Finite

Mathematical Structures

Finite Mathematical Structures

JOHN G. KEMENY
Professor of Mathematics, Dartmouth College
HAZLETON MIRKIL
Assistant Professor of Mathematics, Dartmouth College
J. LAURIE SNELL
Associate Professor of Mathematics, Dartmouth College
GERALD L. THOMPSON
Professor of Mathematics, Ohio Wesleyan University

PRENTICE-HALL, INC.
Englewood Cliffs, N. J., 1959

Library of Congress Catalog Card Number: 59-12841

PRINTED IN THE UNITED STATES OF AMERICA
31736

Preface

The Committee on the Undergraduate Program of the Mathematical Association of America has recommended that every student should receive instruction in both the calculus and in certain modern topics as part of his early college mathematics training. At Dartmouth College this recommendation was implemented in two ways, one for students in the biological and social sciences, and another for students in the physical and engineering sciences.

The book *Introduction to Finite Mathematics*, written by three of us, was designed for a freshman modern mathematics course for students in the biological and social sciences. The prerequisites for the level of exposition of that book were deliberately kept as elementary as possible. The applications in that book were aimed toward the biological and social sciences.

Physical and engineering science students are introduced to modern topics at Dartmouth at the beginning of their sophomore year. We felt the need for a book that would take advantage of the greater maturity of students who have had a full year's course in the calculus. We also wanted to slant applications more to the physical sciences. We have written the present book to fill this need.

While additional maturity is important for the reader of the present book, the calculus actually is used only in Section 13 of Chapter 3, in Section 14 of Chapter 4, in all of Chapter 7, and in a small number of exercises in other sections. In every case only the calculus of functions of one variable is used. In fact, at Dartmouth we use the linear algebra material in Chapter 4 to introduce functions of more than one variable.

There is considerable overlap between the present volume and the first six chapters of *Introduction to Finite Mathematics*. But the content and method of presentation of the various topics differ greatly.

While many topics taken up in *Finite Mathematical Structures* are not in themselves finite problems, they do have finite counterparts which are fully developed in the text before the jump to the "infinite" problem is made. This emphasis on the finite case suggested the title to us.

Chapters 1 and 2 present selected topics in elementary mathematical logic and set theory. The concepts of logical possibilities, operations on statements, sets, operations on sets, and functions, presented in the unasterisked sections of these chapters, are used throughout the rest of the book. Chapter 3 is an introduction to elementary probability theory. Chapter 4, which is independent of Chapter 3, is an introduction to linear algebra. Chapter 5, which deals with convex sets in general and linear programming in particular, is built on the algebra content of Chapter 4 but is independent of Chapter 3. The introduction to Markov chains presented in Chapter 6 depends only on Chapter 3 and on the first three sections of Chapter 4. And the final chapter, 7, which introduces the concept of probabilities relating to a continuous space, depends on Chapter 3 but is completely independent of Chapters 4, 5, and 6. Chapter 7 does require a good understanding of the calculus of functions of one variable.

Every section of this book contains numerous examples and exercises. Wherever possible, the point of a section is illustrated by applications. In addition, more difficult applications of the materials of each chapter are contained in special sections at the end of each chapter. These extra sections we hope will provide additional material for special topics and outside reading.

At Dartmouth College the unasterisked sections of the first four chapters of this book are used in a course following the freshman one-variable calculus course and just preceding the multi-variable calculus course in the sophomore year. Besides introducing the student to modern mathematical ideas, it serves as a bridge between the one-variable calculus and the multi-variable calculus.

This book is written so that it can also be used for a semester's course in linear algebra or for a semester's course in probability. Both of these courses would start with the unasterisked sections of Chapters 1 and 2. Then a linear algebra course would take up Chapters 4 and 5. And a probability course would follow the unasterisked sections of 1 and 2 with Chapters 3, Sections 1, 2, and 3 of Chapter 4, and Chapters 6 and 7.

In addition to these uses, the entire book is suitable for a year's course designed to introduce students to a wide variety of topics in modern mathematics. It might be attractive as training for some students who would otherwise take only traditional courses in mathematics. For instance, it would be suitable for prospective high school teachers.

We would like to thank Dartmouth College for releasing us from part of our teaching duties in order to prepare this book. Great thanks are also due our departmental secretaries, Mrs. Margaret P. Andrews and Mrs. Helen A. Hanchett for their painstaking work in the preparation of the manuscript. And to the numerous undergraduate assistants who have labored energetically in helping us "debug" the manuscript we extend hearty gratitude.

J. G. K.
H. M.
J. L. S.
G. L. T.

Contents

CHAPTER 1 | **COMPOUND STATEMENTS** 1

1. Purpose of the theory 1
2. The most common connectives 4
3. Other connectives 9
4. Logical possibilities 13
5. Tree diagrams 20
6. Logical relations 24

*7. A systematic analysis of logical relations 28
*8. Valid arguments 32
*9. Variants of the conditional 36
*10. Statements having given truth tables 41
*11. Applications to switching circuits 45

CHAPTER 2 | **SETS AND FUNCTIONS** 51

1. Introduction 51
2. Operations on subsets 56
3. The relationship between sets and compound statements 60
4. Open statements 65
5. Functions 70
6. Numerical functions 74
7. The basis of a possibility space 80
8. Counting problems 85
9. The binomial coefficients 90

*10. Quantifiers 96
*11. The binary number system 99
*12. Cardinal numbers 102
*13. The hierarchy of cardinals 107

CHAPTER 3 | **PROBABILITY THEORY** 112

1. Introduction 112
2. Properties of a probability measure 116

3. The equiprobable measure . . . 120
*4. Two nonintuitive examples . . . 124
5. Conditional probability . . . 129
6. Trees, path weights, and branch weights . . . 137
7. Stochastic processes . . . 146
8. Independent trials process . . . 152
9. Mean of a function . . . 159
10. Variance of a function . . . 165
11. The law of large numbers . . . 172
12. Binomial measures and the Poisson approximation . . . 180
13. The central limit theorem . . . 187
*14. A problem of decision . . . 197

CHAPTER 4 | **ELEMENTARY LINEAR ALGEBRA** 205

1. Matrices, column vectors, row vectors . . . 205
2. Matrix multiplication . . . 214
3. Simultaneous linear equations . . . 223
*4. Simultaneous linear equations (cont.) . . . 234
5. The inverse of a square matrix . . . 240
6. Geometric vectors . . . 245
7. Abstract vector spaces . . . 250
8. Linear transformations . . . 255
9. More examples of vector spaces and transformations . . . 260
10. Linear independence and bases . . . 265
11. Uniqueness of dimension . . . 274
12. The matrix of a transformation . . . 278
*13. Functionals . . . 288
*14. Application of vector space ideas to differential equations 294
15. Three-dimensional vector geometry . . . 299
16. Further topics in vector geometry . . . 306
17. Three-dimensional euclidean geometry . . . 320
18. Abstract euclidean vector spaces . . . 330

CHAPTER 5 | **CONVEX SETS** 337

1. Polyhedral convex sets . . . 337
2. Extreme points of polyhedral convex sets . . . 344
*3. Bases for polyhedral convex sets . . . 350
4. Extreme values of functionals on convex sets . . . 355
5. Linear programming problems . . . 359
6. The dual problem and the duality theorem . . . 363
7. The simplex method . . . 372

CHAPTER 6 | **FINITE MARKOV CHAINS** 384

1. Basic concepts and examples . . . 384
2. Ergodic Markov chains . . . 391

*3. Proof of the basic theorems for regular chains 399
4. Absorbing Markov chains 404
5. Mean first passage time for ergodic chains 411
6. Markov chain examples from physics: entropy 415
7. Random walks 423
8. Application of random walks to electric circuits 428
*9. An application of linear algebra 434

CHAPTER 7 | **CONTINUOUS PROBABILITY THEORY** **439**

1. Introduction 439
2. The determination of a distribution 446
3. The mean and variance of functions 453
4. Independent functions 460
5. Sums of independent functions 467
6. Errors in measurement and computation 474

INDEX **481**

Finite

Mathematical Structures

CHAPTER 1

Compound Statements

1. PURPOSE OF THE THEORY

We propose in this first chapter to study ways of putting statements together to form other statements. For example, from the statement "I have a pair of aces" and the statement "You have a straight flush" we can form the more complicated statement "Either I have a pair of aces or else you do not have a straight flush." This new statement is called a *compound* statement, while the statements out of which it is compounded are called its *simple* parts. Any statement (even though already compound) can be used as one of the simple parts of another compound statement.

It might seem natural first to make a thorough study of statements themselves, before one studies ways of putting them together. But we have chosen not to undertake an investigation of the inner nature of statements because (1) such an investigation would be difficult, belonging more to linguistics than to mathematics, and (2) we do not need to know very much about statements in order to understand the various methods of compounding them. It has been found in mathematics that it is often fruitful to take such a by-pass—to assume temporarily that a difficult first problem has been solved, and then go on to show how the solution of the next problem would depend on the various possible solutions of the first.

Hence all we will care to know about a statement is whether it is true or false, and we will proceed then to show how the truth or falsity of a compound statement depends on the truth or falsity of its simple parts. We will also allow for the fact that a statement like "I have a pair of aces" is sometimes true and sometimes false, depending on what hand I hold. The possible five-card poker hands I might hold (and we will see in the next chapter that there are 2,598,960 of these) are an instance of what we will call *logical possibilities* in Section 4 of the present chapter. Before considering any statement we determine in advance the logical possibilities to which it applies. For each one of these possibilities the statement is definitely either true or false. Usually it will be true when applied to some possibilities, false when applied to others, though there exist statements that are true in all cases and statements that are false in all cases.

Our problem now is twofold: (1) What are the various ways in which statements can be *compounded*? (2) How do we determine the *truth value* (i.e., the truth or falsity) of a compound statement, given the truth values of its simple parts? While the first systematic treatment of ideas related to this twofold problem is found in the writings of Aristotle, mathematical methods were first employed by George Boole about 100 years ago. The more polished techniques now available are the product of twentieth-century mathematical logicians.

Examples. As examples of simple statements let us take "The weather is nice" and "It is very hot." We will let p stand for the former and q for the latter.

Suppose we wish to make the compound statement that both are true: "The weather is nice *and* it is very hot." We shall symbolize this statement by $p \wedge q$. The symbol $\wedge$, which can be read "and," is our first connective.

In place of the strong assertion above we might want to make the weak (cautious) assertion that one or the other of the statements is true: "The weather is nice *or* it is very hot." We symbolize this assertion by $p \vee q$. The symbol $\vee$, which can be read "or," is the second connective which we shall use.

Suppose we believed that one of the statements above was false, for example, "It is *not* very hot." Symbolically we would write $\sim q$. Our third connective is then $\sim$, which can be read "not."

More complex compound statements can now be made. For example, $p \wedge \sim q$ stands for "The weather is nice *and* it is *not* very hot."

EXERCISES

1. The following are compound statements or may be so interpreted. Find their simple components.
   (a) It is hot and it is raining.
   (b) It is hot but it is not very humid.
   [*Ans.* "It is hot"; "it is very humid."]
   (c) It is raining or it is very humid.
   (d) Jack and Jill went up the hill.
   (e) The murderer is Jones or Smith.
   (f) It is neither necessary nor desirable.
   (g) Either Jones wrote this book or Smith did not know who the author was.

2. In Exercise 1 assign letters to the various components, and write the statements in symbolic form. [*Ans.* (b) $p \wedge {\sim}q$.]

3. Write the following statements in symbolic form, letting p be "Fred is smart" and q be "George is smart."
   (a) Fred is smart and George is stupid.
   (b) George is smart and Fred is stupid.
   (c) Fred and George are both stupid.
   (d) Either Fred is smart or George is stupid.
   (e) Neither Fred nor George is smart.
   (f) Fred is not smart, but George is stupid.
   (g) It is not true that Fred and George are both stupid.

4. Assume that Fred and George are both smart. Which of the seven compound statements in Exercise 3 are true?

5. Write the following statements in symbolic form.
   (a) Fred likes George. (Statement p.)
   (b) George likes Fred. (Statement q.)
   (c) Fred and George like each other.
   (d) Fred and George dislike each other.
   (e) Fred likes George, but George does not reciprocate.
   (f) George is liked by Fred, but Fred is disliked by George.
   (g) Neither Fred nor George dislikes the other.
   (h) It is not true that Fred and George dislike each other.

6. Suppose that Fred likes George and George dislikes Fred. Which of the eight statements in Exercise 5 are true?

7. For each statement in Exercise 5 give a condition under which it is false. [*Ans.* (c) Fred does not like George.]

8. Let p be "Stock prices are high," and q be "Stocks are rising." Give a verbal translation for each of the following.

(a) $p \wedge q$.
(b) $p \wedge \sim q$.
(c) $\sim p \wedge \sim q$.
(d) $p \vee \sim q$.
(e) $\sim(p \wedge q)$.
(f) $\sim(p \vee q)$.
(g) $\sim(\sim p \vee \sim q)$.

9. Using your answers to Exercise 8, parts (e), (f), (g), find simpler symbolic statements expressing the same idea.

10. Let p be "I have a dog," and q be "I have a cat." Translate into English and simplify: $\sim[\sim p \vee \sim \sim q] \wedge \sim \sim p$.

2. THE MOST COMMON CONNECTIVES

The truth value of a compound statement is determined by the truth values of its components. When discussing a connective we will want to know just how the truth of a compound statement made with this connective depends upon the truth of its components. A very convenient way of tabulating this dependency is by means of a *truth table.*

Let us consider the compound $p \wedge q$. Statement p could be either true or false and so could statement q. Thus there are four possible pairs of truth values for these statements and we want to know in each case whether or not the statement $p \wedge q$ is true. The answer is straightforward: If p and q are both true, then $p \wedge q$ is true, and otherwise $p \wedge q$ is false. This seems reasonable since the assertion $p \wedge q$ says no more and no less than that p and q are both true.

Figure 1 gives the truth table for $p \wedge q$, the *conjunction* of p and q. The truth table contains all the information that we need to know about the connective $\wedge$, namely it tells us the truth value of the conjunction of two statements given the truth values of each of the statements.

p	q	$p \wedge q$
T	T	T
T	F	F
F	T	F
F	F	F

Figure 1

p	q	$p \vee q$
T	T	?
T	F	T
F	T	T
F	F	F

Figure 2

We next look at the compound statement $p \vee q$, the *disjunction* of p and q. Here the assertion is that one or the other of these statements is true. Clearly, if one statement is true and the other false, then the disjunction is true, while if both statements are false, then the disjunction is certainly false. Thus we can fill in the last three rows of the truth table for disjunction (see Figure 2).

Observe that one possibility is left unsettled, namely, what happens if both components are true? Here we observe that the everyday usage of "or" is ambiguous. Does "or" mean "one or the other or both" or does it mean "one or the other but not both"?

Let us seek the answer in examples. The sentence "this summer I will date Jean or Pat," allows for the possibility that the speaker may date both girls. However the sentence "I will go to Dartmouth or to Princeton," indicates that only one of these schools will be chosen. "I will buy a TV set or a phonograph next year," could be used in either sense; the speaker may mean that he is trying to make up his mind which one of the two to buy, but it could also mean that he will buy *at least one* of these—possibly both. We see that sometimes the context makes the meaning clear but not always.

A mathematician would never waste his time on a dispute as to which usage "should" be called the disjunction of two statements. Rather he recognizes two perfectly good usages, and calls one the *inclusive disjunction* (p or q or both) and the other the *exclusive disjunction* (p or q but not both). The symbol $\vee$ will be used for inclusive disjunction, and the symbol $\underline{\vee}$ will be used for exclusive disjunction. The truth tables for these are found in Figures 3 and 4 below. Unless we state otherwise, our disjunctions will be inclusive disjunctions.

p	q	$p \vee q$
T	T	T
T	F	T
F	T	T
F	F	F

Figure 3

p	q	$p \underline{\vee} q$
T	T	F
T	F	T
F	T	T
F	F	F

Figure 4

The last connective we shall discuss in this section is *negation*. If p is a statement, the symbol $\sim p$, called the negation of p, asserts that p is false. Hence $\sim p$ is true when p is false, and false when p is true. The truth table for negation is shown in Figure 5.

p	$\sim p$
T	F
F	T

Figure 5

Besides using these basic connectives singly to form compound statements, several can be used to form a more complicated compound statement, in much the same way that complicated algebraic expressions can be formed by means of the basic arithmetic operations. For example, $\sim(p \wedge q)$, $p \wedge \sim p$, and $(p \vee q) \vee \sim p$ are all compound statements. They are to be read "from the inside out" in the same way that algebraic expressions are, namely, quantities inside the innermost parentheses are first grouped together, then these parentheses are grouped together, etc. Each compound statement has a truth table which can be constructed in a routine way. The following examples show how to construct truth tables.

Example 1. Consider the compound statement $p \vee \sim q$. We begin the construction of its truth table by writing in the first two columns the four possible pairs of truth values for the statements p and q. Then we write the proposition in question, leaving plenty of space between symbols so that we can fill in columns below. Next we copy the truth values of p and q in the columns below their occurrences in the proposition. This completes step 1 of the construction, see Figure 6.

p	q	p	$\vee \sim q$
T	T	T	T
T	F	T	F
F	T	F	T
F	F	F	F
Step No.		1	1

Figure 6

Next we treat the innermost compound, the negation of the variable q, completing step 2, see Figure 7.

p	q	p	$\vee$	$\sim$	q
T	T	T		F	T
T	F	T		T	F
F	T	F		F	T
F	F	F		T	F
Step No.		1		2	1

Figure 7

Finally we fill in the column under the disjunction symbol, which gives us the truth value of the compound statement for various truth values of its variables. To indicate this we place two parallel lines on each side of the final column, completing step 3 as in Figure 8.

p	q	p	$\vee$	$\sim$	q
T	T	T	T	F	T
T	F	T	T	T	F
F	T	F	F	F	T
F	F	F	T	T	F
Step No.		1	3	2	1

Figure 8

The next two examples show truth tables of more complicated compounds worked out in the same manner. There are only two basic rules which the student must remember when working these: first, work from the "inside out"; and second, the truth values of the compound statement are found in the last column filled in during this procedure.

Example 2. The truth table for the statement $(p \vee \sim q) \wedge \sim p$ together with the numbers indicating the order in which the columns are filled in appears in Figure 9.

p	q	$(p$	$\vee$	$\sim$	$q)$	$\wedge$	$\sim$	p
T	T	T	T	F	T	F	F	T
T	F	T	T	T	F	F	F	T
F	T	F	F	F	T	F	T	F
F	F	F	T	T	F	T	T	F
Step No.		1	3	2	1	4	2	1

Figure 9

Example 3. The truth table for the statement $\sim[(p \wedge q) \vee (\sim p \wedge \sim q)]$ together with the numbers indicating the order in which the columns are filled appears in Figure 10.

p	q	$\sim$	$[(p$	$\wedge$	$q)$	$\vee$	$(\sim$	p	$\wedge$	$\sim$	$q)]$
T	T	F	T	T	T	T	F	T	F	F	T
T	F	T	T	F	F	F	F	T	F	T	F
F	T	T	F	F	T	F	T	F	F	F	T
F	F	F	F	F	F	T	T	F	T	T	F
Step No.		5	1	3	1	4	2	1	3	2	1

Figure 10

EXERCISES

1. Give a compound statement which symbolically states "p or q but not both," using only $\sim$, $\vee$, and $\wedge$.

2. Construct the truth table for your answer to Exercise 1, and compare this with Figure 4.

3. Construct the truth table for the symbolic form of each statement in Exercise 3 of Section 1. How does Exercise 4 of Section 1 relate to these truth tables?

4. Construct a truth table for each of the following:

(a) $\sim(p \wedge q)$. [*Ans.* FTTT.]

(b) $p \wedge \sim p$. [*Ans.* FF.]

(c) $(p \vee q) \vee \sim p$. [*Ans.* TTTT.]

(d) $\sim[(p \vee q) \wedge (\sim p \vee \sim q)]$. [*Ans.* TFFT.]

5. Let p stand for "Jones passed the course" and q stand for "Smith passed the course" and translate into symbolic form the statement "It is not the case that Jones and Smith both failed the course." Construct a truth table for this compound statement. State *in words* the circumstances under which the statement is true.

6. Construct a simpler statement about Jones and Smith that has the same truth table as the one in Exercise 5.

7. Let $p \mid q$ express that "p and q are not both true." Write a symbolic expression for $p \mid q$ using $\sim$ and $\wedge$.

8. Write a truth table for $p \mid q$.

9. Write a truth table for $p \mid p$. [*Ans.* Same as Figure 5.]

10. Write a truth table for $(p \mid q) \mid (p \mid q)$. [*Ans.* Same as Figure 1.]

11. Construct a truth table for each of the following:

(a) $\sim(p \vee q) \vee \sim(q \vee p)$. [*Ans.* FFFT.]

(b) $\sim(p \vee q) \wedge p$. [*Ans.* FFFF.]

(c) $\sim(p \veebar q)$. [*Ans.* TFFT.]

(d) $\sim(p \mid q)$. [*Ans.* TFFF.]

12. Construct two symbolic statements, using only $\sim$, $\vee$, and $\wedge$, which have the truth tables (a) and (b), respectively:

p	q	(a)	(b)
T	T	T	T
T	F	F	F
F	T	T	F
F	F	T	T

3. OTHER CONNECTIVES

Suppose we did not wish to make an outright assertion but rather an assertion containing a condition. As examples consider the following sentences. "If the weather is nice, I will take a walk." "If the following statement is true, then I can prove the theorem." "If the cost of living continues to rise, then the government will impose rigid curbs." Each of these statements is of the form "*if* p *then* q." The *conditional* is then a new connective which is symbolized by the arrow $\rightarrow$.

Of course the precise definition of this new connective must be made by means of a truth table. If both p and q are true, then $p \rightarrow q$ is certainly true, and if p is true and q false, then $p \rightarrow q$ is certainly false. Thus the first two lines of the truth table can easily be filled in, see Figure 11a. Suppose now that p is false; how shall we fill in the last two

p	q	$p \rightarrow q$
T	T	T
T	F	F
F	T	?
F	F	?

Figure 11a

p	q	$p \rightarrow q$
T	T	T
T	F	F
F	T	T
F	F	T

Figure 11b

lines of the truth table in Figure 11a? At first thought one might suppose that it would be best to leave it completely undefined. However, to do so would violate our basic principle that a statement is either true or false.

Therefore we make the completely arbitrary decision that the conditional, $p \rightarrow q$, is *true* whenever p is false, regardless of the truth value of q. This decision enables us to complete the truth table for the conditional and it is given in Figure 11b. A glance at this truth table shows that the conditional $p \rightarrow q$ is considered false only if p is true and q is false. If we wished we might rationalize the arbitrary decision made above by saying that if statement p happens to be false then we give the conditional $p \rightarrow q$ the "benefit of the doubt" and consider it true (see Exercise 1).

In everyday conversation it is customary to combine simple statements only if they are somehow related. Thus we might say "It is raining today and I will take an umbrella," but we would not say "I read a good book and I will take an umbrella." However, the rather ill-defined concept of relatedness is difficult to enforce. Concepts related to each other in one person's mind need not be related in another's. In our study of compound statements no requirement of relatedness is imposed on two statements in order that they be compounded by any of the connectives. This freedom sometimes produces strange results in the use of the conditional. For example, according to the truth table in Figure 11b the statement "If $2 \times 2 = 5$, then black is white" is true, while the statement "If $2 \times 2 = 4$, then cows are monkeys" is false. Since we use the "if . . . then . . ." form usually only when there is a causal connection between the two statements, we might be tempted to label both of the above statements as nonsense. At this point it is important to remember that no such causal connection is intended in the usage of $\rightarrow$; the meaning of the conditional is contained in Figure 11b and nothing more is intended. This point will be discussed again in Section 6 with regard to implication.

p	q	$p \leftrightarrow q$
T	T	T
T	F	F
F	T	F
F	F	T

Figure 12

Closely related to the conditional connective is the *biconditional* statement, $p \leftrightarrow q$, which may be read "*p if and only if q.*" The biconditional statement asserts that if p is true, then q is true, and if p is false, then q is false. Hence the biconditional is true in these cases and false in the others so that its truth table can be filled in as in Figure 12.

The biconditional is the last of the five connectives which we shall use in this chapter. The table below gives a summary of them together with the numbers of the figures giving their truth tables. Remember

Name	Symbol	Translated as	Truth Table
Conjunction	$\wedge$	"and"	Figure 1
Disjunction (inclusive)	$\vee$	"or"	Figure 3
Negation	$\sim$	"not"	Figure 5
Conditional	$\rightarrow$	"if . . . then . . ."	Figure 11b
Biconditional	$\leftrightarrow$	". . . if and only if . . ."	Figure 12

that the complete definition of each of these connectives is given by its truth table. The examples below show the use of the two new connectives.

Examples. In Figures 13 and 14 the truth tables of two statements are worked out following the procedure of Section 2. The statement in Figure

p	q	p	$\rightarrow$	$(p$	$\vee$	$q)$
T	T	T	T	T	T	T
T	F	T	T	T	T	F
F	T	F	T	F	T	T
F	F	F	T	F	F	F
Step No.		1	3	1	2	1

Figure 13

13 is said to be *logically true* (see Section 4). The statement in Figure 14 has the same truth table as $p \rightarrow q$ and is said to be *equivalent* to it (see Section 6).

It is also possible to form compound statements from three or more simple statements. The next example is a compound formed from three simple statements p, q, and r. Notice that there will be a total of eight

p	q	$\sim$	p	$\leftrightarrow$	$(p$	$\rightarrow$	$\sim$	$q)$
T	T	F	T	T	T	F	F	T
T	F	F	T	F	T	T	T	F
F	T	T	F	T	F	T	F	T
F	F	T	F	T	F	T	T	F
Step No.		2	1	4	1	3	2	1

Figure 14

possible triples of truth values for these three statements so that the truth table for our compound will have eight rows as shown in Figure 15.

p	q	r	$[p$	$\rightarrow$	$(q$	$\vee$	$r)]$	$\wedge$	$\sim$	$[p$	$\leftrightarrow$	$\sim$	$r]$
T	T	T	T	T	T	T	T	T	T	T	F	F	T
T	T	F	T	T	T	T	F	F	F	T	T	T	F
T	F	T	T	T	F	T	T	T	T	T	F	F	T
T	F	F	T	F	F	F	F	F	F	T	T	T	F
F	T	T	F	T	T	T	T	F	F	F	T	F	T
F	T	F	F	T	T	T	F	T	T	F	F	T	F
F	F	T	F	T	F	T	T	F	F	F	T	F	T
F	F	F	F	T	F	F	F	T	T	F	F	T	F
Step No.			1	3	1	2	1	5	4	1	3	2	1

Figure 15

EXERCISES

1. One way of filling in the question-marked squares in Figure 11a is given in Figure 11b. There are three other possible ways.

(a) Write the three other truth tables.

(b) Show that each one of these truth tables has an interpretation in terms of the connectives now available to us.

2. Write truth tables for $q \vee p$, $q \wedge p$, $q \rightarrow p$, $q \leftrightarrow p$. Compare these with the truth tables in Figures 3, 1, 11b, and 12, respectively.

3. Construct truth tables for:

(a) $p \rightarrow (q \vee r)$. [*Ans.* TTTFTTTT.]

(b) $(p \vee r) \wedge (p \rightarrow q)$. [*Ans.* TTFFTFTF.]

(c) $(p \vee q) \leftrightarrow (q \vee p)$. [*Ans.* TTTT.]

(d) $p \wedge \sim p$. [*Ans.* FF.]

(e) $(p \rightarrow p) \vee (p \rightarrow \sim p)$. [*Ans.* TT.]

(f) $(p \vee \sim q) \wedge r$. [*Ans.* TFTFFFTF.]

(g) $[p \rightarrow (q \rightarrow r)] \rightarrow [(p \rightarrow q) \rightarrow (p \rightarrow r)]$. [*Ans.* TTTTTTTT.]

4. For each of the following statements (i) find a symbolic form, and (ii) construct the truth table. Use the notation: p for "Joe is smart," q for "Jim is stupid," r for "Joe will get the prize."

(a) If Joe is smart and Jim is stupid, then Joe will get the prize. [*Ans.* TFTTTTTT.]

(b) Joe will get the prize if and only if either he is smart or Jim is stupid. [*Ans.* TFTFTFFT.]

(c) If Jim is stupid but Joe fails to get the prize, then Joe is not smart. [*Ans.* Same as (a).]

5. Construct truth tables for each of the following, and give an interpretation.

(a) $(p \rightarrow q) \wedge (q \rightarrow p)$. (Compare with Figure 12.)

(b) $(p \wedge q) \rightarrow p$.

(c) $q \rightarrow (p \vee q)$.

(d) $(p \rightarrow q) \leftrightarrow (\sim p \vee q)$.

6. The truth table for a statement compounded from two simple statements has four rows, and the truth table for a statement compounded from three simple statements has eight rows. How many rows would the truth table for a statement compounded from four simple statements have? How many for five? For n? Devise a systematic way of writing down these latter truth tables.

7. Let p be "It is raining," and q be "The wind is blowing." Translate each of the following into symbolic form.

(a) If it rains, then the wind blows.

(b) If the wind blows, then it rains.
(c) The wind blows if and only if it rains.
(d) If the wind blows, then it does not rain.
(e) It is not the case that the wind blows if and only if it does not rain.

8. Construct truth tables for the statements in Exercise 7.
[*Ans.* TFTT, TTFT, TFFT, FTTT, TFFT.]

9. Construct a truth table for
(a) $(p \vee q) \leftrightarrow (\sim r \wedge \sim s)$.
(b) $(p \wedge q) \rightarrow \sim[\sim p \wedge (r \vee s)]$.

10. Construct a truth table for $\sim[(\sim p \wedge \sim q) \wedge (p \vee r)]$.
[*Ans.* TTTTTTFT.]

11. Find a simpler statement having the same truth table as the one found in Exercise 10.

4. LOGICAL POSSIBILITIES

In using ordinary language we often write or speak the same sentence many times, each time applying it to a different situation. To know whether or not "you have a straight flush" we must know what hand you have been dealt. It is proper that we try to incorporate this feature of ordinary language into the structure of elementary logic. Hence we make each statement relative to certain *logical possibilities*. These we think of as fixed in advance, and we agree that a sentence does not "make sense," is not in fact a statement at all, until its possibilities are specified. When we are considering several statements at once (and we usually are, since our main business in this chapter is the compounding of statements) we must arrange to have each of these statements apply to exactly the same logical possibilities. And in solving a scientific problem we regularly draw up a list of logical possibilities first, before considering the various statements relative to these possibilities.

Example 1. Let us analyze the logical possibilities for the following situation, one that arises in the theory of probability. Suppose there are two

Possibility	Urn	First Ball	Second Ball
1	1	black	black
2	1	black	white
3	1	white	black
4	2	black	white
5	2	white	black
6	2	white	white

Figure 16

urns, the first containing two black balls and one white ball, the second containing one black ball and two white balls, all balls being of different sizes. We are to select an urn at random and draw two balls in succession from it. Figures 16 and 17 show two different ways of analyzing the logical possibilities.

Possibility	Urn	First Ball	Second Ball
1′	1	small black	large black
2′	1	large black	small black
3′	1	small black	white
4′	1	large black	white
5′	1	white	small black
6′	1	white	large black
7′	2	black	small white
8′	2	black	large white
9′	2	small white	black
10′	2	large white	black
11′	2	small white	large white
12′	2	large white	small white

Figure 17

In Figure 16 we have analyzed the possibilities as far as colors of balls drawn was concerned. Such an analysis may be sufficient for many purposes. In Figure 17 we have carried out a finer analysis, in which we distinguish between sizes of balls when they are of the same color. For some purposes the finer analysis may be necessary.

It is important to realize that the possibilities in a given problem may be analyzed in many different ways, from a very rough grouping to a highly refined one. The *main requirement* on an analysis of logical possibilities is that under any conceivable circumstances one and only one of these possibilities must be the case.

Possibility	Truth Value of "Two black balls are drawn from the first urn"
1	T
2	F
3	F
4	F
5	F
6	F

Figure 18

Once the logical possibilities are listed we can then make statements relative to them. "Two black balls are drawn from the first urn" makes sense both for the regular analysis above, and also for the finer analysis.

Possibility	Truth Value of "Two black balls are drawn from the first urn"
1′	T
2′	T
3′	F
4′	F
5′	F
6′	F
7′	F
8′	F
9′	F
10′	F
11′	F
12′	F

Figure 19

Its truth tables for the two analyses are shown in Figures 18 and 19. On the other hand, "the small white ball is drawn after the large white ball from the second urn" makes sense only relative to the finer analysis of possibilities. It is true for case 12′ of this analysis, and false in the other eleven cases. Thus if we intend to study a certain statement in connection with a scientific problem we must be sure to make our analysis of possibilities fine enough so that the truth value of the statement will be determined for each possibility. It is clear that if a given English sentence makes sense for a rough analysis of possibilities it will still make sense for any finer analysis. The last sentence quoted above, on the other hand, provides an example of a statement relative to a fine analysis that does not make sense relative to a rougher analysis.

Although a typical statement is true in some cases and false in others, we can have a statement that is true for all possible cases under consideration. Such a statement is called *logically true* (or a *tautology*). Its logical truth in general follows from the meaning of the words and the form of the statement, together with the context of the problem about which the statement is made. For instance, "At most two black balls are drawn" is logically true for either list of possibilities in Example 1 above. And in fact a sentence that is logically true for one analysis of possibilities in a given problem will be logically true for any other analysis of possibilities in this problem. Similarly, a statement that is false in every possible case under consideration is said to be *logically false* (or a *self-contradiction*). The statement that "the sum of the spots is 13" applied to all possible rolls of a pair of dice is always false.

The (horizontal) rows of a truth table provide an especially important example of logical possibilities. Suppose that we have three simple statements p, q, r. Then for the truth values of these statements we have 8 possibilities. Any statement s compounded from p, q, r can be looked at as a statement relative to these possibilities. For instance if s is the compound statement $p \rightarrow (\sim q \vee r)$ then Figure 20 below is simply a disguise for the truth table of $p \rightarrow (\sim q \vee r)$.

Possibility	Truth Value of s
TTT	T
TTF	F
TFT	T
TFF	T
FTT	T
FTF	T
FFT	T
FFF	T

Figure 20

There is no reason to suppose, however, that every combination of truth values for p, q, r can always occur. Suppose, for instance, that in the urns and balls situation of Example 1, and with the rough analysis of possibilities listed in Figure 16, we have the following three statements p, q, r: "Urn 1 is selected" is p. "The first ball drawn is white" is q. And "The second ball drawn is black" is r. Figure 21 lists the truth values of p, q, r for each of the six rough possibilities of Example 1.

Possibility	p	q	r
1	T	F	T
2	T	F	F
3	T	T	T
4	F	F	F
5	F	T	T
6	F	T	F

Figure 21

Here the truth table rows TTF and FFT never occur. Hence for these particular statements p, q, r we must delete the possibilities TTF and FFT from Figure 20, leaving only the six rows shown in Figure 22. Now the compound statement s is logically true, since its only F occurs in a row that no longer corresponds to a logical possibility.

Possibility	Truth Value of s
TTT	T
TFT	T
TFF	T
FTT	T
FTF	T
FFF	T

Figure 22

When three statements p, q, r are such that all eight truth-table rows are logical possibilities, we say that these three statements are (logically) *independent.* This property of statements will be investigated more thoroughly in Section 7. In situations where we lack precise knowledge of the interrelatedness of p, q, r it is usual to assume p, q, r *independent* in carrying out a truth-table analysis of a statement compounded from them. And, in fact, if a compound expression involving (say) the letters p and q and r turns out to be a logically true statement for just one choice of independent simple statements p and q and r, then it is logically true by virtue of its form alone, and will be logically true for every other choice of statements p and q and r, independent or not. For instance the compound statement "If I have a pair of aces and you have a straight flush, then I have a pair of aces," is logically true regardless of what relation may exist between the simple statement "I have a pair of aces" and the simple statement "You have a straight flush."

Example 2. As a more complicated example let us consider the classification of human beings according to height, hair color, and sex that is carried out in Figure 23. Whether this analysis into 24 cases is adequate will depend on the problem. For example, if we want to allow for white hair or baldness, we must have more cases.

The statement "He is a tall man," is true in cases 1, 3, 5, 7, and false in the others. "She is a woman who is neither short nor redhaired" will be true in cases 2, 4, 6, 10, 12, and 14. On the other hand, the statement "The person is tall, medium, or short," furnishes no information. It is true

Case	Height	Hair Color	Sex
1	tall	blond	male
2	tall	blond	female
3	tall	brown	male
4	tall	brown	female
5	tall	black	male
6	tall	black	female
7	tall	red	male
8	tall	red	female
9	medium	blond	male
10	medium	blond	female
11	medium	brown	male
12	medium	brown	female
13	medium	black	male
14	medium	black	female
15	medium	red	male
16	medium	red	female
17	short	blond	male
18	short	blond	female
19	short	brown	male
20	short	brown	female
21	short	black	male
22	short	black	female
23	short	red	male
24	short	red	female

Figure 23

in every case, hence logically true. On the other hand the statement "He is a man of less than medium height, not blond, brown, or red-haired, and not a short black-haired man" is a self-contradiction.

Of all the logical possibilities, one and only one represents the facts as they are. That is, for a given person one and only one of the 24 cases is a correct description. To know which one, we need factual information. When we say that a certain statement is "true," without qualifying it, we mean that it is true in this one case. But, as we have said before, what the case actually is lies outside the domain of logic. Logic can tell us only what the circumstances (logical possibilities) are for which a statement is true.

EXERCISES

1. Prove that the negation of a logically true statement is logically false, and the negation of a logically false statement is logically true.

2. Classify the following as (i) logically true, (ii) a self-contradiction, (iii) neither.
   (a) $p \leftrightarrow p$. [*Ans.* Logically true.]
   (b) $p \rightarrow \sim p$.
   (c) $(p \vee q) \leftrightarrow (p \wedge q)$. [*Ans.* Neither.]
   (d) $(p \rightarrow \sim q) \rightarrow (q \rightarrow \sim p)$.
   (e) $(p \rightarrow q) \wedge (q \rightarrow r) \wedge \sim(p \rightarrow r)$. [*Ans.* Self-contradiction.]
   (f) $(p \rightarrow q) \rightarrow p$.
   (g) $[(p \rightarrow q) \rightarrow p] \rightarrow p$.

3. Figure 23 gives the possible classifications of one person according to height, color of hair, and sex. How many cases do we get if we classify two people jointly? [*Ans.* 576.]

4. For each of the 24 cases in Figure 23 state whether the following statement is true: "The person has red hair, and, if the person is a woman, then she is short"

5. In Example 1, with the logical possibilities given by Figure 16, state the cases in which the following statements are true.
   (a) Urn one is selected.
   (b) At least one white ball is drawn.
   (c) At most one white ball is drawn.
   (d) If the first ball drawn is white, then the second is black.
   (e) Two balls of different color are drawn if and only if urn one is selected.

6. In Example 1 give two logically true and two logically false statements (other than those in the text).

7. In a college using grades A, B, C, D, and F, how many logically possible report cards are there for a student taking four courses? [*Ans.* 625.]

8. A man has nine coins totaling 78 cents. What are the logical possibilities for the distribution of the coins? [*Hint:* There are three possibilities.]

9. In Exercise 8, which of the following statements are logically true and which are logically false?
   (a) He has at least one penny. [*Ans.* Logically true.]
   (b) He has at least one nickel. [*Ans.* Neither.]
   (c) He has exactly two nickels. [*Ans.* Logically false.]
   (d) He has exactly three nickels if and only if he has exactly one dime. [*Ans.* Logically true.]

10. In Exercise 8, we are told that the man has no nickel in his possession. What can we infer from this?

11. Two dice are rolled. Which of the following analyses satisfy the main requirement for logical possibilities? What is wrong with the others? The sum of the numbers shown is:
(a): (1) 6, (2) not 6.
(b): (1) an even number, (2) less than 6, (3) greater than 6.
(c): (1) 2, (2) 3, (3) 4, (4) more than 4.
(d): (1) 7 or 11, (2) 2, 3, or 12, (3) 4, 5, 6, 8, 9, or 10.
(e): (1) 2, 4, or 6, (2) an odd number, (3) 10 or 12.
(f): (1) less than 5 or more than 8, (2) 5 or 6, (3) 7, (4) 8.
(g): (1) more than 5 and less than 10, (2) at most 4, (3) 7, (4) 11 or 12.
[*Ans.* (a), (c), (d), (f) satisfy the condition.]

12. Assume that p and q are so related that they must have the same truth value. Retest the compound statements in Exercise 2(c) and in 2(f) under this assumption.

13. Let p be the statement "Jim is over five feet in height," q be "Jim is under six feet in height," and r be "Jim is exactly 5 ft 10 in." Write down the eight truth table cases, and eliminate those that are not possible. How many cases remain? [*Ans.* 4.]

14. Give a verbal interpretation for the statement s whose truth table is shown in Figure 22. Verify from the interpretation that s is logically true.

5. TREE DIAGRAMS

A very useful tool for analyzing logical possibilities is the drawing of a "tree." This device will be illustrated by several examples.

Example 1. Consider again the example in Figure 23. Suppose we let the classification proceed as follows: first consider all human beings before classification as being all in one class; next split this large class into three

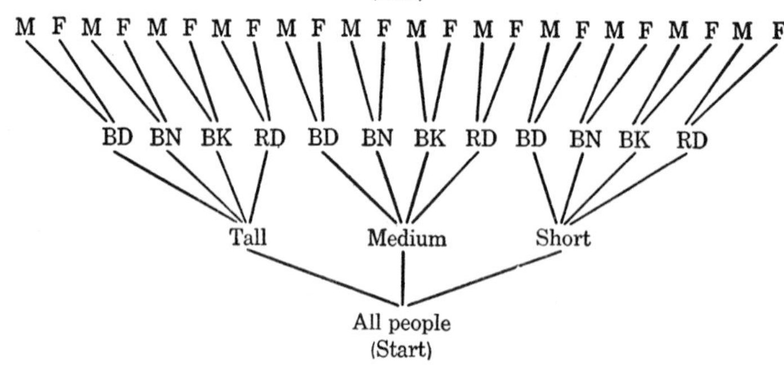

Figure 24

subclasses by putting the short people in one class, the medium height in another, and the tall people in the third; next split up each of these subclasses into four smaller subclasses (making a total of twelve in all) according to hair color; finally, split each of these subclasses into two parts by grouping males together and females together. The final classification then divides the class of all human beings into 24 subclasses. Figure 24 gives a graphical representation of the process described above.

For obvious reasons we shall call a figure like Figure 24, which starts at a point and branches out, a *tree*.

Observe that the tree contains all the information relevant for the classification problem. Each *path* through the tree from the start to the end (bottom to top) represents a logical possibility. There are 24 in all, one for each end point of the tree, and similarly there are 24 cases in Figure 23. The order in which we performed the classification is arbitrary, that is, we might equally well have first classified people according to hair color, then sex, and finally height. We would still get 24 logical possibilities but the tree that we would obtain would differ from that of Figure 24 (see Exercise 1).

Example 2. Next let us consider the example of Figure 16. This is a three-stage process, first we select an urn, then draw a ball and then draw a second ball. The tree of logical possibilities is shown in Figure 25. We

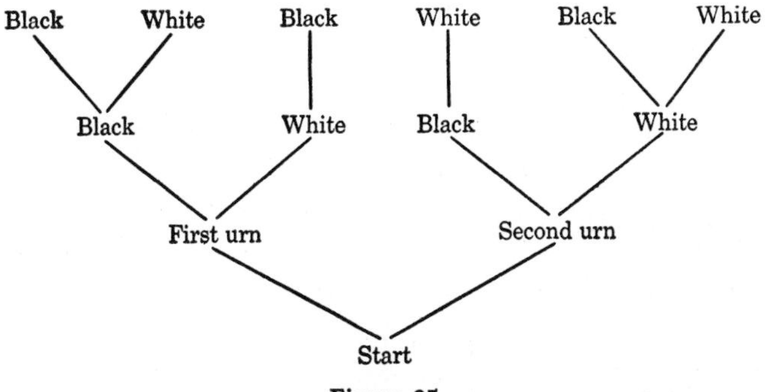

Figure 25

note that six is the correct number of logical possibilities. The reason for this is: if we choose the first urn (which contains two black balls and one white ball) and draw from it a black ball, then the second draw may be of either color; however, if we draw a white ball first, then the second ball drawn is necessarily black. Similar remarks apply if the second urn is chosen.

The reader should observe that in the tree of Figure 24 each point on the same level has the same number of *branches* leading out of it (for instance, four branches for each point on the second level), while in the tree of Figure 25 this is not the case.

Example 3. As a final example let us construct the tree of logical possibilities for the outcomes of a World Series played between the Dodgers and the Yankees. In Figure 26 is shown half of the tree, corresponding to the

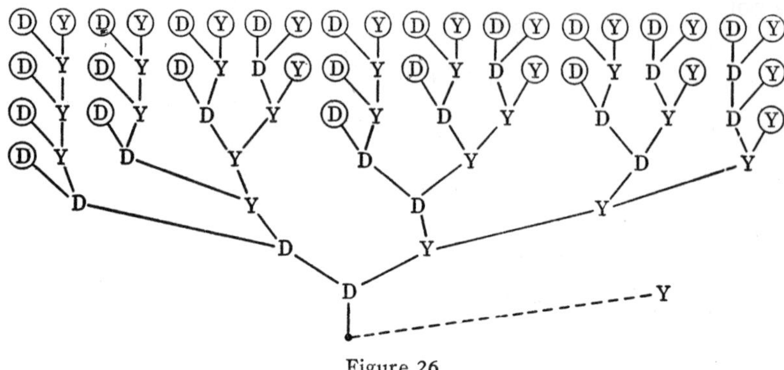

Figure 26

case when the Dodgers win the first game (the dotted line at the bottom leads to the other half of the tree). In the figure a 'D' stands for a Dodger win and 'Y' for a Yankee win. There are 35 possible outcomes (corresponding to the circled letters) in the half-tree shown, so that the World Series can end in 70 ways.

This example is different from the previous two in that the paths of the tree end at different levels, corresponding to the fact that the World Series ends whenever one of the teams has won four games.

Not always do we wish as detailed an analysis as that provided in the examples above. If, in Example 2, we wanted to know only the color and order in which the balls were drawn and not which urn they came from, then there would be only four logical possibilities instead of six. Then in Figure 25 the second and fourth paths (counting from the left) represent the same outcome, namely, a black ball followed by a white ball. Similarly the third and fifth paths represent the same outcome. Finally, if we cared only about the color of the balls drawn, not the order, then there are only three logical possibilities: two black balls, two white balls, or one black and one white ball.

A less detailed analysis of the possibilities for the World Series is also possible. For example we can analyze the possibilities as follows: Dodgers in 4, 5, 6, or 7 games; and Yankees in 4, 5, 6, or 7 games. The new classification reduced the number of possibilities from 70 to 8. The other possibilities have not been eliminated but merely grouped together. Thus the statement "Dodgers in 4 games" can happen in only one way, while "Dodgers in 7 games" can happen in 20 ways (see Figure 26). A still less detailed analysis would be a classification according to the number of games in the series. Here there are only four logical possibilities.

The reader will find that it often requires several trials before the "best" way of listing logical possibilities is found for a given problem.

EXERCISES

1. Construct the tree for Example 1 if the order of classification is hair color, sex, and height. Do the same if the order of classification is sex, height, and hair color. Are there any other ways of performing this classification?

2. In 1955 the Dodgers lost the first two games of the World Series, but won the series in the end. In how many ways can the series go so that the losing team wins the first two games? [*Ans.* 10.]

3. In how many ways can the World Series be played (see Figure 26) if the Dodgers win the first game and
   (a) No team wins two games in a row. [*Ans.* 1.]
   (b) The Dodgers win at least the odd-numbered games. [*Ans.* 5.]
   (c) The winning team wins four games in a row. [*Ans.* 4.]
   (d) The losing team wins four games. [*Ans.* 0.]

4. A man is considering the purchase of one of four types of stocks. Each stock may go up, go down, or stay the same after his purchase. Draw the tree of logical possibilities.

5. For the tree constructed in Exercise 4 give a statement which:
   (a) Is true in half the cases.
   (b) Is false in all but one case.
   (c) Is true in all but one case.
   (d) Is logically true.
   (e) Is logically false.

6. We set up an experiment similar to that of Figure 16, but urn one has two black balls and two white balls, while urn two has one white ball and four black balls. We select an urn, and draw three balls from it. Construct the tree of logical possibilities. How many cases are there? [*Ans.* 10.]

7. From the tree constructed in Exercise 6 answer the following questions.
   (a) In how many cases do we draw three black balls?
   (b) In how many cases do we draw two black balls and one white ball?
   (c) In how many cases do we draw three white balls?
   (d) How many cases does this leave? [*Ans.* 3.]

8. In Exercise 6 we wish to make a rougher classification of logical possibilities. What branches (in the tree there constructed) are identified if:

(a) We do not care about the order in which the balls are drawn.
(b) We care neither about the order of balls, nor about the number of the urn selected.
(c) We care only about what urn is selected, and whether the balls drawn are all the same color.

9. Work Exercise 7 of the last section, by sketching a tree diagram.

10. A menu has a choice of soup or orange juice for an appetizer, a choice of steak, chicken, or fish for the entree, and a choice of pie or cake for dessert. A complete dinner consists of one choice in each case. Draw the tree for the possible complete dinners.
(a) How many different complete dinners are possible? [*Ans.* 12.]
(b) How many complete dinners are there which have chicken for the entree? [*Ans.* 4.]
(c) How many complete dinners are there available for a man who will eat pie only if he had steak for the entree? [*Ans.* 8.]

11. Let us define three arithmetical operations. The operation A adds 2 to a given number. The operation R raises the number to the second power, and D divides the number by 2. Draw a tree showing the possible orders in which the operations can be applied (using each operation once). How many orders are there? [*Ans.* 6.]

12. Use the tree constructed in Exercise 11 to show the result of applying all three operations to the number 0, in various orders.

13. Use the tree of Exercise 11 to show what happens if the three operations are applied to a number x, in various orders. For each of the six cases decide whether there is an x which is left unchanged after the three operations.

6. LOGICAL RELATIONS

Until now we have considered statements in isolation. Sometimes, however, we want to consider the relationship between pairs of statements. The most interesting such relation is that one statement (logically) *implies* the other one. If p implies q we also say that q follows from p, or that q is (logically) deducible from p. For example, in any mathematical theorem the hypothesis implies the conclusion.

If we have listed all logical possibilities for a pair of statements p and q, then we shall characterize implication as follows: p implies q if q is true whenever p is true, i.e., if q is true in all the logically possible cases in which p is true.

For compound statements having the same simple parts truth tables provide a convenient method for testing this relation. In Figure 27 we

p	q	$p \leftrightarrow q$	$p \rightarrow q$	$p \vee q$
T	T	T	T	T
T	F	F	F	T
F	T	F	T	T
F	F	T	T	F

Figure 27

illustrate this method. Let us take $p \leftrightarrow q$ as our hypothesis. Since it is true only in the first and fourth cases and $p \rightarrow q$ is true in both these cases we see that the statement $p \leftrightarrow q$ implies $p \rightarrow q$. On the other hand the statement $p \vee q$ is false in the fourth case and hence it is not implied by $p \leftrightarrow q$. Again, a comparison of the last two columns of Figure 27 shows that the statement $p \rightarrow q$ does not imply and is not implied by $p \vee q$.

The relation of implication has a close affinity to the conditional statement, but it is important not to confuse the two. The conditional is a new *statement* compounded from two given statements, while implication is a *relation* between the two statements. The connection is the following: *p implies q* if and only if the conditional *$p \rightarrow q$ is logically true.*

That this is the case is shown by a simple argument. The statement p implies the statement q if q is true whenever p is true. This means that there is no case in which p is true and q false, i.e., no case in which $p \rightarrow q$ is false. But this in turn means that $p \rightarrow q$ is logically true. In Exercise 1 this result will be applied to Figure 27.

Let us now take up the "paradoxes" of the conditional. Conditional statements sound paradoxical when the components are not related. For example, it sounds strange to say that "If it is a nice day, then chalk is made of wood" is true on a rainy day. It must be remembered that the conditional statement just quoted means no more and no less than that one of the following holds: (1) It is a nice day and chalk is made of wood, or (2) It is not a nice day and chalk is made of wood, or (3) It is not a nice day and chalk is not made of wood. [See Figure 11b.] And on a rainy day number 3 happens to be correct.

But it is by no means true that "It is a nice day" implies that "Chalk is made of wood." It is logically possible for the former to be true and for the latter to be false (indeed, this is the case on a nice day, with the usual method of chalk manufacture), hence the implication does not hold. Thus while the conditional quoted in the previous paragraph is true on a given day, it is not logically true.

In common parlance "if . . . then . . ." is usually asserted on logical grounds. Hence any usage in which such an assertion happens to be true, but is not logically true, sounds paradoxical. Similar remarks apply to the common usage of "if and only if."

If the biconditional $p \leftrightarrow q$ is not only true but logically true, then this establishes a relation between p and q. Since $p \leftrightarrow q$ is true in every logically possible case, the statements p and q have the same truth value in every case. We say, under these circumstances, that p and q are (logically) *equivalent*. For compound statements having the same simple parts, the truth table provides a convenient means of testing for equivalence. We merely have to verify that the compounds have the same truth table. Figure 28 establishes that $p \rightarrow q$ is equivalent to $\sim p \vee q$.

p	q	$p \rightarrow q$	$\sim p \vee q$
T	T	T	T
T	F	F	F
F	T	T	T
F	F	T	T

Figure 28

A pair of statements p and q are said to be *inconsistent* if knowing that one of them is true assures us that the other is false. In other words, p and q are inconsistent if it is impossible for both of them to be true. This concept can be extended to the case of any number of statements: The statements $p_1, p_2, \ldots, p_n$ are inconsistent if it is impossible for all of them to be true. In particular a single statement ($n = 1$) is inconsistent when it is self-contradictory.

If the statements are compounded from the same simple parts, then there is an easy method for testing the consistency of the statements. We construct a truth table for each statement and examine the truth tables one case at a time. If there is a case in which all statements are true (a row of all T's) then the statements are consistent, otherwise they are inconsistent. This method is illustrated in Figure 27. If we examine the three truth tables, we find that they are all T in the first case, hence $p \leftrightarrow q$, $p \rightarrow q$, and $p \vee q$ are consistent. But if we add any statement that is false in the first case, e.g., $\sim p$, then the resulting four statements will be inconsistent.

EXERCISES

1. Show that $(p \leftrightarrow q) \rightarrow (p \rightarrow q)$ is logically true, but that $(p \leftrightarrow q) \rightarrow (p \vee q)$ is not logically true.

2. Prove that p is equivalent to q just in case p implies q and q implies p.

3. Construct truth tables for the following compounds, and test for implications and equivalences.
(a) $p \wedge q$.
(b) $p \rightarrow \sim q$.
(c) $\sim p \vee \sim q$.
(d) $\sim p \vee q$.
(e) $p \wedge \sim q$. [*Ans.* (b) equiv. (c); (a) impl. (d); (e) impl. (b), (c).]

4. Construct truth tables for the following compounds, and arrange them in order so that each compound implies all the following ones.
(a) $\sim p \leftrightarrow q$.
(b) $p \rightarrow (\sim p \rightarrow q)$.
(c) $\sim[p \rightarrow (q \rightarrow p)]$.
(d) $p \vee q$.
(e) $\sim p \wedge q$. [*Ans.* (c), (e), (a), (d), (b).]

5. At most how many of the following assertions can one person consistently believe?
(a) Joe is smart.
(b) Joe is unlucky.
(c) Joe is lucky but not smart.
(d) If Joe is smart, then he is unlucky.
(e) Joe is smart if and only if he is lucky.
(f) Either Joe is smart, or he is lucky, but not both. [*Ans.* 4.]

6. Show that the five statements in Exercise 3 are not consistent. Are any four of these five statements consistent?

7. Given 9 compound statements containing only the letters p and q, prove that if they are consistent then there must be at least one equivalent pair among them.

8. If p is logically true, prove that:
(a) $p \vee q$ is logically true.
(b) $\sim p \wedge q$ is logically false.
(c) $p \wedge q$ is equivalent to q.
(d) $\sim p \vee q$ is equivalent to q.

9. If p and q are logically true and r is logically false, what is the status of $(p \vee \sim q) \wedge \sim r$? [*Ans.* Logically true.]

10. Prove that the conjunction or disjunction of a statement with itself is equivalent to the statement.

11. Prove that the double negation of a statement is equivalent to the statement.

12. Prove that a statement which implies its own negation is a self-contradiction.

13. What is the status of a statement equivalent to its own negation?

14. What relation exists between two logically true statements? Between two self-contradictions?

15. Prove that a logically true statement is implied by every statement, and that a self-contradiction implies every statement.

*7. A SYSTEMATIC ANALYSIS OF LOGICAL RELATIONS

The relation of implication is characterized by the fact that it is impossible for the hypothesis to be true and the conclusion to be false. If two statements are equivalent, it is impossible for one to be true and the other to be false. Thus we see that for an implication one truth table case must not occur, and for an equivalence two of the four truth table cases must not occur. The absence of one or more truth table cases is thus characteristic of logical relations. In this section we shall investigate all conceivable relations that can exist between two statements.

We shall say that two statements are *independent* if each of the four truth table cases (see Figure 29) can occur. The two statements are *dependent* if one or more of the four cases in Figure 29 cannot occur. [Cf. Section 4.]

p	q	Case No.
T	T	1
T	F	2
F	T	3
F	F	4

Figure 29

If p and q are statements such that exactly one of the cases in Figure 29 is excluded, then we say that there is a *onefold* relation between them. Obviously there are four possible onefold relations which we list below. (a) If case 1 is excluded, the two statements cannot both be true. In this case p and q are *inconsistent*. [Cf. Section 6.] Traditional logic calls them a pair of "contraries." (b) If case 2 is excluded, then [cf. Section 6] p *implies* q. (c) If case 3 is excluded, it is false that q is true and p is false, that is, q *implies* p. (d) If case 4 is excluded, both statements cannot be false, i.e., one of them must be true. Such a pair of statements is called a pair of *subcontraries*.

If p and q are statements such that exactly two of the cases in Figure 29 are excluded, then we say that there is a *twofold* relation between them. There are six ways in which two cases can be selected from four, but several of these do not produce interesting relations. For example, suppose cases 1 and 2 are excluded; then p cannot be true, i.e., it is logically false. Similarly, if cases 1 and 3 are excluded, then q is logically false. On the other hand, if cases 3 and 4 are excluded, then p is logically true; and if 2 and 4 are excluded, then q is logically true. Hence we see that these choices do not give us new relations; they merely indicate that one of the two statements is logically true or false. We now have only two alternatives remaining: (A) cases 2 and 3 are excluded which means that the two statements are equivalent; and (B) cases 1 and 4 are excluded, which means that the two statements cannot both be true and cannot both be false; in other words, one must be true and the other false. We shall then say that p and q are *contradictories.*

It is not hard to see that there are no threefold relations, for if three of the cases in Figure 29 are excluded, then there is only one possibility for each of the two statements, so that each must be either logically true or logically false.

We have already noted the connection of implication and equivalence to the conditional and the biconditional, respectively. We can do the same for the three remaining relations. If p and q are subcontraries, then they cannot both be false; since this is the only case in which their disjunction is false, we see that p and q are subcontraries if and only if $p \vee q$ is logically true. If p and q are inconsistent, then they cannot both be true; since this is the only case in which their conjunction is true, we see that p and q are inconsistent if and only if $p \wedge q$ is logically false. Finally, if p and q are contradictories, then cases 1 and 4 of Figure 29 are excluded, hence $p \leftrightarrow q$ is logically false. (Note also that, if p and q are contradictories, then $p \veebar q$ is logically true.) The table in Figure 30 gives a summary of the relevant facts about the six relations we have derived.

Case(s) Excluded	Relation	Alternate Definition
T-T	Inconsistent	$p \wedge q$ logically false
F-F	Subcontraries	$p \vee q$ logically true
T-F	First implies second	$p \rightarrow q$ logically true
F-T	Second implies first	$q \rightarrow p$ logically true
T-F and F-T	Equivalents	$p \leftrightarrow q$ logically true
T-T and F-F	Contradictories	$p \leftrightarrow q$ logically false

Figure 30

Subcontraries are not of great theoretical interest, but inconsistent statements and contradictories are very important. Each of these relations can be generalized to hold for more than two statements. We have already defined the notion of inconsistency for n statements. They cannot all be true simultaneously, i.e., their conjunction must be false. On the other hand, if we have n different statements such that one and only one of them can be true, then we say they form a *complete set of alternatives*. If $n = 1$, then we have a single logically true statement; and if $n = 2$, then we have a pair of contradictories.

Truth tables again furnish a method for recognizing when relations hold between statements. The examples below show how the method works.

Examples. Consider the five compound statements, all having the same components, which appear in Figure 31. Find all relations which exist between pairs of these statements.

p	q	$p \wedge q$	$\sim p \vee \sim q$	$\sim p \vee q$	$\sim p$	$p \rightarrow q$
T	T	T	F	T	F	T
T	F	F	T	F	F	F
F	T	F	T	T	T	T
F	F	F	T	T	T	T
Statement number:		1	2	3	4	5

Figure 31

First of all we note that statements 3 and 5 have identical truth tables, hence they are equivalent. Therefore we need consider only one of them, say statement 3. Statements 1 and 2 have exactly opposite truth tables, hence they are contradictories. Upon comparing statements 1 and 3 we find no T-F case, so that 1 implies 3. Since numbers 1 and 4 are never both true they are inconsistent, while numbers 2 and 3 are never both false, so that they are subcontraries. Finally, upon comparing either 2 or 3 to 4 we find no F-T case and hence both are implied by 4. Thus the six relations we found above are all exemplified in Figure 31. Observe also that statements p and q give an example of a pair of independent statements. [Cf. Section 4.]

EXERCISES

1. Construct truth tables for the following four statements and state what relation (if any) holds between each of the six pairs formable.
   (a) $\sim p$.
   (b) $\sim q$.

(c) $p \wedge \sim q$.
(d) $\sim(\sim p \vee q)$.

[*Ans.* (a) and (b) independent; (a) and (c), (d) inconsistent; (c), (d) imply (b); (c) equiv. (d).]

2. Construct truth tables for each of the following six statements. Give an example of an independent pair, and an example of each of the six possible relations among these.
(a) $p \leftrightarrow q$.
(b) $p \rightarrow q$.
(c) $\sim p \wedge \sim q$.
(d) $(p \wedge q) \vee (\sim p \wedge \sim q)$.
(e) $\sim q$.
(f) $p \wedge \sim q$.

3. Prove the following assertions:
(a) The disjunction of two contradictory statements is logically true.
(b) Two statements are equivalent if and only if either one implies the other one.
(c) The negations of two inconsistent statements are subcontraries.

4. What is the relation between the following pair of statements?
(a) $p \rightarrow [p \wedge \sim(q \vee r)]$.
(b) $\sim p \vee (\sim q \wedge \sim r)$. [*Ans.* Equivalent.]

5. Suppose that any two of the statements p, q, and r are independent. And let us further suppose that there are only four possible truth table cases for the three statements. Prove that either r is equivalent to $p \leftrightarrow q$, or r is equivalent to $p \veebar q$.

6. Prove the following assertions.
(a) The negations of two equivalent statements are equivalent.
(b) In a complete set of alternatives any two statements are inconsistent.
(c) If p and q are subcontraries, and if each implies r, then r is logically true.

7. Pick out a complete set of (four) alternatives from:
(a) It is raining but the wind is not blowing.
(b) It rains if and only if the wind blows.
(c) It is not the case that it rains and the wind blows.
(d) It is raining and the wind is blowing.
(e) It is neither raining nor is the wind blowing.
(f) It is not the case that it is raining or the wind is not blowing.

[*Ans.* (a), (d), (e), (f).]

8. What is the relation between $[p \vee \sim(q \vee r) \vee (p \wedge s)]$ and $\sim(p \wedge q \wedge r \wedge s)$? [*Ans.* Subcontraries.]

9. Suppose that p and q are inconsistent. What is the relation between
   (a) p and $\sim q$.
   (b) $\sim p$ and q.
   (c) $\sim p$ and $\sim q$.
   (d) p and $\sim p$.

10. Let p, q, and r be three statements such that any two of them are independent. Discuss the possible relations among the three statements. [*Hint:* If we ignore the order of the statements, there are 14 such relations. The relations are at most fourfold. There are two fourfold relations, and the other relations are found from these by excluding fewer cases.]

11. Construct the set of logical possibilities which classify a person with respect to sex and marital status.
    (a) Show that "if the person is a bachelor then he is unmarried" is logically true.
    (b) Find the relation between "the person is a man" and "the person is a bachelor."
    (c) Find a simple statement that is a subcontrary of "the person is a man," and is consistent with it.

*8. VALID ARGUMENTS

One of the most important tasks of a logician is the checking of *arguments.* By an argument we shall mean the assertion that a certain statement (the *conclusion*) follows from other statements (the *premises*). An argument will be said to be *valid* if and only if the conjunction of the premises implies the conclusion, i.e., whenever the premises are all true, the conclusion is also true.

It is important to realize that the truth of the conclusion is irrelevant as far as the test of the validity of the argument goes. A true conclusion is neither necessary nor sufficient for the validity of the argument. The two examples below show this, and they also show the form in which we shall state arguments, i.e., first we state the premises, then draw a line and then state the conclusion.

Example 1.

If the United States is a democracy, then its
citizens have the right to vote.
Its citizens do have the right to vote.
____
Therefore the United States is a democracy.

The conclusion is, of course, true. However, the argument is not valid since the conclusion does not follow from the two premises.

Example 2.

In a democracy the chief executive is elected directly
by the people.
In England the Prime Minister is the chief executive.
The British Prime Minister is not directly elected.
———
Therefore England is not a democracy.

Here the conclusion is false, but the argument is valid since the conclusion follows from the premises. If we observe that the first premise is false, the paradox disappears. There is nothing surprising in the correct derivation of a false conclusion from false premises.

If an argument is valid, then the conjunction of the premises implies the conclusion. Hence if all the premises are true, then the conclusion is also true. However, if one or more of the premises is false, so that the conjunction of all the premises is false, then the conclusion may be either true or false. In fact all the premises could be false, the conclusion true, and the argument valid, as the following example shows.

Example 3.

All dogs have two legs.
All two-legged animals are carnivorous.
———
Therefore, all dogs are carnivorous.

Here the argument is valid and the conclusion is true, but both premises are false!

Each of these examples underlines the fact that neither the truth value nor the content of any one of the statements appearing in an argument determines the validity of the argument. In Figures 32 and 33 are two valid forms of arguments:

$$\begin{array}{l} p \rightarrow q \\ \underline{p\qquad} \\ \therefore\ q \end{array}$$

Figure 32

$$\begin{array}{l} p \rightarrow q \\ \underline{\sim q\qquad} \\ \therefore\ \sim p \end{array}$$

Figure 33

The symbol ∴ means "therefore." The truth tables for these argument forms appear in Figure 34.

p	q	$p \rightarrow q$	p	q	$p \rightarrow q$	$\sim q$	$\sim p$
T	T	T	T	T	T	F	F
T	F	F	T	F	F	T	F
F	T	T	F	T	T	F	T
F	F	T	F	F	T	T	T

Figure 34

For the argument of Figure 32, we see in Figure 34 that there is only one case in which both premises are true, namely, the first case, and in this case the conclusion is true, hence the argument is valid. Similarly, in the argument of Figure 33, both premises are true in the fourth case only, and in this case the conclusion is also true, hence the argument is valid.

An argument that is not valid is called a *fallacy*. Two examples of fallacies are the following argument forms:

$$\begin{array}{l} p \rightarrow q \\ \underline{q \quad\quad} \\ \therefore\ p \end{array} \qquad \textit{Fallacies} \qquad \begin{array}{l} p \rightarrow q \\ \underline{\sim p \quad\quad} \\ \therefore\ \sim q \end{array}$$

In the first fallacy both premises are true in the first and third cases of Figure 34, but the conclusion is false in the third case, so that the argument is invalid. (This is the form of Example 1.) Similarly, in the second fallacy we see that both premises are true in the last two cases, but the conclusion is false in the third case.

We say that an argument depends only upon its form in that it does not matter what the components of the argument are. The truth tables in Figure 34 show that if both premises are true, then the conclusions of the arguments in Figures 32 and 33 are also true. For the fallacies above, the truth tables show that it is possible to choose both premises true without making the conclusion true, namely, choose a false p and a true q.

Example 4. Consider the following argument:

$$\begin{array}{l} p \rightarrow q \\ \underline{q \rightarrow r} \\ \therefore\ p \rightarrow r \end{array}$$

The truth table of the argument appears in Figure 35.

p	q	r	$p \rightarrow q$	$q \rightarrow r$	$p \rightarrow r$
T	T	T	T	T	T
T	T	F	T	F	F
T	F	T	F	T	T
T	F	F	F	T	F
F	T	T	T	T	T
F	T	F	T	F	T
F	F	T	T	T	T
F	F	F	T	T	T

Figure 35

Both premises are true in the first, fifth, seventh, and eighth rows of the truth table. Since in each of these cases the conclusion is also true, the argument is valid. (Example 3 can be written in this form.)

EXERCISES

1. Test the validity of the following arguments:

(a)
$$\begin{array}{l} p \leftrightarrow q \\ \underline{p \qquad} \\ \therefore q \end{array}$$

(b)
$$\begin{array}{l} p \vee q \\ \underline{\sim p \qquad} \\ \therefore \quad q \end{array}$$

(c)
$$\begin{array}{l} p \wedge q \\ \underline{\sim p \rightarrow q} \\ \therefore \sim q \end{array}$$

[*Ans.* (a), (b) are valid.]

2. Test the validity of the following arguments:

(a)
$$\begin{array}{l} p \rightarrow q \\ \underline{\sim q \rightarrow \sim r} \\ \therefore r \rightarrow p \end{array}$$

(b)
$$\begin{array}{l} p \rightarrow q \\ \underline{\sim r \rightarrow \sim q} \\ \therefore \sim r \rightarrow \sim p \end{array}$$

[*Ans.* (b) is valid.]

3. Test the validity of the argument

$$\begin{array}{l} p \leftrightarrow q \\ q \vee r \\ \underline{\sim r \qquad} \\ \therefore \sim p \end{array}$$

[*Ans.* Not valid.]

4. Test the validity of the argument

$$\begin{array}{c} p \veebar q \\ \sim q \rightarrow r \\ \underline{\sim p \vee \sim r} \\ \sim p \end{array}$$

5. Test the validity of the argument

$$\begin{array}{c} p \rightarrow q \\ \sim p \rightarrow \sim q \\ \underline{p \wedge \sim r} \\ s \end{array}$$

6. Given are the premises $\sim p \rightarrow q$ and $\sim r \rightarrow \sim q$. We wish to find a valid conclusion involving p and r (if there is any).

(a) Construct truth tables for the two premises.

(b) Note the cases in which the conclusion must be true.

(c) Construct a truth table for a combination of p and r only, filling in T wherever necessary.

(d) Fill in the remainder of the truth table with F's.

(e) What combination of p and r has this truth table? This is a valid conclusion. [*Ans.* $p \vee r$.]

7. Show that the method described in Exercise 6 can always be used to find a conclusion connecting two given variables. Prove that it yields the strongest possible conclusion (in the sense that it implies any other such conclusion).

8. Use the method described in Exercise 6 to find a conclusion connecting p and q in the following argument.

$$\begin{array}{c} p \rightarrow r \\ q \leftrightarrow \sim s \\ \underline{\sim r \vee s} \\ ?\ ?\ ? \end{array}$$

9. Use the method described in Exercise 6 to find a conclusion connecting p and q in the following argument.

$$\begin{array}{l} q \leftrightarrow r \\ r \rightarrow (s \vee (t \wedge u)) \\ \sim p \rightarrow (t \wedge \sim s) \\ \underline{p \vee \sim u} \\ ?\ \ ?\ \ ? \end{array}$$

10. Use the method described in Exercise 6 to find the strongest conclusion connecting "I will pass the course" and "I will study" in the following argument.

If I am lucky I will pass the course.
I will either study or I will be lucky (but not both)
? ? ?

11. Translate the following argument into symbolic form, and test its validity.

If this is a good course, then it is worth taking.
Either the grading is lenient, or the course is not worth taking.
But the grading is not lenient.
Therefore, this is not a good course. [*Ans.* Valid.]

*9. VARIANTS OF THE CONDITIONAL

The conditional of two statements differs from the biconditional and from disjunctions and conjunctions of these two in that it lacks symmetry. Thus $p \vee q$ is equivalent to $q \vee p$, $p \wedge q$ is equivalent to $q \wedge p$, and $p \leftrightarrow q$ is equivalent to $q \leftrightarrow p$; but $p \rightarrow q$ is *not equivalent to* $q \rightarrow p$. The latter statement, $q \rightarrow p$, is called the *converse* of $p \rightarrow q$. Many of the most common fallacies in thinking arise from a confusion of a statement with its converse.

Let us consider four important conditional statements formed from p and q. The truth tables of these four conditionals together with their names are tabulated in Figure 36. We note that $p \to q$ is equivalent to $\sim q \to \sim p$. The latter is called the *contrapositive* of the former. For many arguments the contrapositive is a very useful form of the conditional. In the same manner the statement $\sim p \to \sim q$ is the converse of the contrapositive. Since the contrapositive is equivalent to $p \to q$, the converse of the former is equivalent to the converse of the latter as can be seen in Figure 36.

		Conditional	Converse of Conditional	Converse of Contrapositive	Contrapositive
p	q	$p \to q$	$q \to p$	$\sim p \to \sim q$	$\sim q \to \sim p$
T	T	T	T	T	T
T	F	F	T	T	F
F	T	T	F	F	T
F	F	T	T	T	T

Figure 36

The use of conditionals seems to cause more trouble than the use of the other connectives, perhaps because of the lack of symmetry, but also perhaps because there are so many different ways of expressing conditionals. In many cases only a careful analysis of a conditional statement shows whether the person making the assertion means the given conditional or its converse. Indeed, sometimes he means both of these, i.e., he means the biconditional. (See Exercise 10.)

The statement, "I will go for a walk only if the sun shines," is a variant of a conditional statement. A statement of the form "p only if q" is closely related to the statement "If p then q," but just how? Actually the two express the same idea. The statement "p only if q" states that "If $\sim q$ then $\sim p$" and hence is equivalent to "If p then q." Thus the statement at the beginning of the paragraph is equivalent to the statement, "If I go for a walk, then the sun will be shining."

Other phrases, in common use by mathematicians, which indicate a conditional statement are, "a necessary condition" and "a sufficient condition." To say that p is a sufficient condition for q means that if p takes place, then q will also take place. Hence the sentence "p is a sufficient condition for q" is equivalent to the sentence "If p then q."

Similarly, the sentence "p is a necessary condition for q" is equivalent to "q only if p." Since we know that the latter is equivalent to "If q then p," it follows that the assertion of a necessary condition is the converse of the assertion of a sufficient condition.

Finally, if both a conditional statement and its converse are asserted, then effectively the biconditional statement is being asserted. Hence the assertion "p is a necessary and sufficient condition for q" is equivalent to the assertion "p if and only if q."

A proof is an argument which shows that a conditional statement of the form $p \rightarrow q$ is logically true. (Namely, p is the conjunction of the premises, and q is the conclusion of the argument.) Sometimes it is more convenient to show that an equivalent conditional statement is logically true.

Example 1. Let x and y be positive integers.

THEOREM. If xy is an odd number, then x and y are both odd.

Proof. Suppose, on the contrary, that they are not both odd. Then one of them is even, say $x = 2z$. Then $xy = 2zy$ is an even number, contrary to hypothesis. Hence we have proved our theorem.

Example 2. "He did not know the first name of the president of the Jones Corporation, hence he cannot be an employee of that firm. Why? Because every employee of that firm calls the boss by his first name (behind his back). Therefore, if he were really an employee of Jones, then he would know Jones's first name."

These are simple examples of a very common form of argument, frequently used both in mathematics and in everyday discussions. Let us try to unravel the form of the argument.

Given:	xy is an odd number.	He doesn't know Jones's first name.	p
To prove:	x and y are both odd numbers.	He doesn't work for Jones.	q
Suppose:	x and y are not both odd numbers.	He does work for Jones.	$\sim q$
Then:	xy is an even number.	He must know what Jones's first name is.	$\sim p$

In each case we assume the contradictory to the conclusion and derive, by a valid argument, a result contradictory to the hypothesis. This is one form of the *indirect* method of proof.

To restate, what we want to do is to show that the conditional $p \rightarrow q$ is logically true; what we actually show is that the contrapositive $\sim q \rightarrow \sim p$ is logically true. Since these two statements are equivalent our procedure is valid.

There are several other important variants of this method of proof.

It is easy to check that the following statements have the same truth table as (that is, are equivalent to) the conditional $p \to q$:

(1) $$(p \wedge \sim q) \to \sim p,$$

(2) $$(p \wedge \sim q) \to q,$$

(3) $$(p \wedge \sim q) \to (r \wedge \sim r).$$

The first of these shows that in the indirect method of proof we may make use of the original hypothesis in addition to the contradictory assumption $\sim q$. The second shows that we may also use this double hypothesis in the direct proof of the conclusion q. The third shows that if, from the double hypothesis p and $\sim q$ we can arrive at a contradiction of the form $r \wedge \sim r$, then the proof of the original statement is complete. This last form of the method is often referred to as *reductio ad absurdum.*

These forms of the method are very useful for the following reasons: First of all we see that we can always take $\sim q$ as a hypothesis in addition to p. Secondly we see that besides q there are two other conclusions ($\sim p$ or a contradiction) which are just as good.

EXERCISES

1. Construct indirect proofs for the following assertions:
(a) If x^2 is odd, then x is odd (x an integer).
(b) If I am to pass this course, I must do homework regularly.
(c) If he earns a great deal of money (more than $20,000), he is not a college professor.

2. Give a symbolic analysis of the following argument:

"If he is to succeed, he must be both competent and lucky. Because, if he is not competent, then it is impossible for him to succeed. If he is not lucky, something is sure to go wrong."

3. Construct indirect proofs for the following assertions:
(a) If $p \vee q$ and $\sim q$, then p.
(b) If $p \leftrightarrow q$ and $q \to \sim r$ and r, then $\sim p$.

4. Give a symbolic analysis of the following argument:

"If Jones is the murderer, then he knows the exact time of death and the murder weapon. Therefore, if he does not know the exact time or does not know the weapon, then he is not the murderer."

5. Verify that forms (1), (2), and (3) given above are equivalent to $p \to q$.

6. Give an example of an indirect proof of some statement in which from p and $\sim q$ a contradiction is derived.

7. Give a statement equivalent to $(p \wedge q) \rightarrow r$, which is in terms of $\sim p$, $\sim q$, and $\sim r$. Show how this can be used in a proof where there are two hypotheses given.

8. Let p stand for "I will pass this course" and q for "I will do homework regularly." Put the following statements into symbolic form.
(a) I will pass the course only if I do homework regularly.
(b) Doing homework regularly is a necessary condition for me to pass this course.
(c) Passing this course is a sufficient condition for me to do homework regularly.
(d) I will pass this course if and only if I do homework regularly.
(e) Doing homework regularly is a necessary and sufficient condition for me to pass this course.

9. Take the statement in part (a) of the previous exercise. Form its converse, its contrapositive, and the converse of its contrapositive. Give a verbal form of each of them.

10. Prove that the conjunction of a conditional and its converse is equivalent to the biconditional.

11. To what is the conjunction of the contrapositive and its converse equivalent? Prove it.

12. Prove that
(a) $\sim\sim p$ is equivalent to p.
(b) The contrapositive of the contrapositive is equivalent to the original conditional.

13. "For a matrix to have an inverse it is necessary that its determinant be different from zero." Which of the following statements follow from this? [No knowledge of matrices is required.]
(a) For a matrix to have an inverse it is sufficient that its determinant be zero.
(b) For its determinant to be different from zero it is sufficient for the matrix to have an inverse.
(c) For its determinant to be zero it is necessary that the matrix have no inverse.
(d) A matrix has an inverse if and only if its determinant is not zero.
(e) A matrix has a zero determinant only if it has no inverse.

[*Ans.* (b), (c), (e).]

14. "A function that is differentiable is continuous." This statement is true for all functions, but its converse is not always true. Which of the following statements are true for all functions? [No knowledge of functions is required.]
(a) A function is differentiable only if it is continuous.
(b) A function is continuous only if it is differentiable.

(c) Being differentiable is a necessary condition for a function to be continuous.

(d) Being differentiable is a sufficient condition for a function to be continuous.

(e) Being differentiable is a necessary and sufficient condition for a function to be differentiable. [*Ans.* (a), (d), (e).]

15. Prove that the negation of, "p is a necessary and sufficient condition for q," is equivalent to, "p is a necessary and sufficient condition for $\sim q$."

16. Write the following argument in symbolic form, and test its validity:

"For the candidate to win it is sufficient that he carry New York. He will carry New York only if he takes a strong stand on civil rights. He will not take a strong stand on civil rights. Therefore, he will not win."

17. Write the following argument in symbolic form and test its validity:

"Father praises me only if I can be proud of myself. Either I do well in sports or I cannot be proud of myself. If I study hard, then I cannot do well in sports. Therefore, if father praises me, then I do not study hard."

18. Supply a conclusion to the following argument, making it a valid argument. [Adapted from Lewis Carroll.]

"If he goes to a party, he does not fail to brush his hair.
To look fascinating it is necessary to be tidy.
If he is an opium eater, then he has no self-command.
If he brushes his hair, he looks fascinating.
He wears white kid gloves only if he goes to a party.
Having no self-command is sufficient to make one look untidy.
Therefore . . ."

*10. STATEMENTS HAVING GIVEN TRUTH TABLES

In Sections 2 and 3 we showed how to construct the truth table for any compound statement. It is also interesting to consider the converse problem, namely, given a truth table to find one or more statements having this truth table. The converse problem always has a solution, and in fact, a solution using only the connectives $\wedge$, $\vee$, and $\sim$. The discussion which we give here is valid only for a truth table in three variables but can easily be extended to cover the case of n variables.

As observed in the last section a truth table with three variables has eight rows, one for each of the eight possible triples of truth values. Suppose that our given truth table has its last column consisting entirely of F's. Then it is easy to check that the truth table of the statement $p \wedge \sim p$ also has only F's in its last column, so that this statement serves as an answer to our problem. We now need consider only truth tables having one or more T's. The method that we shall use is to construct statements that are true in one case only, and then to construct the desired statement as a disjunction of these.

It is not hard to construct statements that are true in only one case. In Figure 37 are listed eight such statements, each true in exactly one

p	q	r	Basic Conjunctions
T	T	T	$p \wedge q \wedge r$
T	T	F	$p \wedge q \wedge \sim r$
T	F	T	$p \wedge \sim q \wedge r$
T	F	F	$p \wedge \sim q \wedge \sim r$
F	T	T	$\sim p \wedge q \wedge r$
F	T	F	$\sim p \wedge q \wedge \sim r$
F	F	T	$\sim p \wedge \sim q \wedge r$
F	F	F	$\sim p \wedge \sim q \wedge \sim r$

Figure 37

case. We shall call such statements *basic conjunctions*. Such a basic conjunction contains each variable or its negation, depending on whether the line on which it appears in Figure 37 has a T or an F under the variable. Observe that the disjunction of two such basic conjunctions will be true in exactly two cases, the disjunction of three in three cases, etc. Therefore, to find a statement having a given truth table simply form the disjunction of those basic conjunctions which occur in Figure 37 on the rows where the given truth table has T's.

Example 1. Find a statement whose truth table has T's in the first, second, and last rows, and F's in the other rows. The required statement is the disjunction of the first, second, and eighth basic conjunctions, that is,

$$(p \wedge q \wedge r) \vee (p \wedge q \wedge \sim r) \vee (\sim p \wedge \sim q \wedge \sim r).$$

In Exercise 2 you will show that this statement has the required truth table.

Example 2. A logician is captured by a tribe of savages and placed in a jail having two exits. The savage chief offers the captive the following chance to escape: "One of the doors leads to certain death and the other to freedom. You can leave by either door. To help you in making a decision, two of my warriors will stay with you and answer any one question which you wish to ask of one of them. I must warn you, however, that one of my warriors is completely truthful while the other always lies." The chief then leaves, believing that he has given his captive only a sporting chance to escape.

After thinking a moment, our quick-witted logician asks one question and then chooses the door leading to freedom. What question did he ask?

Let p be the statement "The first door leads to freedom," and q be the statement "You are truthful." It is clear that p and q are useless questions in themselves, so let us try compound statements. We want to ask a single question for which a "yes" answer means that p is true and a "no" answer means that p is false, regardless of which warrior is asked the question. The answers desired to these questions are listed in Figure 38.

The next thing to consider is, what would be the truth table of a question having the desired answers. If the warrior answers "yes" and if he is truthful, that is if q is true, then the truth value is T. But if he answers "yes" and he is a liar, that is if q is false, then the truth value is F. A similar analysis holds if the answer is "no." The truth values of the desired question are shown in Figure 38.

p	q	Desired Answer	Truth Table of Question
T	T	yes	T
T	F	yes	F
F	T	no	F
F	F	no	T

Figure 38

Therefore we have reduced the problem to that of finding a statement having the truth table of Figure 38. Following the general method outlined above, we see that the statement

$$(p \wedge q) \vee (\sim p \wedge \sim q)$$

will do. Hence the logician asks the question: "Does the first door lead to freedom and are you truthful, or does the second door lead to freedom and are you lying?" The statement $p \leftrightarrow q$ also has the truth table given in Figure 38, hence a shorter equivalent question would be: "Does the first door lead to freedom if and only if you are truthful?"

As can be seen in Example 2, the method does not necessarily yield the simplest possible compound statement. However it has two advantages: (1) It gives us a mechanical method of finding a statement that solves the problem. (2) The statement appears in a standard form.

The latter will be made use of in designing switching circuits (see Section 11).

EXERCISES

1. Show that each of the basic conjunctions in Figure 37 has a truth table consisting of one T appearing in the row in which the statement appears in Figure 37, and all the rest F's.

2. Find the truth table of the compound statement constructed in Example 1.

3. In Example 2 there is a second question, having a different truth table from that in Figure 38, which the logician can ask. What is it?

4. Construct one or more compound statements having each of the following truth tables, (a), (b), and (c).

p	q	r	(a)	(b)	(c)
T	T	T	T	F	T
T	T	F	F	F	T
T	F	T	T	F	T
T	F	F	F	T	F
F	T	T	F	F	T
F	T	F	F	F	T
F	F	T	T	F	F
F	F	F	F	F	T

5. Using only $\vee$, $\wedge$ and $\sim$, write a statement equivalent to each of the following:
   (a) $p \leftrightarrow q$.
   (b) $p \rightarrow q$.
   (c) $\sim(p \rightarrow q)$.

6. Using only $\vee$ and $\sim$ write down a statement equivalent to $p \wedge q$. Use this result to prove that any truth table can be represented by means of the two connectives $\vee$ and $\sim$.

In Exercises 7-10 we will study the new connective $\downarrow$, where $p \downarrow q$ expresses "neither p nor q."

7. Construct the truth table of $p \downarrow q$.

8. Construct the truth table for $p \downarrow p$. What other compound has this truth table? [*Ans.* Same as Figure 5.]

9. Construct the truth table for $(p \downarrow q) \downarrow (p \downarrow q)$. What other compound has this truth table? [*Ans.* Same as Figure 3.]

10. Use the results of Exercises 6, 8, and 9 to show that any truth table can be represented by means of the single connective $\downarrow$.

11. Use the results of Exercises 9, 10 following Section 2 to show that any truth table can be represented by means of the single connective $|$.

12. Write down a compound of p, q, r which is true if and only if exactly one of the three components is true.

13. The "basic conjunctions" for statements having only one variable are p and $\sim p$. Discuss the various compound statements that can be formed by disjunctions of these. How do these relate to the possible truth tables for statements of one variable? What can be asserted about an arbitrary compound, no matter how long, that contains only the variable p? [*Ans.* There are four possible truth tables.]

14. A student is confronted with a true-false exam, consisting of five questions. He knows that his instructor always has more true than false questions, and that he never has three questions in a row with the same answer. From the nature of the first and last questions he knows that these must have the opposite answer. The only question to which he knows the answer is number two. And this *assures* him of having all answers correct. What did he know about question two? What is the answer to the five questions? [*Ans.* TFTTF.]

*11. APPLICATIONS TO SWITCHING CIRCUITS

The theory of compound statements has many applications to subjects other than pure mathematics. As an example we shall develop a theory of simple switching networks.

A switching network is an arrangement of wires and switches which connect together two terminals T_1 and T_2. Each switch can be either "open" or "closed." An open switch prevents the flow of current, while a closed switch permits flow. The problem that we want to solve is the following: given a network and given the knowledge of which switches are closed, determine whether or not current will flow from T_1 to T_2.

Figure 39 Figure 40

Figure 39 shows the simplest kind of network in which the terminals are connected by a single wire containing a switch P. If P is closed, then current will flow between the terminals, and otherwise it will not. The network in Figure 40 has two switches P and Q in "series." Here the current flows only if both P and Q are closed.

To see how our logical analysis can be used to solve the problem stated above let us associate a statement with each switch. Let p be the statement "Switch P is closed" and let q be the statement "Switch Q is closed." Then in Figure 39 current will flow if and only if p is true. Similarly in Figure 40 the current will flow if and only if both p and q are true, that is, if and only if $p \wedge q$ is true. Thus the first circuit is represented by p and the second by $p \wedge q$.

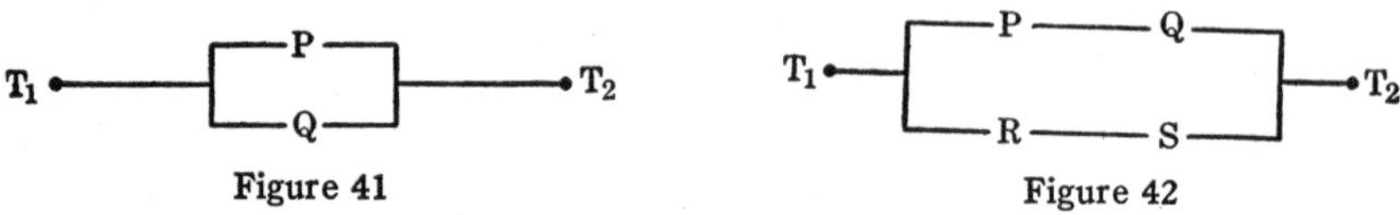

Figure 41

Figure 42

In Figure 41 is shown a network with switches P and Q in "parallel." In this case the current flows if either of the switches is closed, so the circuit is represented by the statement $p \vee q$.

The network in Figure 42 combines the series and parallel types of connections. The upper branch of the network is represented by the statement $p \wedge q$ and the lower by $r \wedge s$; hence the entire circuit is represented by $(p \wedge q) \vee (r \wedge s)$. Since there are four switches and each one can be either open or closed, there are $2^4 = 16$ possible settings for these switches. Similarly, the statement $(p \wedge q) \vee (r \wedge s)$ has four variables, so that its truth table has 16 rows in it. The switch settings for which current flows correspond to the entries in the truth table for which the above compound statement is true.

Switches need not always act independently of each other. It is possible to couple two or more switches together so that they open and close simultaneously, and we shall indicate this in diagrams by giving all such switches the same letter. It is also possible to couple two switches together, so that if one is closed, the other is open. We shall indicate this by giving the first switch the letter P and the second the letter P′. Then the statement "P is closed" is true if and only if the statement "P′ is closed" is false. Therefore if p is the statement "P is closed," then $\sim p$ is the statement "P′ is closed."

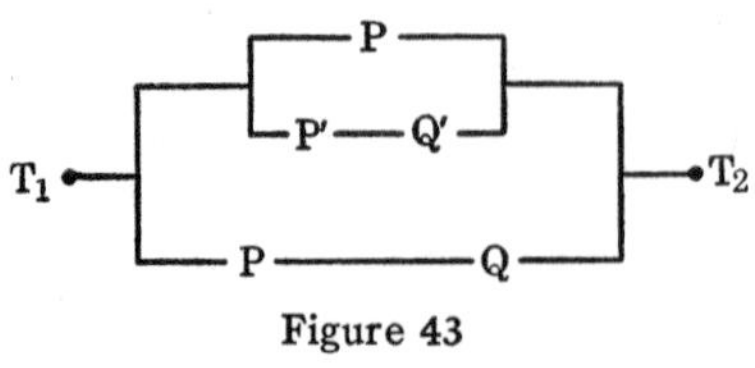

Figure 43

Such a circuit is illustrated in Figure 43. The associated compound statement is $[p \vee (\sim p \wedge \sim q)] \vee [p \wedge q]$. Since the statement is false only if p is false and q is true, the current will flow unless P is open and Q is closed. We can also check directly. If P is closed, current will flow through the top branch regardless of Q's setting. If both switches are open, then P′ and Q′ will be closed, so that current will flow through the middle branch. But if P is open and Q is closed, none of the branches will pass current.

Notice that we never had to consider current flow through the bottom branch. The logical counterpart of this fact is that the statement associated with the network is equivalent to $[p \vee (\sim p \wedge \sim q)]$ whose associated network is just the upper two branches of Figure 43. Thus the electrical properties of the circuit of Figure 43 would be the same if the lower branch were omitted. (See Exercise 7.)

As a last problem we shall consider the design of a switching network having certain specified properties. An equivalent problem, which we solved in Section 10, is that of constructing a compound statement having a given truth table. As in that section, we shall limit ourselves to statements having three variables, although our methods could easily be extended.

In Section 10 we developed a general method for finding a statement having a given truth table not consisting entirely of F's (The circuit which corresponds to a statement whose truth table consists entirely of F's is one in which current never flows, and hence is not of interest.) Each such statement could be constructed as a disjunction of basic conjunctions. Since the basic conjunctions were of the form $p \wedge q \wedge r$, $p \wedge q \wedge \sim r$, etc., each will be represented by a circuit consisting of three switches in series and will be called a *basic series circuit*. The disjunction of certain of these basic conjunctions will then be represented by the circuit obtained by putting several basic series circuits in parallel. The resulting network will not, in general, be the simplest possible such network fulfilling the requirements, but the method always suffices to find one.

p	q	r	Desired Truth Value	Corresponding Basic Conjunction
T	T	T	T	$p \wedge q \wedge r$
T	T	F	T	$p \wedge q \wedge \sim r$
T	F	T	T	$p \wedge \sim q \wedge r$
T	F	F	F	$p \wedge \sim q \wedge \sim r$
F	T	T	T	$\sim p \wedge q \wedge r$
F	T	F	F	$\sim p \wedge q \wedge \sim r$
F	F	T	F	$\sim p \wedge \sim q \wedge r$
F	F	F	F	$\sim p \wedge \sim q \wedge \sim r$

Figure 44

Example. A three-man committee wishes to employ an electric circuit to record a secret simple majority vote. Design a circuit so that each member can push a button for his "yes" vote (not push it for a "no" vote), and so that a signal light will go on if a majority of the committee members vote yes.

Let p be the statement "committee member 1 votes yes," let q be the statement "member 2 votes yes," and let r be "member 3 votes yes." The truth table of the statement "majority of the members vote yes" appears in Figure 44. From that figure we can read off the desired compound statement as

$$(p \wedge q \wedge r) \vee (p \wedge q \wedge \sim r) \vee (p \wedge \sim q \wedge r) \vee (\sim p \wedge q \wedge r).$$

The circuit desired for the voting procedure appears in Figure 45.

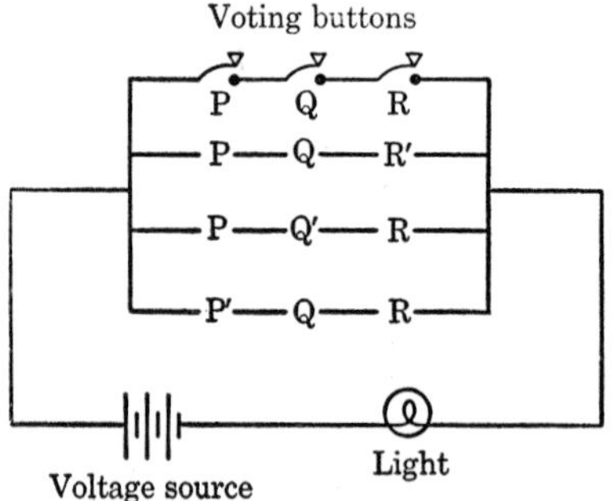

Figure 45

EXERCISES

1. What kind of a circuit has a logically true statement assigned to it? Give an example.
2. Construct a network corresponding to

$$[(p \wedge \sim q) \vee (\sim p \wedge q)] \vee (\sim p \wedge \sim q).$$

3. What compound statement represents:

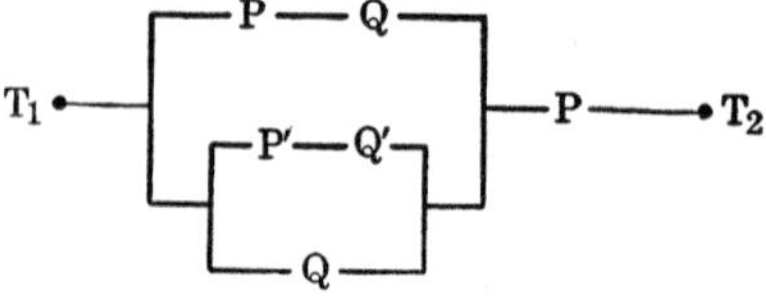

4. Work out the truth table of the statement in Exercise 3. What does this tell us about the circuit?
5. Design a simpler circuit than the one in Exercise 3, having the same properties.

6. Construct a network corresponding to

$$[(p \vee q) \wedge \sim r] \vee [(\sim p \wedge r) \vee q].$$

7. Find the simplest circuit equivalent to that in Figure 43.

8. Design a circuit for an electrical version of the game of matching pennies: At a given signal each of the two players either opens or closes a switch under his control. If they both do the same, A wins; if they do the opposite, then B wins. Design the circuit so that a light goes on if A wins.

9. In a large hall it is desired to turn the lights on or off from any one of four switches on the four walls. This can be accomplished by designing a circuit which turns the light on if an even number of switches are closed, and off if an odd number are closed. (Why does this solve the problem?) Design such a circuit.

10. A committee has five members. It takes a majority vote to carry a measure, except that the chairman has a veto (i.e., the measure carries only if he votes for it). Design a circuit for the committee, so that each member votes for a measure by pressing a button, and the light goes on if and only if the measure is carried.

11. A group of candidates is asked to take a true-false exam, with four questions. Design a circuit such that a candidate can push the buttons of those questions to which he wants to answer "true," and that the circuit will indicate the number of correct answers. [*Hint:* Have five lights, corresponding to 0, 1, 2, 3, 4 correct answers, respectively.]

12. Devise a scheme for working truth tables by means of switching circuits.

SUGGESTED READING

Tarski, A., *Introduction to Logic*, Oxford University Press, New York, 2d rev. ed., 1946, Chapters I, II.

Cohen, M. R., and E. Nagel, *An Introduction to Logic and Scientific Method*, Harcourt, Brace, New York, 1934.

Church, A., *Introduction to Mathematical Logic*, Volume I, Princeton University Press, 1956.

Suppes, P., *Introduction to Mathematical Logic*, Van Nostrand, Princeton, 1957.

Hilbert, D., and W. Ackermann, *Principles of Mathematical Logic*, Chelsea, New York, 2d ed., 1950.

Allendoerfer, C. B., and C. O. Oakley, *Principles of Mathematics*, McGraw-Hill, New York, 1955, Chapter I.

Johnstone, H. W., Jr., *Elementary Deductive Logic*, Crowell, New York, 1954, Parts One and Two.

Hohn, Franz, "Some Mathematical Aspects of Switching," *The American Mathematical Monthly*, **62** (1955), pp. 75–90.

CHAPTER 2

Sets and Functions

1. INTRODUCTION

A well-defined collection of objects is known as a *set*. This concept, in its complete generality, is of great importance in mathematics since all of mathematics can be developed by starting from it.

The various pieces of furniture in a given room form a set. So do the books in a given library, or the integers between 1 and 1,000,000, or all the ideas that mankind has had, or the human beings alive between one billion B.C. and ten billion A.D. These examples are all examples of *finite* sets, that is, sets having a finite number of elements. Examples of infinite sets are the set of all integers, the set of real numbers, and the set of sentences in the English language.

There are two essentially different ways of specifying a set. One can give a rule by which it can be determined whether or not a given object is a member of the set, or one can give a complete list of the elements in the set. We shall say that the former is a *description* of the set and the latter is a *listing* of the set. For example, we can define a set of four people as (a) the members of the quartet which played in town last night, or (b) the people whose names are Jones, Smith, Brown, and Green. It is customary to use braces to surround the listing of a set;

thus the set above should be listed {Jones, Smith, Brown, Green}. However, a listing is practical only for finite sets.

We shall frequently be interested in sets of logical possibilities, since the analysis of such sets is very often a major task in the solving of a problem. Suppose, for example, that we were interested in the successes of three candidates who enter the presidential primaries (we assume there are no other entries). Suppose that the key primaries will be held in New Hampshire, Minnesota, Wisconsin, and California. Assume that candidate A enters all the primaries, that B does not contest in New Hampshire's primary, and C does not contest in Wisconsin's. A list of the logical possibilities is given in Figure 1. Since the New Hampshire and Wisconsin primaries can each end in two ways, and the Minnesota and California primaries can each end in three ways, there are in all $2 \cdot 2 \cdot 3 \cdot 3 = 36$ different logical possibilities as listed in Figure 1.

A set that consists of some members of another set is called a *subset* of that set. For example, the set of those logical possibilities in Figure 1 for which the statement "Candidate A wins at least three primaries" is true, is a subset of the set of all logical possibilities. This subset can also be defined by listing its members: {P1, P2, P3, P4, P7, P13, P19}.

In order to discuss all the subsets of a given set, let us introduce the following terminology. We shall call the original set the *universal set*, one-element subsets will be called *unit sets*, and the set which contains no members the *empty set*. We do not introduce special names for other kinds of subsets of the universal set. As an example, let the universal set $\mathcal{U}$ consist of the three elements $\{a, b, c\}$. The *proper subsets* of $\mathcal{U}$ are those sets containing some but not all of the elements of $\mathcal{U}$. The proper subsets consist of three two-element sets, namely, $\{a, b\}$, $\{a, c\}$, and $\{b, c\}$ and three unit sets, namely, $\{a\}$, $\{b\}$, and $\{c\}$. To complete the picture we also consider the universal set a subset (but not a proper subset) of itself, and we consider the empty set $\mathcal{E}$, that contains no elements of $\mathcal{U}$, as a subset of $\mathcal{U}$. At first it may seem strange that we should include the sets $\mathcal{U}$ and $\mathcal{E}$ as subsets of $\mathcal{U}$, but the reasons for their inclusion will become clear later.

We saw that the three element set above had $8 = 2^3$ subsets. In general, a set with n elements has 2^n subsets, as can be seen in the following manner. We form subsets P of $\mathcal{U}$ by considering each of the elements of $\mathcal{U}$ in turn and deciding whether or not to include it in the subset P. If we decide to put every element of $\mathcal{U}$ into P we get the universal set, and if we decide to put no element of $\mathcal{U}$ into P we get the empty set. In most cases we will put some but not all the elements into P and thus obtain a proper subset of $\mathcal{U}$. We have to make n decisions,

Possibility Number	Winner in New Hampshire	Winner in Minnesota	Winner in Wisconsin	Winner in California
P1	A	A	A	A
P2	A	A	A	B
P3	A	A	A	C
P4	A	A	B	A
P5	A	A	B	B
P6	A	A	B	C
P7	A	B	A	A
P8	A	B	A	B
P9	A	B	A	C
P10	A	B	B	A
P11	A	B	B	B
P12	A	B	B	C
P13	A	C	A	A
P14	A	C	A	B
P15	A	C	A	C
P16	A	C	B	A
P17	A	C	B	B
P18	A	C	B	C
P19	C	A	A	A
P20	C	A	A	B
P21	C	A	A	C
P22	C	A	B	A
P23	C	A	B	B
P24	C	A	B	C
P25	C	B	A	A
P26	C	B	A	B
P27	C	B	A	C
P28	C	B	B	A
P29	C	B	B	B
P30	C	B	B	C
P31	C	C	A	A
P32	C	C	A	B
P33	C	C	A	C
P34	C	C	B	A
P35	C	C	B	B
P36	C	C	B	C

Figure 1

one for each element of the set, and for each decision we have to choose between two alternatives. We can make these decisions in $2 \cdot 2 \cdot \ldots \cdot 2 = 2^n$ ways, and hence this is the number of different subsets of $\mathcal{U}$ that can be formed. Observe that our formula would not have been so simple if we had not included the universal set and the empty set as subsets of $\mathcal{U}$.

This same formula, that a set with n elements has 2^n subsets, also holds for infinite sets—if the numbers are properly interpreted. Indeed, this is one of the basic formulas of the theory of infinite cardinal numbers (see Section 13).

In the example of the voting primaries above there are 2^{36} or about 70 billion subsets. Of course, we cannot deal with this many subsets in a practical problem, but fortunately we are usually interested in only a few of the subsets. The most interesting subsets are those which can be defined by means of a simple rule such as "The set of all logical possibilities in which C loses at least two primaries." It would be difficult to give a simple description for the subset containing the elements {P1, P4, P14, P30, P34}. On the other hand, we shall see in the next section how to define new subsets in terms of subsets already defined.

Examples. We illustrate the two different ways of specifying sets in terms of the primary voting example. Let the universal set $\mathcal{U}$ be the logical possibilities given in Figure 1.

1. What is the subset of $\mathcal{U}$ in which candidate B wins more primaries than either of the other candidates? *Answer:* {P11, P12, P17, P23, P26, P28, P29}.

2. What is the subset in which the primaries are split two and two? *Answer:* {P5, P8, P10, P15, P21, P30, P31, P35}.

3. Describe the set {P1, P4, P19, P22}. *Answer:* The set of possibilities for which A wins in Minnesota and California.

4. How can we describe the set {P18, P24, P27}? *Answer:* The set of possibilities for which C wins in California, and the other primaries are split three ways.

If we take as $\mathcal{U}$ the set of all integers, this will have both finite and infinite subsets. For example, the set of all even numbers and the set of all perfect squares are infinite subsets, while the set of all integers between ten and a hundred is a finite subset.

EXERCISES

1. In the primary example, give a listing for each of the following sets.
   (a) The set in which C wins at least two primaries.

(b) The set in which the first three primaries are won by the same candidate.
(c) The set in which B wins all four primaries.

2. The primaries are considered decisive if a candidate can win three primaries, or if he wins two primaries including California. List the set in which the primaries are decisive.

3. Give simple descriptions for the following sets (referring to the primary example).
(a) {P33, P36}.
(b) {P10, P11, P12, P28, P29, P30}.
(c) {P6, P20, P22}.

4. Joe, Jim, Pete, Mary, and Peg are to be photographed. They want to line up so that boys and girls alternate. List the set of all possibilities.

5. In Exercise 4, list the following subsets.
(a) The set in which Pete and Mary are next to each other.
(b) The set in which Peg is between Joe and Jim.
(c) The set in which Jim is in the middle.
(d) The set in which Mary is in the middle.
(e) The set in which a boy is at each end.

6. Pick out all pairs in Exercise 5 in which one set is a subset of the other.

7. A TV producer is planning a half-hour show. He wants to have a combination of comedy, music, and commercials. If each is allotted a multiple of five minutes, construct the set of possible distributions of time. (Consider only the total time allotted to each.)

8. In Exercise 7, list the following subsets.
(a) The set in which more time is devoted to comedy than to music.
(b) The set in which no more time is devoted to commercials than to either music or comedy.
(c) The set in which exactly five minutes is devoted to music.
(d) The set in which all three of the above conditions are satisfied.

9. In Exercise 8, find two sets, each of which is a proper subset of the set in (a) and also of the set in (c).

10. Let $\mathcal{U}$ be the set of all positive integers. Which of the following subsets are finite?
(a) The set of odd integers. [*Ans.* Infinite.]
(b) The set of all integers below 100. [*Ans.* Finite.]
(c) The set of all integers above 100.
(d) The set of all those integers which are both perfect squares and cubes.

11. In Exercise 10 give a listing of the subset of $\mathcal{U}$ in which conditions (a), (b), and (c) are all satisfied.

12. In each of the following equations state whether the set of solutions is finite or infinite.

(a) $x + 5 = 7$. [*Ans.* Finite.]

(b) $2x - 4 = 2(x - 2)$.

(c) $x^2 - 3x + 2 = 0$.

(d) $x = |x|$. [*Ans.* Infinite.]

2. OPERATIONS ON SUBSETS

In Chapter 1 we considered the ways in which one could form new statements from given statements. Now we shall consider an analogous procedure, the formation of new sets from given sets. We shall assume that each of the sets that we use in the combination is a subset of some universal set, and we shall also want the newly formed set to be a subset of the same universal set. As usual, we can specify a newly formed set either by a description or by a listing.

If P and Q are two sets we shall define a new set $P \cap Q$, called the *intersection* of P and Q as follows: $P \cap Q$ is the set that contains those and only those elements which belong to both P and Q. As an example, consider the logical possibilities listed in Figure 1. Let P be the subset in which candidate A wins at least three primaries, i.e., the set {P1, P2, P3, P4, P7, P13, P19}; let Q be the subset in which A wins the first two primaries, i.e., the set {P1, P2, P3, P4, P5, P6}. Then the intersection $P \cap Q$ is the set in which both events take place, i.e., where A wins the first two primaries *and* wins at least three primaries. Thus $P \cap Q$ is the set {P1, P2, P3, P4}.

If P and Q are two sets we shall define a new set $P \cup Q$ called the *union* of P and Q as follows: $P \cup Q$ is the set that contains those and only those elements that belong either to P or to Q (or to both). In the example in the paragraph above, the union $P \cup Q$ is the set of possibilities for which either A wins the first two primaries *or* wins at least three primaries, i.e., the set {P1, P2, P3, P4, P5, P6, P7, P13, P19}.

To help in visualizing these operations we shall draw diagrams, called Venn diagrams, which illustrate them. We let the universal set be a rectangle and let subsets be circles drawn inside the rectangle. In Figure 2 we show two sets P and Q as shaded circles. Then the doubly crosshatched area is the intersection $P \cap Q$ and the total shaded area is the union $P \cup Q$.

If P is a given subset of the universal set $\mathcal{U}$, we can define a new set $\tilde{P}$ called the *complement* of P as follows: $\tilde{P}$ is the set of all elements of $\mathcal{U}$ that are *not* contained in P. For example, if, as above, Q is the set in which candidate A wins the first two primaries, then $\tilde{Q}$ is the set

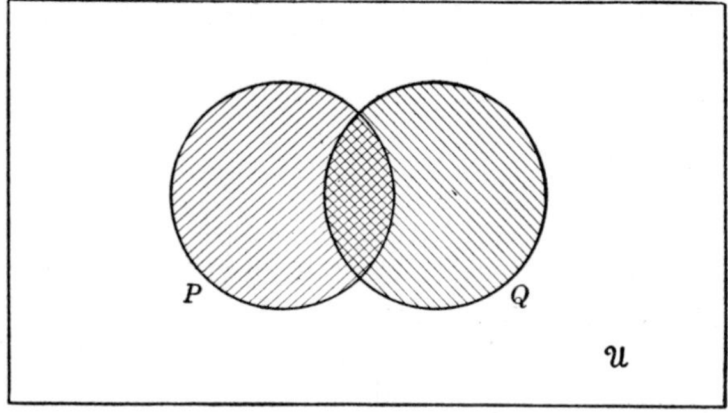

Figure 2

{P7, P8, . . . , P36}. The shaded area in Figure 3 is the complement of the set P. Observe that the complement of the empty set $\mathcal{E}$ is the universal set $\mathcal{U}$, and also that the complement of the universal set is the empty set.

Sometimes we shall be interested in only part of the complement of a set. For example, we might wish to consider the part of the complement of the set Q that is contained in P, i.e., the set $P \cap \tilde{Q}$. The shaded area in Figure 4 is $P \cap \tilde{Q}$.

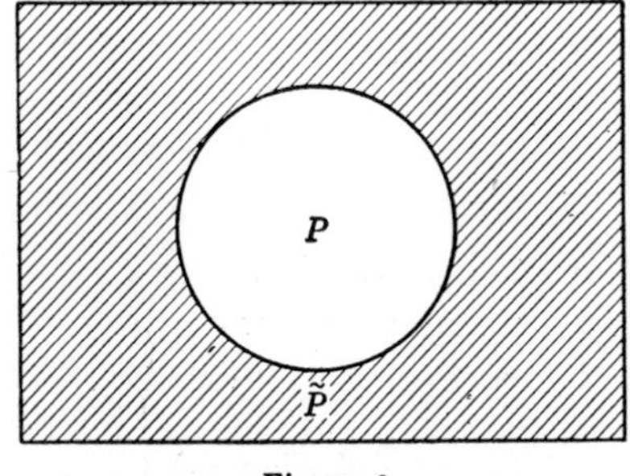

Figure 3

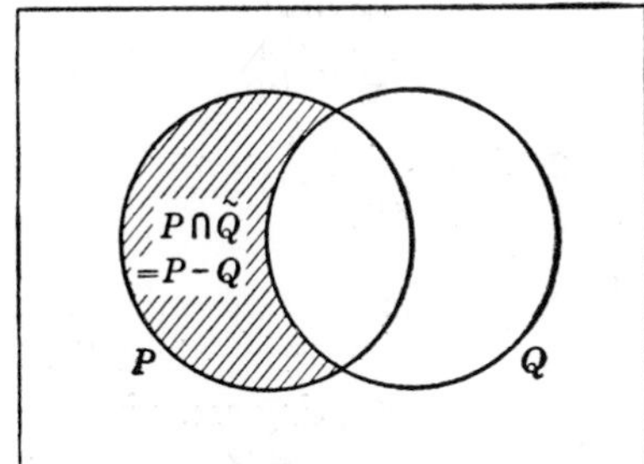

Figure 4

A somewhat more suggestive definition of this set can be given as follows: let $P - Q$ be the *difference* of P and Q, that is, the set that contains those elements of P that do not belong to Q. Figure 4 shows that $P \cap \tilde{Q}$ and $P - Q$ are the same set. In the primary voting example above the set $P - Q$ can be listed as {P7, P13, P19}.

The complement of a subset is a special case of a difference set, since we can write $\tilde{Q} = \mathcal{U} - Q$. If P and Q are nonempty subsets whose intersection is the empty set, i.e., $P \cap Q = \mathcal{E}$, then we say that they are *disjoint* subsets.

Example 1. In the primary voting example let R be the set in which A wins the first three primaries, i.e., the set {P1, P2, P3}; let S be the set in which A wins the last two primaries, i.e., the set {P1, P7, P13, P19, P25, P31}. Then $R \cap S =$ {P1} is the set in which A wins the first three primaries and also the last two, that is he wins all the primaries. We also have

$$R \cup S = \{\text{P1, P2, P3, P7, P13, P19, P25, P31}\},$$

which can be described as the set in which A wins the first three primaries or the last two. The set in which A does not win the first three primaries is $\tilde{R} =$ {P4, P5, . . . , P36}. Finally, we see that the difference set $R - S$ is the set in which A wins the first three primaries but not both of the last two. This set can be found by taking from R the element {P1} which it has in common with S, so that $R - S =$ {P2, P3}.

Example 2. Let $\mathcal{U}$ be the set of positive integers, R the set of even integers, and S the set of integers from 1 to 10. Then $\tilde{R}$ is the set of odd integers; $\tilde{S}$ is the set of all integers greater than 10. The intersection $R \cap S$ is the set {2, 4, 6, 8, 10}. The difference $S - R$ is the set {1, 3, 5, 7, 9}, while the difference $R - S$ consists of all even integers above 10. The union $R \cup S$ contains all the integers up to 10 and all even integers beyond 10.

EXERCISES

1. Draw Venn diagrams for $P \cap Q$, $P \cap \tilde{Q}$, $\tilde{P} \cap Q$, $\tilde{P} \cap \tilde{Q}$.

2. Give a step-by-step construction of the diagram for $(\tilde{P} - Q) \cup (P \cap \tilde{Q})$.

3. Venn diagrams are also useful when three subsets are given. Construct such a diagram, given the subsets P, Q, and R. Identify each of the eight resulting areas in terms of P, Q, and R.

4. On a smooth curve let us classify points as to whether (a) the first derivative is positive (the curve is rising), and (b) the second derivative is positive (the curve is concave upwards). Draw a Venn diagram to show the four possibilities.

5. In Exercise 4 illustrate each of the four cases by drawing a piece of a curve having both properties at all points.

6. Classify the integers according to whether (a) they are even, (b) they are perfect squares, and (c) their last digit in decimal notation is a 5. Draw a Venn diagram. Give, if possible, an example for each of the eight resulting cases.

7. This tabulation records the reaction of a number of spectators to a television show. All the categories can be defined in terms of the fol-

	Liked very much	Liked slightly	Disliked slightly	Disliked very much
Men	1	3	5	10
Women	6	8	3	1
Boys	5	5	3	2
Girls	8	5	1	1

lowing four: M (male), G (grown-up), L (liked), Vm (very much). How many people fall into each of the following categories:

(a) M. [*Ans.* 34.]
(b) $\tilde{L}$.
(c) Vm.
(d) $M \cap \tilde{G} \cap \tilde{L} \cap Vm$. [*Ans.* 2.]
(e) $\tilde{M} \cap G \cap L$.
(f) $(M \cap G) \cup (L \cap Vm)$.
(g) $\widetilde{(M \cap G)}$. [*Ans.* 48.]
(h) $(\tilde{M} \cup \tilde{G})$.
(i) $(M - G)$.
(j) $[\tilde{M} - (G \cap L \cap \widetilde{Vm})]$.

8. In a survey of 100 students, the numbers studying various languages were found to be: Spanish, 28; German, 30; French, 42; Spanish and German, 8; Spanish and French, 10; German and French, 5; all three languages, 3.

(a) How many students were studying no language? [*Ans.* 20.]
(b) How many students had French as their only language? [*Ans.* 30.]
(c) How many students studied German if and only if they studied French? [*Ans.* 38.]

[*Hint:* Draw a Venn diagram with three circles, for French, German, and Spanish students. Fill in the numbers in each of the eight areas, using the data given above. Start from the end of the list and work back.]

9. In a later survey of the 100 students (see Exercise 8), numbers studying the various languages were found to be: German only, 18; German but not Spanish, 23; German and French, 8; German, 26; French, 48; French and Spanish, 8; no language, 24.

(a) How many students took Spanish? [*Ans.* 18.]
(b) How many took German and Spanish but not French? [*Ans.* None.]

(c) How many took French if and only if they did not take Spanish? [*Ans.* 50.]

10. The report of one survey of the 100 students (see Exercise 8) stated that the numbers studying the various languages were: all three languages, 5; German and Spanish, 10; French and Spanish, 8; German and French, 20; Spanish, 30; German, 23; French, 50. The surveyor who turned in this report was fired. Why?

11. A recent survey of 100 Dartmouth students has revealed the information about their dates that is summarized in the following table.

	Beautiful and Intelligent	Plain and Intelligent	Beautiful and Dumb	Plain and Dumb
Blonde	6	9	10	20
Brunette	7	11	15	9
Redhead	2	3	8	0

Let BL = blondes, BR = brunettes, R = redheads, BE = beautiful girls, D = dumb girls. Determine the number of girls in each of the following classes.

(a) $BL \cap BE \cap D$. [*Ans.* 10.]

(b) BR.

(c) $R \cap \tilde{D}$.

(d) $(BR \cup R) \cap (BE \cup \tilde{D})$. [*Ans.* 46.]

(e) $\widetilde{BL} \cup \widetilde{(\widetilde{BE} \cap D)}$.

12. In Exercise 11, which set of each of the following pairs has more girls as members?

(a) $\widetilde{(BL \cup BR)}$ or R.

(b) $D \cap \widetilde{BE}$ or $BL - (D \cap \widetilde{BE})$.

(c) $\mathcal{E}$ or $R \cap \widetilde{BE} \cap D$.

3. THE RELATIONSHIP BETWEEN SETS AND COMPOUND STATEMENTS

The reader may have observed several times in the preceding sections that there was a close connection between sets and statements, and between set operations and compounding operations. In this section we shall formalize these relationships.

Let $\mathcal{U}$ be a set of logical possibilities. If we have a number of statements relative to $\mathcal{U}$ under consideration, there is a natural way of assigning a set to each one of these statements: To each statement we assign the subset of logical possibilities of the universal set for which that statement is true. This idea is so important that we embody it in a formal definition.

DEFINITION. Let $\mathcal{U}$ be a set of logical possibilities, and $p, q, r, \ldots$ be statements relative to $\mathcal{U}$; let $P, Q, R, \ldots$ be the subsets of $\mathcal{U}$ for which statements $p, q, r, \ldots$ are respectively true; then we call $P, Q, R, \ldots$ the *truth sets* of statements $p, q, r, \ldots$.

If p and q are statements, then $p \vee q$ and $p \wedge q$ are also statements and hence must have truth sets. To find the truth set of $p \vee q$ we observe that it is true whenever p is true or q is true (or both). Therefore we must assign to $p \vee q$ the logical possibilities which are in P or in Q (or both); that is, we must assign to $p \vee q$ the set $P \cup Q$. On the other hand, the statement $p \wedge q$ is true only when both p and q are true, so that we must assign to $p \wedge q$ the set $P \cap Q$.

Thus we see that there is a close connection between the logical operation of disjunction and the set operation of union, and also between conjunction and intersection. A careful examination of the definitions of union and intersection shows that the word "or" occurs in the definition of union and the word "and" occurs in the definition of intersection. Thus the connection between the two theories is not surprising.

Since the connective "not" occurs in the definition of the complement of a set, it is not surprising that the truth set of $\sim p$ is $\tilde{P}$. This follows since $\sim p$ is true when p is false, so that the truth set of $\sim p$ contains all logical possibilities for which p is false, that is, the truth set of $\sim p$ is $\tilde{P}$.

The truth sets of two statements p and q are shown in Figure 5. Also marked on the diagram are the various logical possibilities for these two statements. The reader should pick out in this diagram the truth sets of the statements $p \vee q$, $p \wedge q$, $\sim p$, and $\sim q$.

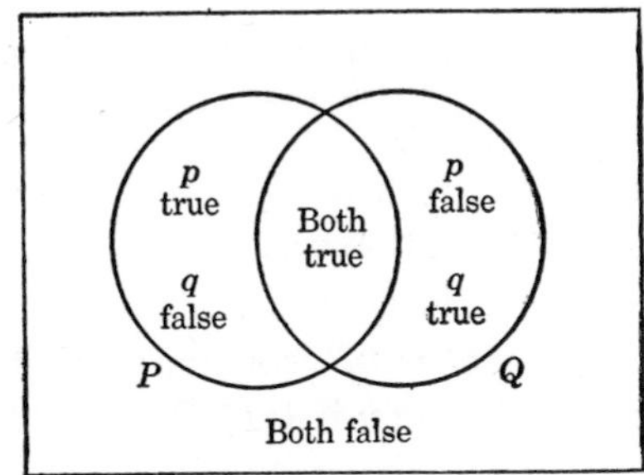

Figure 5

The connection between a statement and its truth set makes it possible to "translate" a problem about compound statements into a problem about sets. It is also possible to go in the reverse direction. Given a problem about sets, think of the universal set as being a set of logical possibilities and think of a subset as being the truth set of a statement. Hence we can "translate" a problem about sets into a problem about compound statements.

So far we have discussed only the truth sets assigned to compound statements involving $\vee$, $\wedge$, and $\sim$. All the other connectives can be defined in terms of these three basic ones, so that we can deduce what truth sets should be assigned to them. For example, we know that $p \rightarrow q$ is equivalent to $\sim p \vee q$ (see Figure 31 of Chapter 1). Hence the truth set of $p \rightarrow q$ is the same as the truth set of $\sim p \vee q$, that is, it is $\tilde{P} \cup Q$. The Venn diagram for $p \rightarrow q$ is shown in Figure 6, where the shaded area is the truth set for the statement. Observe that the unshaded area in Figure 6 is the set $P - Q = P \cap \tilde{Q}$ which is the truth set of the statement $p \wedge \sim q$. Thus the shaded area is the set $\widetilde{(P - Q)} = \widetilde{P \cap \tilde{Q}}$ which is the truth set of the statement $\sim[p \wedge \sim q]$. We have thus discovered the fact $(p \rightarrow q)$, $(\sim p \vee q)$, and $\sim(p \wedge \sim q)$ are equivalent. It is always the case that two compound statements are equivalent if and only if they have the same truth sets. We also see that Venn diagrams can be used to discover relations between statements.

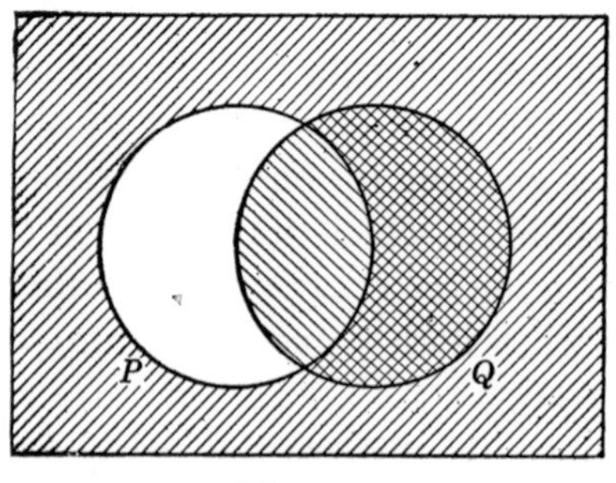

Figure 6

Suppose now that p is a statement that is logically true. What is its truth set? Now p is logically true if and only if it is true in every logically possible case, so that the truth set of p must be $\mathcal{U}$. Similarly, if p is logically false, then it is false for every logically possible case, so that its truth set is the empty set $\mathcal{E}$.

Finally, let us consider the implication relation. Recall that p implies q if and only if the conditional $p \rightarrow q$ is logically true. But $p \rightarrow q$ is logically true if and only if its truth set is $\mathcal{U}$, that is $\widetilde{(P - Q)} = \mathcal{U}$, or $(P - Q) = \mathcal{E}$. From Figure 4 we see that if $P - Q$ is empty, then P is contained in Q. We shall symbolize the containing relation as follows: $P \subset Q$ means "P is a subset of Q." We conclude that $p \rightarrow q$ is logically true if and only if $P \subset Q$.

Let us briefly summarize the above discussion. To each statement there corresponds a truth set. To each logical connective there corresponds a set operation. To each relation between statements there corresponds a relation between the truth sets. The truth sets of the statements $p \vee q$, $p \wedge q$, $\sim p$, and $p \rightarrow q$ are $P \cup Q$, $P \cap Q$, $\tilde{P}$, and $\widetilde{(P - Q)}$, respectively. Statement p is logically true if $P = \mathcal{U}$ and logically false if $P = \mathcal{E}$. Statements p and q are equivalent if and only if $P = Q$, and p implies q if and only if $P \subset Q$.

Example 1. Prove by means of a Venn diagram that the statement $[p \vee (\sim p \vee q)]$ is logically true. The assigned set of this statement is $[P \cup (\tilde{P} \cup Q)]$, and its Venn diagram is shown in Figure 7. In that figure the set P is shaded vertically, and the set $\tilde{P} \cup Q$ is shaded horizontally. Their union is the entire shaded area, which is $\mathcal{U}$, so that the compound statement is logically true.

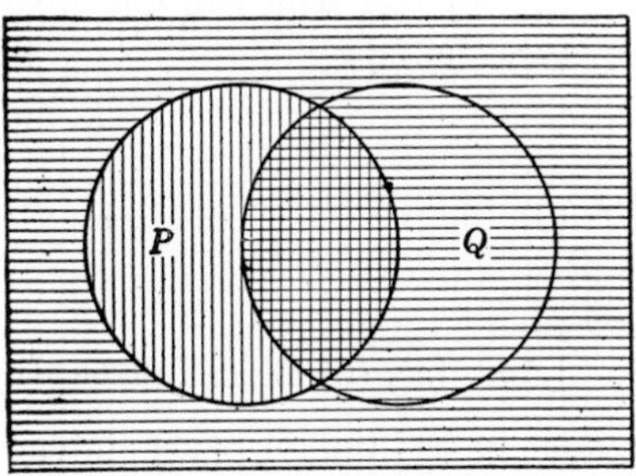

Figure 7

Example 2. Prove by means of Venn diagrams that $p \vee (q \wedge r)$ is equivalent to $(p \vee q) \wedge (p \vee r)$. The truth set of $p \vee (q \wedge r)$ is the entire shaded area of Figure 8, and the truth set of $(p \vee q) \wedge (p \vee r)$ is the doubly shaded area in Figure 9. Since these two sets are equal, we see that the two statements are equivalent.

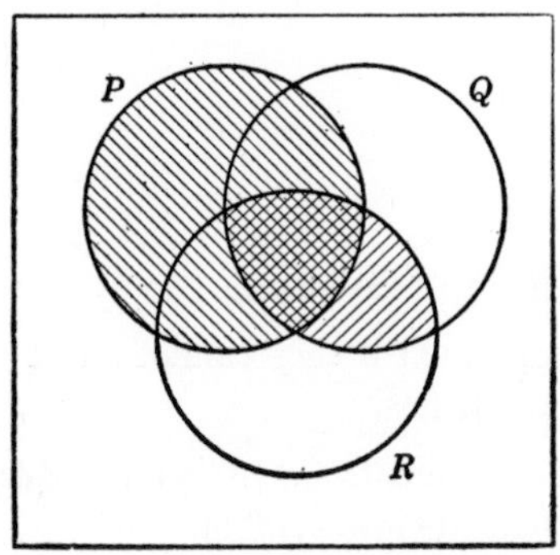

Figure 8

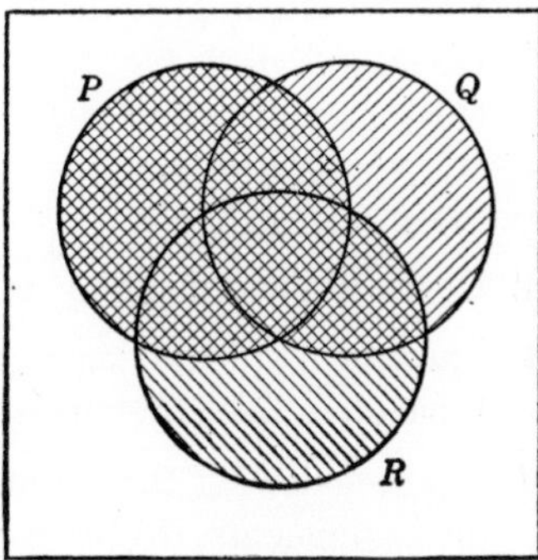

Figure 9

Example 3. Show by means of a Venn diagram that q implies $p \rightarrow q$. The truth set of $p \rightarrow q$ is the shaded area in Figure 6. Since this shaded area includes the set Q we see that q implies $p \rightarrow q$.

Example 4. In Sections 1 and 2 we have already constructed various truth sets for the primary election example. For example, in Section 1 we found that the truth set of "B wins more primaries than either of the other candidates" is {P11, P12, P17, P23, P26, P28, P29}, though we did not at that time call it a truth set. In Section 2 we used truth sets of various compound statements relative to this possibility space as examples of unions, intersections, and complements.

EXERCISES

Note: In Exercises 1, 2, and 3, find first the truth set of each statement.

1. Use Venn diagrams to test which of the following statements are logically true or logically false.
   (a) $p \vee \sim p$.
   (b) $p \wedge \sim p$.
   (c) $p \vee (\sim p \wedge q)$.
   (d) $p \to (q \to p)$.
   (e) $p \wedge \sim(q \to p)$.
   [*Ans.* (a), (d) logically true; (b), (e) logically false.]

2. Use Venn diagrams to test the following statements for equivalences.
   (a) $p \vee \sim q$.
   (b) $\sim(p \wedge q)$.
   (c) $\sim(q \wedge \sim p)$.
   (d) $p \to \sim q$.
   (e) $\sim p \vee \sim q$.
   [*Ans.* (a) and (c) equivalent; (b) and (d) and (e) equivalent.]

3. Use Venn diagrams for the following pairs of statements to test whether one implies the other.
   (a) p; $p \wedge q$.
   (b) $p \wedge \sim q$; $\sim p \to \sim q$.
   (c) $p \to q$; $q \to p$.
   (d) $p \wedge q$; $p \wedge \sim q$.

4. Devise a Venn diagram test for the inconsistency of two statements.

5. Three or more statements are inconsistent if they cannot all be true. What does this state about their truth sets?

6. In the following three compound statements (a) assign variables to the components, (b) bring the statements into symbolic form, (c) find the truth sets, and (d) test for consistency.

   If this is a good course, then I will work hard in it.
   If this is not a good course, then I shall get a bad grade in it.
   I will not work hard, but I will get a good grade in this course.
   [*Ans.* Inconsistent.]

Note: In Exercises 7–9 assign to each set a statement having it as a truth set.

7. Use truth tables to find which of the following sets are empty.
(a) $(P \cup Q) \cap (\tilde{P} \cup \tilde{Q})$.
(b) $(P \cap Q) \cap (\tilde{Q} \cap R)$.
(c) $(P \cap Q) - P$.
(d) $(P \cup R) \cap (\tilde{P} \cup \tilde{Q})$. [*Ans.* (b) and (c).]

8. Use truth tables to find out whether the following sets are all different.
(a) $P \cap (Q \cup R)$.
(b) $(R - Q) \cup (Q - R)$.
(c) $(R \cup Q) \cap \widetilde{(R \cap Q)}$.
(d) $(P \cap Q) \cup (P \cap R)$.
(e) $(P \cap Q \cap \tilde{R}) \cup (P \cap \tilde{Q} \cap R) \cup (\tilde{P} \cap Q \cap \tilde{R}) \cup (\tilde{P} \cap \tilde{Q} \cap R)$.

9. Use truth tables for the following pairs of sets to test whether one is a subset of the other.
(a) $P; P \cap Q$.
(b) $P \cap \tilde{Q}; Q \cap \tilde{P}$.
(c) $P - Q; Q - P$.
(d) $\tilde{P} \cap \tilde{Q}; P \cup Q$.

10. Show, both by the use of truth tables and by the use of Venn diagrams, that $p \wedge (q \vee r)$ is equivalent to $(p \wedge q) \vee (p \wedge r)$.

11. In Section 2 various subsets of the set of 36 possible outcomes of the primary elections were constructed. Identify these subsets as truth sets.

12. In the primary election example find the truth sets of the following statements:
(a) A wins all the primaries. [*Ans.* {P1}.]
(b) A and B both win two elections.
(c) C wins exactly two primaries.
[*Ans.* {P15, P18, P21, P24, P27, P30, P31, P32, P34, P35.}]
(d) C wins all the elections.

4. OPEN STATEMENTS

A statement in which one or more unrestricted variables occur is called an *open statement.* We will be concerned only with statements that have a single such variable, and we will usually let x be this variable.

In algebra one meets open statements very frequently, for example, in an equation such as $x^2 - 3x + 2 = 0$. The unrestricted variable x may take on any number as its value. For certain numbers x (namely, $x = 1$ and $x = 2$) the assertion of the equation is true, for others it is false. In such a situation, where the truth or falsity of an open statement depends only on the value x takes on, we may think of the set of all permissible values of x as the possibility set $\mathcal{U}$, and of the set of all such values that make the assertion true as its truth set. In the above example the set $\mathcal{U}$ consists of all the real numbers, while the truth set is $\{1, 2\}$.

The introduction of a truth set for open statements enables us to apply previously derived results to all kinds of open statements. For example, we know that the truth set of the conjunction of two statements is the intersection of the truth sets. When we are asked to solve an equation, we are asked to find one element (or all elements) of its truth set. When we are asked to solve two equations simultaneously, we are in effect given the open statement which is the conjunction of the two equations. Hence we are looking for elements in the intersection of the two truth sets. If this intersection is empty, then the equations have no simultaneous solution. Such equations are inconsistent, since their truth sets have no value of x in common.

Example 1. Solve simultaneously the equations

$$x^2 - 3x + 2 = 0 \quad \text{and} \quad x^2 = 1.$$

Take as $\mathcal{U}$ the set of all real numbers. We have already noted that the former equation has as its truth set $\{1, 2\}$. The truth set of the latter is $\{1, -1\}$. The intersection of these is the unit set $\{1\}$, hence they have a unique common solution.

Example 2. Let $\mathcal{U}$ consist of the population of the United States. We consider the open statements p: "x is over 6 feet in height," and q: "x is over 30 years of age," and r: "x is under 10 years of age." The truth sets P, Q, and R are the sets of people over 6 feet, over 30 years old, and under 10 years old, respectively. The truth set of $p \wedge q$ is $P \cap Q$, that is, the set of all people who are over 6 feet tall and over 30 years of age. Since no person fulfills both conditions, the truth set of $p \wedge r$ is empty. Hence, p and r are inconsistent statements.

It is useful to apply the concept of a truth set to inequalities as well as to equalities. If $\mathcal{U}$ consists of all real numbers, then the truth set of $x < 0$ consists of the negative real numbers. The truth set of $x > -3$ consists of all real numbers larger than -3. If we assert these two inequalities simultaneously, we get as a truth set the intersection of the two original truth sets, which consists of the numbers between -3 and 0.

Example 3. We again take $\mathcal{U}$ to be the set of real numbers. Let us consider the two open statements

$$p: \; x^3 - x = 0 \quad \text{and} \quad q: \; x^2 < \tfrac{1}{4}.$$

The truth sets are $P = \{-1, 0, 1\}$, and Q which contains the numbers between $-\frac{1}{2}$ and $+\frac{1}{2}$. Since $P \cap Q = \{0\}$, the two conditions together uniquely determine the number 0.

These concepts serve to clarify the distinction between an equation and an identity. When we give someone an equation to solve, we ask him (as noted above) to find one or all elements of the truth set of the equation. But when we assert that $(x - 1)(x + 1)$ identically equals $x^2 - 1$, which is symbolized as $(x - 1)(x + 1) \equiv x^2 - 1$, we assert that the equation holds for all x. Thus an identity is an equation whose truth set is $\mathcal{U}$ itself. An identity is an example of a logically true statement.

It is instructive to follow a correct and an incorrect solution of the cubic equation in Example 3. Let us first solve it correctly. Given

$$x^3 - x = 0,$$

then:

(1) $$x(x - 1)(x + 1) = 0$$

(2) $$x = 0 \quad \text{or} \quad x - 1 = 0 \quad \text{or} \quad x + 1 = 0$$

(3) $$x = 0 \quad \text{or} \quad x = 1 \quad \text{or} \quad x = -1$$

(4) $$x = 0 \quad \text{or} \quad 1 \quad \text{or} \ -1.$$

Step (1) rewrites the given equation in an equivalent form. Since equivalent statements have the same truth set, this is permissible. In step (2) we have rewritten the equation as a disjunction of three equations. This is because a product of numbers is 0 if and only if one of its factors is 0. Hence we know that the disjunction is equivalent to the original equation, and we have not changed the truth set. In step (3) we have rewritten each of the three equations in equivalent form. Finally, we note that the truth set of a disjunction is the union of truth sets; in (3) it is clear that each of the three equations has a single element in its truth set, so that we finally know that the truth set of the original equation has three elements.

Next we consider an incorrect solution. Given

$$x^3 - x = 0,$$

then we divide through by x, and obtain

(5) $$x^2 - 1 = 0$$

(6) $$x^2 = 1$$

Therefore

(7) $$x = 1.$$

We have succeeded in finding one element in the truth set of the original equation, but not the entire truth set. The reason for this is that twice, going to steps (5) and (7), we wrote a new equation that was not equivalent to the previous one. It is quite true that (5) implies the original equation, but it is not equivalent to it. This means that (5) has a smaller truth set than the original equation. For any x that has the property (5) the original equation also holds, but not conversely in the case of $x = 0$. (Recall that we may multiply an equation by 0, but may not divide by 0.) Hence we "lost" 0 from the truth set.

Again, it is true that if $x = 1$, then necessarily $x^2 = 1$. Hence (7) implies (6). But the converse does not hold, hence (7) has a smaller truth set than (6). Indeed, in this step we lost -1 from the truth set.

In solving an equation the safe procedure is to go from a given equation to an equivalent one in each step. This assures us that the original truth set remains unchanged. If we go to an equation that implies the previous one but is not equivalent to it, then we have reduced the truth set; while if we deduce an equation that follows from the original one, but is not equivalent to it, then we have increased the truth set. In the former case we have "lost some roots" while in the latter we have "introduced extraneous roots."

EXERCISES

1. Let $\mathcal{U}$ be the set of real numbers. Describe the truth sets of each of the following open statements.
(a) $x^2 - 4 = 0$. [*Ans.* The truth set is $\{2, -2\}$.]
(b) $x^2 + 4 = 0$. [*Ans.* The truth set is $\mathcal{E}$.]
(c) $x^2 - 4x + 3 = 0$.
(d) $x^2 - 4x + 4 = 0$.
(e) $x^2 - 4x + 5 = 0$.

2. What happens to the truth set of an equation if both sides are multiplied by k, where
(a) $k \neq 0$?
(b) $k = 0$?

3. What happens to the truth set of an inequality such as $x^2 < 2x - 1$ if both sides are multiplied by k, where
(a) $k > 0$?
(b) $k = 0$?
(c) $k < 0$?

4. Find the truth set of the conjunctions of the following open statements. ($\mathcal{U}$ is the set of real numbers.)
(a) $x^2 + x - 2 = 0$ and $x^2 = 4$. [*Ans.* The truth set is $\{-2\}$].
(b) $x^2 - 4 = 0$ and $x^2 - 4x + 4 = 0$.

(c) $x^3 - 6x^2 + 11x - 6 = 0$ and $x^2 - 4x + 3 = 0$.

[*Ans.* The truth set is $\{1, 3\}$.]

(d) $x^3 = 1$ and $x^2 - 4x + 4 = 0$.

5. Find the truth sets of the conjunctions of the following pairs of inequalities. ($\mathcal{U}$ is the set of all integers.)

(a) $x \geq 3$ and $x \leq 10$.

[*Ans.* The truth set is $\{3, 4, 5, 6, 7, 8, 9, 10\}$.]

(b) $x^2 \leq 4$ and $x - 1 \geq 1$.

(c) $x \leq 0$ and $x^2 - 2x \leq 0$.

6. Let $\mathcal{U}$ be the set of real numbers $0 \leq x < 2\pi$. Find the truth sets of each of the following trigonometric equations.

(a) $\sin x = \cos x$. $\left[\textit{Ans.}\text{ The truth set is }\left\{\frac{\pi}{4}, \frac{5\pi}{4}\right\}.\right]$

(b) $\sin x = \sin 2x$.

(c) $\tan x = 1$. [*Ans.* Same as (a).]

(d) $\sin x = 3 + \sin x$.

(e) $\sin^2 x = 1 - \cos^2 x$.

7. Analyze the following argument:

Given that $x = 5$,

then $x^2 = 25$

$$x^2 - 5x = 25 - 5x$$

$$x(x - 5) = -5(x - 5)$$

therefore, $x = -5$

and $5 = -5$.

8. Analyze the following argument:

We are to solve $x - 1 = 0$.

Add -1 to each side, $x - 2 = -1$.

Squaring,

$$x^2 - 4x + 4 = 1.$$

Subtracting 1,

$$x^2 - 4x + 3 = 0.$$

Dividing by $x - 1$,

$$x - 3 = 0.$$

Adding 3, $x = 3$.

9. Give an example of an open statement that is a self-contradiction (has an empty truth set).

10. Prove that if we can deduce a self-contradiction from a set of equations, then the equations have no common solution.

11. Prove that if a set of equations has no common solution, then their conjunction implies any equation.

12. Use the results of Exercises 10 and 11 to show that a set of equations has *no* common solution if and only if it is possible to deduce the equation $1 = 0$ from them.

13. For the following pair of equations (a) show that they have no common solution and (b) show that $1 = 0$ is deducible from them:

$$2x + 1 = 0$$

$$3x + 2 = 0.$$

14. Use the method of Exercise 10 to show that $x^2 - 3x + 1 = 0$ and $2x^2 - 6x + 1 = 0$ have no common solution.

15. Use the method of Exercise 10 to show that the pair of inequalities $x \geq 1$ and $x^2 + 2x + 1 < 3$ has no common solution.

5. FUNCTIONS

A rule that assigns to every element of a given set some definite object is called a *function*. Functions and sets lie at the basis of all branches of mathematics.

More specifically, we are given a set D, which is called the *domain* of the function, and we are given a rule **f** that assigns some object to every element of D. (We shall always write a letter that stands for a function in **boldface**.) Then **f** is called a *function on D*. If x is any element of D, we denote the object assigned to x by $\mathbf{f}(x)$, and call it the *value* of **f** at x. This object may itself be an element of D, but it need not

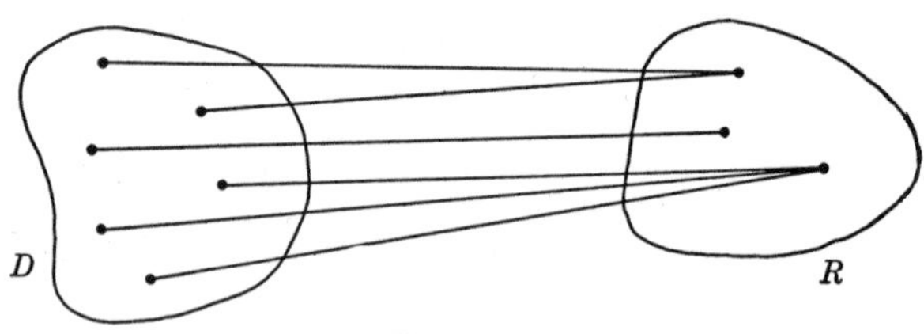

Figure 10

be. The various objects so assigned may be all different, or all the same, or any kind of a mixture. The set R of all objects $\mathbf{f}(x)$ which are used in the assignment is called the *range* of **f**. This is illustrated in Figure 10.

Example 1. Let D be a set of human beings. Say it is the present population of the United States. Let $\mathbf{f}(x)$ be the age of x, expressed to the nearest year. The range of **f** consists of a set of whole numbers, starting with 0, presumably including all integers up to 100, and even having a few integers above 100 in the set.

Example 2. Let D consist of all the citizens of the United States, and let

$f(x)$ be the first name of citizen x. Then the range is a set consisting of a very large number of different names.

Example 3. Let D be the set of adults in the State of New York, and let $f(x)$ be the height of x measured in inches. Then the range of f consists of real numbers, perhaps some real numbers between 30 and 100, allowing for midgets and giants.

Example 4. Let $D = \{0, 1, 2, 3, 4\}$. Let $f(0) = 2$, $f(1) = 2$, $f(2) = 17$, $f(3) = 0$, $f(4) = 17$. The range of f is $\{0, 2, 17\}$. (See Figure 11.)

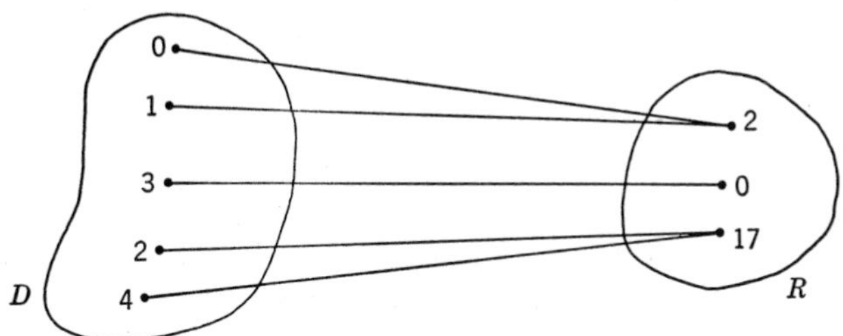

Figure 11

Example 5. Let D be the set of all real numbers. Let $f(x) = x^2 - 3$. The range will again be a set of real numbers, but not all real numbers. (See Exercise 1.)

Example 6. Let D be any set. Let $f(x) = x$ for every x in D. Then the range is D itself. This function is called the *identity function on D*.

Example 7. Let D be any set. Let $f(x) = a$ for every x in D, where a is some fixed object. Then the range is the unit set $\{a\}$, and f is called a *constant function*.

These few examples should illustrate the wide variety of functions, domains, and ranges possible. The domain of a function may be finite as in Examples 1–4, or infinite as in Example 5. The function may be given by a verbal description as in Examples 1–3, or by the explicit listing of all its values as in Example 4, or by some sort of formula as in Example 5. Of course, a listing is possible only if D is finite, and practical only if D is not too big. And a formula is possible only if both D and the range R consist of numbers.

The range R may be the same as D, as in Example 6; or a subset of D, as in Example 5; or overlap D, as in Example 4; or be of a totally different nature from D, as in Examples 1–3. It may have the same number of elements as D, for example, when f is an identity function; or have fewer elements, as in Examples 1–4. It may even happen that D is infinite and yet R is finite, as when f is a constant function. But R

can never have more elements than D, since every element of R has at least one element of D corresponding to it. This idea will be extended in Sections 12–13 of the present chapter.

In short, D and R may be quite arbitrary sets. The only restriction is that **f** should assign a unique element of R to each element of D, and that every element of R be so used.

We can introduce the concept of the equality of two functions.

DEFINITION. The functions **f** and **g** are said to be *equal*, symbolized $\mathbf{f} = \mathbf{g}$, if they have the same domain D, and if for every element x of D we have $\mathbf{f}(x) = \mathbf{g}(x)$.

Naturally, equal functions have the same range. (See Exercise 2.) Functions that are equal in this sense should be thought of as "the same function" in all uses. Thus, for example, $x^2 - 1$ and $(x - 1)(x + 1)$ are two formulas for the same function.

As a more complicated example observe that over the domain $D = \{0, 1\}$ the function defined by the formulas $x^2 + 1$ and $2x^2 - x + 1$ are equal. Of course, if the above domain were changed, these functions might no longer be equal. But that is beside the point, because over the stated domain they *are* equal.

Example 8. Let D be any set. Let A be a subset of D. We define a function **f** on D as follows: If x is in A, then $\mathbf{f}(x) = 1$; if x is in $\tilde{A}$, then $\mathbf{f}(x) = 0$. This function is called the *characteristic function of the subset A*. The range of the characteristic function is normally the set $\{0, 1\}$. (See Exercises 3–6.) This function may be used to represent the subset A.

If **f** is any function defined on D, and a is an element of its range, then $\mathbf{f}(x) = a$ is an open statement with D as its possibility set. The truth set of such a statement consists of all elements of D to which **f** assigns the value a. These truth sets play a key role in probability theory. For example, if D consists of all possible outcomes of an experiment, and **f** is a certain measurement made during the experiment, then the truth set of $\mathbf{f}(x) = a$ is the set of all possible outcomes in which the measurement yields value a. If we want to compute the probability that we will get this value for the measurement, we must certainly know what the truth set is.

The concept of the equality of two functions is also clarified if we think of it in terms of truth sets. Let **f** and **g** be two functions defined on the same domain D. The open statement $\mathbf{f}(x) = \mathbf{g}(x)$ has a certain truth set, that consists of points x for which the two functions happen to have the same value. Of course this truth set may be empty, if the two functions have no common value. It may also happen that the truth set is all of D, and in this case we say that $\mathbf{f} = \mathbf{g}$. In other words, the two functions are equal if $\mathbf{f}(x) = \mathbf{g}(x)$ is an identity, or if it is logically true, or if its truth set is the entire domain.

In Section 3 we constructed truth sets for statements that were not open statements. But in each such case there is a simple method for finding an equivalent open statement, that is, an open statement having the same truth set. Thus, if we wish, we may always think of truth sets as associated with open statements. We may even restrict ourselves to open statements of the form $\mathbf{f}(x) = a$.

Example 9. For the primary voting problem of Section 1 consider the truth set of "A wins in California." If we wish, we may define the function **f** on the set of 36 possibilities whose value for each case is the winner in California. Then "A wins in California" is equivalent to "$\mathbf{f}(x) = \text{A}$," and hence our truth set may be thought of as the truth set of an open statement.

The trick used in this example will work in most cases. But there is a simpler method, though a less natural one, that will work in all cases. Let p be any statement relative to $\mathcal{U}$. Let **f** be the characteristic function of its truth set. Then $\mathbf{f}(x) = 1$ if p is true in case x, and $\mathbf{f}(x) = 0$ if p is false in that case. This function is also called the *characteristic function* of the statement p. Quite clearly, the statement p is equivalent to the open statement "$\mathbf{f}(x) = 1$."

EXERCISES

1. Find the range of the function in Example 5.
2. From the definition of the equality of two functions, prove that equal functions have the same range.
3. In Example 8 it was stated that the characteristic function of a subset A "normally" has two elements in its range. What are the two subsets A which are an exception to this rule?
4. Let A and B be two subsets of D. Let **f** and **g** be their characteristic functions, respectively. Let $\mathbf{h}(x)$ be the lesser of the two numbers $\mathbf{f}(x)$ and $\mathbf{g}(x)$, for every x in D. Prove that **h** is the characteristic function of $A \cap B$.
5. In analogy to Exercise 4, find the characteristic function of $A \cup B$.
6. In analogy to Exercise 4, find the characteristic function of $\tilde{A}$.
7. Let D be the population of the United States. Which of the following **f**'s are functions on D?

   (a) $\mathbf{f}(x)$ is the father of x. [*Ans.* Is a function.]

(b) f(x) is the son of x. [*Ans.* Is not a function.]
(c) f(x) is the grandfather of x.
(d) f(x) is the maternal grandfather of x.
(e) f(x) is the oldest daughter of x.

8. For the f's in Exercise 7 that are functions on D, find the range of each.

9. Describe a function having D as domain and R as range, where
(a) D is $\{1, 2, 3\}$ and R is $\{3, 5\}$.
(b) D is the set of all integers and R is the set of all even integers.
(c) D is the set of all integers and R is $\{0, 1, 2\}$.
(d) D is the set of all real numbers and R is $\{5\}$.

10. Let f be given by the following tables. In each case describe the domain and range of f.

x	f(x)
1	a
2	b
3	a
4	a
5	a

(a)

x	f(x)
1	5
2	2
3	1
4	3
5	4

(b)

x	f(x)
a	!
b	0
c	*
d	*
e	!

(c)

11. Find a nonempty domain D for which the functions defined by the formulas f(x) $= 2x^2 - 1$ and g(x) $= 1 - 3x$ are equal. Find another domain D' for which f and g are unequal.

12. Let D be any set, let f be the identity function on D, and let g be a constant function whose only value is an element d of D. What is the truth set of f(x) = g(x)?

13. Let f and g be constant functions on D. Prove that the truth set of f(x) = g(x) is either D or $\mathcal{E}$.

14. In the primary election example in Section 1, let D be the set of 36 possible outcomes, and let f give the number of primaries that C wins. What is the truth set of f(x) = 2?

15. A coin is tossed twice. If $\mathcal{U} = \{\text{HH, HT, TH, TT}\}$, find two different open statements equivalent to the statement "two heads come up."

6. NUMERICAL FUNCTIONS

An important special class of functions is that of functions whose ranges consist of numbers. These functions are called *numerical functions.* In many cases the exact range of such functions is not so significant as the fact that the range is some subset of the set of all numbers, and hence these functions are simply described as numerical functions on a given domain D. It is not required that the domain should also consist of numbers.

It is possible to define operations of addition and multiplication for numerical functions having the same domain. If $\mathbf{f}$ and $\mathbf{g}$ are both numerical functions having D as domain, we define their *sum* $\mathbf{h} = \mathbf{f} + \mathbf{g}$ by requiring that $\mathbf{h}(x) = \mathbf{f}(x) + \mathbf{g}(x)$ for every x belonging to D. Since $\mathbf{f}(x)$ and $\mathbf{g}(x)$ are numbers, their sum is already defined. Thus the sum of two functions is defined by adding corresponding values. Similarly, the product of two functions is defined by multiplying corresponding values: the *product* $\mathbf{k} = \mathbf{fg}$ of the functions $\mathbf{f}$ and $\mathbf{g}$ is defined by requiring that $\mathbf{k}(x) = \mathbf{f}(x)\mathbf{g}(x)$ for all x belonging to D.

Example 1. Let D be the set $\{a, b, c, d\}$, and let the functions $\mathbf{f}$ and $\mathbf{g}$ be defined by the second and third columns in Figure 12. Then the sum $\mathbf{h}$ and the product $\mathbf{k}$ are as shown in Figure 12.

x	$\mathbf{f}(x)$	$\mathbf{g}(x)$	$\mathbf{h}(x)$	$\mathbf{k}(x)$
a	1	2	3	2
b	2	0	2	0
c	1/2	4	9/2	2
d	5	−2	3	−10

Figure 12

Example 2. Let D be the set of real numbers. Let $\mathbf{f}(x) = x^2$ and let $\mathbf{g}$ be the constant function having the value 3 always, which we denote by $\mathbf{g} = \mathbf{3}$. (We shall always indicate a constant function by writing the constant in **boldface**.) Then the sum $\mathbf{h}$ is given by $\mathbf{h}(x) = x^2 + 3$, and the product $\mathbf{k}$ is determined by $\mathbf{k}(x) = 3x^2$.

Various other operations on functions are commonly in use. For example, by $\mathbf{f}^2$ we mean the product of $\mathbf{f}$ by itself, that is, $\mathbf{ff}$. By $3\mathbf{f}$ we mean the product of the constant function $\mathbf{3}$ and the function $\mathbf{f}$. By $-\mathbf{f}$ we mean the function whose value for x in D is $-\mathbf{f}(x)$. Similarly we can define $\mathbf{f} - \mathbf{g}$, and $\mathbf{f}/\mathbf{g}$, and so on.

When $\mathbf{f}$ and $\mathbf{g}$ are given by formulas, then a combination of $\mathbf{f}$ and $\mathbf{g}$ will be determined by the formula resulting from performing the same combinations on the given formulas.

Example 3. Let $\mathbf{f}(x) = x - 3$ and $\mathbf{g}(x) = x^2 - 2x + 5$, where the domain is the set of real numbers. Then $\mathbf{f} + \mathbf{g}$ is given by $x^2 - x + 2$, the product $\mathbf{fg}$ by $(x - 3)(x^2 - 2x + 5)$, or more simply by $x^3 - 5x^2 + 11x - 15$, the difference **g** − **f** by $x^2 - 3x + 8$, the quotient **f**/**g** by $(x - 3)/(x^2 - 2x + 5)$, and **g**/**f** by $(x^2 - 2x + 5)/(x - 3)$.

From the definition of the quotient of two numerical functions it is clear that a precaution must be taken. The value is well defined only if the denominator is not 0. Hence if in the quotient **g**/**f** the function **f** ever takes on the value 0, then the quotient is not well defined. This is often taken care of by choosing as domain for **g**/**f** the subset of D on which $\mathbf{f}(x) \neq 0$. Thus in Example 3, **g**/**f** is well defined on the set of all real numbers, excluding the number 3. On the other hand **f**/**g** is well defined for the set of all real numbers, since $x^2 - 2x + 5$ cannot be 0.

If the functions are given by a listing or tabulation, then the combinations are easily computed one value at a time.

Example 4. Let **f** and **g** be as in Figure 12. Let $\mathbf{m} = \mathbf{f} - 2\mathbf{g}$, $\mathbf{n} = 3\mathbf{f} - 5\mathbf{g}^3$, and let $\mathbf{p} = \mathbf{g}^2/\mathbf{f}$. These functions are defined by Figure 13.

x	$\mathbf{m}(x)$	$\mathbf{n}(x)$	$\mathbf{p}(x)$
a	−3	−37	4
b	2	6	0
c	−15/2	−637/2	32
d	9	55	4/5

Figure 13

Example 5. We ask a friend to perform the following computations: "Choose a number; add 3; multiply by 6; subtract 6; divide by 3; add 10; divide by 2." When he finishes we ask him what his answer is. He says that it is 10. So we surprise him by saying that his original number was 3. These instructions are actually a complicated way of defining a very simple function. Let us suppose that the original number was x. By working through the above instructions we find that the answer is $x + 7$. Hence we need only subtract 7 from his answer to find the original number. The element of surprise enters because he does not realize how simple a function he is computing.

Example 6. Let us now ask the friend to perform the following operations: "Choose a positive number; add 6; multiply by the original number; add 9; take the (positive) square root; add 10; subtract the original number." And to his surprise we announce that his result was 13, even though we do not know what number he chose. This series of operations defines the constant function **13**, in a complicated way.

An interesting numerical function is the function **n** which assigns to a set the number of elements in the set. We may take as the domain of

$\mathbf{n}$ all the subsets of a given set of k elements, and its range will consist of the numbers 0, 1, . . . , k. A basic property of this function is

(1) $$\mathbf{n}(A \cup B) = \mathbf{n}(A) + \mathbf{n}(B) - \mathbf{n}(A \cap B).$$

This result is easily seen in terms of a Venn diagram. Let us suppose that elements are distributed as in Figure 14. Then $\mathbf{n}(A \cup B) = a + b + c$, while the right side of (1) is

$$(a + b) + (b + c) - b = a + b + c.$$

We also see that if A and B have no elements in common, then (1) simplifies to

$$\mathbf{n}(A \cup B) = \mathbf{n}(A) + \mathbf{n}(B).$$

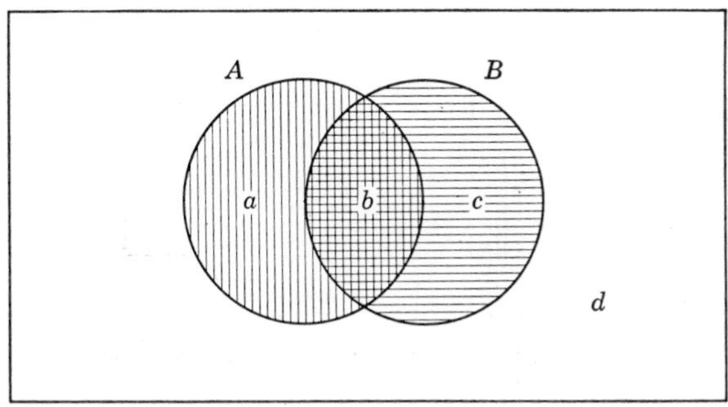

Figure 14

Example 7. We are told that 200 students take mathematics, and 150 take economics. How many students take one or the other course? This question is not answerable on the basis of the given information. If A is the set of math students, and B the set of economics students, then we want to find $\mathbf{n}(A \cup B)$. However, $\mathbf{n}(A \cup B) = \mathbf{n}(A) + \mathbf{n}(B) - \mathbf{n}(A \cap B)$, and the last number is not given. If we know that 20 students take both subjects, then we know that the number taking one or the other (or both) is $200 + 150 - 20 = 330$. If no student takes both courses, then our answer is 350. If every student taking economics is required to take mathematics, then our answer is 200.

Example 8. *More than two sets.* It is possible to derive formulas for the number of elements in a set which is the union of more than two sets (see Exercise 9), but usually it is easier to work with Venn diagrams. For example, suppose that the registrar of a school reports the following statistics about a group of 30 students:

19 take mathematics.
17 take music.
11 take history.

12 take mathematics and music.
7 take history and mathematics.
5 take music and history.
2 take mathematics, history, and music.

We draw the Venn diagram in Figure 15 and fill in the numbers for the number of elements in each subset working from the bottom of our list to the top. That is, since two students take all three courses, and five take music and history, then three take history and music but not mathematics,

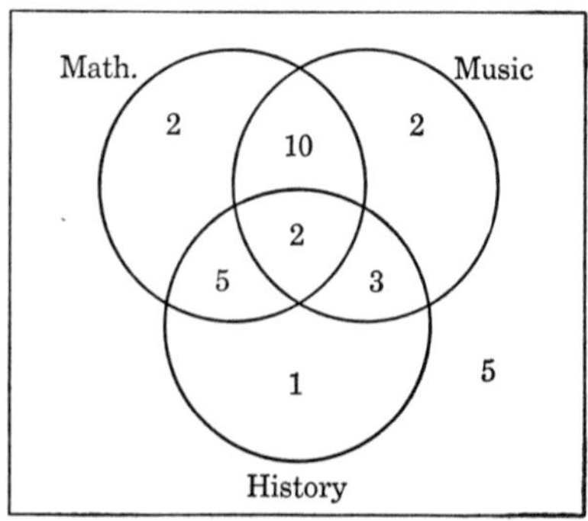

Figure 15

etc. Once the diagram is completed we can read off the number who take any combination of the courses. For example, the number who take history but not mathematics is $3 + 1 = 4$.

EXERCISES

1. Let D be the set of real numbers. Write a formula for the identity function on D.

2. Let D be the set of real numbers, $\mathbf{i}$ the identity function on D, and $\mathbf{j}$ the constant function whose only value is 1. Write formulas for
   (a) $\mathbf{i}^2$. [*Ans.* x^2]
   (b) $\mathbf{i} + 3\mathbf{j}$.
   (c) $3\mathbf{i}^3 - 5\mathbf{i}^2 + 2\mathbf{j}/\mathbf{i} + \mathbf{j}$.

3. Let $\mathbf{f}$ and $\mathbf{g}$ be the characteristic functions of two subsets of D. Prove that $\mathbf{fg}$ is the characteristic function of the intersection of the two subsets.

4. Let $\mathbf{f}$ be the characteristic function of a subset A of D, and $\mathbf{j}$ the constant function having value 1 on D. Prove that $\mathbf{j} - \mathbf{f}$ is the characteristic function of the set $\tilde{A}$. What set has $\mathbf{j}$ as its characteristic function?

5. Check the values in Figure 13.

6. Let f and g be given by the table below.

x	f(x)	g(x)
a	1	5
b	0	-1
c	-2	-3

Write tables for the functions
(a) f + g. [*Ans.* 6, -1, -5.]
(b) fg.
(c) f − g.
(d) f/g. [*Ans.* $\frac{1}{5}$, 0, $\frac{2}{3}$.]
(e) $f^2 - fg + 2$.

7. Let $D = \{0, 1\}$. For each of the following pairs of functions on D state whether f = g.
(a) $f(x) = x$ and $g(x) = x^2$.
(b) $f(x) = 2x + 1$ and $g(x) = 2x^3 + 1$.
(c) $f(x) = x$ and $g(x) = -x$.
(d) f is the constant function 1 and $g(x) = 2x^2 - x + 1$.

8. Let $\mathcal{U}$ be a set of k elements. Find $n(\mathcal{U})$ and $n(\mathcal{E})$.

9. Prove that

$$n(A \cup B \cup C) = n(A) + n(B) + n(C) - n(A \cap B) - n(A \cap C) - n(B \cap C) + n(A \cap B \cap C).$$

[*Hint:* Use a Venn diagram.]

10. A friend tells us to perform the following operations: "Choose a number; add 3; multiply by the original number; add 3; multiply by the original number; add 1; take the cube root; add 4; subtract the original number." At this point he is in a position to make a surprising announcement. What is it? What function is defined by his operations?

11. In Example 8 find:
(a) The number of students that take mathematics but do not take history. [*Ans.* 12.]
(b) The number that take exactly two of the three courses.
(c) The number that take one or none of the courses.

12. In a chemistry class there are 20 students, and in a psychology class there are 30 students. Find the number in either the psychology class or the chemistry class if:
(a) The two classes meet at the same hour. [*Ans.* 50.]
(b) The two classes meet at different hours and 10 students are enrolled in both courses. [*Ans.* 40.]

13. Analyze the data given below and draw a Venn diagram like that in Figure 15. Assuming that every student in the school takes one of the courses, find the total number of students in the school.

(a)	(b)	
28	36	students take English.
23	23	students take French.
23	13	students take German.
12	6	students take English and French.
11	11	students take English and German.
8	4	students take French and German.
5	1	students take all three courses.

Comment on the result in (b).

14. Suppose that in a survey concerning the reading habits of students it is found that:

60 per cent read magazine A.
50 per cent read magazine B.
50 per cent read magazine C.
30 per cent read magazines A and B.
20 per cent read magazines B and C.
30 per cent read magazines A and C.
10 per cent read all three magazines.

(a) What per cent read exactly two magazines? [*Ans.* 50.]
(b) What per cent do not read any of the magazines? [*Ans.* 10.]

15. If p and q are equivalent statements and $\mathbf{n}(P) = 10$, what is $\mathbf{n}(P \cup Q)$?

16. If p implies q, prove that $\mathbf{n}(P \cup \tilde{Q}) = \mathbf{n}(P) + \mathbf{n}(\tilde{Q})$.

17. On a transcontinental airliner, there are 9 boys, 5 American children, 9 men, 7 foreign boys, 14 Americans, 6 American males, and 7 foreign females. What is the number of people on the plane? [*Ans.* 33.]

18. A certain college administers three qualifying tests. They announce the following results: "Of the students taking the tests 2 per cent failed all three tests, 6 per cent failed tests A and B, 5 per cent failed A and C, 8 per cent failed B and C, 29 per cent failed test A, 32 per cent failed B, and 16 per cent failed C." How many students passed all three qualifying tests? How many failed on exactly one test?

19. If p and q are inconsistent statements, show that the number of elements in the truth set of $p \vee q$ is the sum of the elements in the truth sets of p and q.

7. THE BASIS OF A POSSIBILITY SPACE

Let $\mathbf{f}_1, \mathbf{f}_2, \ldots, \mathbf{f}_n$ be functions on $\mathcal{U}$, and let x be any point in $\mathcal{U}$. Then the values $\mathbf{f}_1(x) = a_1, \mathbf{f}_2(x) = a_2, \ldots, \mathbf{f}_n(x) = a_n$ are uniquely determined by x. We can then ask whether x is the only element of $\mathcal{U}$ that leads to these values. If so, we can say that x is uniquely described by the functions. If the functions have the property that they describe every element of $\mathcal{U}$ uniquely, then we say that the functions *describe* $\mathcal{U}$.

Let us suppose that a sequence of n experiments is performed. It is natural to choose as the possibility space the set of all possible sequences of outcomes, whose graphical representation is a tree. We then define the n *outcome functions*, $\mathbf{f}_1, \mathbf{f}_2, \ldots, \mathbf{f}_n$, to be functions whose domain is the set of paths in this tree, and such that $\mathbf{f}_i$ gives the outcome of the ith experiment. The function $\mathbf{f}_i$ may also be thought of as labeling the ith branch of each path in the tree. The n outcome functions describe the possibility space.

Example 1. Let us reconsider the example in Chapter 1, Figure 16. The possibility set consists of six cases, as shown in the figure. Let $\mathbf{f}_1(x) = 1$

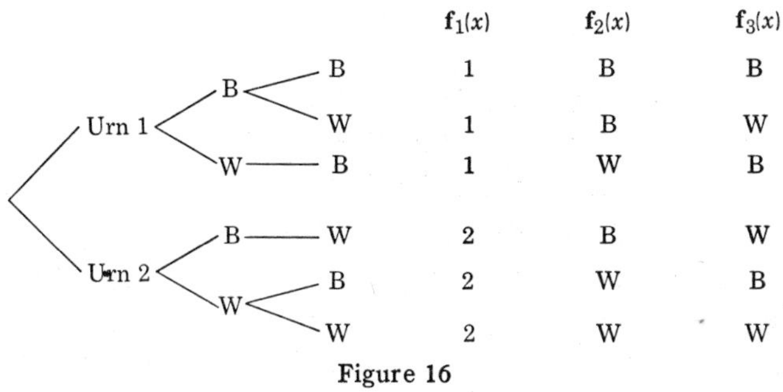

Figure 16

or 2, depending on which urn is chosen; and let $\mathbf{f}_2$ and $\mathbf{f}_3$ give the color of the first and second ball drawn, respectively. Then the three outcome functions describe the possibility space, as is easily seen from the figure. The tree diagram for this example is shown in Figure 16.

Example 2. A coin is tossed, and then a die is rolled. This may be thought of as a sequence of two experiments, where the outcome functions $\mathbf{f}_1$ and $\mathbf{f}_2$ have the ranges $R_1 = \{H, T\}$ and $R_2 = \{1, 2, 3, 4, 5, 6\}$, respectively. The possibility space $\mathcal{U}$ has 12 elements, which are uniquely described by the outcome functions. The tree diagram for this example is shown in Figure 17.

When a sequence of functions describes a possibility space, we know that each element of $\mathcal{U}$ is described by a combination of function values. But it will not be true, in general, that every such combination of values describes a point of $\mathcal{U}$. Thus, in Example 1 the combination $\mathbf{f}_1(x) = 1$, $\mathbf{f}_2(x) =$ white, and $\mathbf{f}_3(x) =$ white is impossible. Indeed, if every combination of values were possible, $\mathcal{U}$ would have $2 \cdot 2 \cdot 2 = 8$ elements instead

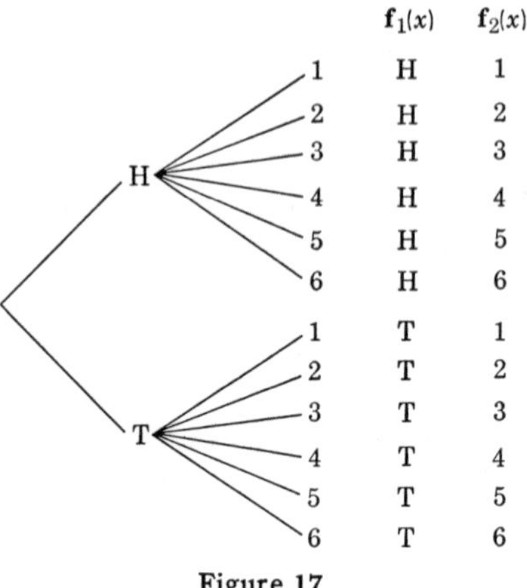

Figure 17

of 6. On the other hand, in Example 2 every combination of values is possible.

DEFINITION. If $\mathbf{f}_1, \mathbf{f}_2, \ldots, \mathbf{f}_n$ are functions on a given set $\mathcal{U}$, and if every combination of function values is possible, then we say that the functions are *logically independent*. If the functions are logically independent, and if they also describe $\mathcal{U}$, then we say that they form a *basis* for $\mathcal{U}$.

In a sequence of experiments the outcome functions describe the possibility space. But they are not, in general, logically independent. To say that they are logically independent means that the outcomes of any subset of the experiments cannot limit the possibilities for the remaining experiments, as is the case in Example 1 above. The outcome functions in Example 2 are logically independent, and hence they form a basis for $\mathcal{U}$.

Example 3. Let p and q be two independent statements. The possibility space is taken to consist of the four truth table cases TT, TF, FT, and FF. Let $\mathbf{f}_1$ and $\mathbf{f}_2$ be the characteristic functions of the two statements p and q, that is, each function is 1 if its statement is true and 0 if it is false. Then the set $\mathcal{U}$ and the values of the functions are as shown in Figure 18. From this figure we see that the characteristic functions describe the possibility space. We also note that all four possible combinations of values occur, hence the functions are logically independent, and they form a basis.

p	q	$\mathbf{f}_1$	$\mathbf{f}_2$	$\mathbf{f}_3$
T	T	1	1	1
T	F	1	0	0
F	T	0	1	0
F	F	0	0	0

Figure 18

If the original statements had not been independent, then at least one case would be missing, and hence the functions would not be logically independent. Thus the concept of the logical independence of functions is a generalization of the concept of the independence of statements.

The function $\mathbf{f}_3$ tabulated in Figure 18 is the characteristic function of the compound statement $p \wedge q$. It is clear that neither the pair of functions $\mathbf{f}_1$ and $\mathbf{f}_3$ nor the pair $\mathbf{f}_2$ and $\mathbf{f}_3$ forms a basis for $\mathfrak{U}$ since neither pair of functions describes the possibility space.

Example 4. Let $\mathbf{f}_1, \mathbf{f}_2, \ldots, \mathbf{f}_7$ be the outcome functions for a World Series played between the Dodgers and the Yankees. Then the range of the first four functions is $\{D, Y\}$, indicating the winning team. But the range of the last three functions is $\{D, Y, N\}$, where N indicates that the game was not played. The possibility space for this situation is given by the tree of Figure 26 on page 22 if we make the following change: the paths of the tree that do not have 7 branches are extended by adding branches labeled N so that every path in the tree has exactly 7 branches. We can see that the outcome functions describe the possibility space, but they do not form a basis. Indeed, if they did form a basis, there would be $2 \cdot 2 \cdot 2 \cdot 2 \cdot 3 \cdot 3 \cdot 3 = 432$ possible outcomes, instead of the actual 70.

If we are interested only in the outcome of the first three games, we can take the three-stage tree, which has 8 paths, as our possibility space. Since the first three functions, when restricted to this possibility space, are logically independent, they form a basis for the new possibility space. Again, if we wish to compute the function $\mathbf{g}$ that gives the number of times the Dodgers win in the first three games, then this simpler possibility space will suffice.

The question may be raised as to whether every possibility space has a basis. It is easily seen that there is at least one basis for every space. For if we let $\mathbf{f}$ be the identity function on $\mathfrak{U}$, then $\mathbf{f}$ itself forms a basis for $\mathfrak{U}$ (see Exercise 6). A basis that consists of a single function will be called a *trivial basis* of $\mathfrak{U}$.

A second interesting question is whether or not a function can be added to a basis. If $\mathbf{f}_1, \ldots, \mathbf{f}_n$ form a basis of $\mathfrak{U}$, then every combination of values of these functions occurs once and only once on $\mathfrak{U}$. Suppose that we try to add a function $\mathbf{g}$ to the basis. Let $\mathbf{f}_1(x) = a_1, \ldots, \mathbf{f}_n(x) = a_n$ be one combination of function values; which occurs for exactly one x. If $\mathbf{g}(x) = b$, then b is the only value of $\mathbf{g}$ that can occur in combination with the given values of the n functions. Hence if $\mathbf{g}$ takes on any other value on $\mathfrak{U}$, then it is not logically independent of the n functions. On the other hand, if it is a constant function, then we have a new larger basis. So we can add as many constant functions to a basis as we wish, but no other function can be added. It is usually assumed that there are no constant functions in a basis, since these are redundant, and under this convention a given basis cannot be enlarged.

Since we have noted that the identity function in itself forms a basis for $\mathcal{U}$, we may raise the question of what other functions have this property. If **f** is a function on $\mathcal{U}$, and if it is to form a basis by itself, then it must describe the space and it must be logically independent of all the other functions in the basis (a condition that is trivially fulfilled). For **f** to describe the space it is necessary that **f** have different values for different elements of $\mathcal{U}$. A function that never takes on the same value twice is known as a *one-one function*, since it matches uniquely one element of the domain with one of the range. Any such one-one function will form a trivial basis.

Example 5. Let $\mathcal{U}$ consist of the soldiers in the United States Army. Let $\mathbf{f}(x)$ be the serial number of soldier x. Then **f** is a one-one function, and hence it forms a basis. This enables the Army to refer to each soldier by his serial number.

EXERCISES

1. A coin is tossed first, and then a number from 1 to 4 is picked. Describe $\mathcal{U}$ and the two outcome functions. Show that the outcome functions form a basis.

2. A coin is tossed first. If it comes up heads, another coin is tossed. If it comes up tails, a die is rolled. Draw the tree diagram. Use the two outcome functions (one for each experiment) to describe $\mathcal{U}$. Show that the outcome functions do not form a basis.

3. Let $\mathbf{f}_1$ and $\mathbf{f}_2$ be the characteristic functions of the independent statements p and q. What is the characteristic function of
(a) $p \wedge q$?
(b) $p \vee q$?
(c) $\sim p$?

4. Let p and q be two statements such that p implies q. Do the two characteristic functions form a basis in this case?

5. Prove that if $\mathbf{f}_1$, $\mathbf{f}_2$, and $\mathbf{f}_3$ form a basis for $\mathcal{U}$, and their ranges have n_1, n_2, n_3 elements, respectively, then $\mathcal{U}$ has $n_1n_2n_3$ elements. What can be said if the functions describe $\mathcal{U}$, but are not logically independent?

6. Let $\mathcal{U}$ be any set and let **f** be its identity function. Prove that **f** by itself forms a basis for $\mathcal{U}$.

7. Suppose that $\mathcal{U}$ has seven elements. Prove that, if we do not allow the use of constant functions, then any basis for $\mathcal{U}$ must be a trivial basis. [*Hint:* See Exercise 5.]

8. Let the functions be defined as in Example 4. Which of the following sets of functions are logically independent?

(a) $\mathbf{f}_1, \mathbf{f}_2$. [*Ans.* Independent.]
(b) $\mathbf{f}_1, \mathbf{f}_2, \mathbf{f}_3, \mathbf{f}_4$.
(c) $\mathbf{f}_1, \mathbf{f}_2, \mathbf{f}_3, \mathbf{f}_4, \mathbf{f}_5$. [*Ans.* Not independent.]
(d) $\mathbf{f}_4, \mathbf{f}_5$.
(e) $\mathbf{f}_5, \mathbf{f}_6$.

9. Let $\mathcal{U}$ be the set of real numbers. Which of the following functions are one-one?

(a) $\mathbf{f}(x) = x$.
(b) $\mathbf{f}(x) = x^2$.
(c) $\mathbf{f}(x) = x^3$.
(d) $\mathbf{f}(x) = \sin x$.
(e) $\mathbf{f}(x) = e^x$. [*Ans.* (a), (c), (e).]

10. Consider the following sequence of two experiments: A number is selected at random from 1 to 5. If this integer is n, we then select a second integer at random, from 1 to n. Draw the tree diagram, and for each path of the tree compute the values of $\mathbf{f}$ and $\mathbf{g}$, where $\mathbf{f}$ gives the sum of the two numbers chosen, and $\mathbf{g}$ their difference. Do these functions describe the tree? Do they form a basis?

11. In Exercise 10 prove that no basis can have $\mathbf{f}$ in it.

12. A set of functions is said to *separate* two points x and y if there is a function $\mathbf{f}$ in the set such that $\mathbf{f}(x) \neq \mathbf{f}(y)$. Prove that a set of functions separates all pairs of points in $\mathcal{U}$ if and only if they describe $\mathcal{U}$.

13. A die is rolled three times. As possibility space we choose the 216 possible sequences of outcomes. Let $\mathbf{f}_1, \mathbf{f}_2, \mathbf{f}_3$ be the outcome functions. Which of the following sets of functions describe the space? Which form a basis?

(a) $\mathbf{f}_1, \mathbf{f}_2, \mathbf{f}_3$.
(b) $\mathbf{f}_1 + \mathbf{f}_2, \mathbf{f}_1 - \mathbf{f}_2, \mathbf{f}_3$.
(c) $\mathbf{f}_1, \mathbf{f}_1 + \mathbf{f}_2, \mathbf{f}_1 + \mathbf{f}_2 + \mathbf{f}_3$.
(d) $\mathbf{f}_1 + \mathbf{f}_2, \mathbf{f}_1 + \mathbf{f}_3, \mathbf{f}_2 + \mathbf{f}_3$.

[*Ans.* They all describe the space; only (a) forms a basis.]

8. COUNTING PROBLEMS

An important type of counting problem concerns the number of functions of a given kind that can be defined on a given domain. Let us choose the set $D = \{x_1, \ldots, x_n\}$ as our domain. We specify the range of our functions to be $R = \{a_1, \ldots, a_m\}$, where, of course, $m \leq n$, and we specify how many times each value of the function is to occur. Say that we require that the value a_i be used n_i times, where the sum of the n_i's must be n. We then inquire as to the number of such functions that can be defined on D.

We may reformulate this type of problem in a highly intuitive way. Let us think of the a_i's as various types of labels that we may attach to the x's. The function to be defined may be thought of as carrying out the labeling. And we are told exactly how many objects are labeled in a given way, where the sum of the labels must equal the number of x's.

Example 1. Let D have five elements, and let $R = \{\text{red, blue}\}$, and let $n_1 = 1, n_2 = 4$. That means that we have five given objects, we have one red label and four blue labels, and we ask how many ways the objects can be labeled. Clearly, if we have once assigned the red label, all the other objects must have blue labels. Hence there are five possible methods of labeling, differing only in which element is labeled red.

Normally we will have $m < n$. In Example 1 we had $n = 5$ and $m = 2$. But a particularly interesting special case is when $m = n$. This means that we have n different labels, and hence each label can be used only once. For such problems the following general principle is useful.

If one thing can be done in exactly r different ways, for each of these a second thing can be done in exactly s different ways, for each of the first two a third can be done in exactly t ways, etc., then the sequence of things can be done in $r \cdot s \cdot t \ldots$ *ways.*

The validity of the above general principle can be established by thinking of a tree representing all the ways in which the sequence of things can be done. There would be r branches from the starting position. From the ends of each of these r branches there would be s new branches, and from each of these t new branches, etc. The number of paths through the tree would be given by the product $r \cdot s \cdot t \ldots$.

Suppose that we wish to count the number of ways that three objects may be labeled with three different labels. The first object may be assigned any one of the three labels, the second any one of the two remaining labels, and the third must be assigned the one remaining label. Hence the labeling can, according to the above principle, be carried out in $3 \cdot 2 \cdot 1 = 6$ ways.

More generally, if we wish to label n objects with n different labels, then the first object may be assigned one of n labels, the next one of the remaining $n - 1$ labels, etc. This gives us $n(n - 1) \cdot \ldots \cdot 2 \cdot 1$ different ways. The number obtained in this way occurs so often that we give it a symbol, namely $n!$, which is read "n factorial." Thus, for example,

$3! = 3 \cdot 2 \cdot 1 = 6$, and $4! = 4 \cdot 3 \cdot 2 \cdot 1 = 24$. For reasons which will be made clear later we define $0! = 1$ (see Exercise 10).

Thus the number of different ways of labeling n objects with labels that are all different is $n!$. Or we can state this result as saying that if we have a given domain with n elements and a given range with the same number of elements, then there are $n!$ different functions having this domain and range.

Example 2. Let us suppose that there are n people in a room, and we want to line them up. In how many orders can we do this? The ways of ordering a set of objects are known as the *permutations* of the set. It is an immediate consequence of the above result that n objects have $n!$ permutations. Namely, a permutation may be thought of as a function having range $\{1, 2, \ldots, n\}$ and assigning place numbers to the people. Hence there are $n!$ permutations. For example, three people may be ordered in six ways, as is shown in the following:

Jones, Smith, Brown	Smith, Brown, Jones
Jones, Brown, Smith	Brown, Jones, Smith
Smith, Jones, Brown	Brown, Smith, Jones.

Let us now attack the more general problem. Here we have normally fewer than n kinds of labels, and we are to use n_i of the labels a_i.

Let us introduce the symbol

$$\binom{n}{n_1, n_2, \ldots, n_k}$$

to stand for the number of ways that n objects can be labeled with k different labels, if we use the ith label n_i times. If $n_1 + n_2 + \ldots + n_k$ does not equal n, then the labeling is impossible, and hence the symbol equals 0. If the sum of the n_i's is equal to n, then there is always at least one way of carrying out the labeling, and hence the symbol has a positive integral value.

Example 3. Let us suppose that we have six objects, and we have 2 red, 3 blue, and 1 black label. The number of ways of labeling the objects is by definition $\binom{6}{2, 3, 1}$. Let us suppose that when we are through labeling, we decide that we prefer to have six different colored labels, every object having a different label. We must then replace the two red labels, say by two shades of red, which can be done in $2!$ ways. The three blue labels can be replaced by three different shades of blue in $3!$ ways, and the black label is replaced (or kept) in $1!$ ways. This gives us the equation

$$\binom{6}{2, 3, 1} 2!3!1! = 6!,$$

since we know that there are 6! ways of assigning distinct labels. Hence we have

$$\binom{6}{2, 3, 1} = \frac{6!}{2!3!1!} = \frac{720}{2 \cdot 6 \cdot 1} = 60.$$

The argument carried out in Example 3 is applicable in the general case. We suppose that we have labeled n objects with k labels (using label a_i a total of n_i times) in one of

$$\binom{n}{n_1, n_2, \ldots, n_k} \quad \text{ways.}$$

We can then obtain a labeling by distinct labels if we associate n_i of the distinct labels with label a_i, and introduce them by relabeling the n_i objects previously labeled by a_i. This can be done in $n_i!$ ways, for each i. We can see that every labeling by the n distinct labels can be obtained in this manner exactly once, hence

$$\binom{n}{n_1, n_2, \ldots, n_k} n_1!n_2! \ldots n_k! = n!$$

and thus

$$\binom{n}{n_1, n_2, \ldots, n_k} = \frac{n!}{n_1!n_2! \ldots n_k!}. \tag{1}$$

Example 4. A college has scheduled nine football games for a season. How many ways can the season end in 4 wins, 2 ties, and 3 losses? We think of D as the set of nine games, and of R as {win, tie, lose}, and then the problem is one of "labeling" the nine games with one of the three possible labels, using the labels 4, 2, and 3 times, respectively. Hence the answer is

$$\binom{9}{4, 2, 3} = \frac{9!}{4!2!3!} = 1260.$$

This type of counting problem occurs frequently in probability theory.

Example 5. A coin is tossed ten times. In how many different ways can we get 7 heads and 3 tails? Here we are trying to label each of ten tosses as "heads" or as "tails," using the former label 7 times and the latter 3 times. Hence the answer is

$$\binom{10}{7, 3} = 120.$$

More generally, if we toss the coin n times, and we want to know the number of ways that we can get r heads (and hence $n - r$ tails), the answer will be

$$\binom{n}{r, n - r}.$$

Example 6. Let us compute the number of different possible bridge deals. In the game of bridge there are four players, often called North, South,

East, and West; and a deal consists of distributing 52 cards among the four players, giving 13 cards to each. If we think of the distribution of the cards, this does not appear to be a labeling problem, since each player receives several cards. But we may think instead of each card being assigned a label, such as "North." Then we are asking for the number of ways that 52 cards can be labeled with four different labels, using each label 13 times, and hence there are

$$\binom{52}{13, 13, 13, 13},$$

or about 54 billion billion billion possible deals.

EXERCISES

1. Compute the following numbers.

(a) $\binom{7}{5, 2}$. (b) $\binom{4}{2, 2}$. (c) $\binom{6}{3, 1, 3}$.

(d) $\binom{250}{248, 1, 1}$. (e) $\binom{5}{1, 2, 2}$. (f) $\binom{4}{2, 0, 2}$.

(g) $\binom{6}{2, 2, 2}$. (h) $\binom{2}{1, 1, 1}$.

[*Ans.* (a) 21; (d) 62,250; (f) 6.]

2. A quarterback on a football team has ten different plays. His coach instructs him to run through the ten plays, without repetition. In how many different orders can he carry out the instructions of his coach?

3. How many ways can nine students be assigned to three triple rooms? How many ways if one particular pair of students refuse to room together? [*Ans.* 1680; 1260.]

4. A group of seven boys and ten girls attends a dance. If all the boys dance in a particular dance, how many possibilities are there for the girls who dance? For the girls who do not dance? How many possibilities are there for the girls who do not dance, if three of the girls are sure to be asked to dance?

5. Suppose that a course is given at three different hours. If fifteen students sign up for the course

(a) How many possibilities are there for the ways the students could distribute themselves in the classes? [*Ans.* 3^{15}.]

(b) How many of the ways would give the same number of students in each class? [*Ans.* 756,756.]

6. There are three different routes connecting city A to city B. How many ways can a round trip be made from A to B and back? How many ways if it is desired to take a different route on the way back? [*Ans.* 9; 6.]

7. How many different ways can a ten question multiple choice exam be answered if each question has three possible choices, labeled a, b, and c? How many ways can it be answered if we choose each letter at least 3 times?

8. In arranging people around a circular table we take into account only their seats relative to each other, not the actual position of any one person. Show that n people can be arranged around a circular table in $(n - 1)!$ ways.

9. A committee of eight men decides to divide itself into three subcommittees of 3, 2, and 3 men, respectively, with no man serving on two subcommittees. In how many ways can this subdivision be accomplished? [*Ans.* 560.]

10. In how many ways can four objects be labeled with two red and two blue labels? In how many ways can they be labeled with red, blue, and green labels if we use two red and two blue labels and don't use the green label? Use your answers to justify the convention that $0! = 1$.

11. Prove that

$$\binom{n}{n_1, n_2, n_3} = \binom{n}{n_2, n_3, n_1}$$

from formula (1). Interpret this result in terms of labeling problems.

12. Prove that the formula for the number of permutations of n objects is a special case of formula (1).

13. Show that in labeling 12 objects in three different colors there are more possibilities when we use each label exactly four times than in any uneven distribution of labels.

9. THE BINOMIAL COEFFICIENTS

This section will be devoted to the most important special case of the counting problems discussed in the previous section. This is the case where two kinds of labels are available.

Let us suppose that we wish to label n objects with two kinds of labels, using exactly j of the first kind of label. Then we must use exactly $n - j$ of the second kind of label, and the labeling can be carried out in

$$\binom{n}{j, n - j} \quad \text{ways.}$$

When there are only two kinds of labels, it suffices to know j, the number of times the first label is used, and hence the $n - j$ in the above symbol is redundant. We can thus abbreviate the symbol to $\binom{n}{j}$.

Example 1. There are ten students in an honors course, and they are sure to receive A's or B's. In how many ways can the grades be assigned so that there will be the same number of A's and B's? In our previous notation this number would be $\binom{10}{5,\,5}$, but we can now write this simply as $\binom{10}{5}$. The answer in any case is

$$\frac{10!}{5!5!} = 252.$$

Example 2. Given a set D of eight elements. We wish to select a subset of three elements. In how many ways can this subset be selected? We know that we may identify a subset by its characteristic function. Hence we are searching for a characteristic function, that is, a function with 0's and 1's as values, which has the value 1 exactly three times. But this is precisely one of our labeling problems, and hence the answer is $\binom{8}{3,\,5}$, or more simply $\binom{8}{3}$ which equals

$$\frac{8!}{3!5!} = 56.$$

Example 2 illustrates the fact that we have an alternate interpretation for the symbol $\binom{n}{j}$. This is the number of ways that we can select j elements from n given ones, hence it is the number of j-element subsets of a set of n elements. These numbers are known as *binomial coefficients*, due to an important use of the numbers in algebra, which will not appear in this book. It will be important for our future work to develop some of the properties of these numbers.

A basic symmetry property of these numbers is the identity

$$\binom{n}{j} = \binom{n}{n-j}.$$

We can establish this in several different ways. If we recall that in unabbreviated form the left side is $\binom{n}{j,\,n-j}$ and the right side is $\binom{n}{n-j,\,j}$, then it becomes obvious that it makes no difference whether the red label is used j times and the blue label $n - j$ times, or vice versa. In terms of subsets the same result may be established as follows. The number $\binom{n}{j}$ is the number of ways that we can select j elements from n given ones. But selecting j of the elements is the same as rejecting $n - j$ elements. Hence the number must be the same as the number of different $n - j$ element subsets that we can reject, and this is $\binom{n}{n-j}$.

Example 3. Sixty students try out for football. The coach must select three full squads, that is a total of 33 men. Hence he must reject 27 candidates. If we think of the number of ways that he can pick his 33 qualifiers, he may end up with one of $\binom{60}{33}$ different possibilities, while if we think of the number of different lists of rejected candidates that he may post, there are $\binom{60}{27}$ possibilities; hence these two numbers are the same. Thus the coach may make his decision in any one of about a billion billion ways.

Example 4. In Example 6 of the last section we computed the number of different possible bridge deals. Let us compare this with the number of possible bridge hands that a given player can get. This number is clearly $\binom{52}{13}$, which is about 635 billion. While the number of different hands is also very large, it is not nearly so great as the number of different possible deals.

A convenient way to obtain the binomial coefficients is by constructing the Pascal triangle, shown in Figure 19. To obtain the triangle we

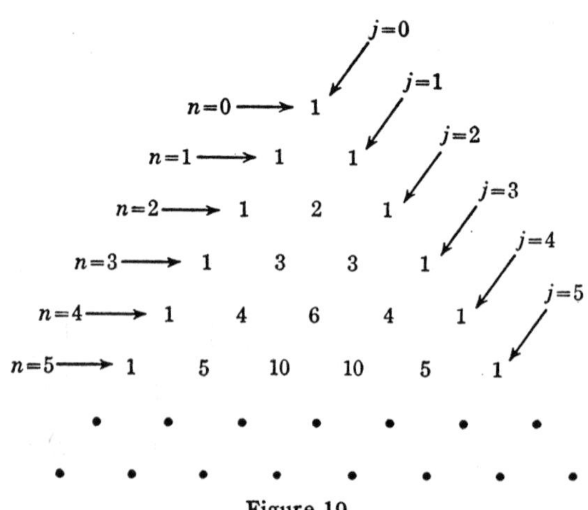

Figure 19

first write the 1's down the sides. Any of the other numbers in the triangle has the property that it is the sum of the two adjacent numbers in the row just above. Thus the next row in the triangle is 1, 6, 15, 20, 15, 6, 1. To find the number $\binom{n}{j}$ we look in the row corresponding to the number n and see where the diagonal line corresponding to the value of j intersects this row. For example, $\binom{4}{2} = 6$ is in the row marked $n = 4$ and the diagonal marked $j = 2$.

The property of the numbers $\binom{n}{j}$ upon which the triangle is based is

$$\binom{n+1}{j} = \binom{n}{j-1} + \binom{n}{j}.$$

This fact can be verified directly, but the following argument is interesting in itself. The number $\binom{n+1}{j}$ is the number of subsets with j elements that can be formed from a set of $n + 1$ elements. Select one of the $n + 1$ elements, x. The $\binom{n+1}{j}$ subsets can be divided into those that contain x, and those that do not. The latter are subsets of j elements formed from n objects, and hence there are $\binom{n}{j}$ such subsets. The former are constructed by adding x to a subset of $j - 1$ elements formed from n elements, and hence there are $\binom{n}{j-1}$ of them. Thus

$$\binom{n+1}{j} = \binom{n}{j-1} + \binom{n}{j}.$$

If we look again at the Pascal triangle, we observe that the numbers in a given row increase for a while, and then decrease. We can prove this fact in general by considering the ratio of two successive terms,

$$\frac{\binom{n}{j+1}}{\binom{n}{j}} = \frac{n!}{(j+1)!(n-j-1)!} \cdot \frac{j!(n-j)!}{n!} = \frac{n-j}{j+1}.$$

The numbers increase as long as the ratio is greater than 1, i.e., $n - j > j + 1$. This means that $j < \frac{1}{2}(n - 1)$. We must distinguish the case of an even n from an odd n. For example, if $n = 10$, j must be less than $\frac{1}{2}(10 - 1) = 4.5$. Hence the last increase is in going from $j = 4$ to 5. Thus $\binom{10}{5}$ is the largest term, and from $j = 5$ on the terms decrease. For $n = 11$, j must be less than $\frac{1}{2}(11 - 1) = 5$. For $j = 5$,

$(n - j)/(j + 1) = 1$. Hence, up to $j = 5$ the terms increase, then $\binom{11}{5} = \binom{11}{6}$, and then the terms decrease.

Example 5. There is a simple model for statistical mechanics, due to T. Ehrenfest which will be discussed in Chapter 6. In that model we consider a gas contained in a volume that is divided into two regions by a permeable membrane. The gas has n molecules, and we are concerned with how many molecules there are in each region. Of course, at any moment of time our set of molecules is divided into two subsets. A subdivision with i elements in the first set can be achieved in $\binom{n}{i}$ ways. We then define the *entropy* of this configuration of molecules to be

$$e_i^n = \log\left[\binom{n}{i}\right].$$

In this it makes little difference what base we choose for the logarithm, since this will change only the units in which we measure entropy.

We can now apply our knowledge concerning binomial coefficients to the concept of entropy. We know that

$$\binom{n}{i} = \binom{n}{n-i}.$$

Hence a configuration with i molecules in the first region has the same entropy as one with i molecules in the second region. We also know that $\binom{n}{i}$ is largest for a given n when $i = n/2$, or is as near as possible. Hence the most even arrangement of molecules has the largest entropy. Furthermore, the less even the division of molecules the smaller the entropy. In the extreme case where all the molecules are in one region we have

$$e_n^n = e_0^n = \log\left[\binom{n}{0}\right] = \log\,[1] = 0.$$

1. Extend the Pascal triangle to $n = 16$. Save the result for later use.
2. Prove that

$$\binom{n}{0} + \binom{n}{1} + \binom{n}{2} + \dots + \binom{n}{n} = 2^n,$$

using the fact that a set with n elements has 2^n subsets.

3. For a set of ten elements prove that there are more subsets with five elements than there are subsets with any other fixed number of elements.

4. Using the fact that

$$\binom{n}{r+1} = \frac{n-r}{r+1} \cdot \binom{n}{r},$$

compute $\binom{30}{s}$ for $s = 1, 2, 3, 4$ from the fact that $\binom{30}{0} = 1$.

[*Ans.* 30; 435; 4060; 27,405.]

5. There are $\binom{52}{13}$ different possible bridge hands. Assume that a list is made showing all these hands, and that in this list the first card in every hand is crossed out. This leaves us with a list of twelve-card hands. Prove that at least two hands in the latter list contain exactly the same cards.

6. A college professor anticipates teaching the same course for the next 35 years. So not to become bored with his jokes, he decides to tell exactly three jokes every year and in no two years to tell exactly the same three jokes. What is the minimum number of jokes that will accomplish this? What is the minimum number if he determines never to tell the same joke twice?

7. From three Republicans and three Democrats, find the number of committees of three which can be formed,

(a) With no restrictions. [*Ans.* 20.]
(b) With three Republicans and no Democrats. [*Ans.* 1.]
(c) With two Republicans and one Democrat. [*Ans.* 9.]
(d) With one Republican and two Democrats. [*Ans.* 9.]
(e) With no Republicans and three Democrats. [*Ans.* 1.]

What is the relation between your answer in part (a) and the answers to the remaining four parts?

8. Problem 7 suggests that the following should be true.

$$\binom{2n}{n} = \binom{n}{0}\binom{n}{n} + \binom{n}{1}\binom{n}{n-1} + \binom{n}{2}\binom{n}{n-2} + \ldots + \binom{n}{n}\binom{n}{0}$$

$$= \binom{n}{0}^2 + \binom{n}{1}^2 + \ldots + \binom{n}{n}^2$$

Show that it is true.

9. By a method analogous to that used for binomial coefficients in this section show that

$$\binom{n+1}{i,j,k} = \binom{n}{i-1,j,k} + \binom{n}{i,j-1,k} + \binom{n}{i,j,k-1}.$$

10. In Example 5 find the change in entropy as one molecule is added to the first cell; i.e., find a simple expression for $e_{i+1}^n - e_i^n$. Use this result to show that entropy increases if and only if the distribution is made more even.

11. Show that n identical objects can be placed into r boxes in

$$\binom{n+r-1}{n} \text{ ways.}$$

[*Hint:* Think of the n objects as placed in some order, with $r - 1$ walls placed at certain positions. Thus, it is a problem of placing n objects and $r - 1$ walls in a row.]

*10. QUANTIFIERS

A statement which asserts that an open statement has all of $\mathcal{U}$ as its truth set is called a *universal statement.* Thus an identity or an assertion of the equality of two functions are examples of universal statements. An equally important type of assertion is that which states that an open statement has a non-empty truth set; such a statement is called an *existential statement.* Universal statements may be put in the form "For all x in $\mathcal{U}$ . . . ," while existential statements are of the form "There is at least one x in $\mathcal{U}$ such that . . . ."

The expressions "For all x in $\mathcal{U}$" and "There is at least one x in $\mathcal{U}$" are examples of quantifiers. A *quantifier* applied to an open statement (with only one kind of variable) in effect "closes" the statement, that is it creates a new statement that is independent of the variable. The statement "For all x in $\mathcal{U}$, $\mathbf{f}(x)$ is 0" is either true or false, depending on the nature of $\mathcal{U}$ and of the function $\mathbf{f}$, but not depending on a choice of x. Other examples of quantifiers are "There are exactly three x's in $\mathcal{U}$ such that . . ." and "There are at most ten x's in $\mathcal{U}$ such that . . . ."

Let us consider the negation of an existential statement. Consider the statement "There is an x in $\mathcal{U}$ such that $\mathbf{f}(x) = \mathbf{g}(x)$." If we deny this, we assert that no x has this property. This is equivalent to the assertion "For all x in $\mathcal{U}$, $\mathbf{f}(x) \neq \mathbf{g}(x)$." Thus the denial of an existential statement is a universal statement. More generally, let $p(x)$ be an open statement. Let P be its truth set. The existential statement "For at least one x in $\mathcal{U}$, $p(x)$" asserts that $P \neq \mathcal{E}$. Hence its negation asserts that $P = \mathcal{E}$. The truth set of $\sim p(x)$ is $\tilde{P}$. The negation of the existential statement asserts that $\tilde{P} = \mathcal{U}$, that is, that "For all x in $\mathcal{U}$, $\sim p(x)$."

Similarly, the negation of a universal statement is existential. The statement "For all x in $\mathcal{U}$, $p(x)$" asserts that $P = \mathcal{U}$. Its negation asserts that $P \neq \mathcal{U}$, hence that $\tilde{P} \neq \mathcal{E}$. Thus it is equivalent to the assertion "For some x in $\mathcal{U}$, $\sim p(x)$." For example, to assert that $\mathbf{f} \neq \mathbf{g}$ is equivalent to the assertion that for some x we have $\mathbf{f}(x) \neq \mathbf{g}(x)$.

Example 1. Number theory deals with the properties of integers, and is a very good area in which to find simple examples of universal and existential statements. Let us first of all define prime numbers. An integer is a *prime number* if it is divisible by exactly two integers, namely, 1 and itself. Thus 2, 3, 5, 7, 11 are examples of primes.

If we examine the primes, say up to 100, we may be led to the following conjecture: any set of ten consecutive integers contains a prime. To make this more precise, let $\mathcal{U}$ consist of all sets of ten consecutive integers. Of course, $\mathcal{U}$ is an infinite set. Then our conjecture has the form: For every X in $\mathcal{U}$, X has a prime element. Since this is a universal statement, a single example where X has no prime in it will disprove it. Such a "counterexample" is given by the set of integers from 114 to 123 inclusive, which contains no primes.

The following is a famous unproved (and undisproved) universal statement known as the *Goldbach conjecture.* Let the possibility set $\mathcal{U}$ for x consist of all even integers ≥ 4. The Goldbach conjecture then is that for all x in $\mathcal{U}$, it is possible to write x as the sum of two primes.

On the other hand, the following universal statement was proved by Schnirelmann early in the present century, and represented the first substantial advance toward cracking the Goldbach conjecture: Let x have the same possibility set $\mathcal{U}$ as above. For all x in $\mathcal{U}$ it is possible to write x as the sum of fewer than 300,000 primes.

Here is an example of a true existential statement that anyone can check for himself. Let the possibility set $\mathcal{U}$ for x be all primes. There exists an x in $\mathcal{U}$ such that $2^x - 1$ is not a prime (see Exercise 7).

Let us elaborate on the way that universal statements are proved and disproved. It is much easier to prove an existential statement than a universal statement. To prove the statement "There is at least one x such that $p(x)$" we need only give a single x having the desired property. That is, an existential statement is most commonly proved by giving an example. The denial of a universal statement is existential, hence it can be proved by an example. Such a "counterexample" proves that the universal statement is false. Thus to prove that "For all x in $\mathcal{U}$, $p(x)$" is false, we need only show a single x in $\mathcal{U}$ which does not have the stated property. For example, the assertion "All prime numbers are odd" is disproved by showing that the number two is an even prime.

Example 2. It is very common in mathematics that a mathematician makes a conjecture and another mathematician disproves it by constructing a counterexample. For example, the eminent number-theorist Fermat conjectured that $2^{2^x} + 1$ is a prime number for every integer x. But Euler later showed that for $x = 5$ we do not get a prime number.

When $\mathcal{U}$ is an infinite set, we cannot prove the truth of a universal assertion by considering all x's separately. More powerful methods of proof are necessary. Mathematical induction is such a method. But sometimes the truth of the universal assertion is provable by the indirect method. Let us suppose that we want to prove "For all x, $p(x)$." We assume its negation, which is equivalent to "There is an x such that $\sim p(x)$." We then take an object that fails to have the property, and show that the existence of such an object leads to a contradiction.

Example 3. Let us prove "Every prime number greater than 2 is odd" by this method. Suppose that the assertion were false. Then we have an integer n which is prime and even. But if it is even, then it is divisible by 2. By hypothesis 2 is not n itself, hence n is not prime—which is a contradiction.

EXERCISES

1. Form the denial of each of the following statements.
   (a) For every x in $\mathcal{U}$, $x^2 > 4$. [*Ans.* For some x in $\mathcal{U}$, $x^2 \leq 4$.]
   (b) For every x in $\mathcal{U}$, $x + 1 = x^3 - 2$.
   (c) For some x in $\mathcal{U}$, $x^2 - 2x + 1 = 0$.
   (d) For some x in $\mathcal{U}$, $1 < x < 2$.

2. Let $\mathcal{U}$ consist of the population of the United States. Classify each of the following statements as universal or existential, and form its negation (in as simple a form as possible).
   (a) All men are mortal. [*Ans.* Some men are not mortal.]
   (b) Some men are children.
   (c) All men are at least five feet tall.
   (d) Some men are at least seven feet tall or at most four feet in height.

3. Give an existential version to the denial of an identity. What does this suggest for the way to *dis*prove an identity?

4. Use the method of Exercise 3 to disprove each of the following supposed identities. ($\mathcal{U}$ is the set of real numbers.)
   (a) $\sqrt{x^2} = x$.
   (b) $\sin x + \cos x = 1$.
   (c) $a^x + b^x = (a + b)^x$.

5. Let $\mathcal{U}$ be the set of all real numbers. Show that each of the following assertions holds for at least one x in $\mathcal{U}$, but does not hold for all x in $\mathcal{U}$.
   (a) $x^2 > x$.
   (b) $(x + 1)^3 = x^3 + 1$.
   (c) $\sin x = -\cos x$.

6. Prove that if a universal statement is true in a given possibility space, it is also true in every subset of the space. But show that the same does not always hold for an existential statement.

7. Show that $2^p - 1$ is prime for $p = 2, 3, 5, 7$ but not for $p = 11$.

*11. THE BINARY NUMBER SYSTEM

Let us consider the way numbers up to (but not including) 1000 are represented in our decimal representation. For example, what does the string of symbols 638 represent?

The first digit, 6, is the quotient when 638 is divided by 100. We then have a remainder of 38. The next digit, 3, is the quotient when the previous remainder is divided by 10. And finally we have a remainder of 8, which is the last digit. This last digit may also be thought of as the quotient when the final remainder is divided by 1.

Thus we perform a sequence of "experiments": First we divide by 100. Then we divide the remainder by 10. Finally we divide the remainder by 1. Let $\mathbf{f}_2$, $\mathbf{f}_1$, $\mathbf{f}_0$ be the three outcome functions, respectively. If $\mathcal{U}$ is the set of integers from 0 to 999, each outcome function has as its range the numbers from 0 to 9, and the result of the experiments is described by the three outcome functions. Hence our outcome functions describe the possibility space, i.e., they give a unique representation of the integers from 0 to 999.

But more than this can be asserted. Since each function has 10 possible values, there are $10 \times 10 \times 10 = 1000$ possible combinations. And since $\mathcal{U}$ has exactly 1000 elements, the outcome functions must be logically independent, i.e., each combination of values actually represents a number. Thus the three functions form a basis for $\mathcal{U}$. Finally, a combination of values is conveniently represented by a string of digits. Thus $\mathbf{f}_2 = 6$, $\mathbf{f}_1 = 3$, and $\mathbf{f}_0 = 8$ is represented by 638.

The key idea in this representation was that in the first experiment we divided by 10^2, which was the largest power of 10 in $\mathcal{U}$; then the remainder is divided by 10^1, and the final remainder by 10^0. This method can be extended to larger numbers. Let $\mathcal{U}$ consist of the integers up to (but not including) 10^n. We let $\mathbf{f}_n$ be the quotient when an element of $\mathcal{U}$ is divided by 10^n, $\mathbf{f}_{n-1}$ the quotient when the remainder is divided by 10^{n-1}, and so on, until $\mathbf{f}_1$ gives the quotient of division by 10^1, and $\mathbf{f}_0$ the final remainder. Then the outcome functions form a basis for $\mathcal{U}$. From this we see that if we represent the elements of $\mathcal{U}$ by the values of the outcome functions, written as a string of digits, then the string $a_n a_{n-1} \ldots a_1 a_0$ represents

$$a_n \cdot 10^n + a_{n-1} \cdot 10^{n-1} + \ldots + a \cdot 10^1 + a_0 \cdot 10^0$$

uniquely.

The important thing to note is that there was no magic in the choice of the number ten for this role. If in place of ten we had used a number

b (called the *base*), we would also have obtained a unique representation. If $\mathcal{U}$ contains all integers up to b^4, for example, then we have a unique representation by dividing by b^3, b^2, b^1, and b^0, successively. Each quotient will be a digit 0 to $b - 1$, and we arrive at a string of four such digits.

Example 1. Let $b = 6$. Let $\mathcal{U}$ contain the integers up to $6^4 = 1296$, that is the integers from 0 to 1295. Our method yields a unique representation of all these numbers by four digit strings "to the base 6." For example, let us represent 1000 to the base 6: First we divide by $216 = 6^3$. Our quotient is 4 and we have a remainder of 136. If we divide this by $36 = 6^2$, our quotient is 3 and the remainder 28. If we divide this by $6 = 6^1$, our quotient is 4 and the remainder is 4. Finally we divide by $1 = 6^0$, which yields a quotient of 4, and there is, of course, no remainder. Thus 1000 represented to the base 6 is written as 4344.

The base must be a positive integer, and 1 is the only integer that will not serve as a base, since all its powers are equal to 1. Hence the simplest possible base is $b = 2$. The resulting system of notation is called the *binary number system*.

In this system we divide by successive powers of 2, and hence the quotient must always be 0 or 1. Thus our numbers will be represented as strings of 0's and 1's.

Example 2. In the binary number system we can represent all numbers up to (but not including) 2^4 by a string of four 0's and 1's. For example, when we choose ten and divide it by 2^3 we have a quotient of 1 and a remainder of 2. When we divide by 2^2 we have a quotient of 0 and hence the same remainder 2. When we divide by 2^1 we have a quotient of 1 and 0 remainder, and hence the final digit is 0. Thus ten represented in the binary system appears as 1010.

The binary system of notation results in a great simplification of arithmetical operations. To add two numbers we need only two rules: Adding 0 to the number does not change the number, and $1 + 1 = 10$ Let us use these rules to add ten and eleven:

$$\begin{array}{r} 1010 \\ 1011 \\ \hline 10101 \end{array}$$

The procedure is perfectly straightforward, if we remember that $1 + 1 = 10$, and hence we have a carry in the second and fourth columns (from the right). The result is

$$1 \times 2^4 + 0 \times 2^3 + 1 \times 2^2 + 0 \times 2^1 + 1 \times 2^0 = 21.$$

Multiplication is in a sense even simpler. We multiply digit by digit, as in the decimal system, and add the results. We have two very simple rules to guide us: Any number multiplied by 0 is 0, and any number multiplied by 1 is the number itself. Let us multiply ten by ten:

```
   1010
   1010
-------
   0000
  1010
 0000
1010
-------
1100100
```

The result is

$$1 \times 2^6 + 1 \times 2^5 + 1 \times 2^2 = 100.$$

The fact that arithmetic in the binary system is so very simple has made this the system of notation used in high-speed computing machines. Each digit is represented by a vacuum tube (or similar electronic device), and the digit is 1 if the tube is on, 0 if the tube is off. The arithmetical rules described above are carried out by simple electric circuits.

EXERCISES

1. Translate each of the following numbers into the binary system.
(a) 20. [*Ans*. 10100.]
(b) 75.
(c) 128.
(d) 80. [*Ans*. 1010000.]
(e) 200.

2. Using the results of Exercise 1 carry out the following additions in the binary system. Check your results.
(a) $20 + 80$.
(b) $75 + 80$.
(c) $128 + 128$.
(d) $128 + 200$.
(e) $80 + 200$.

3. Using the results of Exercise 1, carry out the following multiplications in the binary system. Check your results.
(a) 20×20.
(b) 20×80.
(c) 128×128.

4. Using the results of Exercise 1, carry out the subtraction $200 - 128$ in the binary number system.

5. Prove that the following method serves to number all subsets of a given set: Arrange the elements in order. For any given subset form the characteristic function of the subset. Write down the values of the characteristic function in order, and let the resulting string be the number assigned to the subset, in the binary system.

6. Use the method described in Exercise 5 to number all subsets of the set $\{a, b, c\}$.

7. Use the method of Exercise 5 to prove that a set with n elements has 2^n subsets.

8. If a number is written in the binary number system, how can one tell whether it is even or odd?

9. In a multiple choice test, in which each question has four possible answers, the answers are numbered 1, 2, 4, and 8. The students are told that in each question there may be no correct answer, one correct answer, or several correct answers. They are told to *add* together the numbers of the correct answers (or to write 0 if there is no correct answer).
   (a) Show that the resulting number gives the instructor all the information he desires.
   (b) On a given question the correct sum was 7. Three students put down 4, 8, and 15 respectively. Which answer was most nearly correct? Which was the worst? [*Ans.* 15 best, 8 worst.]

10. Express the numbers 80 and 200 in the number system using base 8 (called the *octal number system*). Add the resulting numbers in the octal system, and check your result.

11. Compare the addition in Exercise 10 with that in Exercise 2(e). From this describe how the octal system can be used as a shorthand for the binary system. [*Hint.* Each octal digit takes the place of three binary digits.]

*12. CARDINAL NUMBERS

Let D be a finite set, **f** any function on D, and let R be the range of the function. Since each element y of R originates from an element x of D, through the relation $\mathbf{f}(x) = y$, we know that R can have no more elements than D. And if **f** happens to be one-one, then there must be exactly the same number of elements in D and R. While these ideas originate from the study of finite domains, they also play a central role in the theory of transfinite (infinite) numbers.

It will be convenient to have a certain list of infinite sets at our disposal, to serve as illustrations. We will use the following: V is the set of all positive integers, W the set of even positive integers, Z the set of all positive rational numbers, Q the set of real numbers between 0 and 1, and R the set of all real numbers. We will also make use of the set V_2 of two-component column vectors with integer components. These will be studied in detail in Chapter 4, and may be thought of for the present purpose simply as an array $\begin{pmatrix} m \\ n \end{pmatrix}$, where m and n are integers.

Let us suppose that we have two sets, A and B, and we wish to know which set has more elements. If these are finite sets, then we may count the number of elements in each set independently for the purpose of comparison. An alternative method is to try to match up the elements of A and B. If we succeed in matching them, there are the same number of elements in both sets; if we use up all the elements of one set before the other is exhausted, then the latter is larger. This method is often more practical than counting.

Example 1. Let A be the set of all students present in a large lecture hall, and let B be the set of all seats in the hall. We wish to determine which set is larger. The procedure of counting the number of students and counting the number of seats may be very lengthy, and is far from optimal. Instead, we could ask all the students to sit down. If every student is seated and there are still empty seats, we can conclude that there are more seats than students; if some students are forced to stand, then the set A is larger than B; while if every student finds a seat and no empty seats remain, then the two sets have the same number of elements. This method of trying to "match" seats and students is the fastest way of having our question answered.

It frequently happens in the history of mathematics that two ideas look equally good at first, but when we attempt to generalize our results we find that one of the ideas allows us to progress much further than the other. The German mathematician G. Cantor showed late in the last century that the concept of "the number of elements in a set" can be extended to infinite sets if we take the method of matching as our basic tool. Cantor succeeded not only in founding the theory of transfinite numbers; he also proved many of its most important theorems.

Let us summarize what we know about comparing two finite sets A and B. We know that one and only one of the following must be the case:

I. There is a one-one function with domain A and range B. (A and B can be matched.)

II. There is a one-one function with a proper subset of A as domain and with range B. (Part of A can be matched with B.)

III. There is a one-one function with A as domain and a proper subset of B as range. (A can be matched with part of B.)

These three cases can be described, respectively, as stating that the two sets are equally large, that A is larger, or that B is larger. If we make use of the concept of the number of elements in a set K, or the *cardinal number* of K, denoted by $\mathbf{n}(K)$, then we have: I. $\mathbf{n}(A) = \mathbf{n}(B)$; II. $\mathbf{n}(A) > \mathbf{n}(B)$; III. $\mathbf{n}(A) < \mathbf{n}(B)$.

If we attempt to relate pairs of infinite sets by exactly the same method, we run into insuperable difficulties. This can be seen by means of the following example.

Example 2. We can show that the set of positive integers V and the set of even positive integers W satisfy all three of the conditions I–III. Let us define three functions: Let $\mathbf{f}_1$ have V as domain and $\mathbf{f}_1(x) = 2x$, let $\mathbf{f}_2$ have W as domain and $\mathbf{f}_2(x) = x$, and let $\mathbf{f}_3$ have V as domain and $\mathbf{f}_3(x) = 4x$. Each of these is a one-one function. Since $\mathbf{f}_1$ has W as its range, it demonstrates relation I. The function $\mathbf{f}_2$ has a proper subset of V as its domain, and it has W as its range, so it demonstrates II. And finally, $\mathbf{f}_3$ has V as domain and a proper subset of W as its range, demonstrating III.

Thus we see that one method of matching may match two given infinite sets, while another will match one of the sets with a proper subset of the other set. The following illustration of the same idea is due to one of the greatest mathematicians of this century, David Hilbert.

Example 3. Suppose that a certain hotel has all its rooms occupied. For simplicity we shall assume that all rooms are single rooms. If this is a finite hotel, and if an additional person asks for a room, he must be turned away. But if this is an infinite hotel, we have no trouble in accommodating him. Suppose, for example, that the rooms are numbered 1, 2, 3, . . . , with one room for each integer. If a new guest arrives we simply ask the guest in room number n to move to room $n + 1$. Guest number 1 moves to room 2, guest 2 to room 3, etc. This will leave room 1 vacant, and we can put the latest arrival in there. Even if the number of new guests arriving equals the number we already have, we should not be embarrassed. Just ask guest number n to move into room number $2n$. This will leave all the odd numbered rooms vacant, in which we can accommodate the infinite number of new arrivals.

The transition to infinite sets was made by Cantor by proposing that the relation I be taken as basic. If we can match two sets by any means, no matter how complex, we will say that they have the same cardinal number. We will consider relations II and III only for sets that cannot possibly be matched. For these sets the relations will have the usual interpretation. Indeed, it can be shown that for any pair of sets A and B one and only one of the following holds (whether the sets be finite or infinite):

I′. There is a one-one function with domain A and range B. Then $\mathbf{n}(A) = \mathbf{n}(B)$.

II′. There is no one-one function having A as domain and B as range, but there is a one-one function with a proper subset of A as domain and B as range. Then $\mathbf{n}(A) > \mathbf{n}(B)$.

III′. There is no one-one function having A as domain and B as range, but there is a one-one function having A as domain and a proper subset of B as range. Then $\mathbf{n}(A) < \mathbf{n}(B)$.

Thus, in comparing two infinite sets we must first decide whether or not they can be matched exactly. If not, we must find a matching that uses up one but not the other, and then we know that the latter set is larger.

Suppose that we find a one-one function with A as domain and a proper subset of B as range. What can we conclude about the cardinal numbers of the two sets? If the sets are finite, then we have relation III, and we know that $\mathbf{n}(A) < \mathbf{n}(B)$. However, for infinite sets we must still ask whether or not some other function will match A and B. If it does, then we have I′, and $\mathbf{n}(A) = \mathbf{n}(B)$. If no such matching exists, then we have III′, and hence $\mathbf{n}(A) < \mathbf{n}(B)$. Hence all we can conclude in the infinite case is that $\mathbf{n}(A) \leq \mathbf{n}(B)$.

Let us apply this to the "axiom" that the whole is greater than any of its parts. This assertion means that if A is a proper subset of B then $\mathbf{n}(A) < \mathbf{n}(B)$. Since we know that A is a proper subset of B, the identity function on A is a one-one function with a proper subset of B as range. But we know that this establishes the desired result only for finite sets. For infinite sets we can only conclude that $\mathbf{n}(A) \leq \mathbf{n}(B)$, i.e., that the part cannot be greater than the whole. Indeed, in Example 2 the set W is a proper subset of V, but they have the same cardinal number.

Example 4. Let us compare the set V of positive integers with the set V_2 of all two-component column vectors with integer components. It is easily seen that $\mathbf{n}(V) \leq \mathbf{n}(V_2)$. We simply introduce the function $\mathbf{f}$ on the set V for which $\mathbf{f}(n) = \begin{pmatrix} n \\ 0 \end{pmatrix}$. This has a proper subset of V_2 as range, hence the inequality follows.

But we must still ask whether some other matching might not succeed in using up all of V_2. Indeed such a matching was found by Cantor himself. We write the elements of V_2 in a two-dimensional array, as in Figure 20, and then we pick them as successive values of the matching function $\mathbf{g}$, proceeding by diagonals. (See the arrows in Figure 20.) Thus

$$\mathbf{g}(1) = \begin{pmatrix}1\\1\end{pmatrix}, \quad \mathbf{g}(2) = \begin{pmatrix}1\\2\end{pmatrix}, \quad \mathbf{g}(3) = \begin{pmatrix}2\\1\end{pmatrix}, \quad \mathbf{g}(4) = \begin{pmatrix}1\\3\end{pmatrix}, \quad \text{etc.}$$

This function is one-one and matches all of V to all of V_2. Naturally, an explicit formula could also be written for $\mathbf{g}$.

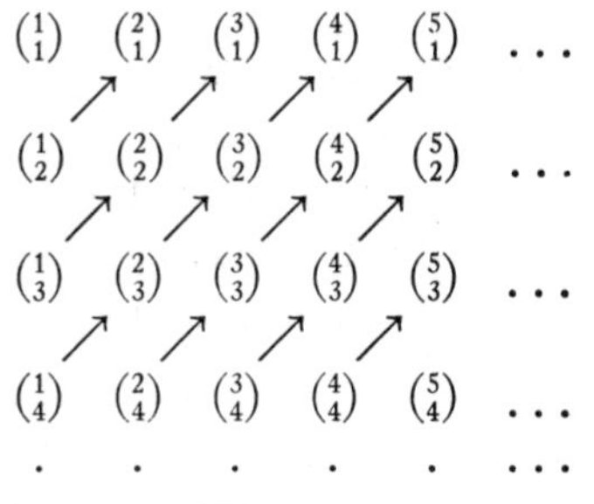

Figure 20

Example 5. Let Z be the set of all positive rational numbers, and let us ask how $\mathbf{n}(Z)$ compares with $\mathbf{n}(V)$. A positive rational number is of the form p/q, where p and q are positive integers. But we must recall that not all such fractions are distinct, since a fraction is not changed when we multiply both numerator and denominator by the same number. Let us suppose that we consider only fractions in which p and q have no common factor, to get a unique representation. Let $\mathbf{f}$ be a function with Z as domain, and let $\mathbf{f}(p/q) = \begin{pmatrix}p\\q\end{pmatrix}$. Then $\mathbf{f}$ will have a subset of V_2 as its range. Thus $\mathbf{n}(Z) \leq \mathbf{n}(V_2)$. Next we construct the function $\mathbf{g}$ with V as domain and $\mathbf{g}(n) = n/1$. This has a subset of Z as range. Hence we have $\mathbf{n}(V) \leq \mathbf{n}(Z) \leq \mathbf{n}(V_2)$. But from Example 4 we know that $\mathbf{n}(V) = \mathbf{n}(V_2)$, hence all three cardinal numbers must be equal. This type of argument, which we know to be valid for finite cardinals, can also be justified for infinite cardinals. Hence we conclude that the cardinal of the set of positive rational numbers is the same as that of the set of integers.

We have so far investigated four infinite sets, V, W, V_2, and Z. We found that these all have the same cardinal number. Since each of these sets can be matched with the integers, they are said to be *denumerably infinite*. We will see in the next section that denumerably infinite sets are the smallest possible infinite sets, and that there are infinitely many cardinals larger than $\mathbf{n}(V)$. We will show that there is a highly complex infinite hierarchy of larger and larger transfinite cardinals.

EXERCISES

1. In Example 2, what is the set $V - W$? Construct a one-one function with domain V and range $V - W$.

2. Prove that there are as many negative integers as positive integers.

3. Prove that the set of integers above 100 has the same cardinal number as the set of integers.

4. Suppose that we define the addition of infinite cardinals so that for any sets A and B having no element in common we have $\mathbf{n}(A \cup B) = \mathbf{n}(A) + \mathbf{n}(B)$. Use the results of Example 2 and Exercise 1 to prove that $\mathbf{n}(V) + \mathbf{n}(V) = \mathbf{n}(V)$.

5. Write the set of integers as the union of three disjoint sets, each having cardinal number $\mathbf{n}(V)$.

6. Sketch a proof to show that if a function (not necessarily one-one) has domain A and range B, then $\mathbf{n}(A) \leq \mathbf{n}(B)$.

7. Prove that if $\mathbf{n}(A) = \mathbf{n}(B)$, and $\mathbf{n}(B) = \mathbf{n}(C)$, then $\mathbf{n}(A) = \mathbf{n}(C)$, using only relation I′ on page 105.

8. Let $\mathbf{h}$ be a function with V_2 as domain and

$$\mathbf{h}\left(\begin{pmatrix} p \\ q \end{pmatrix}\right) = \frac{1}{2}(p + q - 1)(p + q - 2) + p.$$

Prove that this is a one-one matching of V_2 and V. [*Hint:* Show that $\mathbf{h}$ is the inverse function of the function $\mathbf{g}$ constructed in Example 4.]

9. Let V_3 be the set of all three-component column vectors with positive integer components. Sketch a proof that V_3 is denumerably infinite.

10. Prove that the set of all binomial coefficients is denumerably infinite.

*13. THE HIERARCHY OF CARDINALS

The previous section dealt with the basic ideas of the theory of transfinite cardinals. However, we only found one transfinite cardinal. All the infinite sets that we considered had $\mathbf{n}(V)$ as their cardinal number. It can be shown that this is the smallest transfinite number. The usual notation for transfinite numbers is a Hebrew "aleph" with a subscript. Thus our $\mathbf{n}(V)$ is denoted by $\aleph_0$. The next lowest cardinal is called $\aleph_1$, the next $\aleph_2$, etc.

Let us now search for larger infinite sets. In this we are aided by a very strong theorem due to Cantor.

Theorem. If A is any set and S_A is the set of all subsets of A, then $\mathbf{n}(A) < \mathbf{n}(S_A)$.

Proof. It is easily seen that $\mathbf{n}(A) \leq \mathbf{n}(S_A)$. If x is an element of A, then the unit set $\{x\}$ is a subset of A, and hence an element of S_A. Thus the function $\mathbf{f}$ for which $\mathbf{f}(x) = \{x\}$ is a one-one function matching A with a subset of S_A.

We must still ask whether some other function may match A with all of S_A. We will assume that there is a function **g** with A as domain and S_A as range, and we will show that this leads to a contradiction.

The function **g** takes elements of A as arguments and has subsets of A as values. Let us consider the statement "x is not an element of the subset $\mathbf{g}(x)$." Let G be the truth set of this open statement. Since this truth set is a subset of A, it is an element of S_A. Hence G is in the range of **g**. That means that for some element y of A we have $\mathbf{g}(y) = G$. Is this y an element of G? By the definition of G, y is in it if and only if the statement "y is not in the subset $\mathbf{g}(y)$" is true. But that means that y is in G if and only if it is not in G. This is a self-contradiction.

An alternate way to state the proof is to consider a function **g** with domain A and range a subset of S_A. We then construct the subset G. The given argument shows that G is not in the range of **g**, hence the range of **g** is a proper subset of S_A.

This theorem provides us with a method of finding larger and larger sets. We can start with V. Its cardinal number is the smallest infinite cardinal. Then we form the set of all subsets of V, the set S_V, and we are assured that this has a larger infinite cardinal number. Thus it is our first example of a nondenumerably infinite set. We can then form the set of all subsets of S_V, which will have an even larger cardinal number, etc. We thus see that there are infinitely many different infinite cardinal numbers.

As a matter of fact, this does not begin to show how complex the hierarchy of transfinite numbers is. Let us have a sequence of sets so that $\mathbf{n}(A_1) < \mathbf{n}(A_2) < \mathbf{n}(A_3) < \ldots$. If we form the union of these sets A_i, then the union must be larger than any individual set. This is seen as follows: If we want to show that the union is larger than some given A_i, we recall that A_{i+1} is a subset of the union. Hence the union is at least as great as A_{i+1}, and thus greater than A_i.

We now see that from a given set we can form larger and larger sets by means of the theorem. Then we form the union of the resulting infinite sequence. But this union also cannot be the last infinite set, since the theorem guarantees a larger infinite set. We thus get a new infinite sequence of larger and larger infinite sets. And then we can form the union of these, etc.

Let us examine the set S_V. Its elements are subsets of V, hence sets of integers. We know that we can identify a subset of a set with its characteristic function (see Section 5). In our case a characteristic function is a function with V as domain and with values 0 or 1. We can represent such a characteristic function as an infinite decimal expansion with 0's and 1's. We simply let $\mathbf{f}(n)$ be the nth digit in the decimal expansion.

> **Example.** Let W be the set of even integers. Its characteristic function $\mathbf{f}(n)$ is 1 if n is even and 0 if n is odd. We thus have the decimal expansion representation .010101 . . . . This is the decimal expansion of 1/99. Thus the number 1/99 may also be thought of as the representative of the set W.

We thus see that each set of integers can be represented by a decimal expansion, and in a unique way. The function that assigns the decimal expansion to the set of integers is a one-one function with domain S_V. Its range is a subset of the set Q of real numbers between 0 and 1. Hence $\mathbf{n}(S_V) \leq \mathbf{n}(Q)$. But we may equally well think of the expansion as being a binary expansion. Thus, for example, the expansion of W, which is .010101 . . . , represents the number 1/3 in the binary system. We may thus consider the one-one function that takes a real number in Q, considers it written in binary notation, and assigns to it the subset of V whose characteristic function it represents. Thus to 1/3 it assigns the set W. This function has Q as domain and a subset of S_V as range (see Exercise 14). Hence $\mathbf{n}(Q) \leq \mathbf{n}(S_V)$, and thus $\mathbf{n}(Q) = \mathbf{n}(S_V)$.

It can further be shown that $\mathbf{n}(Q) = \mathbf{n}(R)$, that is that the set of all real numbers has the same cardinality as the real numbers between 0 and 1 (see Exercise 7). Thus we know that $\mathbf{n}(R) = \mathbf{n}(S_V)$, and R is also a nondenumerably infinite set.

We know that V has the lowest infinite cardinal number. What set has the second lowest infinite cardinal $\aleph_1$? Such a set can be constructed, but its construction presupposes the theory of transfinite ordinal numbers, which is beyond the scope of this book. We would certainly like a more familiar example. The set R suggests itself as a natural candidate. We know that it is larger than V, and know of no set that is in between. The conjecture that $\mathbf{n}(R) = \aleph_1$ is known as the "continuum hypothesis." (The name is due to the fact that the set of real numbers, or its geometric representation—the straight line, is referred to as the *continuum*.) But this problem has not been solved. It is one of the most famous unsolved problems in mathematics.

One of two possibilities must hold. Either the continuum hypothesis is true, in which case we would like to prove that any set with a cardinal larger than $\aleph_0$ has a cardinal at least as large as $\mathbf{n}(R)$. On the other hand, if the hypothesis is false, then we should be able to pick out a subset of the real numbers with cardinality greater than that of the integers, but smaller than that of all the real numbers. Such a set would have to be complicated in view of the fact that we know that the number of points on an interval, no matter how small, is the same as on the entire line. (See Exercises 5–6.)

Let us close by considering names of numbers. A name of a number or of any other object must be a word or a finite sequence of words, as in "ten," "the square root of two," or "the number attained by adding two and two." How many such names can one form in the English language? Certainly the list is infinite, as is shown by the fact that we have a name for every integer. Hence there are at least $\aleph_0$ names. On the other hand, we can imagine a listing of all possible sequences of words, in lexicographic order. We could number the items on the list. Since all names occur on this list, we have matched the set of names against the set of integers. Hence there is a denumerable infinity of possible names.

This creates a peculiar difficulty. We know that $\mathbf{n}(R) > \aleph_0$, but we have only $\aleph_0$ names. Hence most real numbers are unnamable. But in spite of the fact that most real numbers will forever remain unnamed, we can prove theorems about all real numbers. The problem is even worse for functions of real numbers. Such functions have cardinality of at least $\aleph_2$. Hence only a negligible fraction of a negligible fraction of all these functions can conceivably be described. This is a striking example of man's ability to comprehend his own limitations.

EXERCISES

1. Prove that the set of all functions with domain A has a larger cardinal number than A.

2. What is the characteristic function of the set of odd integers? What number do we get if we represent the characteristic function as a decimal expansion? What if as a binary expansion?

[*Ans.* 10/99, 2/3.]

3. What is the characteristic function of the set of all integers divisible by 4? What number do we get if we represent this characteristic function by a decimal expansion? What if as a binary expansion?

4. Use the function $\mathbf{f}(x) = 2x$ to prove that there are the same number of points in the interval $0 \leq x \leq 1$ as in the interval $0 \leq x \leq 2$. Hence prove that $\mathbf{n}(Q) + \mathbf{n}(Q) = \mathbf{n}(Q)$.

5. Prove that there are the same number of points on the interval $0 \leq x \leq 1$ and on the interval $0 \leq x \leq .00001$.

6. Use the function $\mathbf{f}(x) = 1/(1 + x)$ to prove that the cardinal number of the set of real numbers between 0 and 1 is the same as that of all positive real numbers.

7. Use the results of Exercises 4 and 6 to prove that $\mathbf{n}(Q) = \mathbf{n}(R)$.

8. Prove that $\mathbf{n}(R) = \mathbf{n}(S_V)$.

9. Prove that the set of all functions with domain R has cardinal number at least $\aleph_2$.

10. Pick a finite set A. Define a function $\mathbf{g}$ with A as domain and having subsets of A as values. Construct the set G of the proof of the theorem, and verify that this set is not in the range of G.

11. How many subsets does a set of n elements have? Prove that this number is always larger than n (without using the theorem proved in this section) for any finite n.

12. There is a conjecture common among mathematicians, known as the *generalized continuum hypothesis* that for any infinite set A the cardinal number $\mathbf{n}(S_A)$ is the next cardinal after $\mathbf{n}(A)$. Prove that the continuum hypothesis is a consequence of this hypothesis.

13. Prove that the set of irrational numbers is nondenumerably infinite. [*Hint:* This is the set $R - Z$. Use the indirect method of proof.]

14. Prove that the binary expansions .10000 . . . and .011111 . . . represent the same number. Use this fact to show that the function constructed in this section which has Q as domain and a subset of S_V as its range actually has a proper subset of S_V as range.

15. Let $\mathfrak{U}$ be an infinite possibility set. Prove that it is impossible to name all conceivable truth sets of statements relative to $\mathfrak{U}$.

SUGGESTED READING

Birkhoff, G., and S. MacLane, *A Survey of Modern Algebra*, Macmillan, New York, 1953, Chapter XI.

Tarski, A., *Introduction to Logic*, Oxford University Press, New York, 2d rev. ed., 1946, Chapter IV.

Mathematical Association of America, Committee on the Undergraduate Program, *Elementary Mathematics of Sets*, Ann Arbor, Michigan, 1958, Chapters I and III.

Allendoerfer, C. B., and C. O. Oakley, *Principles of Mathematics*, McGraw-Hill, New York, 1955, Chapter V.

Johnstone, H. W., Jr., *Elementary Deductive Logic*, Crowell, New York, 1954, Part Three.

Breuer, Joseph, *Introduction to the Theory of Sets*, Prentice-Hall, Englewood Cliffs, N. J., 1958.

Fraenkel, A. A., *Abstract Set Theory*, North-Holland Publishing Co., Amsterdam, 1953.

CHAPTER 3

Elementary Probability Theory

1. INTRODUCTION

We often hear statements of the following kind, "It is likely to rain today," "I have a fair chance of passing this course," "There is an even chance that a coin will come up heads," etc. In each case our statement refers to a situation in which we are not certain of the outcome, but we express some degree of confidence that our prediction will be verified. The theory of probability provides a mathematical framework for such assertions.

Consider an experiment whose outcome is not known. Suppose that someone makes an assertion p about the outcome of the experiment, and we want to assign a probability to p. When statement p is considered in isolation, we usually find no natural assignment of probabilities. Rather, we look for a method of assigning probabilities to all conceivable statements concerning the outcome of the experiment. At first this might seem to be a hopeless task, since there is no end to the statements we can make about the experiment. However we are aided by a basic principle:

Fundamental assumption. Any two equivalent statements will be assigned the same probability.

As long as there are a finite number of logical possibilities, there are only a finite number of truth sets, and hence the process of assigning probabilities is a finite one. We proceed in three steps: (1) we first determine $\mathcal{U}$, the possibility set, that is, the set of all logical possibilities, (2) to each subset X of $\mathcal{U}$ we assign a number called the measure $\mathbf{m}(X)$, (3) to each statement p we assign $\mathbf{m}(P)$, the measure of its truth set, as a probability. The probability of statement p is denoted by $\mathbf{Pr}[p]$.

The same procedure is followed in finding the probability for an open statement of the form $\mathbf{f}(x) = a$. Let A be the truth set of this statement. Then

$$\mathbf{Pr}[\mathbf{f} = a] = \mathbf{m}\,(A).$$

Notice that we use the abbreviation $\mathbf{Pr}[\mathbf{f} = a]$, to be read "the probability that $\mathbf{f}$ takes on the value a, for the probability of the statement $\mathbf{f}(x) = a$. This abbreviation will be used throughout the rest of the book.

The first step, that of determining the set of logical possibilities, is one that we considered in the previous chapters. It is important to recall that there is no unique method for analyzing logical possibilities. In a given problem we may arrive at a very fine or a very rough analysis of possibilities, causing $\mathcal{U}$ to have many or few elements.

Having chosen $\mathcal{U}$, the next step is to assign a number to each subset A of $\mathcal{U}$, which will in turn be taken to be the probability of any statement having truth set A. We do this in the following way.

ASSIGNMENT OF A MEASURE. Assign to each element x of $\mathcal{U}$ a positive number (weight) $\mathbf{w}(x)$ such that the sum of all the weights assigned is 1. The function $\mathbf{w}$ so defined is called a *weight function*. If A is any subset of $\mathcal{U}$ we define $\mathbf{m}(A)$ to be the sum of the values of $\mathbf{w}(x)$ for x in A. We denote this sum by $\mathbf{m}(A) = \sum_{x \text{ in } A} \mathbf{w}(x)$ and call it the *measure* of A. We define $\mathbf{m}(\mathcal{E}) = 0$. Note that measure may be considered to be a function $\mathbf{m}$ with domain the set of all subsets of $\mathcal{U}$. The range of $\mathbf{m}$ consists of some set of numbers between 0 and 1.

In application of probability to scientific problems, the assignment of measures and the analysis of the logical possibilities may depend upon factual information and hence can best be done by the scientist making the application.

Once the weights are assigned, to find the probability of a particular statement we must find its truth set and find the sum of the weights assigned to elements of the truth set. This problem, which might seem easy, can often involve considerable mathematical difficulty. The development of techniques to solve this kind of problem is the main task of probability theory.

Example 1. An ordinary die is thrown. What is the probability that the number which turns up is less than 4? Here the possibility set is $\mathcal{U} = \{1, 2, 3, 4, 5, 6\}$. The symmetry of the die suggests that each face should have the same probability of turning up. To make this so we assign weight $\frac{1}{6}$ to each of the outcomes, i.e., $\mathbf{w}(i) = \frac{1}{6}$ for $i = 1, 2, \ldots, 6$. The truth set of the statement, "The number which turns up is less than 4," is $\{1, 2, 3\}$. Hence the probability of this statement is $\frac{3}{6} = \frac{1}{2}$, the sum of the weights of the elements in its truth set.

Example 2. A man attends a race involving three horses A, B, and C. He feels that A and B have the same chance of winning but that A (and hence also B) is twice as likely to win as C. What is the probability that A or C wins? We take as $\mathcal{U}$ the set $\{A, B, C\}$. If we were to assign weight a to the outcome C, then we would assign weight $2a$ to each of the outcomes A and B. Since the sum of the weights must be 1, we have $2a + 2a + a = 1$, or $a = \frac{1}{5}$. Hence we assign weights $\frac{2}{5}, \frac{2}{5}, \frac{1}{5}$ to the outcomes A, B, and C, respectively. The truth set of the statement "Horse A or C wins" is $\{A, C\}$. The sum of the weights of the elements of this set is $\frac{2}{5} + \frac{1}{5} = \frac{3}{5}$. Hence the probability that A or C wins is $\frac{3}{5}$.

Example 3. A coin is thrown twice. We take as possibility space the set $\mathcal{U} = \{HH, HT, TH, TT\}$. We choose weight function $\mathbf{w}$ defined by $\mathbf{w}(x) = \frac{1}{4}$ for each x in $\mathcal{U}$. Let $\mathbf{f}$ be a function with domain $\mathcal{U}$ and value the number of heads which turn up. Then the open statement $\mathbf{f}(x) = 1$ has truth set $\{HT, TH\}$. The measure of the set is $\frac{1}{2}$. Hence $\mathbf{Pr}[\mathbf{f} = 1] = \frac{1}{2}$.

EXERCISES

1. Assume that there are n possibilities for the outcome of a given experiment. How should the weights be assigned if it is desired that all outcomes be assigned the same weight?

2. Let $\mathcal{U} = \{a, b, c\}$. Assign weights to the three elements so that no two have the same weight, and find the measures of the eight subsets of $\mathcal{U}$.

3. In an election Jones has probability $\frac{1}{2}$ of winning, Smith has probability $\frac{1}{3}$, and Black has probability $\frac{1}{6}$.
   (a) Construct $\mathcal{U}$.
   (b) Assign weights.
   (c) Find the measures of the eight subsets.
   (d) Give a pair of nonequivalent predictions which have the same probability.

4. Give the possibility set $\mathcal{U}$, for each of the following experiments.
   (a) An election between candidates A and B is to take place.
   (b) A number between 1 and 5 is chosen at random.
   (c) A two-headed coin is thrown.

(d) A student is asked for the day of the year on which his birthday falls.

5. Prove that for any possibility set there is a unique constant weight function. For which of the cases in Exercise 4 might it be appropriate to assign the constant weight function?

6. Suppose that the following probabilities have been assigned to the possible results of putting a penny in a certain defective peanut-vending machine: The probability that nothing comes out is $\frac{1}{2}$. The probability that either you get your money back or you get peanuts (but not both) is $\frac{1}{3}$.

(a) What is the probability that you get your money back and also get peanuts? [*Ans.* $\frac{1}{6}$.]

(b) From the information given, is it possible to find the probability that you get peanuts? [*Ans.* No.]

7. A die is loaded in such a way that the probability of each face is proportional to the number of dots on that face. (For instance, a 6 is three times as probable as a 2.) What is the probability of getting an even number in one throw? [*Ans.* $\frac{4}{7}$.]

8. If a coin is thrown three times, list the eight possibilities for the outcomes of the three successive throws. A typical outcome can be written (HTH). Determine a probability measure by assigning an equal weight to each outcome. Find the probabilities of the following statements:

(r) The number of heads that occur is greater than the number of tails. [*Ans.* $\frac{1}{2}$.]

(s) Exactly two heads occur. [*Ans.* $\frac{3}{8}$.]

(t) The same side turns up on every throw. [*Ans.* $\frac{1}{4}$.]

9. For the statements given in Exercise 8, which of the following equalities are true?

(a) $\mathbf{Pr}[r \vee s] = \mathbf{Pr}[r] + \mathbf{Pr}[s]$

(b) $\mathbf{Pr}[s \vee t] = \mathbf{Pr}[s] + \mathbf{Pr}[t]$

(c) $\mathbf{Pr}[r \vee \sim r] = \mathbf{Pr}[r] + \mathbf{Pr}[\sim r]$

(d) $\mathbf{Pr}[r \vee t] = \mathbf{Pr}[r] + \mathbf{Pr}[t]$

10. Which of the following pairs of statements (see Exercise 8) are inconsistent? (Recall that two statements are inconsistent if their truth sets have no element in common.)

(a) r, s (b) s, t

(c) $r, \sim r$ (d) r, t [*Ans.* (b) and (c).]

11. State a theorem suggested by Exercises 9 and 10.

12. Let $\mathcal{U}$ be a possibility space and $\mathbf{w}$ and $\mathbf{v}$ be two different weight functions with domain $\mathcal{U}$. Prove that $\mathbf{w} + \mathbf{v}$ is not a weight function.

13. Let $\mathbf{u}$ and $\mathbf{v}$ be two different weight functions defined on the same possibility space $\mathcal{U}$. Let a and b be nonnegative numbers with sum 1. Prove that $a\mathbf{u} + b\mathbf{v}$ is a weight function.

14. A coin is thrown three times. Let $\mathcal{U}$ be the set of eight possible outcomes. Assign equal weights to the elements of $\mathcal{U}$. Let $\mathbf{f}$ be a function with domain $\mathcal{U}$ and value the number of heads which turn up. Find the truth sets of the statements $\mathbf{f}(x) = 0$, $\mathbf{f}(x) = 1$, $\mathbf{f}(x) = 2$, $\mathbf{f}(x) = 3$, and from these the probabilities $\mathbf{Pr}[\mathbf{f} = 0]$, $\mathbf{Pr}[\mathbf{f} = 1]$, $\mathbf{Pr}[\mathbf{f} = 2]$ and $\mathbf{Pr}[\mathbf{f} = 3]$. [*Partial Ans.* $\mathbf{Pr}[\mathbf{f} = 3] = \frac{1}{8}$, $\mathbf{Pr}[\mathbf{f} = 1] = \frac{3}{8}$.]

15. A balanced die is thrown twice. Assign equal weights on the set $\mathcal{U}$ consisting of the 36 possible pairs of outcomes. Let $\mathbf{f}$ be a function with domain $\mathcal{U}$ and value the sum of the numbers which turn up. Find $\mathbf{Pr}[\mathbf{f} = a]$ for $a = 2, 3, \ldots, 12$.
[*Partial Ans.* $\mathbf{Pr}[\mathbf{f} = 11] = \frac{1}{18}$, $\mathbf{Pr}[\mathbf{f} = 7] = \frac{1}{6}$.]

2. PROPERTIES OF A PROBABILITY MEASURE

Before studying special probability measures, we shall consider some general properties of such measures that are useful in computations and in the general understanding of probability theory.

Three basic properties of a probability measure are:

(A) $\mathbf{m}(X) = 0$ if and only if $X = \mathcal{E}$.

(B) $0 \leq \mathbf{m}(X) \leq 1$ for any set X.

(C) For two sets X and Y,

$$\mathbf{m}(X \cup Y) = \mathbf{m}(X) + \mathbf{m}(Y)$$

if and only if X and Y are disjoint, i.e., have no elements in common.

The proofs of properties (A) and (B) are left as an exercise (see Exercise 19). We shall prove (C).

We observe first that $\mathbf{m}(X) + \mathbf{m}(Y)$ is the sum of the weights of the elements of X added to the sum of the weights of Y. If X and Y are disjoint, then the weight of every element of $X \cup Y$ is added once and only once, and hence $\mathbf{m}(X) + \mathbf{m}(Y) = \mathbf{m}(X \cup Y)$.

Assume now that X and Y are not disjoint. Here the weight of every element contained in both X and Y, i.e., in $X \cap Y$, is added twice in the sum $\mathbf{m}(X) + \mathbf{m}(Y)$. Thus the sum is greater than $\mathbf{m}(X \cup Y)$ by an amount $\mathbf{m}(X \cap Y)$. By (A) and (B), if $X \cap Y$ is not the empty set, then $\mathbf{m}(X \cap Y) > 0$. Hence in this case we have $\mathbf{m}(X) + \mathbf{m}(Y) > \mathbf{m}(X \cup Y)$. Thus if X and Y are not disjoint, the equality in (C) does not hold. Our proof shows that in general we have

(C′) For any two sets X and Y,

$$\mathbf{m}(X \cup Y) = \mathbf{m}(X) + \mathbf{m}(Y) - \mathbf{m}(X \cap Y)$$

Since the probabilities for statements are obtained directly from the probability measure $\mathbf{m}(X)$, any property of $\mathbf{m}(X)$ can be translated into a property about the probability of statements. For example, the above properties become, when expressed in terms of statements:

(a) $\mathbf{Pr}[p] = 0$ if and only if p is logically false.

(b) $0 \leq \mathbf{Pr}[p] \leq 1$ for any statement p.

(c) The equality

$$\mathbf{Pr}[p \vee q] = \mathbf{Pr}[p] + \mathbf{Pr}[q]$$

holds if and only if p and q are inconsistent.

(c′) For any two statements p and q,

$$\mathbf{Pr}[p \vee q] = \mathbf{Pr}[p] + \mathbf{Pr}[q] - \mathbf{Pr}[p \wedge q].$$

Another property of a probability measure that is often useful in computation is

(D) $\mathbf{m}(\tilde{X}) = 1 - \mathbf{m}(X)$,

or, in the language of statements,

(d) $\mathbf{Pr}[\sim p] = 1 - \mathbf{Pr}[p]$.

The proofs of (D) and (d) are left as an exercise (see Exercise 20).

It is important to observe that our probability measure assigns probability 0 only to statements which are logically false, i.e., which are false for every logical possibility. Hence, a prediction that such a statement will be true is certain to be wrong. Similarly a statement is assigned probability 1 only if it is true in every case, i.e., logically true. Thus the prediction that a statement of this type will be true is certain to be correct. (While these properties of a probability measure seem quite natural, it is necessary, when dealing with infinite possibility sets, to weaken them slightly. This will be discussed in Chapter 7.)

We shall now discuss the interpretation of probabilities that are not 0 or 1. We shall give only some intuitive ideas that are commonly held concerning probabilities. While these ideas can be made mathematically more precise, we offer them here only as a guide to intuitive thinking.

Suppose that, relative to a given experiment, a statement has been assigned probability a. From this it is often inferred that if a sequence of such experiments is performed under identical conditions, the fraction of experiments which yield outcomes making the statement true would be approximately a. The mathematical version of this is the "law of large numbers" of probability theory (which will be treated in Section 11). In cases where there is no natural way to assign a probability measure, the probability of a statement is estimated experimentally. A sequence of experiments is performed and the fraction of the experiments which make the statement true is taken as the approximate probability for the statement.

A second and related interpretation of probabilities is concerned with betting. Suppose that a certain statement p has been assigned probability a. We wish to offer a bet that p will in fact turn out to be true. We agree to give r dollars if p does not turn out to be true, provided that we receive s dollars if it does turn out to be true. What should r and s be to make the bet fair? If it were true that in a large number of such bets we would win s a fraction a of the times and lose r a fraction $1 - a$ of the time, then our average winning per bet would be $sa - r(1 - a)$. To make the bet fair we should make this average winning 0. This will be the case if $sa = r(1 - a)$ or if $r/s = a/(1 - a)$. Notice that this determines only the ratio of r and s. Such a ratio, written $r:s$, is said to give *odds* for the bet.

Example. Assume that a probability of $\frac{3}{4}$ has been assigned to a certain horse winning a race. Then the odds for a fair bet would be $\frac{3}{4}:\frac{1}{4}$. These odds could be equally well written as 3:1, 6:2, or 12:4, etc. A fair bet would be to agree to pay \$3 if the horse loses and receive \$1 if the horse wins. Another fair bet would be to pay \$6 if the horse loses and win \$2 if the horse wins.

EXERCISES

1. Let p and q be statements such that $\mathbf{Pr}[p \wedge q] = \frac{1}{4}$, $\mathbf{Pr}[\sim p] = \frac{1}{3}$, and $\mathbf{Pr}[q] = \frac{1}{2}$. What is $\mathbf{Pr}[p \vee q]$? [*Ans.* $\frac{11}{12}$.]

2. Using the result of Exercise 1, find $\mathbf{Pr}[\sim p \wedge \sim q]$.

3. Let p and q be statements such that $\mathbf{Pr}[p] = \frac{1}{2}$ and $\mathbf{Pr}[q] = \frac{2}{3}$. Are p and q consistent? [*Ans.* Yes.]

4. Show that, if $\mathbf{Pr}[p] + \mathbf{Pr}[q] > 1$, then p and q are consistent.

5. A student is worried about his grades in English and Art. He estimates that the probability of passing English is .4, that he will pass at least one course with probability .6, but that he has only probability .1 of passing both courses. What is the probability that he will pass Art? [*Ans.* .3.]

6. Given that a school has grades A, B, C, D, and F, and that a student has probability .9 of passing a course, and .6 of getting a grade lower than B, what is the probability that he will get a C or D? [*Ans.* $\frac{1}{2}$.]

7. A die is loaded in such a way that the probability of each face turning up is proportional to the number of dots on that face (see Exercise 7

of Section 1). Let f be the outcome function for the experiment; then the range of f consists of the numbers $\{1, 2, \ldots, 6\}$. Compute the following.

(a) $\mathbf{Pr}[(\mathbf{f} = 2) \vee (\mathbf{f} = 4) \vee (\mathbf{f} = 6)]$. [*Ans.* $\frac{4}{7}$.]
(b) $\mathbf{Pr}[(\mathbf{f} = 1) \vee (\mathbf{f} = 2) \vee (\mathbf{f} = 5)]$.
(c) $\mathbf{Pr}[\mathbf{f} \neq 2]$.
(d) $\mathbf{Pr}[\mathbf{f} > 2]$. [*Ans.* $\frac{6}{7}$.]
(e) $\mathbf{Pr}[(\mathbf{f} = 7) \vee (\mathbf{f} \neq 7)]$.
(f) $\mathbf{Pr}[(\mathbf{f} = 4) \vee (\mathbf{f} > 2)]$.

8. A balanced coin is tossed twice. Let $\mathbf{f}_1$ and $\mathbf{f}_2$ be the outcome functions of the first and second experiments, respectively. Then the range of both functions is the set $\{H, T\}$, and the domain is $\mathcal{U} = \{HH, HT, TH, TT\}$. Compute the following probabilities.

(a) $\mathbf{Pr}[(\mathbf{f}_1 = H) \vee (\mathbf{f}_2 \neq H)]$.
(b) $\mathbf{Pr}[\mathbf{f}_1 = T]$.
(c) $\mathbf{Pr}[(\mathbf{f}_1 = H) \vee (\mathbf{f}_2 = H)]$.
(d) $\mathbf{Pr}[\mathbf{f}_2 \neq T]$.

9. A balanced die is rolled twice. Let $\mathbf{f}_1$ and $\mathbf{f}_2$ be the outcome functions of the first and second experiments, respectively. Compute the following probabilities.

(a) $\mathbf{Pr}[(\mathbf{f}_1 = 3) \wedge (\mathbf{f}_2 < 4)]$. [*Ans.* $\frac{1}{12}$.]
(b) $\mathbf{Pr}[(\mathbf{f}_1 \neq 6) \wedge (\mathbf{f}_2 > 3)]$. [*Ans.* $\frac{5}{12}$.]
(c) $\mathbf{Pr}[(\mathbf{f}_1 \neq 7) \vee (\mathbf{f}_2 < 5)]$. [*Ans.* 1.]
(d) $\mathbf{Pr}[(\mathbf{f}_1 = 7) \vee (\mathbf{f}_2 \neq 3)]$. [*Ans.* $\frac{5}{6}$.]

10. What odds should a person give on a bet that a six will turn up when a die is thrown?

11. Referring to Example 2 of Section 1, what odds should the man be willing to give for a bet that either A or B will come in first?

12. Prove that if the odds in favor of a given statement are $r{:}s$, then the probability that the statement will be true is $r/(r + s)$.

13. Using the result of Exercise 12 and the definition of "odds," show that if the odds are $r{:}s$ that a statement is true, then the odds are $s{:}r$ that it is false.

14. A man is willing to give 5:4 odds that the Dodgers will win the World Series. What must the probability of a Dodger victory be for this to be a fair bet? [*Ans.* $\frac{5}{9}$.]

15. A man has found through long experience that if he washes his car it rains the next day 85 per cent of the time. What odds should he give that this will occur next time?

16. A man offers 1:3 odds that A will occur, 1:2 odds that B will occur.

He knows that A and B cannot both occur. What odds should he give that A or B will occur? [*Ans.* 7:5.]

17. A man offers 3:1 odds that A will occur, 2:1 odds that B will occur. He knows that A and B cannot both occur. What odds should he give that A or B will occur?

18. Show from the definition of a probability measure that $\mathbf{m}(X) = 1$ if and only if $X = \mathcal{U}$.

19. Show from the definition of a probability measure that properties (A), (B) of the text are true.

20. Prove property (D) of the text. Why does property (d) follow from this property?

21. Prove that if R, S, and T are three sets that have no element in common,

$$\mathbf{m}(R \cup S \cup T) = \mathbf{m}(R) + \mathbf{m}(S) + \mathbf{m}(T).$$

22. If X and Y are two sets such that X is a subset of Y, prove that $\mathbf{m}(X) \leqslant \mathbf{m}(Y)$.

23. If p and q are two statements such that p implies q, prove that $\mathbf{Pr}[p] \leqslant \mathbf{Pr}[q]$.

24. Suppose that you are given n statements and each has been assigned a probability less than or equal to r. Prove that the probability of the disjunction of these statements is less than or equal to nr.

25. The following is an alternative proof of property (C′) of the text. Give a reason for each step.
(a) $X \cup Y = (X \cap \tilde{Y}) \cup (X \cap Y) \cup (Y \cap \tilde{X})$.
(b) $\mathbf{m}(X \cup Y) = \mathbf{m}(X \cap \tilde{Y}) + \mathbf{m}(X \cap Y) + \mathbf{m}(\tilde{X} \cap Y)$.
(c) $\mathbf{m}(X \cup Y) = \mathbf{m}(X) + \mathbf{m}(Y) - \mathbf{m}(X \cap Y)$.

26. If X, Y, and Z are any three sets, prove that, for any probability measure,

$$\mathbf{m}(X \cup Y \cup Z) = \mathbf{m}(X) + \mathbf{m}(Y) + \mathbf{m}(Z) - \mathbf{m}(X \cap Y) - \mathbf{m}(Y \cap Z) - \mathbf{m}(X \cap Z) + \mathbf{m}(X \cap Y \cap Z).$$

27. Translate the result of Exercise 26 into a result concerning three statements p, q, and r.

28. A man offers to bet "dollars to doughnuts" that a certain event will take place. Assuming that a doughnut costs a nickel, what must the probability of the event be for this to be a fair bet? [*Ans.* $\frac{20}{21}$.]

3. THE EQUIPROBABLE MEASURE

We have already seen several examples where it was natural to assign the same weight to all possibilities in determining the appropriate probability measure. The probability measure determined in this manner is called the *equiprobable measure.* The measure of sets in the case of the equiprobable measure has a very simple form. In fact, if $\mathcal{U}$ has n elements and if the equiprobab'e measure has been assigned, then for any set X, $\mathbf{m}(X)$ is r/n, where r is the number of elements in the set X. This is true since the weight of each element in X is $1/n$, and hence the sum of the weights of elements of X is r/n.

The particularly simple form of the equiprobable measure makes it easy to work with. In view of this it is important to observe that a particular choice for the set of possibilities in a given situation may lead to the equiprobable measure, while some other choice will not. For example, consider the case of two throws of an ordinary coin. Suppose that we are interested in statements about the number of heads which occur. If we take for the possibility set the set $\mathcal{U} = \{\text{HH, HT, TH, TT}\}$ then it is reasonable to assign the same weight to each outcome, and we are led to the equiprobable measure. If, on the other hand, we were to take as possible outcomes the set $\mathcal{U} = \{\text{no H, one H, two H}\}$, it would not be natural to assign the same weight to each outcome, since one head can occur in two different ways, while each of the other possibilities can occur in only one way.

Example 1. Suppose we throw two ordinary dice. Each die can turn up a number from 1 to 6; hence there are $6 \cdot 6 = 36$ possibilities. We assign a weight function $\mathbf{w}(x) = \frac{1}{36}$ for all x in the possibility set $\mathcal{U}$. A prediction that is true in j cases will have probability $j/36$. For example, let $\mathbf{f}$ be a function with domain $\mathcal{U}$ and value the sum of the numbers that turn up. Then the truth set of the statement $\mathbf{f}(x) = 5$ is the set $\{(1, 4), (2, 3), (3, 2), (4, 1)\}$. Since this set has four elements $\mathbf{Pr}[\mathbf{f} = 5] = \frac{4}{36} = \frac{1}{9}$

Example 2. Suppose that two cards are drawn successively from a deck of cards. What is the probability that both are hearts? There are 52 possibilities for the first card, and for each of these there are 51 possibilities for the second. Hence there are $52 \cdot 51$ possibilities for the result of the two draws. We assign the equiprobable measure. The statement "The two cards are hearts" is true in $13 \cdot 12$ of the $52 \cdot 51$ possibilities. Hence the probability of this statement is $13 \cdot 12/52 \cdot 51 = \frac{1}{17}$.

Example 3. Assume that, on the basis of a predictive index applied to students A, B, and C when entering college, it is predicted that after four years of college the scholastic record of A will be the highest, C the second highest, and B the lowest of the three. Suppose, in fact, that these predictions turn out to be exactly correct. If the predictive index has no merit at all and hence the predictions amount simply to guessing, what is the probability that such a prediction will be correct? There are $3! = 6$ orders in which the men might finish. If the predictions were really just guessing, then we would assign an equal weight to each of the six outcomes. In this case the probability that a particular prediction is true is $\frac{1}{6}$. Since this probability is reasonably large, we would hesitate to conclude that the predictive index is in fact useful, on the basis of this one experiment. Suppose, on the other hand, it predicted the order of six men correctly. Then a similar analysis would show that, by guessing, the probability is $1/6! = 1/720$ that such a prediction would be correct. Hence, we might conclude here that there is strong evidence that the index has some merit.

EXERCISES

1. A letter is chosen at random from the word "random." What is the probability that it is an 'n'? That it is a vowel? [*Ans.* $\frac{1}{6}$; $\frac{1}{3}$.]

2. An integer between 3 and 12 inclusive is chosen at random. What is the probability that it is an even number? That it is even and divisible by three?

3. A card is drawn at random from a pack of playing cards.
(a) What is the probability that it is either a heart or the king of clubs? [*Ans.* $\frac{7}{26}$.]
(b) What is the probability that it is either the queen of hearts or an honor card (i.e., ten, jack, queen, king, or ace)? [*Ans.* $\frac{5}{13}$.]

4. A word is chosen at random from the set of words $\mathcal{U}$ = {men, bird, ball, field, book}. Let p, q, and r be the statements:
p: The word has two vowels.
q: The first letter of the word is 'b'.
r: The word rhymes with 'cook'.
Find the probability of the following statements:
(a) p.
(b) q.
(c) r.
(d) $p \land q$.
(e) $(p \lor q) \land \sim r$.
(f) $p \rightarrow q$. [*Ans.* $\frac{4}{5}$.]

5. A single die is thrown. Find the probability that
(a) An odd number turns up.
(b) The number which turns up is greater than two.
(c) A seven turns up.

6. In the primary voting example of Chapter 2, Section 1, assume that all 36 possibilities in the elections are equally likely. Find
(a) The probability that candidate A wins more states than either of his rivals. [*Ans.* $\frac{7}{18}$.]

(b) That all the states are won by the same candidate. [*Ans.* $\frac{1}{36}$.]
(c) That every state is won by a different candidate. [*Ans.* 0.]

7. A single die is thrown twice. What value for the sum of the two outcomes has the highest probability? What value or values of the sum has the lowest probability of occurring?

8. Two boys and two girls are placed at random in a row for a picture. What is the probability that the boys and girls alternate in the picture? [*Ans.* $\frac{1}{3}$.]

9. A certain college has 500 students and it is known that:

300 read French.
200 read German.
50 read Russian.
20 read French and Russian.
30 read German and Russian.
20 read German and French.
10 read all three languages.

If a student is chosen at random from the school, what is the probability that the student:
(a) Reads two and only two languages?
(b) Reads at least one language?

10. Suppose that three people enter a restaurant that has a row of six seats. If they choose their seats at random, what is the probability that they sit with no seats between them? What is the probability that there is at least one empty seat between any two of them?

11. Find the probability of obtaining each of the following poker hands. (A poker hand is a set of five cards chosen at random from a deck of 52 cards.)
(a) Royal flush (ten, jack, queen, king, ace in a single suit.) [*Ans.* $4/\binom{52}{5} = .0000015$.]
(b) Straight flush (five in a sequence in a single suit, but not a royal flush). [*Ans.* $(40 - 4)/\binom{52}{5} = .000014$.]
(c) Four of a kind (four cards of the same face value). [*Ans.* $624/\binom{52}{5} = .00024$.]
(d) Full house (one pair and one triple of the same face value). [*Ans.* $3744/\binom{52}{5} = .0014$.]
(e) Flush (five cards in a single suit but not a straight or royal flush). [*Ans.* $(5148 - 40)/\binom{52}{5} = .0020$.]
(f) Straight (five cards in a row, not all of the same suit). [*Ans.* $(10{,}240 - 40)/\binom{52}{5} = .0039$.]
(g) Straight or better. [*Ans.* .0076.]

12. If ten people are seated at a circular table at random, what is the probability that a particular pair of people are seated next to each other? [*Ans.* $\frac{2}{9}$.]

13. A room contains a group of n people who are wearing badges numbered from 1 to n. If two people are selected at random, what is the probability that the larger badge number is a 3? Answer this problem assuming that $n = 5, 4, 3, 2$. [*Ans.* $\frac{1}{5}$; $\frac{1}{3}$; $\frac{2}{3}$; 0.]

14. In Exercise 13, suppose that we observe two men leaving the room and that the larger of their badge numbers is 3. What might we guess as to the number of people in the room?

15. Find the probability that a bridge hand will have suits of:

(a) 5, 4, 3, and 1 cards. $\left[Ans.\ \dfrac{4!\binom{13}{5}\binom{13}{4}\binom{13}{3}\binom{13}{1}}{\binom{52}{13}} \approx .129.\right]$

(b) 6, 4, 2, and 1 cards. [*Ans.* .047.]

(c) 4, 4, 3, and 2 cards. [*Ans.* .216.]

(d) 4, 3, 3, and 3 cards. [*Ans.* .105.]

16. There are $\binom{52}{13} \approx 6.35 \times 10^{11}$ possible bridge hands. Find the probability that a bridge hand dealt at random will be all of one suit. Estimate *roughly* the number of bridge hands dealt in the entire country in a year. Is it likely that a hand of all one suit will occur sometime during the year in the United States?

17. Three cards are drawn successively from a bridge deck. Let $\mathbf{f}$ be the function whose value is the number of black cards obtained. The range of $\mathbf{f}$ is $\{0, 1, 2, 3\}$. Compute $\mathbf{Pr}[\mathbf{f} = a]$ for $a = 0, 1, 2, 3$.
[*Ans.* $\mathbf{Pr}[\mathbf{f} = 3] = \mathbf{Pr}[\mathbf{f} = 0] = \frac{2}{17}$,
$\mathbf{Pr}[\mathbf{f} = 2] = \mathbf{Pr}[\mathbf{f} = 1] = \frac{13}{34}$.]

18. In Exercise 13, let $\mathbf{f}$ be the function whose value is the sum of the numbers on the badges of the two people selected. The range of $\mathbf{f}$ is then the set $\{3, 4, \ldots, 2n - 1\}$. Compute $\mathbf{Pr}[\mathbf{f} = 5]$ for $n = 5, 4, 3, 2$. [*Ans.* $\frac{1}{5}$, $\frac{1}{3}$, $\frac{1}{3}$, 0.]

19. A man has eight coins in his pocket, three dimes and five nickels. He chooses three coins at random and records the total value of these coins. Let $\mathbf{f}$ be the sum of the three coins and compute the following:

(a) $\mathbf{Pr}[\mathbf{f} > 20]$. [*Ans.* $\frac{2}{7}$.]

(b) $\mathbf{Pr}[\mathbf{f} \neq 22]$.

(c) $\mathbf{Pr}[\mathbf{f} = 10 \vee \mathbf{f} \geq 25]$. [*Ans.* $\frac{2}{7}$.]

*4. TWO NONINTUITIVE EXAMPLES

There are occasions in probability theory when one finds a problem for which the answer, based on probability theory, is not at all in agreement with one's intuition. It is usually possible to arrange wagers that will bring one's intuition into line with the mathematical theory. A particularly good example of this is provided by the matching birthdays problem.

Assume that we have a room with r people in it and we propose the bet that there are at least two people in the room having the same birthday, i.e., the same month and day of the year. We ask for the value of r which will make this a fair bet. Few people would be willing to bet even money on this wager unless there were at least 100 people in the room. Most people would suggest 150 as a reasonable number. However, we shall see that with 150 people the odds are approximately 4,500,000, 000,000,000 to 1 in favor of two people having the same birthday, and that one should be willing to bet even money with as few as 23 people in the room.

Let us first find the probability that in a room with r people, no two have the same birthday. There are 365 possibilities for each person's birthday (neglecting February 29). There are then 365^r possibilities for the birthdays of r people. We assume that all these possibilities are equally likely. To find the probability that no two have the same birthday we must find the number of possibilities for the birthdays which have *no* day represented twice. The first person can have any of 365 days for his birthday. For each of these, if the second person is to have a different birthday, there are only 364 possibilities for his birthday. For the third man, there are 363 possibilities if he is to have a different birthday than the first two, etc. Thus the probability that no two people have the same birthday in a group of r people is

$$q_r = \frac{365 \cdot 364 \cdot \ldots \cdot (365 - r + 1)}{365^r}.$$

The probability that at least two people have the same birthday is then $p_r = 1 - q_r$. In Figure 1 the values of p_r and the odds for a fair bet, $p_r:(1 - p_r)$, are given for several values of r.

We consider now a second problem in which intuition does not lead to the correct answer.

Consider a set $\mathcal{U} = \{x_1, x_2, \ldots, x_n\}$ with n elements. A permutation of these objects is determined by a function $\mathbf{f}$ with domain $\mathcal{U}$ and range $\mathcal{U}$. If $\mathbf{f}$ is such a function we shall say that the permutation has a *fixed point* if, for some x, $\mathbf{f}(x) = x$. A permutation having no fixed point is called a *complete permutation*. For example, if $\mathcal{U} = \{1, 2, 3\}$ the permutation defined by the function $\mathbf{f}$ with $\mathbf{f}(1) = 2$, $\mathbf{f}(2) = 3$, and $\mathbf{f}(3) = 1$ is a complete permutation.

The problem that we now consider can be stated as follows. If a

Number of People in the Room	Probability of at Least Two with Same Birthday	Approximate Odds for a Fair Bet
5	.027	
10	.117	
15	.253	
20	.411	70:100
21	.444	80:100
22	.476	91:100
23	.507	103:100
24	.538	117:100
25	.569	132:100
30	.706	242:100
40	.891	819:100
50	.970	33:1
60	.994	169:1
70		1,200:1
80		12,000:1
90		160,000:1
100		3,300,000:1
125		31,000,000,000:1
150		4,500,000,000,000,000:1

Figure 1

permutation of n numbers is chosen at random, what is the probability that the permutation chosen is a complete permutation? A more colorful but equivalent problem is the following. A hat-check girl has checked n hats, but they have become hopelessly scrambled. She hands back the hats at random. What is the probability that no man gets his own hat? For this problem some people's intuition would lead them to guess that for a large number of hats this probability should be small, while others guess that it should be large. Few people guess that the probability is neither large nor small and essentially independent of the number of hats involved.

To find the desired probability, we assume that all $n!$ possible permutations are equally likely, and hence we need only count the number of complete permutations which there are for n elements. Let w_n be the number of such permutations. Then the desired probability is $p_n = w_n/n!$. If this procedure is carried out (see Exercise 11), the answer is found to be

$$p_n = \frac{1}{2!} - \frac{1}{3!} + \frac{1}{4!} - \cdots \pm \frac{1}{n!}$$

where the + sign is chosen if n is even and the − sign if n is odd. In Figure 2, these numbers are given for the first few values of n.

Number of Hats	Probability p_n That No Man Gets His Hat
2	.500000
3	.333333
4	.375000
5	.366667
6	.368056
7	.367857
8	.367882

Figure 2

We see that p_n is the nth partial sum of the infinite series for e^{-1}. Thus, as the number of hats increases, p_n tends to $e^{-1} = .367879\ldots$. Thus we see, for instance, that p_7 and p_{1000} differ only in the fifth decimal place.

EXERCISES

1. What odds should you be willing to give on a bet that at least two people in the United States Senate have the same birthday?
[*Ans.* More than 160,000:1.]

2. What is the probability that in the House of Representatives at least two men have the same birthday?

3. What odds should you be willing to give on a bet that at least two of the Presidents of the United States have had the same birthday? Would you win the bet?
[*Ans.* More than 3:1; Yes. Polk and Harding were born on Nov. 2.]

4. What odds should you be willing to give on the bet that at least two of the Presidents of the United States have died on the same day of the year? Would you win the bet?
[*Ans.* More than 2.4:1; Yes. Jefferson, Adams, and Monroe all died on July 4.]

5. Four men check their hats. Assuming that the hats are returned at random, what is the probability that *exactly* four men get their own hats? Calculate the answer that exactly 3, 2, 1, 0 men get their own hats.
[*Ans.* $\frac{1}{24}$; 0; $\frac{1}{4}$; $\frac{1}{3}$; $\frac{3}{8}$.]

6. A group of 50 men and their wives attend a dance. The partners for a dance are chosen by lot. What is the approximate probability that no man dances with his wife?

7. Show that the probability that, in a group of r people, *exactly* one pair has the same birthday is

$$t_r = \binom{r}{2} \frac{365 \cdot 364 \ldots (365 - r + 2)}{365^r}.$$

8. Show that $t_r = \binom{r}{2} \frac{q_r}{366 - r}$, where t_r is defined in Exercise 7, and q_r is the probability that no pair has the same birthday.

9. Using the result of Exercise 8 and the results given in Figure 1, find the probability of exactly one pair of people with the same birthday in a group of r people, for $r = 15, 20, 25, 30, 40$, and 50.

[*Ans.* .22; .32; .38; .38; .26; .12.]

10. What is the approximate probability that there has been exactly one pair of Presidents with the same birthday?

11. Let w_n be the number of complete permutations of n numbers.

(a) Show that

$$w_1 = 0,\ w_2 = 1, \ldots,$$
$$w_n = (n-1)w_{n-1} + (n-1)w_{n-2} \qquad n = 2, 3, \ldots.$$

(*Hint:* Any complete permutation of n numbers can be obtained from a complete permutation of $n - 1$ numbers or from a permutation of $n - 1$ numbers that leaves one number fixed. Describe how this can be done, and show that the two terms on the right side of the equation represent the number that can be obtained from each of these methods.)

(b) Let p_n be the probability that a permutation of n numbers chosen at random is a complete permutation. From part (a) show that

$$p_1 = 0, \qquad p_2 = \frac{1}{2},$$

$$p_n = \frac{n-1}{n} p_{n-1} + \frac{1}{n} p_{n-2} \quad \text{for} \quad n = 3, 4, \ldots.$$

(c) Let $v_n = p_n - p_{n-1}$ for $n = 2, 3, 4, \ldots$. From part (b), show that

$$nv_n = -v_{n-1}, \qquad n = 3, \ldots.$$

(d) Using the fact that $p_1 = 0$, and $p_2 = \frac{1}{2}$, find v_2. From the result of part (c) find $v_3, v_4, \ldots, v_n$.

(e) Using the result of part (d), show that

$$p_n = \frac{1}{2!} - \frac{1}{3!} + \ldots \pm \frac{1}{n!}.$$

12. In a well-known game of solitaire a player turns over the cards in a bridge deck one-by-one while reciting their names in a fixed order. His objective is to go through the deck without once naming the card he turns over. What is his probability of winning? What is the probability if he uses only the 13 spades?

5. CONDITIONAL PROBABILITY

Suppose that we have a given $\mathcal{U}$ and that measures have been assigned to all subsets of $\mathcal{U}$. A statement p will have probability $\mathbf{Pr}[p] = \mathbf{m}(P)$. Suppose we now receive some additional information, say that statement q is true. How does this additional information alter the probability of p?

The probability of p after the receipt of the information q is called its *conditional probability*, and it is denoted by $\mathbf{Pr}[p|q]$, which is read "the probability of p given q." In this section we will construct a method of finding this conditional probability in terms of the measure $\mathbf{m}$.

If we know that q is true, then the original possibility set $\mathcal{U}$ has been reduced to Q and therefore we must define our measure on the subsets of Q instead of on the subsets of $\mathcal{U}$. Of course, every subset P of Q is a subset of $\mathcal{U}$, and hence we know $\mathbf{m}(P)$, its measure before q was discovered. Since q cuts down on the number of possibilities, its new measure $\mathbf{m}'(P)$ should be larger.

To define a new measure we must define a new weight function. The definition of this weight function is suggested by the following considerations. If x and y are two outcomes in Q such that x is twice as likely to occur as y, then this should still be the case after we learn that q is true. More generally, if $\mathbf{w}'$ is to be the new weight function, we wish any relation of the form $\mathbf{w}(x) = c\mathbf{w}(y)$ to imply that $\mathbf{w}'(x) = c\mathbf{w}'(y)$ for outcomes x and y in Q. This will be the case if we obtain $\mathbf{w}'$ from $\mathbf{w}$ simply by multiplying the values of $\mathbf{w}$ on Q by a proportionality factor, that is, if we define $\mathbf{w}'$ by

$$\mathbf{w}'(x) = k\mathbf{w}(x) \quad \text{for} \quad x \text{ in } Q.$$

To determine the k we note that we must have,

$$\sum_{x \text{ in } Q} \mathbf{w}'(x) = 1.$$

That is,

$$\sum_{x \text{ in } Q} k\mathbf{w}(x) = 1.$$

This means

$$k = \frac{1}{\sum_{x \text{ in } Q} \mathbf{w}(x)} = \frac{1}{\mathbf{m}(Q)}.$$

Therefore our definition of $\mathbf{w}'$ becomes

$$\mathbf{w}'(x) = \frac{\mathbf{w}(x)}{\mathbf{m}(Q)} \quad \text{for} \quad x \text{ in } Q.$$

If P is any subset of Q, the conditional measure of P, $\mathbf{m}'(P)$ is found from $\mathbf{w}'$ to be

(1) $$\mathbf{m}'(P) = \sum_{x \text{ in } P} \mathbf{w}'(x) = \frac{\sum_{x \text{ in } P} \mathbf{w}(x)}{\mathbf{m}(Q)} = \frac{\mathbf{m}(P)}{\mathbf{m}(Q)}.$$

How does this affect the probability of an arbitrary statement p? First of all the truth set of p has been reduced. Because all elements of $\tilde{Q}$ have been eliminated, the new truth set of p is $P \cap Q$ and therefore

(2) $$\mathbf{Pr}[p|q] = \mathbf{m}'(P \cap Q) = \frac{\mathbf{m}(P \cap Q)}{\mathbf{m}(Q)} = \frac{\mathbf{Pr}[p \wedge q]}{\mathbf{Pr}[q]}.$$

Note that if the original measure $\mathbf{m}$ is the equiprobable measure, then the new measure $\mathbf{m}'$ will also be the equiprobable measure on the set Q.

We must take care that the denominators in (1) and (2) be different from zero. Observe that $\mathbf{m}(Q)$ will be zero if Q is the empty set, which happens only if q is self-contradictory. This is also the only case in which $\mathbf{Pr}[q] = 0$, and hence we make the obvious assumption that our information q is not self-contradictory.

Example 1. In an election, candidate A has a .4 chance of winning, B has .3 chance, C has .2 chance, and D has .1 chance. Just before the election C withdraws. What are now the chances of the other three candidates? Let q be the statement that C will not win, i.e., that A or B or D will win. Observe that $\mathbf{Pr}[q] = .8$, hence all the other probabilities are increased by a factor of $1/.8 = 1.25$. Candidate A now has .5 chance of winning, B has .375, and D has .125.

Example 2. A family is chosen at random from the set of all families having exactly two children (not twins). What is the probability that the family has two boys, if it is known that there is a boy in the family? Without any information being given, we would assign the equiprobable measure on the set $\mathfrak{U} = \{\text{BB, BG, GB, GG}\}$ where the first letter of pair indicates the sex of the younger child and the second that of the older. The information that there is a boy causes $\mathfrak{U}$ to change to $\{\text{BB, BG, GB}\}$, but the new measure is still the equiprobable measure. Thus the conditional probability that there are two boys given that there is a boy is $\frac{1}{3}$. If on the other hand, we know that the first child is a boy, then the conditional probability is $\frac{1}{2}$.

A particularly interesting case of conditional probability is that in which $\mathbf{Pr}[p|q] = \mathbf{Pr}[p]$. Here the information provided by statement q

has no effect on the probability of p, and we then say that p is independent of q relative to the given measure. For the case of independent statements we can replace $\mathbf{Pr}[p|q]$ by $\mathbf{Pr}[p]$ in (2) and cross-multiply, obtaining $\mathbf{Pr}[p \wedge q] = \mathbf{Pr}[p] \cdot \mathbf{Pr}[q]$. In the same way, if we express the condition that q is independent of p, we again arrive at the relation expressed in (3). Hence the two statements are independent of each other. Observe that the question of whether or not statements are independent depends to a large extent on the way in which weights have been assigned to elements of the possibility space, cf. Example 3 below. Notice also that statements p and q can be open statements of the form $\mathbf{f}(x) = a$, cf. Example 4, below. We embody the important idea of independent statements relative to a measure in a formal definition.

DEFINITION. Let $\mathcal{U}$ be a possibility space in which a measure $\mathbf{m}$ is defined and let p and q be statements relative to $\mathcal{U}$. Then p and q are *independent statements relative to the measure* $\mathbf{m}$ if

$$\mathbf{Pr}[p \wedge q] = \mathbf{Pr}[p] \cdot \mathbf{Pr}[q]. \tag{3}$$

Example 3. Consider two throws of an ordinary coin—the four possibilities are then equally likely. Let p be the statement, "A head turns up on the first throw," and let q be the statement, "A tail turns up on the second throw." Then $\mathbf{Pr}[p] = \mathbf{Pr}[q] = \frac{1}{2}$ and $\mathbf{Pr}[p \wedge q] = \frac{1}{4}$ and therefore p and q are independent statements relative to the equiprobable measure.

But now suppose we change the experiment so that we first throw an ordinary coin; if heads comes up we toss the same coin again, and if tails comes up we toss a loaded coin that is three times as likely to turn up tails as heads. Here the possibilities HH and HT each have weight $\frac{1}{4}$ while possibility TH has weight $\frac{1}{8}$ and possibility TT has weight $\frac{3}{8}$. Therefore, if p and q are the same statements as above we have $\mathbf{Pr}[p] = \frac{1}{2}$, $\mathbf{Pr}[q] = \frac{5}{8}$ and $\mathbf{Pr}[p \wedge q] = \frac{1}{4}$ so that, relative to the new measure, statements p and q are *not* independent. This emphasizes the fact that the question of whether or not statements are independent depends upon the way the measure is defined on the possibility space.

Example 4. An ordinary coin is thrown three times. Let $\mathbf{f}$ be the number of heads which turn up. Then $\mathbf{Pr}[\mathbf{f} = 3] = \mathbf{Pr}[\mathbf{f} = 0] = \frac{1}{8}$ and $\mathbf{Pr}[\mathbf{f} = 2] = \mathbf{Pr}[\mathbf{f} = 1] = \frac{3}{8}$. Now consider the two statements "$(\mathbf{f}(x) = 3) \vee (\mathbf{f}(x) = 0)$" and "$\mathbf{f}(x) \leq 1$," that is the statements, "The same side turns up all three times," and "At most one head turns up." On the face of it, these statements do not seem to be independent. However, it can easily be shown (see Exercise 10) that, relative to the equiprobable measure, they are independent. On the other hand, it is not hard (see Exercise 22) to invent measures for the possibility space such that these two statements are not independent relative to these new measures.

The concept of independent statements is easily extended to independent functions.

DEFINITION. Let $\mathcal{U}$ be a possibility space for which a measure $\mathbf{m}$ has been assigned. Let $\mathbf{g}_1, \mathbf{g}_2, \ldots, \mathbf{g}_r$ be functions with domain $\mathcal{U}$. These functions are *independent* relative to the measure $\mathbf{m}$ if

$$\mathbf{Pr}[(\mathbf{g}_1 = a_1) \wedge (\mathbf{g}_2 = a_2) \wedge \ldots \wedge (\mathbf{g}_r = a_r)] = \mathbf{Pr}[\mathbf{g}_1 = a_1] \cdot \mathbf{Pr}[\mathbf{g}_2 = a_2] \ldots \mathbf{Pr}[\mathbf{g}_r = a_r]$$

for every set of range values $a_1, a_2, \ldots, a_r$.

When it is necessary to distinguish the present notion of independence from the notion of logical independence in Chapter 2 (or from the notion of linear independence in Chapter 4) we will sometimes speak of "probabilistic" independence.

It can be proved that if a set of functions is an independent set for a measure $\mathbf{m}$, then the same is true for any subset of the functions. [See Exercise 21.]

Example 5. Consider three throws of a coin. Let $\mathcal{U} = \{\text{HHH, HHT, HTH, HTT, THH, THT, TTH, TTT}\}$. Let $\mathbf{f}_1$, $\mathbf{f}_2$ and $\mathbf{f}_3$ be the three outcome functions. We assign the equiprobable measure to $\mathcal{U}$, then to determine whether or not the set of functions $\mathbf{f}_1, \mathbf{f}_2, \mathbf{f}_3$ are independent for the equiprobable measure we must verify, for example, that

$$\mathbf{Pr}[(\mathbf{f}_1 = \text{H}) \wedge (\mathbf{f}_2 = \text{T}) \wedge (\mathbf{f}_3 = \text{H})] = \mathbf{Pr}[\mathbf{f}_1 = \text{H}] \cdot \mathbf{Pr}[\mathbf{f}_2 = \text{T}] \cdot \mathbf{Pr}[\mathbf{f}_3 = \text{H}].$$

The truth set of the statement on the left side of this equation consists of the single possibility HTH and hence the probability of this statement is $\frac{1}{8}$. Each of the three statements that occur on the right side has probability $\frac{1}{2}$ and hence their product is $\frac{1}{8}$. A similar calculation for the other possible range values shows that $\mathbf{f}_1$, $\mathbf{f}_2$, and $\mathbf{f}_3$ are independent relative to the equiprobable measure. From this it follows that pairs of these functions, for example, $\mathbf{f}_1, \mathbf{f}_3$, also are independent relative to the equiprobable measure.

Let us see the relation between the concept of probabilistic independence and the concept of logical independence defined in Chapter 2. We shall consider only the case of two functions. Let $\mathbf{f}$ and $\mathbf{g}$ be two functions, defined on a possibility space $\mathcal{U}$, that are *not* logically independent. Then there must be range values a and b such that $\mathbf{f}(x) = a$ and $\mathbf{g}(x) = b$ are not logically false statements but $(\mathbf{f}(x) = a) \wedge (\mathbf{g}(x) = b)$ is logically false. Since the probability of a statement is zero if and only if it is logically false we see that no matter what choice of measure we make we will have $\mathbf{Pr}[\mathbf{f} = a] \cdot \mathbf{Pr}[\mathbf{g} = b] \neq 0$, but $\mathbf{Pr}[(\mathbf{f} = a) \wedge (\mathbf{g} = b)] = 0$. Hence if **f** and **g** are not logically independent they cannot be independent in the probabilistic sense. Thus logical independence is a necessary condition for independence in the probabilistic sense. Indeed we can show that logical independence of **f** and **g** is the necessary and sufficient condition for the existence of a measure that will make **f** and **g** probabalistically independent. We have already seen that logical independence is a necessary condition. We will now show that if the functions are logically independent then there exists at least one measure (normally there are many measures) that makes the functions probabilistically independent. Let $a_1, a_2, \ldots, a_m$ be the range values for **f** and $b_1, b_2, \ldots, b_n$ be the range values for **g**. We assign weights to the possibility space $\mathcal{U}$ in such a way that the measure of the truth set of a statement of the form $(\mathbf{f}(x) = a_j) \wedge (\mathbf{g}(x) = b_k)$ has weight $1/mn$. We do this as follows: By logical independence we know that the truth set of such a statement has at least one element in it. Assume that it has t elements. Then we assign weight $1/mnt$ to each element of this truth set. We have mn different truth sets that do not intersect and which include all the elements of $\mathcal{U}$. We have assigned measure $1/mn$ to each and hence measure $mn(1/mn) = 1$ to the set of all elements of $\mathcal{U}$. Thus we have determined a probability measure. We have assigned the measure in such a way that

$$\mathbf{Pr}[(\mathbf{f} = a_j) \wedge (\mathbf{g} = b_k)] = \frac{1}{mn}.$$

We next observe that

$$\begin{aligned}\mathbf{Pr}[\mathbf{f} = a_j] &= \mathbf{Pr}[(\mathbf{f} = a_j) \wedge (\mathbf{g} = b_1)] + \mathbf{Pr}[(\mathbf{f} = a_j) \wedge (\mathbf{g} = b_2)] + \ldots \\ &\qquad + \mathbf{Pr}[(\mathbf{f} = a_j) \wedge (\mathbf{g} = b_n)] \\ &= \frac{n}{nm} = \frac{1}{m}.\end{aligned}$$

Similarly $\mathbf{Pr}[\mathbf{g} = b_j] = 1/n$. Hence

$$\mathbf{Pr}[(\mathbf{f} = a_j) \wedge (\mathbf{g} = b_k)] = \frac{1}{mn} = \mathbf{Pr}[\mathbf{f} = a_j] \cdot \mathbf{Pr}[\mathbf{g} = b_k].$$

Hence the measure constructed makes the functions independent in the probabilistic sense.

Example 5 (Cont.) Let $\mathbf{g}_1$ be a function that is 1 if the first outcome is heads and 0 if it is tails. Let $\mathbf{g}_2$ be the function giving the total number of heads that turn up in the three tosses. Then it is possible for $\mathbf{g}_1$ to have the value 1 and for $\mathbf{g}_2$ to have the value 0, but in no case do both of these values occur. Hence $\mathbf{g}_1$ and $\mathbf{g}_2$ are not logically independent. Therefore no assignment of measure would make them independent in the probabilistic sense.

EXERCISES

1. A card is drawn at random from a pack of playing cards. What is the probability that it is a 5, given that it is between 2 and 7 inclusive?

2. A die is loaded in such a way that the probability of a given number turning up is proportional to that number (e.g., a 6 is three times as likely to turn up as a 2).

(a) What is the probability of rolling a 3 given that an odd number turns up? [*Ans.* $\frac{1}{3}$.]

(b) What is the probability of rolling an even number given that a number greater than 3 turns up? [*Ans.* $\frac{2}{3}$.]

3. A die is thrown twice. What is the probability that the sum of the faces that turn up is greater than 10, given that one of them is a 6? Given that the first throw is a 6? [*Ans.* $\frac{3}{11}$; $\frac{1}{3}$.]

4. Referring to Section 3, Exercise 9, what is the probability that the man selected studies German if:

(a) He studies French?

(b) He studies French and Russian?

(c) He studies neither French nor Russian?

5. In the primary voting example of Chapter 2, Section 1, assuming that the equiprobable measure has been assigned, find the probability that A wins at least two primaries, given that B drops out of the Wisconsin primary? [*Ans.* $\frac{7}{9}$.]

6. If $\mathbf{Pr}[\sim p] = \frac{1}{4}$ and $\mathbf{Pr}[q \mid p] = \frac{1}{2}$, what is $\mathbf{Pr}[p \wedge q]$? [*Ans.* $\frac{3}{8}$.]

7. A student takes a five-question true-false exam. What is the probability that he will get all answers correct if:

(a) He is only guessing?

(b) He knows that the instructor puts more true than false questions on his exams?

(c) He also knows that the instructor never puts three questions in a row with the same answer?

(d) He also knows that the first and last questions must have the opposite answer?

(e) He also knows that the answer to the second problem is "false"?

8. Three persons, A, B, and C, are placed at random in a straight line.

Let r be the statement, "B is to the right of A," and let s be the statement, "C is to the right of A."

(a) What is $\mathbf{Pr}[r \wedge s]$? [*Ans.* $\frac{1}{3}$.]

(b) Are r and s independent relative to the equiprobable measure? [*Ans.* No.]

9. Let a deck of cards consist of the jacks and queens chosen from a bridge deck, and let two cards be drawn from the new deck. Find:

(a) The probability that the cards are both jacks, given that one is a jack. [*Ans.* $\frac{3}{11} = 0.27$.]

(b) The probability that the cards are both jacks, given that one is a red jack. [*Ans.* $\frac{5}{13} = 0.38$.]

(c) The probability that the cards are both jacks, given that one is the jack of hearts. [*Ans.* $\frac{3}{7} = 0.43$.]

10. Prove that the statements in Example 4 are independent relative to the equiprobable measure.

11. The following example shows that r may be probabilistically independent of p and q without being independent of $p \wedge q$ and $p \vee q$. We throw a coin twice. Let p be "The first toss comes out heads," q be "The second toss comes out heads," and r be "The two tosses come out the same." Compute $\mathbf{Pr}[r]$, $\mathbf{Pr}[r \mid p]$, $\mathbf{Pr}[r \mid q]$, $\mathbf{Pr}[r \mid p \wedge q]$, $\mathbf{Pr}[r \mid p \vee q]$. [*Ans.* $\frac{1}{2}, \frac{1}{2}, \frac{1}{2}, 1, \frac{1}{3}$.]

12. Prove that for any two statements p and q,

$$\mathbf{Pr}[p] = \mathbf{Pr}[p \wedge q] + \mathbf{Pr}[p \wedge \sim q].$$

13. Assume that p and q are independent statements relative to a given measure. Prove that each of the following pairs of statements are independent relative to this same measure.

(a) p and $\sim q$.

(b) $\sim q$ and p.

(c) $\sim p$ and $\sim q$.

14. Prove that for any three statements p, q, and r,

$$\mathbf{Pr}[p \wedge q \wedge r] = \mathbf{Pr}[p] \cdot \mathbf{Pr}[q \mid p] \cdot \mathbf{Pr}[r \mid p \wedge q].$$

15. Prove that two statements are independent relative to a given measure if and only if their characteristic functions are independent functions relative to this measure.

16. Prove that there exists a measure making two given statements probabilistically independent if and only if the statements are logically independent.

17. Let $\mathcal{U}$ be the set of eight possible outcomes of three tosses of a coin. Let p be the statement "the first toss comes up heads" and let q be "at least two heads come up."

(a) Are p and q logically independent? [*Ans.* Yes.]

(b) If the equiprobable measure is assigned on $\mathcal{U}$, are p and q probabilistically independent? [*Ans.* No.]

(c) Define a measure on $\mathcal{U}$ so that p and q are probabilistically independent.

18. Let $\mathcal{U}$ be the set of 16 possible outcomes of four tosses of a coin. For each of the following pairs of functions state (i) whether they are logically independent and (ii) whether they are independent relative to the equiprobable measure.

(a) $\mathbf{f}(x)$ is 1 if the second toss is heads and 0 otherwise, $\mathbf{g}(x)$ gives the number of heads in the last two tosses. [*Ans.* Yes; yes.]

(b) $\mathbf{f}(x)$ gives the number of heads on the first three tosses, and $\mathbf{g}(x)$ gives the number of heads on the last two tosses.

(c) $\mathbf{f}(x)$ is the characteristic function of "the first two outcomes are the same" and $\mathbf{g}(x)$ of "at least two tails come up."

19. Let **f**, **g**, and **h** be any three functions. Prove that

$$\mathbf{Pr}[(\mathbf{f} = a) \wedge (\mathbf{g} = b) \wedge (\mathbf{h} = c)] =$$
$$\mathbf{Pr}[\mathbf{f} = a]\cdot\mathbf{Pr}[\mathbf{g} = b \mid \mathbf{f} = a]\cdot\mathbf{Pr}[\mathbf{h} = c \mid (\mathbf{f} = a) \wedge (\mathbf{g} = b)].$$

provided a, b, and c are in the ranges of **f**, **g**, and **h**, respectively.

20. Let **f** and **g** be any two functions independent with respect to a given probability measure. Let a and b be possible values for **f** and **g**, respectively. Prove that

$$\mathbf{Pr}[\mathbf{f} = a \mid \mathbf{g} = b] = \mathbf{Pr}[\mathbf{f} = a].$$

21. Let $\mathbf{f}_1$, $\mathbf{f}_2$, $\mathbf{f}_3$ be independent relative to a given measure. Prove that each of the following sets is independent relative to this measure.

(a) $\mathbf{f}_1$, $\mathbf{f}_2$.

(b) $\mathbf{f}_1 + \mathbf{f}_2$, $\mathbf{f}_3$.

22. Assign weights to the elements of the possibility space of the experiment described in Example 4 in such a way that the two statements considered there are *not* independent. [*Hint:* Use an idea similar to that of Example 3.]

23. Two dice, loaded as described in Exercise 2, are rolled and the sum of the numbers that turn up is recorded. Let **f** be the outcome function of the experiment where the range of **f** is the set $\{2, 3, \ldots, 12\}$. Find $\mathbf{Pr}[\mathbf{f} = a]$ for $a = 2, 3, \ldots, 12$.

[*Partial Ans.* $\mathbf{Pr}[\mathbf{f} = 7] = \frac{8}{63}$; $\mathbf{Pr}[\mathbf{f} = 11] = \frac{20}{147}$.]

24. The 13 hearts are selected from an ordinary bridge deck, and from these 13 cards, two cards are drawn at random. Consider the following statements.

p: "Two face cards are drawn."

q: "The first card drawn is a face card."

r: "At least one face card is drawn."
(Jack, queen, and king are face cards.) Compute the following probabilities.
(a) $\mathbf{Pr}[p \mid q]$. [*Ans.* $\frac{1}{6}$.]
(b) $\mathbf{Pr}[p \mid r]$. [*Ans.* $\frac{1}{11}$.]
(c) $\mathbf{Pr}[q \mid r]$. [*Ans.* $\frac{6}{11}$.]
(d) $\mathbf{Pr}[r \mid q]$. [*Ans.* 1.]

25. Let p and q be two statements such that p implies q. Show that p and q are probabilistically independent statements if and only if q is logically true or p logically false.

26. Let $\mathbf{f}_1$, $\mathbf{f}_2$, and $\mathbf{f}_3$ be the outcome functions of the experiment in which a balanced coin is tossed three times. Compute the probability of each of the following statements.
(a) $\mathbf{Pr}[\mathbf{f}_1 = \text{H} \mid (\mathbf{f}_2 = \text{T}) \vee (\mathbf{f}_3 = \text{H})]$. [*Ans.* $\frac{1}{2}$.]
(b) $\mathbf{Pr}[\mathbf{f}_1 = \text{H} \mid (\mathbf{f}_1 = \text{T}) \vee (\mathbf{f}_2 = \text{H})]$. [*Ans.* $\frac{1}{3}$.]
(c) $\mathbf{Pr}[(\mathbf{f}_1 = \text{H}) \vee (\mathbf{f}_2 = \text{H}) \mid (\mathbf{f}_1 = \text{H}) \vee (\mathbf{f}_2 = \text{H}) \vee (\mathbf{f}_3 = \text{H})]$
[*Ans.* $\frac{6}{7}$.]

27. Let $\mathbf{f}_1$ and $\mathbf{f}_2$ be the outcome functions of the experiment in which a balanced die is rolled twice. Compute the following.
(a) $\mathbf{Pr}[\mathbf{f}_1 = 3 \mid \mathbf{f}_2 > 2]$.
(b) $\mathbf{Pr}[\mathbf{f}_1 < 4 \mid (\mathbf{f}_1 \neq 2) \wedge (\mathbf{f}_2 > 3)]$.
(c) $\mathbf{Pr}[\mathbf{f}_1 = 5 \mid \mathbf{f}_1 + \mathbf{f}_2 = 9]$.
(d) $\mathbf{Pr}[\mathbf{f}_1 = 2 \mid \mathbf{f}_1 + \mathbf{f}_2 = 9]$.

6. TREES, PATH WEIGHTS, AND BRANCH WEIGHTS

In Section 7 of Chapter 2 we considered the description of a sequence of experiments in which the possibilities for one experiment depended upon the outcomes of previous experiments. It turned out that the possibility space that described the entire set of experiments was represented by a tree with the possibilities being the paths through the tree. We defined outcome functions for each experiment and observed that they described the possibility space. Here we shall first discuss some more details about trees, and then show how a probability measure can be assigned to the set of paths of a possibility tree using information about the outcome functions.

Consider a possibility tree for a sequence of experiments. Each possible sequence of outcomes corresponds to a *path* through the tree. The line segments which make up the path are called *branches*. The tree starts from an initial point and the branches which issue from this point constitute the first stage of the tree. We label the ends of the branches with the possible outcomes of the first experiment. From each of these end points we have a new set of branches issuing, and the end points are labeled with the possible outcomes of the second experiment. These branches constitute the second stage of the tree. We continue in this way with as many stages as there are experiments. The points from which branches issue are called branch points. Each *branch point* at the jth stage of the tree corresponds to a unique sequence of outcomes for the first j experiments.

In this section we shall be dealing with two basic concepts: The concept of a path weight function and the concept of a set of branch weights for the tree.

DEFINITION. Let $\mathcal{U}$ be the set of all paths of a tree. A weight function defined on $\mathcal{U}$ is called a *path weight function.*

DEFINITION. An *assignment of branch weights* for a tree is an assignment of weights to the branches of the tree such that the sum of the weights assigned to branches issuing from any branch point is 1.

In any tree the branches from a branch point at the jth level correspond to possible outcomes of the jth experiment knowing the outcomes of the first $j - 1$ experiments. We assign weights to these branches which are appropriate for the experiment that will be performed when this branch point is reached.

Example 1. Let us reconsider Example 1 of Section 7, Chapter 2. We have two urns. Urn 1 contains two black balls and one white ball. Urn 2 contains two white balls and one black ball. An urn is chosen at random and two balls are drawn successively (without replacement) from the urn chosen. The possibility tree is shown in Figure 3. There are six paths, that we have labeled x_1 through x_6.

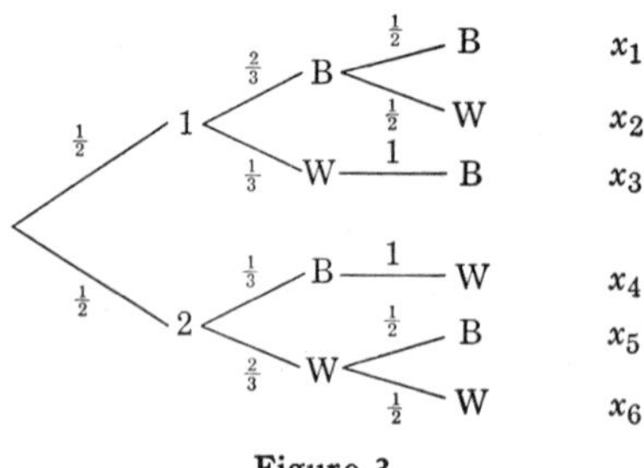

Figure 3

Thus at the first step of the experiment, one of the two urns is selected at random; hence we assign weights $\frac{1}{2}$ to each of the first two alternatives (see Figure 3). If the first urn is chosen, then, since it contains two black and one white ball, there is probability $\frac{2}{3}$ of choosing a black ball and $\frac{1}{3}$ of choosing a white ball. In case urn 2 is chosen, these probabilities are interchanged. On the third step, if urn 1 was chosen and a black ball drawn, then there is probability $\frac{1}{2}$ each of drawing a black or a white ball; but if a white ball was drawn first, there is probability 1 of drawing a black ball. Similarly, the other branch weights can be computed. These are shown in Figure 3.

We shall need a general notation for branch weights. Let $abc \ldots st$ be a possible sequence of outcomes for the first j experiments. Then by

$$p_{ab \ldots s,t}$$

we shall mean the weight appropriate for outcome t given that the first $j - 1$ outcomes are $ab \ldots s$. The weights for the first experiment are indicated by p_a. For instance, in Example 1 we have $p_1 = \frac{1}{2}$, $p_{1,B} = \frac{2}{3}$, and $p_{1B,B} = \frac{1}{2}$.

We wish now to consider statements that relate to the entire sequence of experiments. To find the probabilities for such statements we must assign a weight function to the set of paths of the tree. We want to do this by means of the branch weights and in such a way that the branch weights become conditional probabilities.

Consider the case of three experiments. Let x be any path in the possibility tree. We know that the outcome functions describe the path space so that x is the unique element in the truth set of a statement of the form

$$(\mathbf{f}_1(x) = a) \wedge (\mathbf{f}_2(x) = b) \wedge (\mathbf{f}_3(x) = c).$$

Thus the weight $\mathbf{w}(x)$ which we assign to the point x will be the probability

$$\mathbf{Pr}[(\mathbf{f}_1 = a) \wedge (\mathbf{f}_2 = b) \wedge (\mathbf{f}_3 = c)].$$

But this probability can be rewritten as

$$\mathbf{Pr}[\mathbf{f}_1 = a] \cdot \mathbf{Pr}[\mathbf{f}_2 = b \mid \mathbf{f}_1 = a] \cdot \mathbf{Pr}[\mathbf{f}_3 = c \mid (\mathbf{f}_2 = b) \wedge (\mathbf{f}_1 = a)]$$

(see Exercise 19 of the preceding section). From the way that branch weights are determined it is clear that we would want

$$\mathbf{Pr}[\mathbf{f}_1 = a] = p_a,$$

$$\mathbf{Pr}[\mathbf{f}_2 = b \mid \mathbf{f}_1 = a] = p_{a,b},$$

$$\mathbf{Pr}[\mathbf{f}_3 = c \mid (\mathbf{f}_2 = b) \wedge (\mathbf{f}_1 = a)] = p_{ab,c}.$$

If this is to be the case we see that it is necessary to assign a weight $\mathbf{w}(x)$ by

$$\mathbf{w}(x) = p_a p_{a,b} p_{ab,c}.$$

That is, we must assign a weight to a path equal to the product of the branch weights assigned to the branches of the path.

It can be proved, in general, that if path weights and branch weights are related in this way then the branch weights will be the appropriate conditional probabilities.

Example 1 (Cont.). If we assign branch weights as in Example 1, then the product of these weights along each path is $\frac{1}{6}$ (see Figure 4). There are

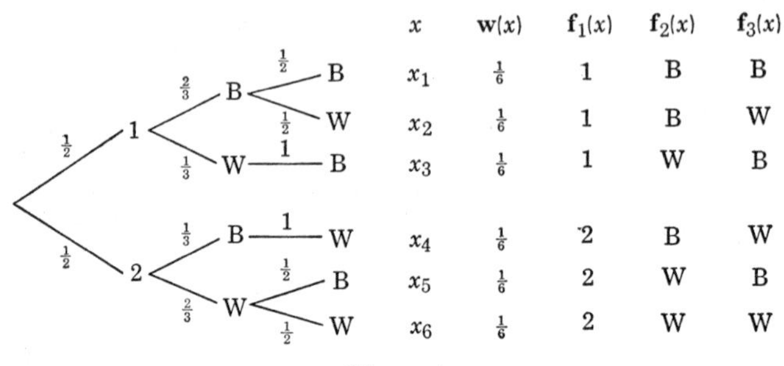

x	$\mathbf{w}(x)$	$\mathbf{f}_1(x)$	$\mathbf{f}_2(x)$	$\mathbf{f}_3(x)$
x_1	$\frac{1}{6}$	1	B	B
x_2	$\frac{1}{6}$	1	B	W
x_3	$\frac{1}{6}$	1	W	B
x_4	$\frac{1}{6}$	2	B	W
x_5	$\frac{1}{6}$	2	W	B
x_6	$\frac{1}{6}$	2	W	W

Figure 4

six paths, so that we do obtain a weight function in this way. Let us now check the desired conditional probabilities along the path x_1.

$$p_1 = \mathbf{Pr}[\mathbf{f}_1 = 1] = \mathbf{w}(x_1) + \mathbf{w}(x_2) + \mathbf{w}(x_3) = \tfrac{1}{2},$$

$$p_{1,B} = \mathbf{Pr}[\mathbf{f}_2 = B \mid \mathbf{f}_1 = 1] = \frac{\mathbf{Pr}[(\mathbf{f}_2 = B) \wedge (\mathbf{f}_1 = 1)]}{\mathbf{Pr}[\mathbf{f}_1 = 1]}$$

$$= \frac{\mathbf{w}(x_1) + \mathbf{w}(x_2)}{\mathbf{w}(x_1) + \mathbf{w}(x_2) + \mathbf{w}(x_3)} = \frac{2}{3},$$

$$p_{1B,B} = \mathbf{Pr}[\mathbf{f}_3 = B \mid (\mathbf{f}_2 = B) \wedge (\mathbf{f}_1 = 1)] = \frac{\mathbf{Pr}[(\mathbf{f}_3 = B) \wedge (\mathbf{f}_2 = B) \wedge (\mathbf{f}_1 = 1)]}{\mathbf{Pr}[(\mathbf{f}_2 = B) \wedge (\mathbf{f}_1 = 1)]}$$

$$= \frac{\mathbf{w}(x_1)}{\mathbf{w}(x_1) + \mathbf{w}(x_2)} = \frac{1}{2}.$$

If the other branch weights are computed it will be found that we again obtain the branch weights of Example 1.

Suppose we have constructed a tree and tree measure for a sequence of n experiments. We sometimes become interested in statements whose truth values depend upon the outcomes of the first m experiments, where $m < n$. We could answer questions about such statements by considering the simpler tree that consists of the first m stages of the n-stage tree. Any probability obtained in this way will be the same as the corresponding one obtained from the n-stage tree.

For instance, in Example 1, consider the statement p which is "The first ball drawn was black." The truth set P is seen from Figure 4 to be the set $P = (x_1, x_2, x_4)$. From this we see that $\mathbf{Pr}[p] = \mathbf{m}(P) = \frac{1}{2}$.

But since this statement relates to only the first two experiments, we could have used the simpler tree given in Figure 5. Considered as a statement relative to this tree, the truth set of p is the set $\{x_1, x_3\}$. Since the measure of this set is $\frac{1}{2}$ we see that $\mathbf{Pr}[p] = \frac{1}{2}$ as before.

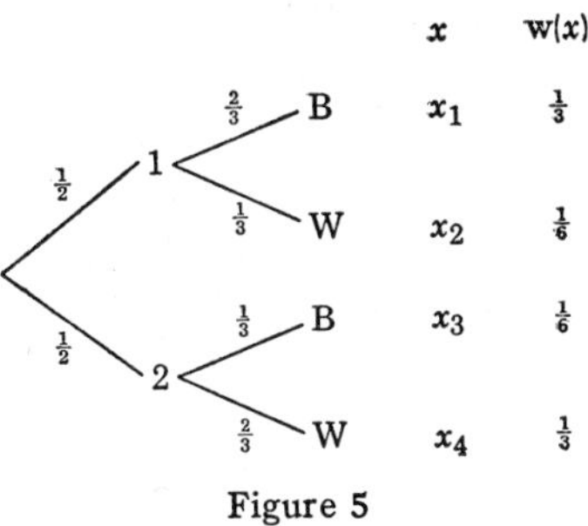

Figure 5

In the above examples we started with branch weights and determined a path weight. It sometimes happens that we are able to determine directly the appropriate path weights. From these it is easy to determine the unique set of branch weights consistent with this path weight function. An example of this is illustrated in the next example.

Example 2. A freshman must choose among mathematics, physics, chemistry, and astronomy as his science course. On the basis of the interest he expressed, his advisor assigns probabilities .4, .3, .2, and .1 to his choosing each of the four courses, respectively. Then, on the basis of the difficulties of these courses, the advisor estimates the probability of the student getting an A in mathematics to be .1, in physics .2, in chemistry .3, and in astronomy .9. This leads to the possibility tree, branch weights, and path weights shown in Figure 6. In that figure the letters M, P, C, and A stand for mathematics, physics, chemistry and astronomy, respectively.

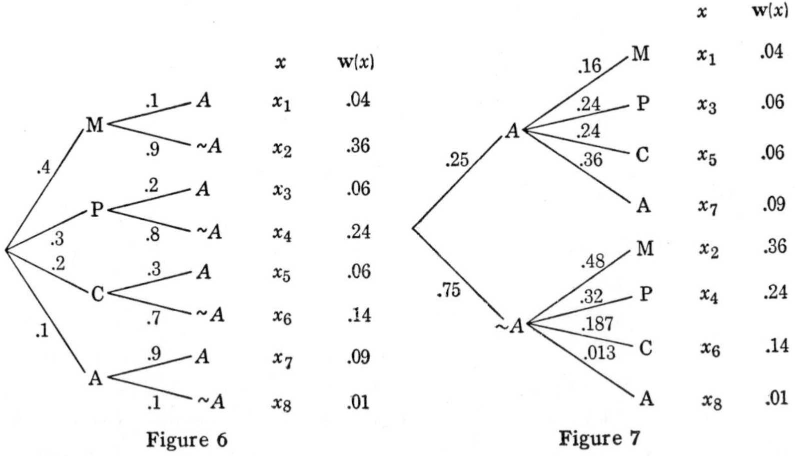

Suppose now that the advisor tries to estimate the probability of the student getting an A or a ~A, that is, a grade lower than an A, without knowing which of the four courses he took. This corresponds to analyzing the possibilities in reverse order, that is, considering first the grade of the student and then what course he takes. The new possibility tree is shown in Figure 7.

A path in the new tree still specifies a grade and a course. We label the paths so that paths in the two trees of Figures 6 and 7, which represent the same grade and course, have the same label. The path weight to be assigned to x_1, for example, will be the probability that the student received an A and took mathematics. But this is the weight assigned to x_1 in the previous tree. Hence the weight assigned to x_1 in the new tree should be the same as the weight assigned to x_1 in the previous tree. Thus corresponding paths are assigned the same weight.

We now have a possibility tree and a path weight function assigned and we wish to find the appropriate branch weights. For example, let us find the branch weights along path x_1; that is, we want p_A and $p_{A,M}$. We know that $p_A = \mathbf{Pr}[\mathbf{f}_1 = A]$ and we know that the statement $\mathbf{f}_1(x) = A$ has truth set $\{x_1, x_3, x_5, x_7\}$. The measure of this set is $.04 + .06 + .06 + .09 = .25$, so that $p_A = .25$. We also know that $p_A \cdot p_{A,M} = \mathbf{w}(x_1) = .04$. And from the last two facts we see that

$$p_{A,M} = \frac{.04}{.25} = .16.$$

The same procedure for each of the paths determines the other branch weights.

From the new tree we can see how the knowledge of his grade affects predictions about the course the student takes. With no knowledge we assigned probability .4 for his taking mathematics. Knowing that he got an A in the course that he took would cause us to decrease this to .16. Knowing that he did not get an A would cause us to increase it to .48.

EXERCISES

1. The fractions of Republicans, Democrats, and Independent voters in cities A and B are

City A: .30 Republican, .40 Democratic, .30 Independent;
City B: .40 Republican, .50 Democratic, .10 Independent.

A city is chosen at random and two voters are chosen successively and at random from the voters of this city. Construct a tree measure and find the probability that two Democrats are chosen. Find the probability that the second voter chosen is an Independent voter.

[*Ans.* .205; .2.]

2. A coin is thrown. If a head turns up a die is rolled. If a tail turns up the coin is thrown again. Construct a tree measure to represent the two experiments and find the probability that the die is thrown and a six turns up.

3. A man wins a certain tournament if he can win two consecutive games out of three played alternately with two opponents A and B. A is a better player than B. The probability of winning a game when B is the opponent is $\frac{2}{3}$. The probability of winning a game when A is his opponent is only $\frac{1}{3}$. Construct a tree measure for the possibilities for three games, assuming that he plays alternately but plays A first. Do the same assuming that he plays B first. In each case find the probability that he will win two consecutive games. Is it better to play two games against the strong player or against the weaker player? [*Ans.* $\frac{10}{27}$; $\frac{8}{27}$; better to play strong player twice.]

4. Construct a tree measure to represent the possibilities for four throws of an ordinary coin. Assume that the probability of a head on any toss is $\frac{1}{2}$ regardless of any information about other throws.

5. A box contains three defective light bulbs and seven good ones. Construct a tree to show the possibilities if three consecutive bulbs are drawn at random from the box (they are not replaced after being drawn). Assign a tree measure and find the probability that at least one good bulb is drawn out. Find the probability that all three are good if the first bulb is good. [*Ans.* $\frac{119}{120}$; $\frac{5}{12}$.]

6. A chess player plays three successive games of chess. His psychological makeup is such that the probability of his winning a given game is $(\frac{1}{2})^{k+1}$, where k is the number of games he has won so far. (For instance, the probability of his winning the first game is $\frac{1}{2}$, the probability of his winning the second game if he has already won the first game is $\frac{1}{4}$, etc.) What is the probability that he will win at least two of the three games?

7. There are two urns, A and B. Urn A contains one black and one red ball. Urn B contains two black and three red balls. A ball is chosen at random from urn A and put into urn B. A ball is then drawn at random from urn B.
   (a) What is the probability that both balls drawn are of the same color? [*Ans.* $\frac{7}{12}$.]
   (b) What is the probability that the first ball drawn was red, given that the second ball drawn was black? [*Ans.* $\frac{2}{5}$.]

8. Assume that in the World Series each team has probability one-half of winning each game, independently of the outcomes of any other game. Assign a tree measure. (See Chapter 1, Section 5 for the tree.) Find the probability that the series ends in 4, 5, 6, and 7 games, respectively.

9. Assume that in the World Series one team is stronger than the other and has probability $\frac{2}{3}$ for winning each of the games. Assign a tree measure and find the following probabilities.

(a) The probability that the stronger team wins in 4, 5, 6, and 7 games, respectively.
(b) The probability that the weaker team wins 4, 5, 6, and 7 games, respectively.
(c) The probability that the series ends in 4, 5, 6, and 7 games, respectively. [*Ans.* .21; .30; .27; .22.]
(d) The probability that the strong team wins the series. [*Ans.* .83.]

10. In the World Series from 1905 through 1958, excluding the nine-game series, there have been 10 four-game series, 13 five-game series, 12 six-game series, and 16 seven-game series. Add the results from 1959 to date to these and use these past records to estimate the probability that a series will last 4, 5, 6, or 7 games. Compare your answers with those obtained theoretically in Exercises 8 and 9(c). Which assumption about the World Series play seems to fit the data better?

11. A student claims to be able to distinguish beer from ale. He is given a series of three tests. In each test he is given two glasses of beer and one of ale and asked to pick out the ale. If he gets two or more correct we will admit his claim. Draw a tree to represent the possibilities (either right or wrong) for his answers. Construct the tree measure which would correspond to guessing and find the probability that his claim will be established if he guesses on every trial. [*Ans.* $\frac{7}{27}$.]

12. During the month of May the probability of a rainy day is .2. The Yankees win on a clear day with probability .7, but on a rainy day only with probability .4. If we know that they won a certain game in May, what is the probability that it rained on that day? [*Ans.* $\frac{1}{8}$.]

13. On a multiple-choice exam there are four possible answers for each question. Therefore, if a student knows the right answer, he has probability one of choosing correctly; if he is guessing, he has probability $\frac{1}{4}$ of choosing correctly. Let us further assume that a good student will know 90 per cent of the answers, a poor student only 50 per cent. If a good student has the right answer, what is the probability that he was only guessing? Answer the same question about a poor student, if the poor student has the right answer. [*Ans.* $\frac{1}{37}$, $\frac{1}{5}$.]

14. Three economic theories are proposed at a given time, which appear to be equally likely on the basis of existing evidence. The state of the American economy is observed the following year, and it turns out that its actual development had probability .6 of happening according to the first theory; and probabilities .4 and .2 according to the others. How does this modify the probabilities of correctness of the three theories? Use the method of Example 2.

15. Let p_1, p_2, p_3, and p_4 be a set of equally likely alternatives. Let

$\mathbf{Pr}[q \mid p_1] = a$, $\mathbf{Pr}[q \mid p_2] = b$, $\mathbf{Pr}[q \mid p_3] = c$, $\mathbf{Pr}[q \mid p_4] = d$. Show that, if $a + b + c + d = 1$, then the revised probabilities of the alternatives relative to q are a, b, c, and d, respectively.

16. In poker, Smith holds a very strong hand and bets a considerable amount. The probability that his opponent, Jones, has a better hand is .05. With a better hand Jones would raise the bet with probability .9, but with a poorer hand Jones would raise only with probability .2. Suppose that Jones raises, what is the new probability that he has a winning hand? Use the method of Example 2. [*Ans.* $\frac{9}{47}$.]

17. A rat is allowed to choose one of five mazes at random. If we know that the probabilities of his getting through the various mazes in three minutes are .6, .3, .2, .1, .1, and we find that the rat escapes in three minutes, how probable is it that he chose the first maze? The second maze? [*Ans.* $\frac{6}{13}$, $\frac{3}{13}$.]

18. A number is chosen at random from the set of integers $U_1 = \{1, 2, 3, 4, 5\}$. If the number n is obtained, a second number is chosen at random from the set $U_2 = \{1, 2, \ldots, n\}$. Construct a tree and tree measure for the two experiments. Let $\mathbf{f}_1$ and $\mathbf{f}_2$ be the two outcome functions and $\mathbf{f}_1 + \mathbf{f}_2$ the sum. Find

(a) $\mathbf{Pr}[\mathbf{f}_1 = a]$, $a = 1, 2, 3, 4, 5$.
(b) $\mathbf{Pr}[\mathbf{f}_2 = a]$, $a = 1, 2, 3, 4, 5$.
(c) $\mathbf{Pr}[\mathbf{f}_1 + \mathbf{f}_2 = a]$, $a = 2, 3, 4, 5, 6, 7, 8, 9, 10$.

19. A population of bacteria increases in the following fashion: in every generation each bacterium creates 0, 1, or 2 new bacteria with probabilities $\frac{1}{4}$, $\frac{1}{2}$, and $\frac{1}{4}$, respectively, and then dies. The individual bacteria act independently of each other. Assuming that we start with a single bacterium, construct a tree and tree measure for the first two generations, taking as outcomes the number of bacteria created in a single generation. If $\mathbf{f}_1$ and $\mathbf{f}_2$ are the outcome functions, compute the following quantities:

(a) $\mathbf{Pr}[\mathbf{f}_1 > 0]$. [*Ans.* $\frac{3}{4}$.]
(b) $\mathbf{Pr}[\mathbf{f}_2 > 0]$. [*Ans.* $\frac{39}{64}$.]
(c) $\mathbf{Pr}[\mathbf{f}_1 = 1 \mid \mathbf{f}_2 = 1]$. [*Ans.* $\frac{4}{5}$.]
(d) Find the probability that no bacteria are alive in the third generation (not counting the original bacterium). $\left[Ans.\ \dfrac{7921}{16{,}384} = .483.\right]$

20. Let $\mathbf{f}_0 = 1$ and let $\mathbf{f}_1$ and $\mathbf{f}_2$ be the outcome functions for the experiment of Exercise 19. ($\mathbf{f}_0$ corresponds to the initial population.) Define $\mathbf{w}_1 = \mathbf{f}_0 + \mathbf{f}_1$ and $\mathbf{w}_2 = \mathbf{f}_0 + \mathbf{f}_1 + \mathbf{f}_2$. What is the interpretation of $\mathbf{w}_1$ and $\mathbf{w}_2$? Find the range of each function and compute the probabilities that $\mathbf{w}_1$ and $\mathbf{w}_2$ take on each of their possible range values.

7. STOCHASTIC PROCESSES

Any sequence of experiments that can be subjected to a probabilistic analysis is called a stochastic process. If the set of possible outcomes is finite we shall say that the process is finite. A finite stochastic process is completely described by a possibility tree together with path (or branch) weights, as described in the previous section. Stochastic processes can be classified by indicating special properties possessed by the outcome functions of the process. Here we shall define and give examples of three important types of stochastic process: the *independent process*, the *independent trials process*, and the *Markov chain process*.

DEFINITION. A finite stochastic process with outcome functions $\mathbf{f}_1$, $\mathbf{f}_2$, $\ldots, \mathbf{f}_n, \ldots$ is an *independent process* if for each n and for any outcome $t, s, r, \ldots, a$

$$(1)\quad \mathbf{Pr}[\mathbf{f}_n = t \mid (\mathbf{f}_{n-1} = s) \wedge (\mathbf{f}_{n-2} = r) \wedge \ldots (\mathbf{f}_1 = a)] = \mathbf{Pr}[\mathbf{f}_n = t].$$

In other words, for an independent process the probability that the outcome of the nth experiment is a certain element of the outcome set is independent of the outcomes of the first $n - 1$ experiments.

To recognize whether a given stochastic process is an independent process or not it is useful to look at the *star* of each branch point. This

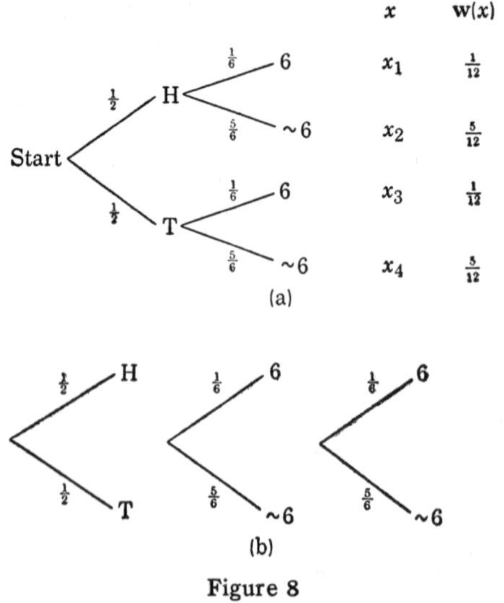

Figure 8

is defined to be the set of all branches *issuing* from this branch point. For instance, for the stochastic process illustrated in Figure 8(a) we have drawn in Figure 8(b) the stars of branch points START, H, and T. Two stars are said to be *equal* if the branches of one have the same probabilities and the same set of end points as the branches of the other. An independent process has the characteristic property that at each fixed stage all stars are equal.

An important conclusion that can be drawn concerning an independent process is the following: Consider the case of three outcome functions. Then

$$\mathbf{Pr}[(\mathbf{f}_1 = a) \wedge (\mathbf{f}_2 = b) \wedge (\mathbf{f}_3 = c)]$$
$$= \mathbf{Pr}[\mathbf{f}_1 = a] \cdot \mathbf{Pr}[\mathbf{f}_2 = b \mid \mathbf{f}_1 = a] \cdot \mathbf{Pr}[\mathbf{f}_3 = c \mid (\mathbf{f}_1 = a) \wedge (\mathbf{f}_2 = b)].$$

If the process is an independent process, then we see that

$$\mathbf{Pr}[(\mathbf{f}_1 = a) \wedge (\mathbf{f}_2 = b) \wedge (\mathbf{f}_3 = c)] = \mathbf{Pr}[\mathbf{f}_1 = a] \cdot \mathbf{Pr}[\mathbf{f}_2 = b] \cdot \mathbf{Pr}[\mathbf{f}_3 = c].$$

That is, the outcome functions $\mathbf{f}_1$, $\mathbf{f}_2$, $\mathbf{f}_3$ are independent relative to the tree measure. In general, for any independent process any subset of the outcome functions is independent relative to the tree measure.

Example 1. As an example of an independent process assume that a coin is thrown and then a die is rolled. In the case of the die experiment we note only whether or not a six turns up. The tree and the tree measure are given in Figure 8. (The notation ~6 means "a number less than 6 turns up.")

An important special type of independent process is the independent trials process which we now define.

DEFINITION. A finite stochastic process is an *independent trials process* if it is an independent process such that

$$\mathbf{Pr}[\mathbf{f}_n = a] = \mathbf{Pr}[\mathbf{f}_m = a] \quad (2)$$

for all m and n and each outcome a.

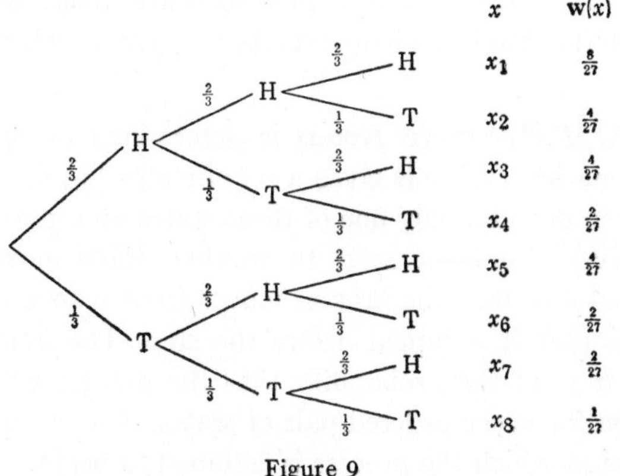

Figure 9

From the above definition we see that in an independent trials process all the stars are equal, while in an independent process stars in different stages are allowed to be unequal. Figure 9 illustrates an independent trials process.

Example 2. Let us choose for each experiment the toss of a biased coin. We assume that the probability of heads is $\frac{2}{3}$ on any one toss. Then for any number of tosses we can construct a tree and tree weights. For instance, for $n = 3$ the tree is indicated in Figure 9. The three outcome functions each have the same range $R = \{\text{H}, \text{T}\}$, and $\mathbf{Pr}[\mathbf{f}_i = \text{H}] = \frac{2}{3}$, $\mathbf{Pr}[\mathbf{f}_i = \text{T}] = \frac{1}{3}$ for each outcome function.

In the case of an independent process the branch weights assigned at a given stage are all the same, and are independent of the outcomes of previous experiments. We now consider a process, the Markov chain process, for which the branch weights assigned at a given stage depend only on the outcomes of the experiment immediately preceding the given one.

Definition. A finite stochastic process with outcome functions $\mathbf{f}_0$, $\mathbf{f}_1$, . . . , $\mathbf{f}_n$ is a *Markov chain process* if the starting state, given by $\mathbf{f}_0$, is fixed and

$$\text{(3)} \qquad \mathbf{Pr}[\mathbf{f}_n = t \mid (\mathbf{f}_{n-1} = s) \wedge (\mathbf{f}_{n-2} = r) \wedge \ldots \wedge (\mathbf{f}_1 = a)] = \mathbf{Pr}[\mathbf{f}_n = t \mid \mathbf{f}_{n-1} = s]$$

$$\text{(4)} \qquad \mathbf{Pr}[\mathbf{f}_n = t \mid \mathbf{f}_{n-1} = s] = \mathbf{Pr}[\mathbf{f}_m = t \mid \mathbf{f}_{m-1} = s]$$

for all $m \geq 1$, $n \geq 2$ and any possible sequence of outcomes $a, \ldots, s, t$.

In other words, the outcome of a given experiment depends only on the outcome of the immediately preceding experiment; and, moreover, this dependence is the same at all stages.

If two branch points in a Markov chain have the same label, whether at the same or different stages, then their stars are equal. Because of the special form of the Markov chain process we give another, equivalent, definition.

Definition. A *Markov chain process* is determined by specifying the following information: There is given a set of states $\{s_1, s_2, \ldots, s_r\}$. The process can be in one and only one of these states at a given time and it moves successively from one state to another. Each move is called a *step*. The probability that the process moves from s_i to s_j depends only on the state s_i that it occupied before the step. The *transition probability* p_{ij}, which gives the probability that the process will move from s_i to s_j, is given for every ordered pair of states. Also an initial *starting state* is specified at which the process is assumed to begin.

With the information given above it is now possible to construct a tree and assign path weights to describe the Markov chain process when it moves through any (finite) number of steps.

Example 3. The Land of Oz is blessed by many things, but not by good weather. They never have two nice days in a row. If they have a nice day they are just as likely to have snow as rain the next day. If they have snow (or rain), they have an even chance of having the same the next day. If there is a change from snow or rain, only half of the time is this a change to a nice day. It is a nice day today in the Land of Oz. With this information we form a Markov chain as follows. We take as states the kinds of weather R, N, S. From the above information we determine the transition probabilities. These are most conveniently represented in a square array as

$$\begin{array}{c c} & \begin{array}{ccc} R & N & S \end{array} \\ \begin{array}{c} R \\ N \\ S \end{array} & \begin{pmatrix} \frac{1}{2} & \frac{1}{4} & \frac{1}{4} \\ \frac{1}{2} & 0 & \frac{1}{2} \\ \frac{1}{4} & \frac{1}{4} & \frac{1}{2} \end{pmatrix} \end{array}$$

The entries in the first row represent the probabilities for the various kinds of weather following a rainy day, those in the second row represent these

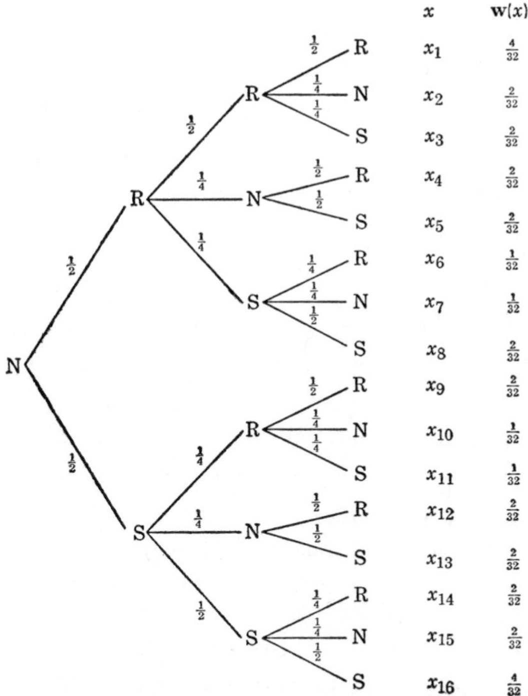

Figure 10

probabilities following a nice day, and the same for a snowy day in the third row. Such a square array is called the *matrix of transition probabilities*. From this we determined a tree and a tree measure for the next three days' weather as indicated in Figure 10.

From this tree we can find the predictions for rain in the next three days. In fact we find

$$\mathbf{Pr}[\mathbf{f}_1 = R] = \tfrac{1}{2}$$
$$\mathbf{Pr}[\mathbf{f}_2 = R] = \tfrac{3}{8}$$
$$\mathbf{Pr}[\mathbf{f}_3 = R] = \tfrac{13}{32}.$$

We shall discuss Markov chains in detail in Chapter 6.

EXERCISES

1. In Example 2, let $\mathbf{f}$ be the number of heads that turns up. Find $\mathbf{Pr}[\mathbf{f} = 0]$, $\mathbf{Pr}[\mathbf{f} = 1]$, $\mathbf{Pr}[\mathbf{f} = 2]$ and $\mathbf{Pr}[\mathbf{f} = 3]$.

2. In Example 3, find $\mathbf{Pr}[\mathbf{f}_1 = N]$, $\mathbf{Pr}[\mathbf{f}_2 = N]$ and $\mathbf{Pr}[\mathbf{f}_3 = N]$.

3. State in each case whether the process indicated is (a) an independent process, (b) an independent trials process, (c) a Markov chain, (d) none of these.

i. A die is rolled a number of times. [*Ans.* (b).]

ii. The World Series under the assumption that each team has an equal chance of winning each game.

iii. A series of games played between two teams where the winner of each game is assumed to have probability 2/3 of winning the next game. [*Ans.* (c).]

iv. A series of games between two teams played alternately at each team's stadium and assuming that the home team wins with probability 2/3.

4. A certain calculating machine uses only the digits 0 and 1. It is supposed to transmit one of these digits through several stages. However, at every stage there is a probability p that the digit which enters this stage will be changed when it leaves. We form a Markov chain to represent the process of transmission by taking as states the digits 0 and 1. What is the matrix of transition probabilities?

5. For the Markov chain in Exercise 4, draw a tree and assign a tree measure, assuming that the process begins in state 0 and moves through three stages of transmission. What is the probability that the machine after three stages produces the digit 0, i.e., the correct digit? What is the probability that the machine never changed the digit from 0? [*Ans.* $(1 - p)^3 + 3p^2(1 - p)$; $(1 - p)^3$.]

6. Assume that a man's profession can be classified as professional, skilled laborer, or unskilled laborer. Assume that of the sons of professional men 80 per cent are professional, 10 per cent are skilled laborers, and 10 per cent are unskilled laborers. In the case of sons of skilled laborers, 60 per cent are skilled laborers, 20 per cent are professional, and 20 per cent are unskilled laborers. Finally, in the case of unskilled laborers, 50 per cent of the sons are unskilled laborers, and 25 per cent each are in the other two categories. Assume that every man has a son, and form a Markov chain by following a given family through several generations. Set up the matrix of transition probabilities. Find the probability that the grandson of an unskilled laborer is a professional man. [*Ans.* .375.]

7. In Exercise 6 we assumed that every man has a son. Assume instead that the probability a man has a son is .8. Form a Markov chain with four states. The first three states are as in Exercise 6, and the fourth state is such that the process enters it if a man has no son, and that the state cannot be left. This state represents families whose male line has died out. Find the matrix of transition probabilities and find the probability that an unskilled laborer has a grandson who is a professional man. [*Ans.* .24.]

8. In Example 1 suppose that the die is rolled first. Draw the tree and construct the tree measure.

9. There are two coins, the first is well balanced while the second turns up heads with probability $\frac{2}{3}$. We proceed by tossing the fair coin if heads came up last time and the biased coin following tails. Assume that the first toss was tails. Draw the tree for the next three tosses, constructing the tree measure. What is the probability of getting at least two heads? [*Ans.* $\frac{2}{3}$.]

10. Show that the process in Exercise 9 is a Markov chain. Write its transition probabilities.

11. In a series of games between teams A and B assume that team A wins with probability .6, loses with .3, and ties with probability .1. Draw the tree and construct the tree measure for a series of three games between the teams.

12. In Exercise 11 let us suppose that 2 points are awarded for a win and 1 for a tie. What is the probability that each team will get 3 points in the series? [*Ans.* .109.]

13. It is known that of the sons of Harvard men 80 per cent go to Harvard and the rest to Yale. Of the sons of Yale men 40 per cent go to Yale, the remainder split evenly between Harvard and Dartmouth. Of the sons of Dartmouth men 70 per cent go to Dartmouth, 20 to Harvard, and 10 to Yale.

(a) Assume that this is a Markov chain, and set up the transition matrix.

(b) If in the present generation we pick a sample consisting of 40 per cent Harvard men, 40 per cent Yale men, and 20 per cent Dartmouth men, what percentage distribution can we expect in the next generation? [*Ans.* 48, 26, 26.]

(c) Suppose that the original assumptions are modified by assuming that the son of a Harvard man always goes to Harvard. Set up the transition matrix.

8. INDEPENDENT TRIALS PROCESS

An independent process arises when experiments are performed in such a way that the outcome of any one experiment does not influence the outcome of any other experiment. If the possible outcomes and the probabilities for these outcomes are the same for every experiment, we have an independent trials process. Consider now an independent trials process, and let $A = \{a, b, \ldots, h\}$ be the common set of possible outcomes for any one experiment. For example, in the case of a sequence of throws of a coin $A = \{\mathrm{H}, \mathrm{T}\}$. Many of the interesting questions about such a sequence of experiments relate to the number of times each of the outcomes occurs in a given number of repetitions of the experiment. For example, in tossing a coin one hundred times we might ask for the probability that half of the tosses will be heads. In this section we shall find the probability that each of the outcomes will occur a specified number of times. The discussion is carried out in terms of an experiment with only three possible outcomes but the general procedure will be clear.

We start then with an experiment with three possible outcomes a, b, and c, where these outcomes occur in each experiment with probabilities p_a, p_b, p_c, respectively. We assume that the experiment is performed three times. The possibility tree and path weights are given in Figure 11.

Let $\mathbf{g}_a$ be a function whose domain is the set of paths and whose value $\mathbf{g}_a(x)$ is the number of times outcome a occurs on path x. For example, $\mathbf{g}_a(x_1) = 3$, $\mathbf{g}_a(x_2) = 2$, etc. Similarly let $\mathbf{g}_b$ be a function whose value $\mathbf{g}_b(x)$ gives the number of times b occurs on x, and $\mathbf{g}_c$ a function whose value $\mathbf{g}_c(x)$ gives the number of times c occurs on x. Then we are interested in probabilities of the form,

$$\mathbf{Pr}[(\mathbf{g}_a = r) \wedge (\mathbf{g}_b = s) \wedge (\mathbf{g}_c = t)].$$

We assume that r, s, and t have sum 3. Otherwise the probability of the above statement is 0. Consider first a special case, say $r = 1$, $s = 2$, and $t = 0$. Then

$$\mathbf{Pr}[(\mathbf{g}_a = 1) \wedge (\mathbf{g}_b = 2) \wedge (\mathbf{g}_c = 0)] = \mathbf{w}(x_5) + \mathbf{w}(x_{11}) + \mathbf{w}(x_{13})$$
$$= 3p_a p_b^2.$$

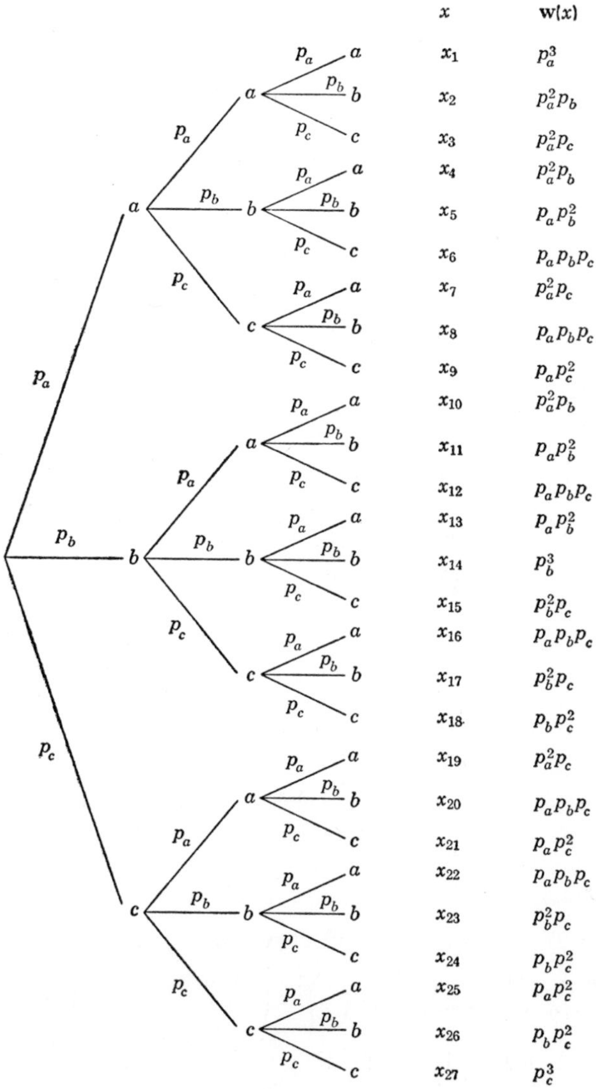

x	$\mathbf{w}(x)$
x_1	p_a^3
x_2	$p_a^2 p_b$
x_3	$p_a^2 p_c$
x_4	$p_a^2 p_b$
x_5	$p_a p_b^2$
x_6	$p_a p_b p_c$
x_7	$p_a^2 p_c$
x_8	$p_a p_b p_c$
x_9	$p_a p_c^2$
x_{10}	$p_a^2 p_b$
x_{11}	$p_a p_b^2$
x_{12}	$p_a p_b p_c$
x_{13}	$p_a p_b^2$
x_{14}	p_b^3
x_{15}	$p_b^2 p_c$
x_{16}	$p_a p_b p_c$
x_{17}	$p_b^2 p_c$
x_{18}	$p_b p_c^2$
x_{19}	$p_a^2 p_c$
x_{20}	$p_a p_b p_c$
x_{21}	$p_a p_c^2$
x_{22}	$p_a p_b p_c$
x_{23}	$p_b^2 p_c$
x_{24}	$p_b p_c^2$
x_{25}	$p_a p_c^2$
x_{26}	$p_b p_c^2$
x_{27}	p_c^3

Figure 11

We notice that the truth set of the statement considered above consisted of three paths each of which was assigned the same weight. Consider now the case of n experiments. We again consider a tree and path weights for these experiments. Each path of the tree carries with it the label at each stage indicating the outcome of the corresponding experiment. We define $\mathbf{g}_a$, $\mathbf{g}_b$, and $\mathbf{g}_c$ as above. Let A be the truth set of the statement $(\mathbf{g}_a(x) = r) \wedge (\mathbf{g}_b(x) = s) \wedge (\mathbf{g}_c(x) = t)$. The set A consists of all paths which have the label a exactly r times, the label b exactly s times, and the label c exactly t times. Furthermore every possible labeling of the n branch points with this property will occur. Hence from Chapter 2 we see that there are

$$\binom{n}{r, s, t} = \frac{n!}{r!s!t!}$$

paths in A. The weight assigned to any path in A is $p_a^r \cdot p_b^s \cdot p_c^t$. Combining these results, we have

$$\mathbf{Pr}[(\mathbf{g}_a = r) \wedge (\mathbf{g}_b = s) \wedge (\mathbf{g}_c = t)] = \binom{m}{r, s, t} p_a^r \cdot p_b^s \cdot p_c^t.$$

We have established above a special case of the following important result.

Theorem. Consider the first n stages of an independent trials process with possible outcomes $a, b, \ldots, h$. Let $\mathbf{g}_a$ be the number of times a occurs, $\mathbf{g}_b$ the number of times b occurs, etc. Then

$$\mathbf{Pr}[(\mathbf{g}_a = r_1) \wedge (\mathbf{g}_b = r_2) \wedge \ldots \wedge (\mathbf{g}_h = r_h)]$$

$$= \binom{n}{r_1, r_2, \ldots, r_h} p_a^{r_1} \cdot p_b^{r_2} \ldots p_h^{r_h}$$

where $r_1, r_2, \ldots, r_h$ are any nonnegative integers such that $r_1 + r_2 + \ldots + r_h = n$.

Example 1. A die is thrown 12 times. What is the probability that each number will come up exactly twice. The experiment that we repeat has possible outcomes 1, 2, 3, 4, 5, 6, each occurring with probability $\frac{1}{6}$. The probability that each outcome occurs twice is then

$$\mathbf{Pr}[(\mathbf{g}_1 = 2) \wedge (\mathbf{g}_2 = 2) \wedge (\mathbf{g}_3 = 2) \wedge (\mathbf{g}_4 = 2) \wedge (\mathbf{g}_5 = 2) \wedge (\mathbf{g}_6 = 2)]$$

$$= \binom{12}{2, 2, 2, 2, 2, 2}\left(\frac{1}{6}\right)^2 \cdot \left(\frac{1}{6}\right)^2 \cdot \left(\frac{1}{6}\right)^2 \cdot \left(\frac{1}{6}\right)^2 \cdot \left(\frac{1}{6}\right)^2 \cdot \left(\frac{1}{6}\right)^2 = .0034.$$

Example 2. Assume that each time a certain team plays a game it wins with probability .6, loses with probability .3 and ties with probability .1. In a three-game series what are the probabilities for the various combinations of wins, losses, and ties that might occur? We consider this as an independent trials process where each experiment has possible outcomes W, L, D occurring with probabilities .6, .3, and .1, respectively. Then for any r, s, and t we have

$$\mathbf{Pr}[(\mathrm{g}_W = r) \wedge (\mathrm{g}_L = s) \wedge (\mathrm{g}_D = t)] = \binom{3}{r,\, s,\, t}(.6)^r(.3)^s(.1)^t.$$

In Figure 12 we have given the probabilities for all possible combinations of wins, ties, and losses. From these probabilities it is easy to find other interesting probabilities. For example the probability that the team wins exactly two games is $.324 + .108 = .432$.

r	s	t	$\mathbf{Pr}[(r \text{ wins}) \wedge (s \text{ losses}) \wedge (t \text{ ties})]$
3	0	0	.216
0	3	0	.027
0	0	3	.001
2	1	0	.324
2	0	1	.108
1	2	0	.162
1	1	1	.108
1	0	2	.018
0	2	1	.027
0	1	2	.009

Figure 12

We consider next the important special case of n repetitions of an experiment with two possible outcomes. Let these outcomes be a and b. Then the statement $\mathrm{g}_a = r$ is equivalent to the statement $(\mathrm{g}_a = r) \wedge (\mathrm{g}_b = n - r)$. Thus the interest in this case is primarily in the probability that one of the outcomes occurs a particular number of times. Let p be the probability that a occurs in a single experiment. Then the probability that b occurs is $1 - p$. Hence from our general result we have the following theorem.

Theorem. An experiment with two outcomes a, b occurring with probabilities p and $1 - p$, respectively, is carried out independently n times. Let g_a be the number of times that a occurs. Then

$$\mathbf{Pr}[\mathrm{g}_a = r] = \binom{n}{r} p^r(1 - p)^{n-r}.$$

Example 3. Consider n throws of an ordinary coin. We assume that the probability is 1/2 for heads on any one throw independently of the outcome of any other throw. Then the probability that exactly r heads will turn up is

$$\mathbf{Pr}[\mathrm{g}_H = r] = \binom{n}{r}\left(\frac{1}{2}\right)^n.$$

For example, in 100 throws the probability that exactly 50 heads will turn up is $\binom{100}{50}\left(\frac{1}{2}\right)^{100}$, which is approximately .08. Thus we see that it is quite unlikely that exactly one-half of the tosses will result in heads. On the other hand, suppose that we ask for the probability that nearly one-half of the tosses will be heads. To be more precise, let us ask for the probability that the number of heads that occur does not deviate by more than 10 from 50. To find this we must add all the various $\mathbf{Pr}[\mathbf{g}_a = r]$ for $r = 40, 41, \ldots, 60$. If this is done, we obtain a probability of approximately .96. Thus, while it is unlikely that exactly 50 heads will occur, it is very likely that the number of heads which occur will be between 40 and 60.

Example 4. Assume that we have a machine which, on the basis of data given, is to predict the outcome of an election as either a Republican victory or a Democratic victory. If two identical machines are given the same data, they should predict the same result. We assume, however, that any such machine has a certain probability q of reversing the prediction that it would ordinarily make, because of a mechanical or electrical failure. To improve the accuracy of our prediction we give the same data to n identical machines, and choose the answer which the majority of the machines give. To avoid ties we assume that n is odd. Let us see how this decreases the probability of an error due to a faulty machine.

A single experiment then consists in giving the data to a single machine. We label the outcomes "success" and "failure" according to whether the machine gives the answer of a correctly operating machine or not. The probability of success is $p = 1 - q$. Carrying out the experiment n times corresponds to giving the data to n different machines. The majority decision will agree with that of a perfectly operating machine if we have more than $n/2$ successes. Suppose, for example, that we have five machines, each of which has probability .1 of reversing the prediction because of parts failure. Let $\mathbf{g}_S$ be the number of machines that operate correctly. Then we need to find

$$\mathbf{Pr}[(\mathbf{g}_S = 3) \vee (\mathbf{g}_S = 4) \vee (\mathbf{g}_S = 5)].$$

But this is

$$\mathbf{Pr}[\mathbf{g}_S = 3] + \mathbf{Pr}[\mathbf{g}_S = 4] + \mathbf{Pr}[\mathbf{g}_S = 5] = \binom{5}{3}(.9)^3(.1)^2 + \binom{5}{4}(.9)^4(.1)^1 + \binom{5}{5}(.9)^5(.1)^0 = .991.$$

Thus the above procedure decreases the probability of error due to machine failure from .1 in the case of one machine to .009 for the case of five machines.

EXERCISES

1. Compute for $n = 4$, $n = 8$, $n = 12$, and $n = 16$ the probability of obtaining exactly one-half heads when an ordinary coin is thrown. [*Ans.* .375; .273; .226; .196.]

2. Compute for $n = 4$, $n = 8$, $n = 12$, and $n = 16$ the probability that the fraction of heads deviates from one-half by less than one-fifth. [*Ans.* .375; .711; .854; .923.]

3. Verify that the probability .991 given in Example 4 is correct.

4. Assume that Peter and Paul match pennies four times. (In matching pennies, Peter wins a penny with probability $\frac{1}{2}$, and Paul wins a penny with probability $\frac{1}{2}$.) What is the probability that Peter wins more than Paul? Answer the same for five throws. For the case of 12,917 throws. [*Ans.* $\frac{5}{16}$; $\frac{1}{2}$; $\frac{1}{2}$.]

5. Suppose that in a city 60 per cent of the population are Democrats, 30 per cent are Republicans, and 10 per cent are Independents. What is the probability that if three people are chosen at random there will be one Republican, one Democrat, and one Independent voter? [*Ans.* .108.]

6. Three horses, A, B, and C compete in four races. Assuming that each horse has an equal chance in each race, what is the probability that A wins two races and B and C win one each? What is the probability that the same horse wins all four races? [*Ans.* $\frac{4}{27}$; $\frac{1}{27}$.]

7. Assume that in a certain large college 40 per cent of the students are freshmen, 30 per cent are sophomores, 20 per cent are juniors, and 10 per cent are seniors. A committee of eight is chosen at random from the student body. What is the probability that there are equal numbers from each class on the committee?

8. Let us assume that when a batter comes to bat, he has probability .6 of being put out, .1 of getting a walk, .2 of getting a single, .1 of getting an extra base hit. If he comes to bat five times in a game, what is the probability that

(a) He gets two walks and three singles? [*Ans.* .0008.]

(b) A walk, a single, an extra base hit (and is out twice)? [*Ans.* .0432.]

(c) Has a perfect day (i.e., never out). [*Ans.* .01024.]

9. If an ordinary die is thrown four times, what is the probability that exactly two 6's will occur?

10. In a ten-question true-false exam, what is the probability of getting 70 per cent or better by guessing? [*Ans.* $\frac{11}{64}$.]

11. Assume that, every time a batter comes to bat, he has probability .3 for getting a hit. Assuming that his hits form an independent trials process and that the batter comes to bat four times, what fraction of the games would he expect to get at least two hits? At least three hits? Four hits? [*Ans.* .3483; .0837; .0081.]

12. A coin is to be thrown eight times. What is the most probable number of heads that will occur? What is the number having the highest probability, given that the first four throws resulted in heads?

13. A small factory has ten workers. The workers eat their lunch at one of two diners, and they are just as likely to eat in one as in the other. If the proprietors want to be more than .95 sure of having enough seats, how many seats must each of the diners have? [*Ans.* Eight seats.]

14. Suppose that five people are chosen at random and asked if they favor a certain proposal. If only 30 per cent of the people favor the proposal, what is the probability that a majority of the five people chosen will favor the proposal?

15. In Example 4, if the probability for a machine reversing its answer due to a parts failure is .2, how many machines would have to be used to make the probability greater than .89 that the answer obtained would be that which a machine with no failure would give?

[*Ans.* Three machines.]

16. Assume that a single torpedo has a probability $\frac{1}{2}$ of sinking a ship, probability $\frac{1}{4}$ of damaging it, and probability $\frac{1}{4}$ of missing. Assume further that two damaging shots sink the ship. What is the probability that four torpedos will succeed in sinking the ship? [*Ans.* $\frac{251}{256}$.]

17. Jones, Smith, and Green live in the same house. The mailman has observed that Jones and Smith receive the same amount of mail on the average, but that Green receives twice as much as Jones (and hence also twice as much as Smith). If he has four letters for this house, what is the probability that each man receives at least one letter?

18. If three dice are thrown, find the probability that there is one six and two fives, given that all the outcomes are greater than three.

[*Ans.* $\frac{1}{9}$.]

19. A man plays a tournament consisting of three games. In each game he has probability $\frac{1}{2}$ for a win, $\frac{1}{4}$ for a loss, and $\frac{1}{4}$ for a draw, independently of the outcomes of other games. To win the tournament he must win more games than he loses. What is the probability that he wins the tournament?

20. Assume that in a certain course the probability that a student chosen at random will get an A is .1, that he will get a B is .2, that he will get a

C is .4, that he will get a D is .2, and that he will get an E is .1. What distribution of grades is most likely in the case of four students?

[*Ans.* One B, two C's, one D.]

21. Let us assume that in a World Series game a batter has probability $\frac{1}{4}$ of getting no hits, $\frac{1}{2}$ for getting one hit, $\frac{1}{4}$ for getting two hits, assuming that the probability of getting more than two hits is negligible. In a four-game World Series, find the probability that the batter gets:
(a) Exactly two hits.
(b) Exactly three hits.
(c) Exactly four hits.
(d) Exactly five hits.
(e) Fewer than two hits or more than five.

[*Ans.* $\frac{7}{64}$, $\frac{7}{32}$, $\frac{35}{128}$, $\frac{7}{32}$, $\frac{23}{128}$.]

9. MEAN OF A FUNCTION

When we are given a large set of numbers it is often useful to replace them by a single number that gives us useful information about the entire set of numbers. The most common number used for this purpose is the average of the numbers. Here we shall give a generalization of this concept to numerical functions defined on a possibility space $\mathfrak{U}$.

DEFINITION. Let **f** be a numerical function defined on a possibility space for which a measure **m** has been defined by a weight function **w**. Then the *mean value of* **f** with respect to the measure **m**, denoted by **M**[**f**], is

$$\mathbf{M}[\mathbf{f}] = \sum_x \mathbf{f}(x)\mathbf{w}(x) \tag{1}$$

Example 1. A die is rolled. Let $\mathfrak{U} = \{1, 2, 3, 4, 5, 6\}$. Let **m** be the equiprobable measure and let **f** be the outcome function. Then

$$\mathbf{M}[\mathbf{f}] = 1\cdot\tfrac{1}{6} + 2\cdot\tfrac{1}{6} + 3\cdot\tfrac{1}{6} + 4\cdot\tfrac{1}{6} + 5\cdot\tfrac{1}{6} + 6\cdot\tfrac{1}{6} = 3\tfrac{1}{2}.$$

Example 2. A coin is thrown twice. Let $\mathfrak{U} = \{\text{HH, HT, TH, TT}\}$. Let **m** be the equiprobable measure and let **f** be the number of heads that turn up. Then

$$\mathbf{M}[\mathbf{f}] = 2\cdot\tfrac{1}{4} + 1\cdot\tfrac{1}{4} + 1\cdot\tfrac{1}{4} + 0\cdot\tfrac{1}{4} = 1.$$

Example 3. Let A be any finite set of numbers. A number is drawn at random from this set. Then the possibility set is the set A. Let **f** be the outcome function. Then **M**[**f**] is the average of the numbers in A. For example, if $A = \{1, 2, 7, 9, 9\}$, then

$$\mathbf{M}[\mathbf{f}] = 1\cdot\tfrac{1}{5} + 2\cdot\tfrac{1}{5} + 7\cdot\tfrac{1}{5} + 9\cdot\tfrac{1}{5} + 9\cdot\tfrac{1}{5}$$
$$= \frac{1 + 2 + 7 + 9 + 9}{5} = 5\frac{3}{5}.$$

In practice the computation of (1) can be shortened. Let us choose those terms $\mathbf{f}(x)\mathbf{w}(x)$ in the sum for which $\mathbf{f}(x)$ has a fixed value j. We get a number of terms of the form $j \cdot \mathbf{w}(x)$, where x is any element of the truth set of $\mathbf{f}(x) = j$. Thus j is multiplied by the sum of all weights in this truth set, i.e., by $\mathbf{Pr}[\mathbf{f} = j]$. Thus for computational purposes we can replace (1) by

(2) $$\mathbf{M}[\mathbf{f}] = \sum_j j \cdot \mathbf{Pr}[\mathbf{f} = j].$$

Example 4. Let $\mathbf{f}$ be the number of rainy days in the three days after a nice day in the Land of Oz. The probabilities of $\mathbf{f}(x) = j$ can be found from Figure 10 on page 149. These are given in Figure 13.

j	$\mathbf{Pr}[\mathbf{f} = j]$
0	8/32
1	11/32
2	9/32
3	4/32

Figure 13

From these probabilities we find, using (2),

$$\mathbf{M}[\mathbf{f}] = 0 \cdot \tfrac{8}{32} + 1 \cdot \tfrac{11}{32} + 2 \cdot \tfrac{9}{32} + 3 \cdot \tfrac{4}{32} = 1\tfrac{9}{32}.$$

Theorem. Let $\mathbf{f}$ and $\mathbf{g}$ be any two functions defined on the possibility space $\mathcal{U}$. Then

(a) $$\mathbf{M}[\mathbf{f} + \mathbf{g}] = \mathbf{M}[\mathbf{f}] + \mathbf{M}[\mathbf{g}].$$

(b) $$\mathbf{M}[a\mathbf{f}] = a\mathbf{M}[\mathbf{f}] \text{ for any constant } a.$$

(c) $$\mathbf{M}[\mathbf{a}] = a \text{ for any constant } a.$$

We first prove (a).

$$\begin{aligned}\mathbf{M}[\mathbf{f} + \mathbf{g}] &= \sum_x (\mathbf{f}(x) + \mathbf{g}(x))\mathbf{w}(x) \\ &= \sum_x \mathbf{f}(x)\mathbf{w}(x) + \sum_x \mathbf{g}(x)\mathbf{w}(x) = \mathbf{M}[\mathbf{f}] + \mathbf{M}[\mathbf{g}].\end{aligned}$$

To prove (b),

$$\mathbf{M}[a\mathbf{f}] = \sum_x a\mathbf{f}(x)\mathbf{w}(x) = a \sum_x \mathbf{f}(x)\mathbf{w}(x) = a \cdot \mathbf{M}[\mathbf{f}].$$

The proof of (c) is similar.

We have stated part (a) of the above theorem for the case of two functions but it is clear that by repeated application of this theorem we can prove that the mean of the sum of any finite number of functions is the sum of the mean values of these functions.

Example 5. Consider an independent trials process with n experiments each of which results in outcome a with probability p or outcome b with with probability $q = 1 - p$. Let $\mathbf{f}_j$ be a function whose value is 1 if outcome a occurs on the jth experiment and 0 otherwise. Then

$$\mathbf{Pr}[\mathbf{f}_j = 1] = p \quad \text{and} \quad \mathbf{Pr}[\mathbf{f}_j = 0] = q.$$

From this we see that $\mathbf{M}[\mathbf{f}_j] = 0 \cdot q + 1 \cdot p = p$. Let $\mathbf{s}_n = \mathbf{f}_1 + \mathbf{f}_2 + \ldots + \mathbf{f}_n$. Then the value of $\mathbf{s}_n$ gives the total number of times a occurs in the n experiments. By our theorem,

$$\mathbf{M}[\mathbf{s}_n] = \mathbf{M}[\mathbf{f}_1] + \mathbf{M}[\mathbf{f}_2] + \ldots + \mathbf{M}[\mathbf{f}_n] = pn.$$

We can easily extend this result to an arbitrary independent trials process with any number of outcomes. Let a be one possible outcome and p its probability. Let us lump all other outcomes of the experiment into outcome b, that a will *not* occur. Then the above analysis applies. Hence in n trials the mean number of occurrences of a is pn.

Example 6. As a specific example of the above procedure consider n rolls of an ordinary die. The probability of a six on any one experiment is $\frac{1}{6}$. Let $\mathbf{s}_n$ be the number of sixes that turn up in n throws. To compute this directly by (2) we would have to evaluate the sum

$$\mathbf{M}[\mathbf{s}_n] = \sum_j j\,\mathbf{Pr}[\mathbf{s}_n = j] = \sum_j j \binom{n}{j}\left(\frac{1}{6}\right)^j\left(\frac{5}{6}\right)^{n-j}.$$

However, by the preceding remarks we know that $\mathbf{M}[\mathbf{s}_n] = np = n/6$.

While it is always true that the mean of the sum of two functions is the sum of the means of the functions, the corresponding result does not always hold for the product of two functions (see Exercise 3).

Theorem. Let $\mathbf{f}$ and $\mathbf{g}$ be any two probabilistically independent functions. Then $\mathbf{M}[\mathbf{f}\cdot\mathbf{g}] = \mathbf{M}[\mathbf{f}]\cdot\mathbf{M}[\mathbf{g}]$.

Proof: Let $\mathbf{h} = \mathbf{f}\cdot\mathbf{g}$. Using (2), we have

$$\mathbf{M}[\mathbf{h}] = \sum_j j \cdot \mathbf{Pr}[\mathbf{h} = j].$$

But if j is in the range of $\mathbf{h}$, then we have numbers a and b in the ranges of $\mathbf{f}$ and $\mathbf{g}$ such that $ab = j$. And we have

$$\mathbf{Pr}[\mathbf{h} = j] = \sum_{a,b} \mathbf{Pr}[(\mathbf{f} = a) \wedge (\mathbf{g} = b)] = \sum_{a,b} \mathbf{Pr}[\mathbf{f} = a]\mathbf{Pr}[\mathbf{g} = b],$$

where the sum is over pairs of numbers a,b such that $ab = j$. The equation is a consequence of the independence of $\mathbf{f}$ and $\mathbf{g}$. Hence

$$\begin{aligned}\mathbf{M}[\mathbf{f}\cdot\mathbf{g}] &= \sum_{a,b} ab \cdot \mathbf{Pr}[\mathbf{f} = a] \cdot \mathbf{Pr}[\mathbf{g} = b] \\ &= \sum_a a \cdot \mathbf{Pr}[\mathbf{f} = a] \cdot \sum_b b \cdot \mathbf{Pr}[\mathbf{g} = b] \\ &= \mathbf{M}[\mathbf{f}] \cdot \mathbf{M}[\mathbf{g}].\end{aligned}$$

It is again easy to extend the result to the product of several independent functions.

Example 7. A die is thrown twice. Let **g** be the product of the numbers obtained. Then $\mathbf{g} = \mathbf{f}_1 \cdot \mathbf{f}_2$, where $\mathbf{f}_1$ and $\mathbf{f}_2$ are the outcome functions. These are probabilistically independent functions and $\mathbf{M}[\mathbf{f}_1] = \mathbf{M}[\mathbf{f}_2] = \frac{7}{2}$. Hence

$$\mathbf{M}[\mathbf{g}] = \tfrac{7}{2} \cdot \tfrac{7}{2} = \tfrac{49}{4}.$$

EXERCISES

1. A die is rolled twice. Find the mean of the sum of the numbers which turn up. Find the mean of the average of the numbers which turn up.

2. A number is chosen at random from the integers 1, 2, 3, 4, 5, 6, 7, 8, 9. Find the mean of the number chosen. Find the mean of the number chosen given that it is an even number. [*Ans.* 5; 5.]

3. In Example 2 let **f** be the number of heads and **g** the number of tails. Does $\mathbf{M}[\mathbf{f} \cdot \mathbf{g}] = \mathbf{M}[\mathbf{f}] \cdot \mathbf{M}[\mathbf{g}]$? [*Ans.* No.]

4. A coin is thrown until the first time a head comes up or until three tails in a row occur. Find the mean number of times the coin is thrown.

5. Referring to Exercise 6 of Section 6, find the mean number of chess games a player wins. [*Ans.* $\frac{75}{64}$.]

6. An urn contains two black and three white balls. Balls are successively drawn from the urn without replacement until a black ball is obtained. Find the mean number of draws required.

7. Using the result of Exercises 8 and 9 of Section 6, find the mean number of games in the World Series (a) under the assumption that each team has probability $\frac{1}{2}$ of winning each game and (b) under the assumption that the stronger team has probability $\frac{2}{3}$ of winning each game. [*Ans.* 5.81; 5.50.]

8. Referring to Exercise 9 of Section 3, find the mean number of languages read by a student chosen at random.

9. Referring to Exercise 5 of Section 4, find the mean number of men who get their own hats. [*Ans.* 1.]

10. Prove that for any two functions **f**, **g**,

$$\mathbf{M}[\mathbf{f} \cdot \mathbf{g}] \leq \frac{\mathbf{M}[\mathbf{f}^2] + \mathbf{M}[\mathbf{g}^2]}{2}.$$

11. Prove that $\mathbf{M}[\mathbf{f}^2] = 0$ if and only if $\mathbf{f} = 0$.

12. A box contains 5 chips, two numbered 1, one numbered 2, and two numbered 3. A chip is drawn at random. If $\mathbf{f}$ is the number obtained, find $\mathbf{M}[\mathbf{f}]$. [*Ans.* 2.]

13. In Exercise 12, assume that a chip is drawn at random, the number noted and the chip replaced. A second draw is then made. Let $\mathbf{f}_1$ and $\mathbf{f}_2$ be the outcome functions for these two experiments. Find $\mathbf{M}[\mathbf{f}_1]$, $\mathbf{M}[\mathbf{f}_2]$, $\mathbf{M}[\frac{1}{2}(\mathbf{f}_1 + \mathbf{f}_2)]$, $\mathbf{M}[\mathbf{f}_1 \cdot \mathbf{f}_2]$. [*Ans.* 2; 2; 2; 4.]

14. In Exercise 13, assume that a chip is drawn and then a second one is drawn without replacing the first chip. Let $\mathbf{f}_1$ and $\mathbf{f}_2$ be the two outcome functions. Find $\mathbf{M}[\mathbf{f}_1]$, $\mathbf{M}[\mathbf{f}_2]$, $\mathbf{M}[\frac{1}{2}(\mathbf{f}_1 + \mathbf{f}_2)]$, and $\mathbf{M}[\mathbf{f}_1 \cdot \mathbf{f}_2]$. Are $\mathbf{f}_1$ and $\mathbf{f}_2$ independent?

15. A die is loaded so that the probability of a given face turning up is proportional to the number on that face. Let $\mathbf{f}$ be the outcome function of the experiment. Find $\mathbf{M}[\mathbf{f}]$. [*Ans.* $\frac{13}{3}$.]

16. Two dice, loaded as described in Exercise 15, are rolled. Let $\mathbf{f}$ be the function that gives the sum of the two numbers that turn up, $\mathbf{g}$ be the function that gives the average of the two numbers, and $\mathbf{h}$ the function that gives the product of the two numbers. Find $\mathbf{M}[\mathbf{f}]$, $\mathbf{M}[\mathbf{g}]$, and $\mathbf{M}[\mathbf{h}]$.

17. Balls marked with the numbers 1, 2, 3, 4, 5, 6, 7 are put into an urn and one is withdrawn at random. Let $\mathbf{f}$ be the outcome function. Find the means of the following functions.

(a) $\mathbf{f}^2$. [*Ans.* 20.]
(b) $\mathbf{g} = 2\mathbf{f} + 4$. [*Ans.* 12.]
(c) $\mathbf{f} + \mathbf{g}$. [*Ans.* 16.]
(d) $7\mathbf{f} - 3\mathbf{g}$. [*Ans.* −8.]

18. Ten chips are marked with the numbers 1, 2, 2, 3, 4, 4, 5, 6, 6, 7 placed in a box and one is withdrawn at random. If $\mathbf{f}$ is the number of the chip chosen, find the means of the following functions:

(a) $\mathbf{f}^2$.
(b) $\mathbf{g} = 5 - 3\mathbf{f}$.
(c) $\mathbf{f} - \mathbf{g}$.
(d) $3\mathbf{f} + 7\mathbf{g}$.

19. An urn is filled with balls marked with the integers from 1 through n. For each k, there are k balls marked with the integer k. A ball is drawn at random. Let $\mathbf{f}$ be the number chosen and find $\mathbf{M}[\mathbf{f}]$ for $n = 2, 3, 4, 5$. Show that, in general,

$$\mathbf{M}[\mathbf{f}] = \frac{2n + 1}{3}$$

[*Hint:* The following sums will be needed:

$$1 + 2 + \ldots + n = \frac{n(n+1)}{2} \quad \text{and}$$

$$1^2 + 2^2 + \ldots + n^2 = \frac{n(n+1)(2n+1)}{6}.]$$

20. Let $\mathcal{U}$ be any set on which a measure is defined and let A be a subset of $\mathcal{U}$. If $\mathbf{f}_A$ is the characteristic function of A show that $\mathbf{M}[\mathbf{f}_A^2] = \mathbf{M}[\mathbf{f}_A]$.

21. Let $\mathbf{f}$ be the function defined on the possibility space $\mathcal{U} = \{a, b\}$ with $\mathbf{f}(a) = \frac{1}{3}$ and $\mathbf{f}(b) = 3$. Find a number p between 0 and 1 so that if weight p is put on outcome a and weight $1 - p$ on outcome b, then, relative to this measure, we will have $\mathbf{M}[\mathbf{f}^2] = \mathbf{M}[\mathbf{f}]$.

[*Ans.* $p = \frac{27}{28}$.]

22. A student takes a three-question multiple choice exam. Each question has three possible answers a, b, and c. He considers the following four ways of guessing the answers:

(a) Choose a random permutation of the three answers and assign them to the questions.

(b) Choose the answer to each question at random from the answers a, b, and c.

(c) Answer all questions with a.

(d) Answer all questions with a random choice of a or b.

In each case find the mean number of correct answers the student will make. [*Ans.* 1; 1; 1; 1.]

23. A group of n men enter a restaurant and check their hats. When they leave, their hats are returned at random. Let $\mathbf{f}_i$ be the function that is equal to 1 if the ith man gets his hat back and equal to 0 if he does not. Let $\mathbf{s}_n = \mathbf{f}_1 + \mathbf{f}_2 + \ldots + \mathbf{f}_n$. For $n = 2, 3, 4$, and 5, find $\mathbf{M}[\mathbf{f}_i]$ and $\mathbf{M}[\mathbf{s}_n]$.

[*Ans.* $\mathbf{M}[\mathbf{f}_i] = \frac{1}{2}, \frac{1}{3}, \frac{1}{4}, \frac{1}{5}$ and $\mathbf{M}[\mathbf{s}_n] = 1$ for $n = 2, 3, 4, 5$.]

24. In Exercise 23 show that, in general, $\mathbf{M}[\mathbf{f}_i] = 1/n$ and $\mathbf{M}[\mathbf{s}_n] = 1$.

25. An urn contains four black and six white balls. A group of three balls is chosen from the urn. Let $\mathbf{f}$ be the number of black balls chosen. Find the mean of $\mathbf{f}$. [*Ans.* $\frac{6}{5}$.]

26. In Exercise 18 of Section 6 find $\mathbf{M}[\mathbf{f}_1]$, $\mathbf{M}[\mathbf{f}_2]$, and $\mathbf{M}[\mathbf{f}_1 + \mathbf{f}_2]$.

27. Let $\mathcal{U}$ be the set of integers $\{1, 2, \ldots, 100\}$ and let $\mathbf{f}$ be the identity function on $\mathcal{U}$. (You may think of $\mathbf{f}$ as the outcome function in picking an element of $\mathcal{U}$ at random.) For a given probability measure $\mathbf{m}$ on $\mathcal{U}$ we say that an integer u is a "median" if $\mathbf{Pr}[\mathbf{f} < u] \leq \frac{1}{2}$ and also $\mathbf{Pr}[\mathbf{f} > u] \leq \frac{1}{2}$.

(a) Prove that for any measure $\mathbf{m}$ there is always at least one median.

(b) Prove that for any measure $\mathbf{m}$ there are at most two medians.

(c) Give an example of a measure on $\mathcal{U}$ such that there are two medians.

10. VARIANCE OF A FUNCTION

The utility of the average of a set of numbers as a number descriptive of the set is greatly increased when most of the numbers do not deviate too much from their average value. We ask for an estimate of the likelihood that the value of the function will be near its mean. Such an estimate is provided by the variance.

DEFINITION. Let **f** be a numerical function with domain $\mathcal{U}$. Assume that a measure **m** has been assigned to $\mathcal{U}$. Then the variance of **f**, relative to **m**, denoted by **V**[**f**], is

$$\mathbf{V}[\mathbf{f}] = \mathbf{M}[(\mathbf{f} - \mathbf{a})^2]$$

where $a = \mathbf{M}[\mathbf{f}]$.

Example 1. Consider the case of one roll of a die. Let **f** be the outcome function. We have seen that $\mathbf{M}[\mathbf{f}] = \frac{7}{2}$. Thus to find the variance of **f** we must form the function $(\mathbf{f} - 7/2)^2$ and take its mean value. The function $(\mathbf{f} - 7/2)^2$ is tabulated in Figure 14.

x	$\mathbf{w}(x)$	$\mathbf{f}(x)$	$(\mathbf{f}(x) - 7/2)^2$
1	1/6	1	25/4
2	1/6	2	9/4
3	1/6	3	1/4
4	1/6	4	1/4
5	1/6	5	9/4
6	1/6	6	25/4

Figure 14

From this table we easily find $\mathbf{M}[(\mathbf{f} - 7/2)^2]$. Thus

$$\mathbf{V}[\mathbf{f}] = \mathbf{M}[(\mathbf{f} - 7/2)^2]$$
$$= \tfrac{25}{4}\cdot\tfrac{1}{6} + \tfrac{9}{4}\cdot\tfrac{1}{6} + \tfrac{1}{4}\cdot\tfrac{1}{6} + \tfrac{1}{4}\cdot\tfrac{1}{6} + \tfrac{9}{4}\cdot\tfrac{1}{6} + \tfrac{25}{4}\cdot\tfrac{1}{6} = \tfrac{35}{12}.$$

Let $\mathcal{U}$ be a space for which a measure has been assigned and let **f** be a function with $\mathbf{M}[\mathbf{f}] = a$. Then $(\mathbf{f}(x) - a)^2$ may be considered as the square of the distance from $\mathbf{f}(x)$ to a. Thus $\mathbf{V}[\mathbf{f}] = \mathbf{M}[(\mathbf{f} - \mathbf{a})^2]$ may be considered the square of the distance from the function **f** to the constant function **a**.

Example 2. In Figure 15 we have defined three functions **f**, **g**, **h** on a space $\mathcal{U} = \{x_1, x_2, x_3, x_4\}$ for which a measure has been assigned. Each function has mean 1.

x	$\mathbf{w}(x)$	$\mathbf{f}(x)$	$(\mathbf{f}(x) - 1)^2$	$\mathbf{g}(x)$	$(\mathbf{g}(x) - 1)^2$	$\mathbf{h}(x)$	$(\mathbf{h}(x) - 1)^2$
x_1	1/2	1	0	0	1	1	0
x_2	1/4	0	1	4	9	1	0
x_3	1/8	0	1	0	1	1	0
x_4	1/8	4	9	0	1	1	0

Figure 15

$$\begin{aligned} \mathbf{V}[\mathbf{f}] &= 0\cdot\tfrac{1}{2} + 1\cdot\tfrac{1}{4} + 1\cdot\tfrac{1}{8} + 9\cdot\tfrac{1}{8} = \tfrac{3}{2} \\ \mathbf{V}[\mathbf{g}] &= 1\cdot\tfrac{1}{2} + 9\cdot\tfrac{1}{4} + 1\cdot\tfrac{1}{8} + 1\cdot\tfrac{1}{8} = 3 \\ \mathbf{V}[\mathbf{h}] &= 0. \end{aligned}$$

Note that $\mathbf{g}$ has its largest deviation from the mean on the point x_2. This outcome occurs with probability $\frac{1}{4}$. The function $\mathbf{f}$ has the same maximum deviation, but it occurs at outcome x_4 which has probability $\frac{1}{8}$ of occurring. This contributes less to the variance and helps to make $\mathbf{V}[\mathbf{f}]$ less than $\mathbf{V}[\mathbf{g}]$.

Example 3. Let $A = \{a_1, a_2, \ldots, a_n\}$ be any set of numbers. Choose a number at random from this set. Let $\mathbf{f}$ be the outcome function. Then we have seen that $\mathbf{M}[\mathbf{f}] = a$ where a is the average of the numbers in A. Thus

$$\mathbf{V}[\mathbf{f}] = \sum_j \frac{(a_j - a)^2}{n}.$$

For example, let $A = \{1, 2, 3, 4, 5\}$. Then the average is 3 and if $\mathbf{f}$ is the outcome function, then

$$\mathbf{V}[\mathbf{f}] = \frac{(1-3)^2 + (2-3)^2 + (3-3)^2 + (4-3)^2 + (5-3)^2}{5} = 2.$$

The variance has quite different properties from the mean. For example, for any constant c, we have $\mathbf{M}[c\mathbf{f}] = c\mathbf{M}[\mathbf{f}]$ and $\mathbf{M}[\mathbf{f} + \mathbf{c}] = \mathbf{M}[\mathbf{f}] + c$. The following theorem shows that the variance has different properties.

Theorem. For any constant c, $\mathbf{V}[c\mathbf{f}] = c^2\mathbf{V}[\mathbf{f}]$, $\mathbf{V}[\mathbf{f} + \mathbf{c}] = \mathbf{V}[\mathbf{f}]$, and $\mathbf{V}[\mathbf{c}] = 0$.

Proof. Let $a = \mathbf{M}[\mathbf{f}]$. Then $\mathbf{M}[c\mathbf{f}] = ca$. Hence,

$$\begin{aligned} \mathbf{V}[c\mathbf{f}] &= \mathbf{M}[(c\mathbf{f} - c\mathbf{a})^2] = \mathbf{M}[c^2(\mathbf{f} - \mathbf{a})^2] \\ &= c^2\mathbf{M}[(\mathbf{f} - \mathbf{a})^2] = c^2\mathbf{V}[\mathbf{f}]. \end{aligned}$$

To prove the second statement, observe that

$$\mathbf{V}[\mathbf{f} + \mathbf{c}] = \mathbf{M}[((\mathbf{f} + \mathbf{c}) - (\mathbf{a} + \mathbf{c}))^2] = \mathbf{M}[(\mathbf{f} - \mathbf{a})^2] = \mathbf{V}[\mathbf{f}].$$

The proof of the last statement is left as an exercise (see Exercise 4).

The next theorem gives us a convenient alternative way to calculate the variance of a function.

Theorem. Let $\mathbf{f}$ be a function defined on $\mathcal{U}$ and assume that $\mathbf{M}[\mathbf{f}] = a$. Then

$$\mathbf{V}[\mathbf{f}] = \mathbf{M}[\mathbf{f}^2] - a^2.$$

Proof: We observe that

$$\mathbf{V}[\mathbf{f}] = \mathbf{M}[(\mathbf{f} - \mathbf{a})^2] = \mathbf{M}[\mathbf{f}^2 - 2a\mathbf{f} + \mathbf{a}^2]$$
$$= \mathbf{M}[\mathbf{f}^2] - 2a\mathbf{M}[\mathbf{f}] + a^2 = \mathbf{M}[\mathbf{f}^2] - a^2.$$

Example 4. In Example 1, it is somewhat easier to find the variance by using the theorem just proved. That is,

$$\mathbf{M}[\mathbf{f}^2] = 1\cdot\tfrac{1}{6} + 4\cdot\tfrac{1}{6} + 9\cdot\tfrac{1}{6} + 16\cdot\tfrac{1}{6} + 25\cdot\tfrac{1}{6} + 36\cdot\tfrac{1}{6} = \tfrac{91}{6}$$

and hence

$$\mathbf{V}[\mathbf{f}] = \mathbf{M}[\mathbf{f}^2] - a^2 = \tfrac{91}{6} - (\tfrac{7}{2})^2 = \tfrac{35}{12}.$$

It is not true in general that $\mathbf{V}[\mathbf{f} + \mathbf{g}] = \mathbf{V}[\mathbf{f}] + \mathbf{V}[\mathbf{g}]$ (see Exercise 3). This is one of the essential differences between the mean and the variance. The following theorem shows that this property holds for the important case of independent functions.

Theorem. Consider a set of probabilistically independent functions; then the variance of the sum of these functions is the sum of the variances of the individual functions.

Proof: Consider the case where there are only two functions $\mathbf{f}$ and $\mathbf{g}$ in the set. Let $\mathbf{M}[\mathbf{f}] = a$ and $\mathbf{M}[\mathbf{g}] = b$. Then

$$\mathbf{V}[\mathbf{f} + \mathbf{g}] = \mathbf{M}[(\mathbf{f} + \mathbf{g})^2] - (a + b)^2$$
$$= \mathbf{M}[\mathbf{f}^2] + 2\mathbf{M}[\mathbf{f}\cdot\mathbf{g}] + \mathbf{M}[\mathbf{g}^2] - a^2 - 2ab - b^2.$$

Since $\mathbf{f}$ and $\mathbf{g}$ are independent, $\mathbf{M}[\mathbf{f}\cdot\mathbf{g}] = \mathbf{M}[\mathbf{f}]\cdot\mathbf{M}[\mathbf{g}] = ab$. Thus

$$\mathbf{V}[\mathbf{f} + \mathbf{g}] = \mathbf{M}[\mathbf{f}^2] - a^2 + \mathbf{M}[\mathbf{g}^2] - b^2 = \mathbf{V}[\mathbf{f}] + \mathbf{V}[\mathbf{g}].$$

Assume now that our set has three functions $\mathbf{f}$, $\mathbf{g}$, and $\mathbf{h}$. Then $\mathbf{f} + \mathbf{g}$, $\mathbf{h}$ form an independent set (see Exercise 21 of Section 5) and by the previous result

$$\mathbf{V}[(\mathbf{f} + \mathbf{g}) + \mathbf{h}] = \mathbf{V}[\mathbf{f} + \mathbf{g}] + \mathbf{V}[\mathbf{h}] = \mathbf{V}[\mathbf{f}] + \mathbf{V}[\mathbf{g}] + \mathbf{V}[\mathbf{h}].$$

This procedure extends the proof to any number of functions in the set.

As an immediate consequence of this theorem we have the following important result.

Theorem. Let $\mathbf{f}_1, \mathbf{f}_2, \ldots, \mathbf{f}_n$ be independent functions with $\mathbf{M}[\mathbf{f}_i] = a$ and $\mathbf{V}[\mathbf{f}_i] = b^2$ for all i. Let $\mathbf{s}_n = \mathbf{f}_1 + \mathbf{f}_2 + \ldots + \mathbf{f}_n$ and $\mathbf{h}_n = \mathbf{s}_n/n$. Then

$$\mathbf{M}[\mathbf{s}_n] = na, \quad \mathbf{V}[\mathbf{s}_n] = nb^2, \quad \mathbf{M}[\mathbf{h}_n] = a, \quad \mathbf{V}[\mathbf{h}_n] = b^2/n.$$

Proof: Since the functions have the same mean, we have

$$\mathbf{M}[\mathbf{s}_n] = \mathbf{M}[\mathbf{f}_1] + \ldots + \mathbf{M}[\mathbf{f}_n] = na.$$

Since they are also independent and have the same variance b^2,

$$\mathbf{V}[\mathbf{s}_n] = \mathbf{V}[\mathbf{f}_1] + \ldots + \mathbf{V}[\mathbf{f}_n] = nb^2.$$

We know that multiplying a function by a constant multiplies the mean by the constant and the variance by the square of the constant. Hence $\mathbf{M}[\mathbf{h}_n] = \mathbf{M}[\mathbf{s}_n/n] = 1/n\, \mathbf{M}[\mathbf{s}_n] = a$ and

$$\mathbf{V}[\mathbf{h}_n] = \mathbf{V}\left[\frac{\mathbf{s}_n}{n}\right] = \frac{1}{n^2}\mathbf{V}[\mathbf{s}_n] = \frac{nb^2}{n^2} = \frac{b^2}{n}.$$

Example 5. Consider n rolls of a die. Let $\mathbf{f}_1, \mathbf{f}_2, \ldots, \mathbf{f}_n$ be the outcome functions and let $\mathbf{s}_n = \mathbf{f}_1 + \mathbf{f}_2 + \ldots + \mathbf{f}_n$ be the sum of the outcomes, and $\mathbf{h}_n = \mathbf{s}_n/n$ be the average of the outcomes. Then, since $\mathbf{M}[\mathbf{f}_i] = \frac{7}{2}$ and $\mathbf{V}[\mathbf{f}_i] = \frac{35}{12}$ for every i, we have $\mathbf{M}[\mathbf{s}_n] = \frac{7}{2}n$, $\mathbf{V}[\mathbf{s}_n] = \frac{35}{12}n$, $\mathbf{M}[\mathbf{h}_n] = \frac{7}{2}$, and $\mathbf{V}[\mathbf{h}_n] = 35/12n$.

An important special case of the previous theorem is the following:

Theorem. Let a be a possible outcome for an experiment and assume that the probability that a occurs is p. Assume that the experiment is carried out n times under independent conditions. Let $\mathbf{s}_n$ be the number of times that the outcome a occurs and $\mathbf{h}_n = \mathbf{s}_n/n$ the fraction of the n times that it occurs. Then

$$\mathbf{M}[\mathbf{s}_n] = np, \quad \mathbf{V}[\mathbf{s}_n] = np(1-p), \quad \mathbf{M}[\mathbf{h}_n] = p, \quad \mathbf{V}[\mathbf{h}_n] = \frac{p(1-p)}{n}.$$

Proof. The probability model for repeating an experiment independently is an independent trials process. We take as outcomes for the individual experiments only the two possibilities 0 and 1, recording 0 if a does not occur and 1 if it does. Then let $\mathbf{f}_1, \mathbf{f}_2, \ldots, \mathbf{f}_n$ be the outcome functions. We have

$$\mathbf{Pr}[\mathbf{f}_1 = 0] = 1 - p$$

$$\mathbf{Pr}[\mathbf{f}_1 = 1] = p.$$

Hence $\mathbf{M}[\mathbf{f}_1] = p$ and, since $\mathbf{f}_1^2 = \mathbf{f}_1$, $\mathbf{M}[\mathbf{f}_1^2] = p$. Hence

$$\mathbf{V}[\mathbf{f}_1] = \mathbf{M}[\mathbf{f}_1^2] - p^2 = p - p^2 = p(1-p).$$

Thus our result follows from the previous theorem.

Example 6. A coin is tossed n times; $\mathbf{s}_n$ is the number of times a head turns up, and $\mathbf{h}_n = \mathbf{s}_n/n$ is the fraction of times a head turns up. Let us find the mean and variance of $\mathbf{s}_n$ and $\mathbf{h}_n$ for the cases in which n is 10, 100, 1000, 10,000, respectively.

The table in Figure 16 gives these values for the required values of n.

n	$\mathbf{M}[\mathbf{s}_n]$	$\mathbf{V}[\mathbf{s}_n]$	$\mathbf{M}[\mathbf{h}_n]$	$\mathbf{V}[\mathbf{h}_n]$
10	5	10/4	1/2	1/40
100	50	100/4	1/2	1/400
1000	500	1000/4	1/2	1/4000
10,000	5000	10,000/4	1/2	1/40,000

Figure 16

Observe that for the function $\mathbf{s}_n$ the mean is always half the number of throws and the variance of $\mathbf{s}_n$ is always one quarter the number of throws. However, the average number of heads obtained, represented by the function $\mathbf{h}_n$, always has mean $\frac{1}{2}$ but the variance steadily decreases. Thus, the more times we toss the coin the less probable it is that the average number of heads should differ by very much from $\frac{1}{2}$. This point will be considered again in Section 11.

If $\mathbf{f}$ is a function defined on a possibility space to which weights have been assigned, then the *standard deviation* of $\mathbf{f}$ is defined to be

$$\mathbf{D}[\mathbf{f}] = \sqrt{\mathbf{V}[\mathbf{f}]}.$$

In Exercise 8 several properties of the standard deviation are derived.

If $\mathbf{f}$ is a function as above it is frequently convenient to replace $\mathbf{f}$ by a standardized function $\mathbf{f}^*$ that has certain simple properties. To do so, let a be the mean and b be the standard deviation of $\mathbf{f}$. Then the *standardized function* $\mathbf{f}^*$ is defined by

$$\mathbf{f}^* = \frac{\mathbf{f} - \mathbf{a}}{b}.$$

Then we have

$$\mathbf{M}[\mathbf{f}^*] = \frac{1}{b}(\mathbf{M}[\mathbf{f}] - a) = \frac{a - a}{b} = 0$$

$$\mathbf{V}[\mathbf{f}^*] = \frac{1}{b^2}\mathbf{V}[\mathbf{f}] = \frac{1}{b^2}b^2 = 1.$$

Thus the standardized function has mean 0 and variance 1. Observe that the standardized function was obtained by subtracting $\mathbf{a}$ from $\mathbf{f}$, and this corresponds to changing the point from which measurements are made. Similarly, dividing by the factor b is equivalent to changing the scale so that the unit of measurement is the standard deviation.

For example, consider an independent trials process with numerical outcome functions $\mathbf{f}_1, \mathbf{f}_2, \ldots, \mathbf{f}_n$ and sum functions $\mathbf{s}_n = \mathbf{f}_1 + \mathbf{f}_2 + \ldots + \mathbf{f}_n$.

If the mean of $\mathbf{f}_j$ is a and its standard deviation is b then $\mathbf{M}[\mathbf{s}_n] = na$ and $\mathbf{V}[\mathbf{s}_n] = nb^2$, so that the standardized function is

$$\mathbf{s}_n^* = \frac{\mathbf{s}_n - na}{b\sqrt{n}}.$$

If we carry out the same computation for $\mathbf{h}_n$, we find that

$$\mathbf{h}_n^* = \frac{(\mathbf{s}_n/n) - a}{b/\sqrt{n}} = \frac{\mathbf{s}_n - na}{b\sqrt{n}} = \mathbf{s}_n^*.$$

Example 7. The standardized function for the coin tossing experiment of Example 6 is given by

$$\mathbf{s}_n^* = 2\frac{\mathbf{s}_n - n(1/2)}{\sqrt{n}}$$

where, as before, $\mathbf{s}_n$ is the number of heads that turn up in n tosses of the coin.

The standardized function can be used to measure how far off the outcome of a given experiment is from the mean. For instance, if we toss a coin 100 times and 70 heads turn up then $\mathbf{s}^*$ is 4. In Section 13 we shall see that a deviation as large as this is very unlikely.

EXERCISES

1. A royal family has children only until they have a boy or until they have had three girls. Let $\mathbf{f}$ be the number of boys and $\mathbf{g}$ the number of girls they have. (Ignore the possibility of twins, triplets, etc.) Find the mean and the variance of $\mathbf{f}$ and $\mathbf{g}$.

[*Ans.* $\mathbf{M}[\mathbf{f}] = \mathbf{M}[\mathbf{g}] = \frac{7}{8}$; $\mathbf{V}[\mathbf{f}] = \frac{7}{64}$; $\mathbf{V}[\mathbf{g}] = \frac{71}{64}$.]

2. A number is chosen at random from each of the following sets of numbers. Find the variance for the number chosen.

(a) $\mathcal{U} = \{0, -1, 0, 1, 1\}$.

(b) $\mathcal{U} = \{10, 0, 5, 10, 100\}$. [*Ans.* 1420.]

(c) $\mathcal{U} = \{100, 99, 100, 101, 101\}$.

(d) $\mathcal{U} = \{1, 1, 1, 1, 1, 1\}$. [*Ans.* 0.]

3. Let $\mathbf{f}$ be any function defined on $\mathcal{U}$. Let $\mathbf{g} = -\mathbf{f}$. Prove that $\mathbf{V}[\mathbf{g}] = \mathbf{V}[\mathbf{f}]$. How does this prove that $\mathbf{V}[\mathbf{f} + \mathbf{g}] = \mathbf{V}[\mathbf{f}] + \mathbf{V}[\mathbf{g}]$ cannot hold in general?

4. Prove that $\mathbf{V}[\mathbf{f}] = 0$ if and only if $\mathbf{f}$ is a constant function.

5. A coin is thrown three times. Let $\mathbf{f}$ be the number of heads that turn up. Find $\mathbf{V}[\mathbf{f}]$. Compare this with the case of one throw.

[*Ans.* $\frac{3}{4}$ for three throws, $\frac{1}{4}$ for one throw.]

6. A number is chosen at random from the integers 1, 2, 3, . . . , n. Let **f** be the outcome function. Prove

$$\mathbf{M}[\mathbf{f}] = \frac{n+1}{2} \quad \text{and} \quad \mathbf{V}[\mathbf{f}] = \frac{(n-1)(n+1)}{12}.$$

7. A number is chosen at random from 1, 2, . . . , n. How must n be selected so that the outcome function has the same mean and variance? (See Exercise 6.)

8. Prove the following facts about the standard deviation.
(a) $\mathbf{D}[\mathbf{f} + \mathbf{c}] = \mathbf{D}[\mathbf{f}]$.
(b) $\mathbf{D}[c\mathbf{f}] = |c|\mathbf{D}[\mathbf{f}]$.

9. Let **f** be a function with $\mathbf{M}[\mathbf{f}] = a$. Let c be any number. Prove that $\mathbf{M}[(\mathbf{f} - \mathbf{c})^2] = \mathbf{M}[(\mathbf{f} - \mathbf{a})^2] + (a - c)^2$. Use this result to prove that $\mathbf{M}[(\mathbf{f} - \mathbf{c})^2]$ is a minimum when $c = a$.

10. Let $A = \{-1, 0, 1\}$. A number is chosen at random from A. Let **f** be the outcome function. Show that $\mathbf{V}[\mathbf{f} + \mathbf{f}^2] = \mathbf{V}[\mathbf{f}] + \mathbf{V}[\mathbf{f}^2]$.
[*Ans.* Both are equal to $\frac{8}{9}$.]

11. Let **f** be a function with range $R = \{0, 1\}$. Prove that $\mathbf{V}[\mathbf{f}] \leq \frac{1}{4}$. Give an example of a function having range $R = \{0, 1\}$ and having variance $\frac{1}{4}$.

12. Using the results of Exercises 8 and 9 of Section 6, find the variance for the number of games in the World Series (a) under the assumption that each team has probability $\frac{1}{2}$ of winning each game and (b) under the assumption that the stronger team has probability $\frac{2}{3}$ of winning each game.

13. In Exercise 18 of Section 6, find $\mathbf{V}[\mathbf{f}_1]$, $\mathbf{V}[\mathbf{f}_2]$, and $\mathbf{V}[\mathbf{f}_1 + \mathbf{f}_2]$.

14. A coin is thrown 10 times. Let **h** be the fraction of tosses that yield a head. Find $\mathbf{h}^*$.
[*Ans.* $\mathbf{h}^* = (2\mathbf{h} - 1)\sqrt{10}$.]

15. In Exercise 14, show that the statement $\mathbf{h}^*(x) < -2$ is equivalent to a statement about **h**.

16. A die is loaded so that the probability of a face coming up is proportional to the number on that face. If the die is rolled once and **f** is the outcome function of the experiment, find $\mathbf{V}[\mathbf{f}]$ and $\mathbf{D}[\mathbf{f}]$.
[*Ans.* $\mathbf{V}[\mathbf{f}] = \frac{20}{9}$, $\mathbf{D}[\mathbf{f}] = 2\sqrt{5}/3$.]

17. Find the variance of the function **f** in Exercise 12 of Section 9.
[*Ans.* $\mathbf{V}[\mathbf{f}] = \frac{4}{5}$.]

18. Find the variances of the functions in Exercise 13 of Section 9.

19. Find the variance of the functions in Exercise 14 of Section 9.

20. Find the variances of the functions **f** and **g** of Exercise 16 of Section 9. [*Hint.* Use theorems from the present section.]

[*Ans.* $\mathbf{V}[\mathbf{f}] = \frac{40}{9}$, $\mathbf{V}[\mathbf{g}] = \frac{10}{9}$.]

21. Find the variances of the functions **f** and **g** given in Exercise 17 of Section 9. [*Ans.* $\mathbf{V}[\mathbf{f}] = 4$; $\mathbf{V}[\mathbf{g}] = 16$.]

22. Find the variances of the functions **f** and **g** given in Exercise 18 of Section 9.

23. In Exercise 19 of Section 9 show that the variance of **f** is given by the following formula.

$$\mathbf{V}[\mathbf{f}] = \tfrac{1}{18}(n^2 + n - 2).$$

[*Hint.* In addition to the sums given in the hint to Exercise 19 of Section 9 the following sum will be needed:

$$1^3 + 2^3 + \ldots + n^3 = \frac{n^2(n+1)^2}{4}.]$$

24. Show that $\mathbf{M}[\mathbf{f}^2] = \mathbf{M}[\mathbf{f}]^2$ if and only if **f** is a constant function. [*Hint.* Use Exercise 4.]

25. If **f** is such that $\mathbf{M}[\mathbf{f}^2] = \mathbf{M}[\mathbf{f}]$ and $\mathbf{V}[\mathbf{f}] = 0$ then either $\mathbf{f} = \mathbf{0}$ or else $\mathbf{f} = \mathbf{1}$. [*Hint.* Use Exercise 4.]

26. If **f** is such that $\mathbf{M}[\mathbf{f}^2] = \mathbf{M}[\mathbf{f}]$ show that $\mathbf{V}[\mathbf{f}] \leq \frac{1}{4}$.

27. If **f** is a function whose range is the set $\{0, 1\}$ show that $\mathbf{M}[\mathbf{f}^2] = \mathbf{M}[\mathbf{f}]$.

28. A biased coin that has probability p of turning up a head on each toss is tossed n times. Let $\mathbf{h}_n$ be the fraction of tosses which turn up heads. Show that, regardless of the value of p, $\mathbf{V}[\mathbf{h}_n] \leq 1/4n$.

29. Carry out the following steps to find the variance of $\mathbf{s}_n$ in the hat check problem of Exercise 23 of Section 9.

(a) Show that $\mathbf{M}[\mathbf{f}_i^2] = \dfrac{1}{n}$.

(b) Show that $\mathbf{M}[\mathbf{f}_i\mathbf{f}_j] = \dfrac{1}{n(n-1)}$ for $i \neq j$.

(c) Use (a) and (b) to prove that

$$\mathbf{M}[\mathbf{s}_n^2] = \mathbf{M}[(\mathbf{f}_1 + \mathbf{f}_2 + \ldots + \mathbf{f}_n)^2] = 2.$$

(d) Show that $\mathbf{V}[\mathbf{s}_n] = 1$.

Note the variance is independent of n, as was the mean. (See Exercise 24 of Section 9.)

11. THE LAW OF LARGE NUMBERS

Let us assume that a die is thrown and we observe whether or not a six turns up. With our usual assignment of probabilities we would assign probability $\frac{1}{6}$ to getting a six. Our experience with dice leads us to believe that if the die is rolled a large number of times approximately $\frac{1}{6}$ of the times a six will turn up. This latter statement relates to an independent trials process. The law of large numbers makes precise this connection under very general circumstances. Before proving this theorem we must prove the following important theorem relating to the variance of a function.

Theorem. (Chebyshev's inequality). Let $\mathbf{f}$ be a function defined on a possibility space $\mathcal{U}$. Let a be the mean value of $\mathbf{f}$ and b^2 its variance. Then for any positive number k,

$$\mathbf{Pr}[|\mathbf{f} - \mathbf{a}| > k] \leq \frac{b^2}{k^2}.$$

Proof: Let A be the truth set of the statement $|\mathbf{f}(x) - a| > k$. Then A is also the truth set of the equivalent statement $(\mathbf{f}(x) - a)^2 > k^2$.

$$\begin{aligned} b^2 = \mathbf{V}[\mathbf{f}] &= \mathbf{M}[(\mathbf{f} - \mathbf{a})^2] \\ &= \sum_{x} (\mathbf{f}(x) - a)^2 \mathbf{w}(x) \\ &= \sum_{x \text{ in } A} (\mathbf{f}(x) - a)^2 \mathbf{w}(x) + \sum_{x \text{ in } \tilde{A}} (\mathbf{f}(x) - a)^2 \mathbf{w}(x). \end{aligned}$$

Both of these sums have only nonnegative elements. If we drop the second sum we can only decrease the result. Thus

$$b^2 \geq \sum_{x \text{ in } A} (\mathbf{f}(x) - a)^2 \mathbf{w}(x).$$

But for x in A, $(\mathbf{f}(x) - a)^2 > k^2$. Thus

$$b^2 \geq \sum_{x \text{ in } A} k^2 \mathbf{w}(x) = k^2 \sum_{x \text{ in } A} \mathbf{w}(x) = k^2 \mathbf{m}(A).$$

Thus

$$\mathbf{m}(A) \leq \frac{b^2}{k^2}$$

or

$$\mathbf{Pr}[|\mathbf{f} - \mathbf{a}| > k] \leq \frac{b^2}{k^2}.$$

The inequality we have just established gives an important interpretation for the standard deviation. Recall that $b = \sqrt{\mathbf{V}[\mathbf{f}]}$ is the standard deviation of $\mathbf{f}$. Since k was an arbitrary positive number we may replace k by tb, where t is an arbitrary positive number. If we do this we have

$$\mathbf{Pr}[|\mathbf{f} - \mathbf{a}| > tb] \leq \frac{1}{t^2}.$$

Thus if we think of b as a unit of measurement, the probability that the value of the function deviates from its mean by a large number of b units is small. For example, the probability is less than or equal to $\frac{1}{9}$ that the function deviates by more than 3 standard deviations from its mean. We shall see later that for a wide class of functions we can make even more precise statements about such deviations.

Example 1. A manufactured lot has a fraction p of defective items, but we do not know the value of p. In order to estimate p we repeat n times the experiment of drawing an item at random from the lot. Let $\mathbf{h}_n$ denote the fraction of defective items drawn. We have seen that $\mathbf{M}[\mathbf{h}_n] = p$ and $\mathbf{V}[\mathbf{h}_n] = pq/n$. Thus

$$\mathbf{Pr}\left[|\mathbf{h}_n - \mathbf{p}| > 4\sqrt{\frac{pq}{n}}\right] \leq \frac{1}{16}.$$

Or since for any p, $\frac{1}{4} \geq pq$, we have

$$\mathbf{Pr}\left[|\mathbf{h}_n - \mathbf{p}| > \frac{2}{\sqrt{n}}\right] \leq \frac{1}{16}.$$

For example, if $n = 400$,

$$\mathbf{Pr}[|\mathbf{h}_{400} - \mathbf{p}| > .1] \leq .063$$

no matter what p is. Hence the value of $\mathbf{h}_n$ may be taken as an estimate for the unknown p. This estimate will, with high probability (.937), not differ by more than .1 from the correct value. It is clear that the larger the number of experiments we perform, the better estimate we get for p.

Theorem. (The law of large numbers.) Let $\mathbf{f}_1, \mathbf{f}_2, \ldots, \mathbf{f}_n$ be independent functions with $\mathbf{M}[\mathbf{f}_i] = a$ and $\mathbf{V}[\mathbf{f}_i] = b^2$ for all i. Let $\mathbf{h}_n = (\mathbf{f}_1 + \ldots + \mathbf{f}_n)/n$. Then for any k

$$\mathbf{Pr}[|\mathbf{h}_n - \mathbf{a}| > k] \leq \frac{b^2}{nk^2} \tag{1}$$

$$\mathbf{Pr}[|\mathbf{h}_n - \mathbf{a}| > k] \to 0 \tag{2}$$

as n tends to infinity.

Proof. We know from the previous section that $\mathbf{M}[\mathbf{h}_n] = a$ and $\mathbf{V}[\mathbf{h}_n] = b^2/n$. Hence Chebyshev's inequality gives (1), and (2) follows immediately from (1).

The result (2) tells us that for any k, by choosing n large enough we can make the probability as small as we please that $\mathbf{h}_n$ differs from its mean by more than k. The stronger result (1) tells us that this probability will be small provided that b^2 is small compared to nk^2.

An alternative way to state (2) is to say that for any $k > 0$,

$$\mathbf{Pr}[|\mathbf{h}_n - \mathbf{a}| \leq k] \to 1.$$

This follows from the fact that

$$\mathbf{Pr}[|\mathbf{h}_n - \mathbf{a}| \leq k] = 1 - \mathbf{Pr}[|\mathbf{h}_n - \mathbf{a}| > k].$$

Thus no matter how small we choose k, by taking n sufficiently large we can make the probability that the average of the outcomes will not deviate from a by more than k as close to 1 as we wish.

The law of large numbers has suggested the following terminology for a gambling game. Let **f** be a player's winnings from a single play of the game. Then the value of the game is taken to be $\mathbf{M}[\mathbf{f}]$. According to the law of large numbers, if the game is repeated a large number of times, it is very likely that the average winnings of the player will be near $\mathbf{M}[\mathbf{f}]$. If $\mathbf{M}[\mathbf{f}] > 0$ the game is called favorable; if $\mathbf{M}[\mathbf{f}] = 0$ it is called fair; and if $\mathbf{M}[\mathbf{f}] < 0$ it is called unfavorable.

Example 2. Consider the game of roulette as played at Monte Carlo. There are several types of bets which the gambler can make, and we consider two of these.

The wheel has the number 0 and the numbers from 1 to 36 marked on equally spaced slots. The wheel is spun and the ball comes to rest in one of these slots. If the player puts a stake, say of \$1, on a given number, and the ball comes to rest in this slot, then he receives from the croupier \$35 in addition to his \$1 bet. Let **f** be his winning on a single play. Then

$$\mathbf{M}[\mathbf{f}] = 35 \cdot \tfrac{1}{37} - 1 \cdot \tfrac{36}{37} = -\tfrac{1}{37} = -.027.$$

Thus the law of large numbers suggests that he will in the long run lose about 2.7 per cent of his stakes.

A second way to play is the following. A player may bet on "red" or "black." The numbers from 1 to 36 are evenly divided between the two colors. If a player bets on "red," and a red number turns up, he receives twice his stake. If a black number turns up, he loses his stake. If 0 turns up then the wheel is spun until it stops on a number different from 0. If this is black, the player loses; but if it is red, he receives only his original stake, not twice it. Again let **f** be his winning on a single play. Then

$$\mathbf{M}[\mathbf{f}] = 1 \cdot \tfrac{18}{37} + 0 \cdot \tfrac{1}{74} - 1 \cdot \tfrac{37}{74} = -\tfrac{1}{74} = -.0135.$$

In this case the player can expect, by the law of large numbers, to lose about 1.35 per cent of his stakes in the long run. Thus the average loss in this case is only half as great as in the previous case.

Example 3. In the game of craps a pair of dice is rolled by one of the players. If the sum of the spots shown is 7 or 11, he wins. If it is 2, 3, or 12, he loses. If it is another sum, he must continue rolling the dice until he either repeats the same sum or rolls a 7. In the former case he wins, in the latter he loses. Let us suppose that he wins or loses \$1. Then the two possible outcomes are $+1$ and -1. We will compute the mean value of the game. First we must find the probability that he will win.

We represent the possibilities by a two-stage tree shown in Figure 17. While it is theoretically possible for the game to go on indefinitely, we do not consider this possibility. This means that our analysis applies only to games which actually stop at some time.

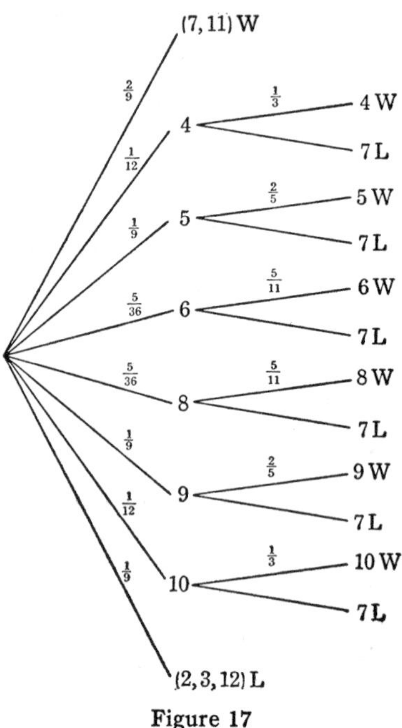

Figure 17

The branch probabilities at the first stage are determined by thinking of the 36 possibilities for the throw of the two dice as being equally likely and taking as the branch probability, in each case, the fraction of the possibilities which correspond to the branch. The probabilities for the branches at the second level are obtained as follows. If, for example, the first outcome was a 4, then when the game ends, a 4 or 7 must have occurred. The possible outcomes for the dice were

$$\{(3,1), (1,3), (2,2), (4,3), (3,4), (2,5), (5,2), (1,6), (6,1)\}.$$

Again we consider these possibilities to be equally likely and assign to the branch considered the fraction of the outcomes which correspond to this branch. Thus to the 4 branch we assign a probability $\frac{3}{9} = \frac{1}{3}$. The other branch probabilities are determined in a similar way. Having the path weights assigned, to find the probability of a win we must simply add the weights of all paths leading to a win. If this is done, we obtain $\frac{244}{495}$. Thus the mean value of the player's winnings is

$$1 \cdot \tfrac{244}{495} + (-1) \cdot \tfrac{251}{495} = -\tfrac{7}{495} = -.0141.$$

Hence he can expect to lose 1.41 per cent of his stakes in the long run. It is interesting to note that this is just slightly less favorable than his losses in betting on "red" in roulette.

The law of large numbers generalizes to processes other than independent trials processes. One useful simple generalization is the following. Assume that we have r different experiments possibly completely unrelated. We now perform a sequence of trials, each of which is made by choosing one of the r experiments to perform. For example, one experiment may be to make a bet at roulette and the other to play a certain slot machine. To describe the process obtained we must have a rule that tells us at each trial which of the r experiments to choose. For example, if there are only two experiments the rule may be to alternate. The rule may be as complicated as we wish, but must be described independently of the outcomes of any of the experiments. Knowing the probabilities for the outcomes of any of the individual experiments and the rule for choosing the experiments, we can construct a tree and tree measure for any number of experiments. We shall call the result an r-experiment independent process. Then the probability that the nth outcome function takes on specific values will depend only on the experiment that was performed. Hence the same holds for the mean and variance of the outcome function. Let a_j and b_j^2 be these quantities when the jth experiment was performed. Then if $\mathbf{f}_1, \mathbf{f}_2, \ldots, \mathbf{f}_n$ are the outcome functions for the first n trials we have

$$\mathbf{M}[\mathbf{f}_1 + \mathbf{f}_2 + \ldots + \mathbf{f}_n] = n_1 a_1 + n_2 a_2 + \ldots + n_r a_r$$

and

$$\mathbf{V}[\mathbf{f}_1 + \mathbf{f}_2 + \ldots + \mathbf{f}_n] = n_1 b_1^2 + n_2 b_2^2 + \ldots + n_r b_r^2$$

where n_j is the number of times that the rule tells us to perform the jth experiment in the first n trials. If

$$\mathbf{h}_n = \frac{\mathbf{f}_1 + \mathbf{f}_2 + \ldots + \mathbf{f}_n}{n}$$

is the average of the outcome functions, then

$$\mathbf{M}[\mathbf{h}_n] = \frac{n_1 a_1 + n_2 a_2 + \ldots + n_r a_r}{n}$$

and

$$\mathbf{V}[\mathbf{h}_n] = \frac{n_1 b_1^2 + n_2 b_2^2 + \ldots + n_r b_r^2}{n^2}.$$

Let K be the largest of the quantities b_j^2. Then

$$\mathbf{V}[\mathbf{h}_n] \leq \frac{K(n_1 + n_2 + \ldots + n_r)}{n^2} = \frac{Kn}{n^2} = \frac{K}{n}.$$

Thus we see that $\mathbf{V}[\mathbf{h}_n]$ tends to 0 as n tends to infinity. Thus by Chebyshev's inequality,

$$\mathbf{Pr}[|\mathbf{h}_n - \mathbf{M}[\mathbf{h}_n]| > k] \to 0$$

as n tends to infinity.

Example 4. Assume that a man decides to play a number on roulette and craps. He decides to make $\frac{1}{3}$ of his plays roulette and $\frac{2}{3}$ craps. The mean winnings on a single play of roulette were found to be $-.027$ and at craps they were $-.0141$. Then on n plays his mean winnings per play will be

$$\tfrac{1}{3}(-.027) + \tfrac{2}{3}(-.0141) = -.009 - .0094 = -.0184.$$

Thus by the generalization of the law of large numbers the player can expect to lose about 1.84 per cent of his stakes in the long run.

EXERCISES

1. Let $\mathbf{h}$ be the fraction of outcomes which result in heads in 10^8 tosses of an ordinary coin. Prove that

$$\mathbf{Pr}[|\mathbf{h} - 1/2| > .001] \leq .0025.$$

2. Assume that a decimal expansion $a_1, a_2, a_3, \ldots$, is written by making each a_j the result of a random choice from the integers $0, 1, 2, \ldots, 9$. What does the law of large numbers tell you about occurrences of 9's in this sequence?

3. Suppose that we modify the game of craps as follows: If his first throw is a 7 or 11 the player wins \$2, if it is a 2, 3, or 12 he loses \$3, if it is a 4, 5, 6, 8, 9, or 10 the game is as usual with the player winning or losing \$1 on subsequent tosses. Find the mean value of the new game, and compare it with the old value. [*Ans.* Same as the old value.]

4. Suppose that in roulette at Monte Carlo we place 50 cents on "red" and 50 cents on "black." What is the mean value on the game? Is this better or worse than placing \$1 on "red"?

5. Betting on "red" in roulette can be described roughly as follows. We win with probability .49, get our money back with probability .01, and lose with probability .50. Draw the tree for three plays of the game, and compute (to three decimals) the probability of each path. What is the probability that we are ahead at the end of three bets? [*Ans.* .485.]

6. Consider the version of roulette for which bets are placed on red or black. (a) Find the mean and variance for the amount the house wins

on a \$1 bet. (b) Find the mean and standard deviation for the total amount of money the house wins on 250,000 \$1 bets.

[*Ans.* (a) .0135, 1; (b) 3375, 500.]

7. Using the result of Exercise 6, prove that the probability that the house loses money on 250,000 bets is less than .03.

8. A bets 50 cents against B's x cents that, if two cards are dealt from a shuffled pack of ordinary playing cards, both cards will be of the same color. What value of x will make this a fair bet?

9. For the decimal expansion chosen as in Exercise 2, show that the probability that the sum of the first 100,000 digits deviates from 450,000 by more than 3,000 is $<.10$.

10. Peter and Paul match pennies. Find the mean and variance for Peter's winnings after three plays. [*Ans.* 0, 3.]

11. In Exercise 10 assume that Peter decides to quit the first time that he is ahead while Paul is willing to play all three matches. Find the mean and variance for Peter's winnings.

12. A penny is tossed until a head appears. If a head appears on the first throw, the player receives \$2 from the bank. If a head appears for the first time on the second throw, the player receives \$4; if for the first time on the third throw, he receives $2^3 = 8$ dollars. In general, if it occurs for the first time on the jth throw he receives 2^j dollars if the bank has this much money, and all the money the bank has if it does not. Assume that the bank has 1,000,000 dollars. What is a fair amount to pay to play the game? [*Hint.* The probability that he wins \$1,000,000 is $2^{-20} + 2^{-21} + 2^{-22} + \ldots = 2^{-19}$.] [*Ans.* \$20.91.]

13. A die is rolled until a 2 or a 5 turns up. If one of these turns up on the first roll, the player receives \$1 from the bank, if on the second roll he receives \$3, and in general, if one of the numbers turns up for the first time on the jth roll he receives 3^j dollars if the bank has that much money, and all the money the bank has if it does not. If the bank has \$1,000,000 what is a fair amount to pay for the game?

14. Prove that if n men in a restaurant are handed their hats at random, the probability that more than 11 get their own hats is at most .01 no matter how large n is. (See Exercise 29 of Section 10.)

15. A die is loaded so that the probability of a number turning up is proportional to that number. We let $\mathbf{f}$ be the outcome function and $a = \mathbf{M}[\mathbf{f}]$. If the die is rolled n times, how large must n be in order that

$$\mathbf{Pr}[|\mathbf{f} - \mathbf{a}| > \tfrac{1}{9}] \leq .001?$$

16. A die, loaded as in Exercise 15, is rolled twice and a player must pay

\$3 if a 7 or an 11 turns up; otherwise he wins \$1. What is the value of this game? [*Ans.* −5.2 cents.]

17. A man tosses three coins n times. One of the coins has two heads, another turns up heads with probability $\frac{2}{3}$ and the third coin is balanced. If $\mathbf{h}_n$ is the average number of heads that turn up in n tosses (all three coins are tossed each time) how large must n be in order that

$$\mathbf{Pr}[|\mathbf{h}_n - \mathbf{M}[\mathbf{h}_n]| > \tfrac{1}{6}] < .01?$$

[*Ans.* $n \geq 1700$.]

18. A potato bin contains a fraction p of rotten potatoes. In order to estimate this fraction we select 100 potatoes at random and find 7 of them are rotten; hence we estimate $p = .07$. Use Chebyshev's inequality to estimate the probability that the true value of p differs from the estimated value by more than .2. [*Ans.* .06.]

19. A certain lake contains a proportion p of pike. It was found that of 900 fish caught 75 were pike. Estimate p and give statements that show what confidence can be placed in the estimate.

12. BINOMIAL MEASURES AND THE POISSON APPROXIMATION

The independent trials process with two outcomes is one of the most important kinds of process from the point of view of applications. The study of this process has also led to important results which apply equally well to more general processes. We consider in this section and the next a detailed treatment of this process.

Consider now an independent trials process where each experiment has only two possible outcomes a or b. We define an equivalent process by

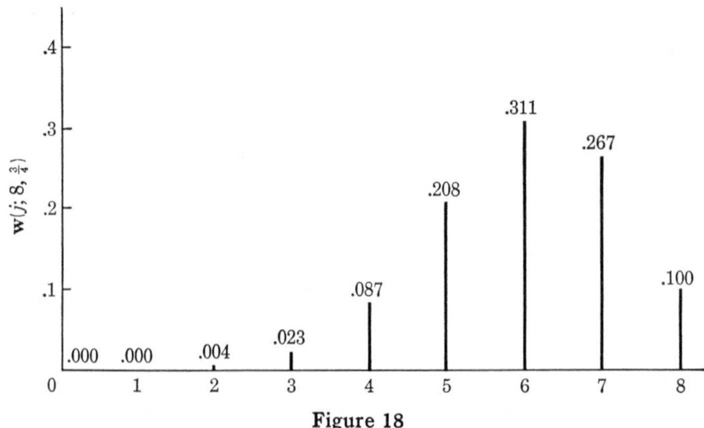

Figure 18

relabeling the outcomes a and b by 1 and 0, respectively. With this new labeling let $\mathbf{f}_1, \mathbf{f}_2, \ldots, \mathbf{f}_n$ be the outcome functions. Then the function $\mathbf{s}_n = \mathbf{f}_1 + \mathbf{f}_2 + \ldots + \mathbf{f}_n$ gives the number of times the outcome a occurs in n experiments. From Section 8 we know that this is

$$\mathbf{Pr}[\mathbf{s}_n = j] = \binom{n}{j} p^j q^{n-j}$$

where p is the probability of an occurrence of an a in any one experiment and $q = 1 - p$ is the probability of the occurrence of b. We will denote these probabilities by $\mathbf{w}(j; n, p)$, and call them binomial probabilities. In Figure 18 we have graphed $\mathbf{w}(j; 8, \frac{3}{4})$. In Figure 19 we have graphed $\mathbf{w}(j; 7, \frac{3}{4})$.

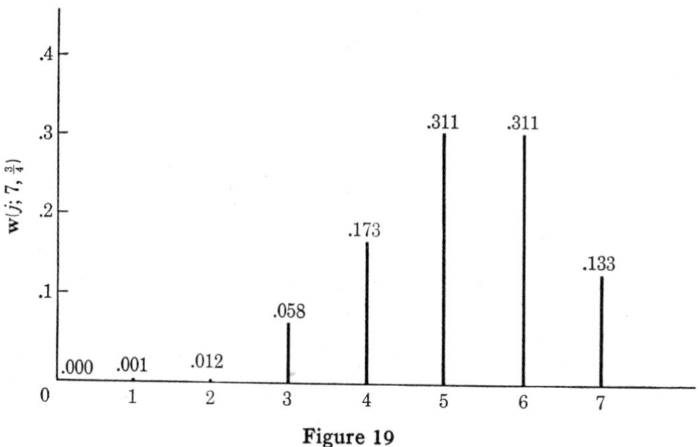

Figure 19

We see in the first case that $\mathbf{w}$ increases up to a maximum value at $j = 6$ and then decreases. In the second case the values increase up to a maximum value at $j = 5$, have the same value for $j = 6$, and then decrease. These two cases are typical of what can happen in general.

Returning to the general case, consider the ratio of succeeding values of $\mathbf{w}$. We see that

$$\frac{\mathbf{w}(j+1; n, p)}{\mathbf{w}(j; n, p)} = \frac{\binom{n}{j+1} p^{j+1} q^{n-j-1}}{\binom{n}{j} p^j q^{n-j}} = \frac{n-j}{j+1} \cdot \frac{p}{q}.$$

This ratio will be greater than one as long as $(n - j)p > (j + 1)q$, or as long as $j < np - q$. If $np - q$ is not an integer, the values of $\mathbf{w}$ increase up to a maximum value, which occurs at the first integer greater than $np - q$, and then decrease. In case $np - q$ is an integer, $\mathbf{w}$ increases up to $j = np - q$, is the same for $j = np - q$ and $j = np - q + 1$, and then decreases. We recall that $\mathbf{M}[\mathbf{s}_n] = np$. Thus we see that, in general, the values of $\mathbf{s}_n$ that have the highest probability are near the mean.

Example 1. A die is rolled six times. Let $\mathbf{s}_6$ be the number of sixes that turn up. Then

$$\mathbf{Pr}[\mathbf{s}_6 = j] = \mathbf{w}(j; 6, \tfrac{1}{6}) = \binom{6}{j}(\tfrac{1}{6})^j(\tfrac{5}{6})^{n-j}.$$

These probabilities are given in Figure 20.

x	$\mathbf{w}(x; 6, 1/6)$
0	.33490
1	.40188
2	.20093
3	.05359
4	.00804
5	.00064
6	.00002

Figure 20

In this case $\mathbf{w}$ has a single maximum at $\mathbf{M}[\mathbf{f}] = 1$. It is of course an exceptional case that the $\mathbf{M}[\mathbf{f}] = np$ is an integer and hence in the range of $\mathbf{f}$.

Note that for fixed n and p, the function $\mathbf{w}$, considered to be a function on the space $\mathcal{U} = \{0, 1, 2, \ldots, n\}$, has all the properties of a weight function. This would be the appropriate weight function if we were to make the coarser analysis of possibilities according to the number of times outcome a occurs. The measure determined this way is usually called the binomial measure.

The values of $\mathbf{w}$ for large n are very difficult to compute. There are, however, approximate methods for dealing with the probabilities for large n. We shall consider one such method in this section and a second method in the next section.

Theorem. For the binomial probability $\mathbf{w}(j; n, p)$, keep j fixed, let n tend to infinity, and p tend to zero, in such a way that $np = m$ stays constant Then

$$\lim_{n\to\infty} \mathbf{w}(j; n, p) = \frac{m^j e^{-m}}{j!}.$$

Proof. We write

$$\mathbf{w}(j; n, p) = \frac{n(n-1)\ldots(n-j+1)}{j!} p^j(1-p)^{n-j}.$$

Since $p = m/n$, the right side is

$$= \frac{n(n-1)\ldots(n-j+1)}{j!}\left(\frac{m}{n}\right)^j\left(1-\frac{m}{n}\right)^{n-j}.$$

We may rewrite this in the form

$$= \frac{1\left(1-\frac{1}{n}\right)\ldots\left(1-\frac{j-1}{n}\right)}{j!}\, m^j\, \frac{\left(1-\frac{m}{n}\right)^n}{\left(1-\frac{m}{n}\right)^j}.$$

We now make use of the result from calculus that

$$\lim_{n\to\infty}\left(1-\frac{m}{n}\right)^n = e^{-m}.$$

Since j and m are fixed,

$$\lim_{n\to\infty} 1\cdot\left(1-\frac{1}{n}\right)\ldots\left(1-\frac{j-1}{n}\right) = 1$$

and

$$\lim_{n\to\infty}\left(1-\frac{m}{n}\right)^j = 1.$$

Thus

$$\lim_{n\to\infty} \mathbf{w}(j, n, p) = \frac{m^j e^{-m}}{j!}.$$

The importance of this theorem is that it shows that for repeated trials with n large and p small, we may approximate the binomial probabilities by the values of

$$\mathbf{w}(j; m) = \frac{m^j e^{-m}}{j!},$$

where $m = np = \mathbf{M}[\mathbf{s}_n]$.

Example 2. Let us assume that a typesetter makes on the average one mistake per 1000 words. Assume that he is setting type for a book with 100 words to a page. Let **s** be the number of mistakes which he makes on a given page. We assume that each word is a single experiment and the probability of a mistake on a single word is .001. Treating this as an independent trials process, we know that $\mathbf{Pr}[\mathbf{s} = j] = \mathbf{w}(j; 100, .001)$. This is given in Figure 21, to five-place accuracy, together with the approximation obtained by using $\mathbf{w}(j; m)$, with $m = \mathbf{M}[\mathbf{s}] = 100(.001) = .1$. That is, $\mathbf{w}(j; .1) = \frac{(.1)^j e^{-(.1)}}{j!}$.

Consider now a hypothetical experiment where the outcome is any positive integer, i.e., $\mathcal{U} = \{0, 1, 2, \ldots\}$. In analogy with the case of a finite number of outcomes we may determine a measure on $\mathcal{U}$ by assigning weights to the outcomes in such a way that their sum is 1. The theorem

j	w(j; 100, .001)	w(j; .1)
0	.90480	.90484
1	.09057	.09048
2	.00449	.00452
3	.00015	.00015
4	.00000	.00000

Figure 21

proved earlier in this section suggests the assignment of weights

$$\mathbf{w}(j;m) = \frac{m^j e^{-m}}{j!}$$

to the possibility of j. Using the infinite series for e^m, we see that

$$\sum_j \mathbf{w}(j;m) = \sum_j \frac{m^j e^{-m}}{j!} = e^{-m} \sum_j \frac{m^j}{j!} = 1$$

so that this choice of $\mathbf{w}$ does define a probability measure on $\mathcal{U}$. This measure is called the *Poisson measure with mean m*. Let $\mathbf{f}$ be the outcome function for this experiment. We define, in analogy with the finite case,

$$\mathbf{M}[\mathbf{f}] = \sum_j j\, \mathbf{w}(j;m).$$

Similarly

$$\mathbf{V}[\mathbf{f}] = \sum_j (\mathbf{f} - \mathbf{M}[\mathbf{f}])^2 \mathbf{w}(j;m).$$

Both of these sums have the value m. Hence for this experiment, $\mathbf{M}[\mathbf{f}] = \mathbf{V}[\mathbf{f}] = m$. We will show this for $\mathbf{M}[\mathbf{f}]$.

$$\mathbf{M}[\mathbf{f}] = \sum j \frac{m^j e^{-m}}{j!} = me^{-m} \sum_{j>0} \frac{m^{j-1}}{(j-1)!}.$$

Letting $k = j - 1$, $\mathbf{M}[\mathbf{f}] = me^{-m} \sum_k \frac{m^k}{k!} = m.$

We have remarked that the binomial probabilities determine a set of weights on the set $\mathcal{U} = \{0, 1, \ldots, n\}$. The Poisson measure is determined by a set of weights on the set $V = \{0, 1, \ldots, n, \ldots\}$ of all integers. Our theorem shows that the weights for the binomial measure determined by n, p should approximate those for the Poisson measure with $m = np$ when n is large and p small. Figure 22 gives several cases of these approximations.

j	Poisson $m = .1$	Binomial $n = 10$ $p = .01$	Poisson $m = 1$	Binomial $n = 100$ $p = .01$	Poisson $m = 10$	Binomial $n = 1000$ $p = .01$
0	.9048	.9044	.3679	.3660	.0000	.0000
1	.0905	.0914	.3679	.3697	.0005	.0004
2	.0045	.0042	.1839	.1849	.0023	.0022
3	.0002	.0001	.0613	.0610	.0076	.0074
4	.0000	.0000	.0153	.0149	.0189	.0186
5			.0031	.0029	.0378	.0374
6			.0005	.0005	.0631	.0627
7			.0001	.0001	.0901	.0900
8			.0000	.0000	.1126	.1128
9					.1251	.1256
10					.1251	.1257
11					.1137	.1143
12					.0948	.0952
13					.0729	.0731
14					.0521	.0520
15					.0347	.0345
16					.0217	.0215
17					.0128	.0126
18					.0071	.0069
19					.0037	.0036
20					.0019	.0018
21					.0009	.0009
22					.0004	.0004
23					.0002	.0002
24					.0001	.0001
25					.0000	.0000

Figure 22

EXERCISES

Note: A table of e^{-m} will be useful in working these problems.

1. Assume that the Poisson measure with mean .3 has been assigned for the outcome of an experiment. Let **f** be the outcome function. Find $\mathbf{Pr}[\mathbf{f} = 0]$, $\mathbf{Pr}[\mathbf{f} = 1]$, and $\mathbf{Pr}[\mathbf{f} > 1]$. [*Ans.* .741, .222, .037.]

2. Assume that 500 raisin cookies are to be made. Estimate the smallest number of raisins which may be used to insure a probability less than .01 that a cookie chosen from the 500 will not have any raisins.

3. Assume that on the average only one person in a thousand has a particular rare blood type.

(a) In a city of 10,000 what is the probability that no person has this blood type? [*Ans.* .00005.]

(b) How many people would have to be canvassed to give a probability greater than one half of finding a person with this blood type?

4. The probability that in a bridge deal one of the four hands has all hearts is $6.3 \cdot 10^{-12}$. The probability expert in a town of 50,000 is called on the average of once a year (usually late at night) and told that the caller has just been dealt a hand of all hearts. Should he suspect that some of these callers are the victims of practical jokes?

[*Ans.* Yes. With fifty deals per day per person the probability is less than .01 that such a hand would occur during the year.]

5. A man never puts money in a five-cent parking meter. He assumes that there is a probability of .05 that he will be caught. The first offense costs nothing, the second costs 50 cents, and subsequent offenses cost one dollar each. Under his assumptions, how does the mean cost in parking 20 times compare with the cost of putting money in the meter each time?

6. An advertiser drops 10,000 leaflets on a city which has 2,000 blocks. Assume that each leaflet has an equal chance to land on each block. What is the probability that a particular block will receive no leaflets? [*Ans.* .007.]

7. Assume that for a certain experiment the Poisson measure with mean m has been assigned. Show that a most probable outcome for the experiment is a value k such that $m - 1 \leq k \leq m$. Under what conditions will there be two most probable values?

8. A man receives an average of ten letters each day. On a certain day he receives no mail and wonders if it is a holiday. To decide this he computes the probability that in ten years he would have at least one day without any mail. He assumes that the number of letters that he receives on a day has a Poisson measure. What probability did he find? [*Hint:* Apply the Poisson measure twice. First to find the probability that on a given day he receives no mail, and a second time to find the probability that in 3000 days he will have no such day—since each year has about 300 days on which mail is delivered.] [*Ans.* .13.]

9. In Example 2 assume that the book has 1000 pages. Let $\mathbf{g}$ be the number of pages with no mistakes. Show that $\mathbf{M}[\mathbf{g}] = 905$ and $\mathbf{V}[\mathbf{g}] = 86$. Using this show that the probability is $\leq .05$ that there will be more than 950 pages without errors or fewer than 860 pages without errors.

10. Prove that the Poisson measure with mean m has variance m.

13. THE CENTRAL LIMIT THEOREM

In this section we shall continue our study of the independent trials process. We consider first the special case of two outcomes. As in the previous section we label one outcome with a 1 and the other with a 0. Let p be the probability of outcome 1 on any experiment and $q = 1 - p$. Let $\mathbf{s}_n$ be the number of times in the first n experiments that outcome 1 occurs. We have seen that $\mathbf{M}[\mathbf{s}_n] = np$ and $\mathbf{V}[\mathbf{s}_n] = npq$. We have also seen that

$$\mathbf{Pr}[\mathbf{s}_n = j] = \binom{n}{j} p^j q^{n-j}.$$

We know that one standard deviation is a useful unit to employ in studying $\mathbf{s}_n$. For example, by Chebychev's inequality, the probability of a deviation of $\mathbf{s}_n$ from its mean value np by a large number of standard deviations is unlikely. Since we know the probability that $\mathbf{s}_n$ takes on any particular value, we can calculate more precisely the probability that $\mathbf{s}_n$ deviates from its mean by any number of standard deviations. More generally we could find the probability of statements of the form

$$c\sqrt{npq} < \mathbf{s}_n(x) - np < d\sqrt{npq}$$

for any numbers c and d with $c < d$. Let $\mathbf{s}_n^*$ be the standardized function (see Section 10)

$$\mathbf{s}_n^* = \frac{\mathbf{s}_n - np}{\sqrt{npq}}.$$

Then for any c, d, the statement about $\mathbf{s}_n$ that we wish to consider is equivalent to the simpler statement

$$c < \mathbf{s}_n^*(x) < d$$

about $\mathbf{s}_n^*$.

In Figure 23 we have computed several of these probabilities for $p = \frac{1}{4}$. We have included in each case one of the end points. We have also included the probability that $\mathbf{s}_n^*(x) = 0$, i.e., that $\mathbf{s}_n(x) = np$. We have chosen values of n for which this is possible. To illustrate a calculation for this table, consider the case $n = 16$. Then $\mathbf{M}[\mathbf{s}_{16}] = 4$ and the standard deviation of $\mathbf{s}_{16}$ is $\sqrt{\frac{1}{4}\cdot\frac{3}{4}\cdot 16} \approx 1.73$. Thus

$$\mathbf{s}_{16}^* = \frac{\mathbf{s}_{16} - 4}{1.73}$$

and the statement

$$1 < \mathbf{s}_{16}^*(x) \leq 2$$

is true only when $\mathbf{s}_{16}$ is equal to 6 or 7. These are the cases when $\mathbf{s}_{16}$ deviates from its mean 4 by more than one and at most two standard deviations. Hence

$$\mathbf{Pr}[1 < s^*_{16} \leq 2] = \binom{16}{6}\left(\frac{1}{4}\right)^6\left(\frac{3}{4}\right)^{10} + \binom{16}{7}\left(\frac{1}{4}\right)^7\left(\frac{3}{4}\right)^9 = .163.$$

$p = 1/4$	$n = 16$	$n = 40$	$n = 120$	$n = 400$	$n = 1000$
$\mathbf{Pr}[s^*_n < -3]$	.000	.000	.001	.001	.001
$\mathbf{Pr}[-3 \leq s^*_n < -2]$	.010	.016	.019	.019	.020
$\mathbf{Pr}[-2 \leq s^*_n < -1]$	.187	.165	.152	.143	.141
$\mathbf{Pr}[-1 \leq s^*_n < 0]$	.208	.258	.293	.318	.326
$\mathbf{Pr}[s^*_n = 0]$	.225	.144	.084	.046	.029
$\mathbf{Pr}[0 < s^*_n \leq 1]$	.180	.237	.280	.310	.321
$\mathbf{Pr}[1 < s^*_n \leq 2]$	.163	.153	.146	.140	.139
$\mathbf{Pr}[2 < s^*_n \leq 3]$	.025	.025	.023	.021	.021
$\mathbf{Pr}[3 < s^*_n]$	.002	.002	.002	.002	.002

Figure 23

We observe from this table several interesting facts. First the values in the row corresponding to $\mathbf{Pr}[s^*_n = 0]$ become smaller and smaller as n increases. It can be proved that as n increases, the probability that s^*_n takes on any given value tends to 0. Consider, however, the probabilities in the other rows. These seem to be approaching limits. We shall see later that this is the case. We also note that as n increases the probabilities of deviations on either side of the mean become more nearly equal. For example, for $n = 1000$, $\mathbf{Pr}[-3 \leq s^*_n < -2] = .020$ and $\mathbf{Pr}[2 < s^*_n \leq 3] = .021$. This symmetry property is surprising in view of the fact that the individual outcome functions do not have such a symmetry. For example, the probability that an outcome function is greater than its mean is $\frac{1}{4}$ and that it is less than its mean is $\frac{3}{4}$. On the other hand, for $n = 1000$ the probability that s_n is less than its mean is .488 and the probability that it is greater than its mean is .483.

We consider next a different value for p, viz., $p = \frac{1}{2}$. In this case $\mathbf{M}[s_n] = (\frac{1}{2})n$ and $\mathbf{V}[s_n] = (\frac{1}{4})n$. Hence

$$s^*_n = \frac{s_n - n(\mathbf{1/2})}{\frac{1}{2}\sqrt{n}}.$$

The probabilities for statements of the form $t < s^*_n(x) < t + 1$ for several values of n are given in Figure 24.

Again we observe that the probabilities in a row apparently tend to a limit. What is, however, even more surprising is that they are approximately the same as the values found for $p = \frac{1}{4}$. We, of course, expect the symmetry property found in the case $p = \frac{1}{4}$, since in the case $p = \frac{1}{2}$ the individual outcome functions have probability $\frac{1}{2}$ of deviating from their mean by $+\frac{1}{2}$ and probability $\frac{1}{2}$ of deviating by $-\frac{1}{2}$ from their mean.

The fact that we obtained similar results for large n for the case $p = \frac{1}{2}$ and $p = \frac{1}{4}$ is explained by a very general theorem called the central limit theorem. We shall state without proof an important special case of this theorem.

$p = 1/2$	$n = 16$	$n = 100$	$n = 800$
$\mathbf{Pr}[s_n^* < -3]$	.000	.001	.001
$\mathbf{Pr}[-3 \leq s_n^* < -2]$	.010	.017	.021
$\mathbf{Pr}[-2 \leq s_n^* < -1]$	.094	.118	.131
$\mathbf{Pr}[-1 \leq s_n^* < 0]$	.297	.325	.333
$\mathbf{Pr}[s_n^* = 0]$	.196	.078	.028
$\mathbf{Pr}[0 < s_n^* \leq 1]$	.297	.325	.333
$\mathbf{Pr}[0 < s_n^* \leq 2]$	.094	.118	.131
$\mathbf{Pr}[2 < s_n^* \leq 3]$	.010	.017	.021
$\mathbf{Pr}[3 < s_n^*]$	.000	.001	.001

Figure 24

Theorem (Central limit theorem). Let $\mathbf{f}_1, \mathbf{f}_2, \ldots, \mathbf{f}_n$ be numerical valued outcome functions for an independent trials process. Let $\mathbf{M}[\mathbf{f}_1] = a$ and $\mathbf{V}[\mathbf{f}_1] = b^2 > 0$. Let

$$\mathbf{s}_n = \mathbf{f}_1 + \mathbf{f}_2 + \ldots + \mathbf{f}_n$$

and let $\mathbf{s}_n^*$ be $\mathbf{s}_n$ standardized, i.e.,

$$\mathbf{s}_n^* = \frac{\mathbf{s}_n - na}{b \cdot \sqrt{n}}.$$

Let $c \leq d$ be any two numbers. Then

$$\mathbf{Pr}[c \leq \mathbf{s}_n^* \leq d] \to \frac{1}{\sqrt{2\pi}} \int_c^d e^{-x^2/2}\, dx \tag{1}$$

as n tends to infinity.

To estimate the probability $\mathbf{Pr}[c \leq \mathbf{s}_n^* \leq d]$ by means of the central limit theorem, we must find the value of

$$\frac{1}{\sqrt{2\pi}} \int_c^d e^{-x^2/2}\, dx.$$

The graph of the function $\frac{1}{\sqrt{2\pi}} e^{-x^2/2}$ is shown in Figure 25. This graph is called the *normal* curve.

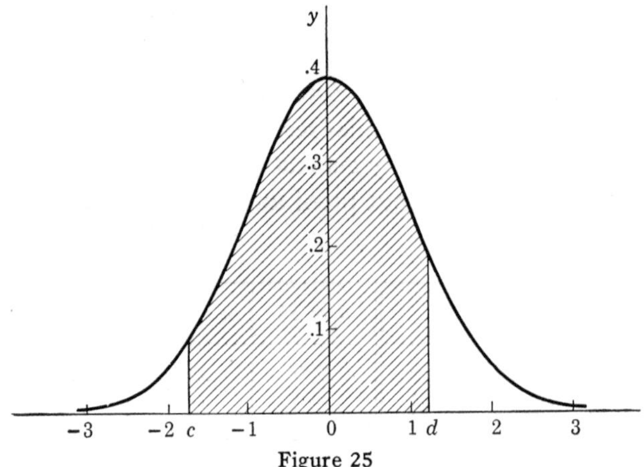

Figure 25

Our estimate for $\mathbf{Pr}[c \le \mathbf{s}_n^* \le d]$ is the area under this curve between c and d. Unfortunately this area cannot be found by elementary integration techniques; hence we must give it in tabular form. In Figure 26 we give the area under the curve from 0 to d. That is the approximation for $\mathbf{Pr}[0 \le \mathbf{s}_n^* \le d]$. From the symmetry of the curve this area is the same as the area from 0 to $-d$, which is the estimate for $\mathbf{Pr}[-d \le \mathbf{s}_n^* \le 0]$. By putting $c = d$ in (1) we see that the probability that $\mathbf{s}_n^*$ takes on any particular value tends to 0. Thus we may include end points of intervals, or not, when discussing limiting probabilities.

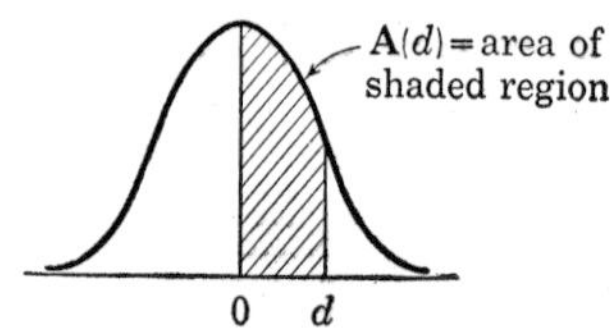

d	$\mathbf{A}(d)$	d	$\mathbf{A}(d)$	d	$\mathbf{A}(d)$	d	$\mathbf{A}(d)$
.0	.000	1.1	.364	2.1	.482	3.1	.4990
.1	.040	1.2	.385	2.2	.486	3.2	.4993
.2	.079	1.3	.403	2.3	.489	3.3	.4995
.3	.118	1.4	.419	2.4	.492	3.4	.4997
.4	.155	1.5	.433	2.5	.494	3.5	.4998
.5	.191	1.6	.445	2.6	.495	3.6	.4998
.6	.226	1.7	.455	2.7	.497	3.7	.4999
.7	.258	1.8	.464	2.8	.497	3.8	.49993
.8	.288	1.9	.471	2.9	.498	3.9	.49995
.9	.316	2.0	.477	3.0	.4987	4.0	.49997
1.0	.341					5.0	.49999997

Figure 26

The table of Figure 26 lists, in effect, the values of definite integrals of the form

$$\frac{1}{\sqrt{2\pi}} \int_0^d e^{-x^2/2}\, dx,$$

where the left-hand end point is 0. When the left-hand end point is some $c \neq 0$, then we must make use of the symmetry of the curve to compute the integral. For instance

$$\frac{1}{\sqrt{2\pi}} \int_{-.4}^0 e^{-x^2/2}\, dx$$

is the same as

$$\frac{1}{\sqrt{2\pi}} \int_0^{.4} e^{-x^2/2}\, dx = .155.$$

Similarly,

$$\frac{1}{\sqrt{2\pi}} \int_{-.3}^{.2} e^{-x^2/2}\, dx = \frac{1}{\sqrt{2\pi}} \int_{-.3}^0 e^{-x^2/2}\, dx + \frac{1}{\sqrt{2\pi}} \int_0^{.2} e^{-x^2/2}\, dx$$

$$= .118 + .079 = .197$$

and

$$\frac{1}{\sqrt{2\pi}} \int_{.2}^{.9} e^{-x^2/2}\, dx = \frac{1}{\sqrt{2\pi}} \int_0^{.9} e^{-x^2/2}\, dx - \frac{1}{\sqrt{2\pi}} \int_0^{.2} e^{-x^2/2}\, dx$$

$$= .316 - .079 = .237.$$

Example 1. Let us return to the case of independent trials with outcome functions having the value 1 with probability p and 0 with probability q. We now see that the central limit theorem explains the results which we obtained by direct calculation for $p = \frac{1}{4}$ and $p = \frac{1}{2}$. It shows further that the probabilities of the form that we calculated may be approximated by the central limit theorem for any value of p. How large a value of n must be chosen for a good approximation by the central limit theorem depends upon p. For small p the Poisson approximation is apt to be better. In Figure 27 we have given the comparison of the values found for the cases $n = 1000$, $p = \frac{1}{4}$ and $n = 800$, $p = \frac{1}{2}$ with the limiting values predicted by the central limit theorem.

	$n = 1000$ $p = 1/4$	$n = 800$ $p = 1/2$	limit as $n \to \infty$
$\Pr[0 < s_n^* \leq 1]$	.321	.333	.341
$\Pr[1 < s_n^* \leq 2]$	.139	.131	.136
$\Pr[2 < s_n^* \leq 3]$	.021	.021	.021
$\Pr[s_n^* > 3]$	.002	.001	.001

Figure 27

The most common use of the central limit theorem is made in the following form. We are interested in the probability that the sum function $\mathbf{s}_n$ or the average function $\mathbf{h}_n$ does not deviate from its mean by more than k standard deviations. From the central limit theorem we see that these probabilities are for given k approximately the area under the normal curve between $-k$ and $+k$. For $k = 1$ this area is approximately .681, for $k = 2$ it is .954, and for $k = 3$ it is .997. Thus we see that a deviation from the mean by more than 2 standard deviations is unlikely, and by more than 3 standard deviations, extremely unlikely.

Example 2. Consider 900 rolls of an ordinary die. Let $\mathbf{s}_{900}$ be the total of the numbers which turn up. We have seen that the mean of each outcome function is 3.5 and the standard deviation is $\sqrt{35/12} \approx 1.7$. The mean of $\mathbf{s}_{900}$ is thus $900 \cdot 3.5 = 3150$ and the standard deviation is $1.7 \cdot \sqrt{900} = 51$. Thus a deviation as great as 153 from the mean number 3150 would be highly unlikely (probability .003). And a total as large as 3500 might be interpreted to mean that the die is not a balanced die. The average of the numbers that turn up has mean 3.5 and standard deviation $1.7/\sqrt{900} \approx .06$. Thus we see that with probability .997 the average will not deviate from 3.5 by more than $3(.06) = .18$, i.e., that the average will lie between 3.32 and 3.68. With probability .954 we would predict that the average would not deviate from 3.5 by more than $2(.06) = .12$, i.e., that the average will lie between 3.38 and 3.62.

Example 3. A student of average ability in a certain college knows that he can get an A in a course with probability .1, a B with probability .2, a C with probability .4, a D with .2, and an E with probability .1. These grades carry 4, 3, 2, 1, and 0 points credit, respectively. The requirement for graduation is that the student should take 40 courses and attain a point average of at least 1.8 (or a total of 72 points credit).

Let $\mathbf{f}_i$ give the number of points that the student earns in course i, and let $\mathbf{s}_{40}$ give the total number of points earned in 40 courses. Then $\mathbf{M}[\mathbf{f}_i] = 2.0$ and $\mathbf{V}[\mathbf{f}_i] = 1.2$. Hence the function $\mathbf{s}_{40}$ has mean 80 and variance 48. Thus its standard deviation is about 6.93. For graduation it is necessary that $\mathbf{s}_{40}$ should not be more than 8 points below its mean, or not more than about 1.15 standard deviations below the mean. From Figure 26 we find that there is a probability of about .12 that the student will fail to graduate.

Let us suppose that the college offers certain special courses (sometimes called "snap courses") in which the student is sure to get exactly a B. Suppose that the student, aware of the danger of not graduating, decides to elect five of these special courses. This will assure him of 15 points, and hence he needs only 57 points in the remaining 35 courses. The sum function has mean 70 and variance 42, and thus a standard deviation of 6.48.

To fail to graduate the student must attain a sum at least 13 points or at least two standard deviations below the mean. He has thus reduced the probability of failure from .12 to about .023.

If he wants to be very sure of graduating, he may elect 10 snap courses (this being the maximum allowed for any one student). These will yield 30 points, and he needs only 42 points in the 30 other courses. The sum function then has mean 60 and variance 36, or standard deviation 6. To fail to graduate the student will have to come out at least three standard deviations below the mean; he will have to be very unlucky indeed.

Example 4. Assume that a particle moves in a straight line as follows. It starts at position 0 and makes a sequence of steps. Each step is a unit step to the right or a unit step to the left. Assume that it moves on any step to the right with probability $\frac{1}{2}$ and hence to the left also with probability $\frac{1}{2}$. We may consider each step to be the outcome function for an independent trials process. The sum of the outcome functions then gives the position of the particle. Each outcome function has value 1 with probability $\frac{1}{2}$ and -1 with probability $\frac{1}{2}$. Thus the mean of an outcome function is 0 and the variance is the mean of the square of the function which is 1. Hence the standard deviation is also 1. By the central limit theorem we see that after n steps the particle will, with probability .954, be at a distance not greater than $2\sqrt{n}$ from its starting position. For example, in 900 steps we would expect to find the particle at a distance not more than 60 units from its starting position.

Assume now that the particle moves one step to the right with probability $\frac{3}{4}$ and to the left with probability $\frac{1}{4}$. Then the mean of each outcome function is $1 \cdot \frac{3}{4} - 1 \cdot \frac{1}{4} = \frac{1}{2}$. The variance is the mean of the square of the function minus the square of the mean which is $1 - \frac{1}{4} = \frac{3}{4}$. Thus after n steps we expect to find the particle with probability .954 at a position not more than $2 \cdot \sqrt{.75n}$ units from a position $n/2$ units to the right of 0. In the case of 900 steps this is within 52 units of 450. This type of process is often called a *random walk*.

In Section 11 and in the present section we have obtained information about sums of independent functions in two ways: first by applying Chebyshev's inequality and second by the central limit theorem. It is instructive to compare the two results.

The first difference is that the central limit theorem is a much deeper result. We were able to prove Chebyshev's inequality, but the proof of the central limit theorem requires results beyond the scope of this book.

The second difference is in the kind of information that each gives. Let us compare the two results as applied to an independent trials process with outcome functions $\mathbf{f}_1, \mathbf{f}_2, \ldots, \mathbf{f}_n$. Let $\mathbf{s}_n = \mathbf{f}_1 + \mathbf{f}_2 + \ldots + \mathbf{f}_n$ and $\mathbf{s}_n^*$ be $\mathbf{s}_n$ standardized.

By Chebyshev's inequality

$$\mathbf{Pr}[|\mathbf{s}_n^*| > k] \leq \frac{1}{k^2}. \tag{1}$$

By the central limit theorem

$$\mathbf{Pr}[|\mathbf{s}_n^*| > k] \approx \frac{2}{\sqrt{2\pi}} \int_k^\infty e^{-x^2/2}\, dx. \tag{2}$$

For example, if $k = 3$, then by (1)

$$\mathbf{Pr}[|\mathbf{s}_n^*| > 3] \leq \tfrac{1}{9};$$

but by (2),

$$\mathbf{Pr}[|\mathbf{s}_n^*| > 3] \approx .003.$$

While (2) appears to be a much stronger result than (1) it must be realized that (1) is the assertion that a certain inequality holds and (2) is only an assertion that an approximation holds. To show that in general (2) gives more precise information it would be necessary to study the nature of this approximation. This is a very difficult problem.

Just as for the law of large numbers, the central limit theorem has also been proved for more general kinds of processes than independent trials. In particular, it is also true for the r-experiment independent process introduced in Section 11. That is, each trial is one of r experiments. We saw that if $\mathbf{s}_n$ is the sum of the first n trials, then

$$A_n = \mathbf{M}[\mathbf{s}_n] = n_1a_1 + \ldots + n_ra_r$$

$$B_n^2 = \mathbf{V}[\mathbf{s}_n] = n_1b_1^2 + \ldots + n_rb_r^2$$

where n_j is the number of times the jth experiment is performed and a_j and b_j^2 are the mean and variance of the outcome function when this experiment is performed. Hence to standardize $\mathbf{s}_n$ we must form the new function

$$\mathbf{s}_n^* = \frac{\mathbf{s}_n - \mathbf{A}_n}{\mathbf{B}_n}.$$

The generalized central limit theorem then tells us that probabilities relating to $\mathbf{s}_n^*$ may be computed from the area under the normal curve.

Example 5. Let us assume that in Example 3 a snap course is such that the student receives an A with probability .3, a B with probability .4, and a C with probability .3. Then if $\mathbf{g}_i$ is his grade in taking the ith snap course, we have $\mathbf{M}[\mathbf{g}_i] = 3$ and $\mathbf{V}[\mathbf{g}_i] = .6$. Assuming that the other courses are unchanged, let us see the effect of this on his passing. If he takes 5 snap courses and 35 regular courses the mean for his total grade will be $5 \cdot 3 + 35 \cdot 2 = 85$. The variance of his sum will be $5 \cdot .6 + 35 \cdot 1.2 = 45$. The standard deviation is then approximately 6.71. To fail to graduate he would have to be 13 points below the mean, or approximately 1.9

standard deviations. Thus his probability of graduating has been reduced only slightly from the case where a B was certain. Assume next that he decides to take ten snap courses. Then the mean of his sum is $10 \cdot 3 + 30 \cdot 2 = 90$ and the variance is $10 \cdot .6 + 30 \cdot 1.2 = 42$. The standard deviation is then approximately 6.48. To fail to graduate in this case the student must get 18 points or more below the mean. This is less than 2.8 standard deviations. In the case that a B was assured we found he would fail to graduate only if he got more than 3 standard deviations below the mean. We thus observe that the school can decrease the probability that a man will graduate without making the courses any harder on the average.

EXERCISES

1. Let $\mathbf{s}_n^*$ be the standardized function for sum of n independent trials with numerical outcomes. Find the limiting probabilities for:
(a) $\mathbf{Pr}[\mathbf{s}_n^* < -2.5]$. [*Ans.* .006.]
(b) $\mathbf{Pr}[\mathbf{s}_n^* < 2.5]$.
(c) $\mathbf{Pr}[\mathbf{s}_n^* \geq -.5]$.
(d) $\mathbf{Pr}[-1.5 < \mathbf{s}_n^* < 1]$. [*Ans.* .774.]

2. In a group of 300 families with three children it was found that there were 500 boys. What is the probability of finding this many or more boys if the probability that each child is a boy is $\frac{1}{2}$.

3. Experience has shown that, because of multiple applications for Ivy League schools, only about $\frac{1}{2}$ of the students which the college is willing to accept finally come to the college. Assume that a college can accommodate at most 820 students. Assume that it sends out 1600 acceptances and that each student comes to the college with probability $\frac{1}{2}$. What is the probability that the school ends up with more students than it can accommodate? Find the largest number that they could accept if they wanted a probability less than .05 of getting more students than they can accommodate. [*Ans.* .159; 1574.]

4. Peter and Paul each have 20 pennies. They agree to match pennies 400 times keeping score but not paying until the 400 matches are over. What is the probability that one of the players will not be able to pay? Answer the same question for the case that Peter has 10 pennies and Paul has 30.

5. A piece of rope is made up of 100 strands. Assume that the breaking strength of the rope is the sum of the breaking strengths of the individual strands. Assume further that this sum may be considered to be the sum of outcome functions for an independent trials process with 100 experiments each having mean 10 pounds and standard deviation

1. Find the approximate probability that the rope will support a weight (a) of 1000 pounds, (b) of 970 pounds.

[*Ans.* (a) .5; (b) .999.]

6. Assume that in a certain large city, 900 people are chosen at random and asked if they favor a certain proposal. Of the 900 asked, 550 say they favor the proposal and 350 are opposed. If, in fact, the people in the city are equally divided on the issue, would it be unlikely that such a large majority would be obtained in a sample of 900 of the citizens?

7. Assume that a calculating machine carries out a million operations to solve a certain problem. In each operation the machine gives the answer 10^{-5} too small, with probability $\frac{1}{2}$, and 10^{-5} too large, with probability $\frac{1}{2}$. Assume that the errors are independent of one another. What is a reasonable accuracy to attach to the answer? What if the machine carries out 10^{10} operations?

[*Ans.* $\pm .02$; ± 2; each with probability .95.]

8. Two railroads are competing for the passenger traffic of 1000 passengers by operating similar trains at the same hour. If a given passenger is equally likely to choose one train as the other, how many seats would the railroad provide if it wants to be sure that its seating capacity is sufficient in 99 out of 100 cases? [*Ans.* 537.]

9. Consider an independent trials process with two outcomes A and B. Let p be the probability for outcome A and $q = 1 - p$ the probability for B. Assume that p is not known and that it is desired to estimate p by the average number of times A occurs in n trials. Using the fact that $\sqrt{pq} < \frac{1}{2}$ estimate the number of trials necessary to ensure that the probability is at least .95 that the fraction of outcomes which are A will be within .02 of the unknown value for p.

10. Assume that a baseball player has probability .37 of getting a hit each time he comes to bat. Find the probability of getting an average of .388 or better if he comes to bat 300 times during the season. (In 1957 Ted Williams had a batting average of .388 and Mickey Mantle had an average of .353. If we assume this difference is due to chance we may estimate the probability of a hit as the combined average, which is about .37.) [*Ans.* .258.]

11. A true-false examination has 48 questions. Assume that the probability that a student knows the answer to any one question is $\frac{3}{4}$. A passing score is 30 or better. Estimate the probability that a student will fail the exam. Estimate the probability that in a group of 100 such students none fail.

12. A thousand particles are started at the same time and at the same position. Each particle moves in a random walk with probability $\frac{1}{2}$

for a step to the right and $\frac{1}{2}$ for a step to the left. Let $\mathbf{w}(x)$ be the approximate probability that after 10,000 steps exactly x will be more than 300 units away from the starting position. Find $\mathbf{w}(x)$ for $x = 0$, 1, 2, 3. (*Hint:* Use Poisson approximation.)

[*Ans.* .074; .193; .251; .218.]

13. In Exercise 11 assume that the questions are divided into three groups, 16 hard questions, 16 medium hard questions, and 16 easy questions. The probability of a student knowing the answer to a hard question is .4, to a medium question .6, and to an easy question .8. Estimate the probability a given student will fail the exam. [Hint: see p. 194.]

14. A game is played in which a player has probability .3 of receiving one dollar and probability .1 of losing one dollar (otherwise he breaks even). What is the probability that in 100 plays of the game he ends up at least 35 dollars ahead? [*Ans.* .006.]

15. A coin is biased in such a way that a head comes up with probability .8 on a single toss. Use the normal approximation to estimate the probability that in a million tosses there are more than 800,400 heads.

16. In Exercise 7 of Section 11 estimate, by using the central limit theorem, the probability that the house loses money.

17. Let $\mathbf{s}$ be the number of heads in 1,000,000 tosses of a balanced coin. Use (a) Chebyshev's inequality, and (b) the central limit theorem to estimate the probability that $\mathbf{s}$ is less than 499,500 or greater than 500,500. Use the same two methods to estimate the probability that $\mathbf{s}$ is less than 499,000 or greater than 501,000. And also the probability that $\mathbf{s}$ is less than 498,500 or greater than 501,500.

[*Ans.* (a) ≤ 1 (i.e., no information); $\leq \frac{1}{4}$; $\leq \frac{1}{9}$.
(b) .318; .046; .003 (approximate answers).]

*14. A PROBLEM OF DECISION

In the preceding sections we have dealt with the problem of calculating the probability of certain statements based on the assumption of a given probability measure. In a statistics problem, one is often called upon to make a decision in a case where the decision would be relatively easy to make if we could assign probabilities to certain statements, but we do not know how to assign these probabilities. For example, if a vaccine for a certain disease is proposed, we may be called upon to decide whether or not the vaccine should be used. We may decide that we could make the decision if we could compare the probability that a person vaccinated will get the disease with the probability that a person not vaccinated will get the disease. Statistical theory develops methods to obtain from experiments some information which will aid in estimating these probabilities, or will otherwise help in making the required decision. We shall illustrate a typical procedure.

Smith claims that he has the ability to distinguish ale from beer and has bet Jones a dollar to that effect. Now Smith does not mean that he can distinguish beer from ale with 100 per cent accuracy, but rather that he believes that he can distinguish them a fraction of the time which is significantly greater than $\frac{1}{2}$.

Assume that it is possible to assign a number p which represents the probability that Smith can pick out the ale from a pair of glasses, one containing ale and one beer. We identify $p = \frac{1}{2}$ with his having no ability, $p > \frac{1}{2}$ with his having some ability, and $p < \frac{1}{2}$ with his being able to distinguish, but having the wrong idea which is the ale. If we knew the value of p, we would award the dollar to Jones if p were $\leq \frac{1}{2}$, and to Smith if p were $> \frac{1}{2}$. As it stands, we have no knowledge of p and thus cannot make a decision. We perform an experiment and make a decision as follows.

Smith is given a pair of glasses, one containing ale and the other beer, and is asked to identify which is the ale. This procedure is repeated ten times, and the number of correct identifications is noted. If the number correct is at least eight, we award the dollar to Smith, and, if it is less than eight, we award the dollar to Jones.

We now have a definite procedure. The mathematical model is the following. The possibility space is the ten-stage tree corresponding to the possible sequences of right or wrong answers which Smith could give. We take the outcome functions $\mathbf{f}_j$ to have the value 1 if the answer given is correct and 0 otherwise. The decision procedure depends only on the value of the sum function $\mathbf{s}_{10} = \mathbf{f}_1 + \mathbf{f}_2 + \ldots + \mathbf{f}_{10}$. If the outcome x is such that $\mathbf{s}_{10}(x) < 8$ we award a dollar to Jones, if $\mathbf{s}_{10}(x) \geq 8$ we award the dollar to Smith. We shall assume that the probability measure is assigned to yield an independent trials process. The actual measure assigned would depend upon our estimate of the probability p of success per experiment. We indicate by $\mathbf{Pr}_p[r]$ the probability of a statement r computed using the measure determined by the choice p. Thus $\mathbf{Pr}_{.5}[r]$ means the probability of the statement r when $p = .5$, i.e., Smith is guessing. The $\mathbf{Pr}_{.8}[r]$ would mean the probability of r under the assumption that he has probability .8 of being correct on each trial.

We shall examine this procedure both from Jones's and Smith's points of view. We can make two kinds of errors. We may award the dollar to Smith when in fact the appropriate value of p is $\leq \frac{1}{2}$, or we may award the dollar to Jones when the appropriate value for p is $> \frac{1}{2}$. There is no way that these errors can be completely avoided. We hope that our procedure is such that each of the bettors will be convinced that, if he is right, he will very likely win the bet.

Jones believes that the true value of p is $\frac{1}{2}$. We shall calculate the probability of Jones losing the bet if this is indeed true. This is $\mathbf{Pr}_{.5}[\mathbf{s}_{10} \geq 8]$. We find the probability from Figure 28 by adding the values of $\mathbf{Pr}_{.5}[\mathbf{s}_{10} = y]$ for values of y greater than or equal to 8. The result is .055. Hence Jones sees that if he is right he will win the bet with probability $1 - .055 = .945$ and is satisfied with the experiment.

Smith, on the other hand, believes that p is significantly greater than .5. If he believes that p is as high as .9 then the probability that he wins the bet is $\mathbf{Pr}_{.9}[\mathbf{s}_{10} \geq 8]$ which may again be found from the table in Figure 28. It is .930. Thus in this case both men would be satisfied.

y \ p	0.10	0.25	0.50	0.75	0.90
0	.349	.056	.001	.000	.000
1	.387	.188	.010	.000	.000
2	.194	.282	.044	.000	.000
3	.057	.250	.117	.003	.000
4	.011	.146	.205	.016	.000
5	.001	.058	.246	.058	.001
6	.000	.016	.205	.146	.011
7	.000	.003	.117	.250	.057
8	.000	.000	.044	.282	.194
9	.000	.000	.010	.188	.387
10	.000	.000	.001	.056	.349

Figure 28. $\mathbf{Pr}_p[\mathbf{s}_{10} = y]$.

Suppose, however, that Smith thinks the value of p is only about .75. Then the probability that he will get eight or more correct and thus win the bet is .526. There is then only an approximately even chance that the experiment will discover his abilities, and he probably will not be satisfied with this. If Smith really thinks his ability is represented by a p value of about $\frac{3}{4}$, we would have to devise a different method of awarding the dollar. We might, for example, propose that Smith win the bet if he gets seven or more correct. Then, if he has probability $\frac{3}{4}$ of being correct on a single trial, the probability that he will win the bet is approximately .776. If $p = \frac{1}{2}$, the probability that Jones will win the bet is about .828 under this new arrangement. Jones's chances of winning are thus decreased, but Smith may be able to convince him that it is a fairer arrangement than the first procedure.

In the above example, it was possible to make two kinds of errors. The probability of making these errors depended on the way we designed the experiment and the method we used for the required decision. In some cases we are not too worried about the errors and can make a relatively simple experiment. In other cases, errors are very important, and the experiment must be designed with that fact in mind. For example, the possibility of error is certainly important in the case that a vaccine for a given disease is proposed, and the statistician is asked to help in deciding whether or not it should be used. In this case it might be assumed that there is a certain probability p that a person will get the disease if not vaccinated, and a probability r that he will get it if he is vaccinated. If we have some knowledge of the approximate value of p, we are then led to construct an experiment to decide whether r is greater than p, equal to p, or less than p. The first case would be interpreted to mean that the vaccine actually tends to produce the disease, the second that it has no effect, and the third that it prevents the disease; so that we can make three kinds of errors. We could recommend acceptance when it is actually harmful, we could recommend acceptance when it has no effect, or finally we could reject it when it actually is effective. The first and third might result in the loss of lives, the second in the loss of time and money of those administrating the test. Here it would certainly be important that the probability of the first and third kinds of errors be made small. To see how it is possible to make the probability of both errors small, we return to the case of Smith and Jones.

Suppose that, instead of demanding that Smith make at least eight correct identifications out of ten trials, we insist that he make at least 60 correct identifications out of 100 trials. (The glasses must be very small.)

Consider first the case that $p = \frac{1}{2}$. Then $\mathbf{M}[\mathrm{s}_{100}] = 50$ and $\mathbf{D}[\mathrm{s}_{100}] = \sqrt{100 \cdot \frac{1}{2} \cdot \frac{1}{2}} = 5$. For Smith to get 60 or more right by guessing he must get 2 standard deviations above the mean. By the central limit theorem we may approximate this by using the probability table of the normal curve. It is .023. Hence Jones is happy.

Assume now that Smith believes his probability to be .75 on each trial. Then

$$\mathbf{M}[\mathrm{s}_{100}] = 75 \quad \text{and} \quad \mathbf{D}[\mathrm{s}_{100}] = \sqrt{100 \cdot \tfrac{3}{4} \cdot \tfrac{1}{4}} \approx 4.3.$$

In this case 60 represents 15, or approximately 3.5 standard deviations, below the mean. From the normal approximation we find that the probability of Smith being as unlucky as this is .0002. Hence Smith is happy.

The probabilities for Smith winning under each possible value of p

is shown in Figure 29. The dotted curve gives, for comparison, the corresponding probabilities for the case of 10 experiments. We have seen that with only 10 experiments we cannot devise a satisfactory test if Smith believes his ability to be .75, but with 100 experiments we can. There are of course always practical limitations on the number of experiments possible. The limitations are obvious in the above experiment.

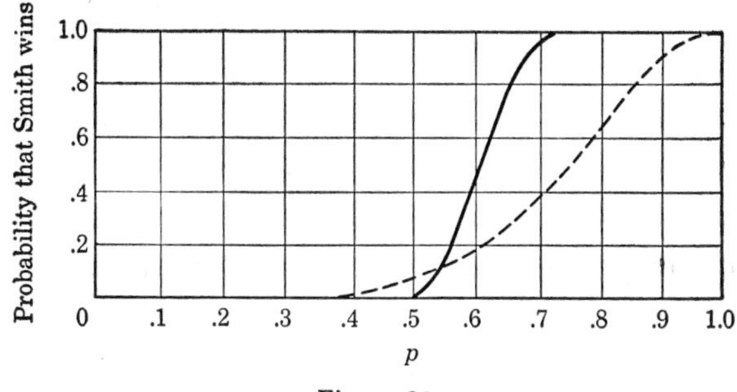

Figure 29

In each of the cases considered so far we started with a particular procedure and analyzed the properties of this procedure. More often the problem is to design a procedure having certain prescribed properties. We now give an example of this.

Example 1. Assume that a manufacturer has a large lot of goods which he is trying to decide to accept or to reject. He expects a certain fraction p of the goods to be defective and is willing to accept the lot if this fraction is not too large. He could determine p by examining each of the objects in the lot. However, this may be a very expensive procedure. It is customary to use instead a statistical test. One such procedure is the following.

The manufacturer first decides on a fraction p_1 such that if a fraction as large as p_1 is defective he wants to be quite sure to reject the lot. Assume that he chooses $p_1 = .3$. He then decides on another fraction p_2 such that if the fraction of defectives is no greater than p_2 he would like to be quite sure to accept the lot. Assume that for this he chooses $p_2 = .1$. We then design a test based on the assumption that one of these two cases is in fact the true situation. The test may of course then be examined for other choices if we wish. Under the assumption just made the manufacturer can make two kinds of errors. He can reject the lot when $p = .1$ and he can accept the lot when $p = .3$. He would like to make the probability of each type of error small. Let us say he wants the chance of each type of error to be no greater than .025.

The procedure that we use is to choose a sample of n items at random from the lot and to test these items. If more than K of the items in the sample are defective the lot is rejected; otherwise it is accepted. We must determine n and K. If the number in the sample is small compared to the total number of items, we can represent the process as an independent trials process just as in the beer-ale example. Let $\mathbf{s}_n$ be the number of defectives in the sample. Assuming $p = .1$, the probability that we will reject the lot is $\mathbf{Pr}_{.1}[\mathbf{s}_n > K]$. We want

(1) $$\mathbf{Pr}_{.1}[\mathbf{s}_n > K] \leq .025.$$

Assuming $p = .3$, the probability that we will accept the lot is $\mathbf{Pr}_{.3}[\mathbf{s}_n \leq K]$. We want also

(2) $$\mathbf{Pr}_{.3}[\mathbf{s}_n \leq K] \leq .025$$

Using the central limit theorem, (1) will be correct if K is 2 standard deviations from the mean when .1 is correct, that is, if

(1′) $$K = \tfrac{1}{10}n + 2\sqrt{n \cdot \tfrac{1}{10} \cdot \tfrac{9}{10}}.$$

The inequality (2) will hold if K is 2 standard deviations below the mean when .3 is correct, that is, if

(2′) $$K = \tfrac{3}{10}n - 2\sqrt{n \cdot \tfrac{3}{10} \cdot \tfrac{7}{10}}.$$

We may equate (1′) and (2′) and solve for n.

Doing this we obtain $n = 57.5$. The corresponding value of K is 10.3. Hence for our test we use $n = 58$ and $K = 10$. Because we had to choose integers for K and n, condition (1) is not quite satisfied while (2) is more than satisfied (see Exercise 11).

EXERCISES

1. Assume that in the beer and ale experiment Jones agrees to pay Smith if Smith gets at least nine out of ten correct.

(a) What is the probability of Jones paying Smith even though Smith cannot distinguish beer and ale, and guesses? [*Ans.* .011.]

(b) Suppose that Smith can distinguish with probability .9. What is the probability of his not collecting from Jones? [*Ans.* .264.]

2. Suppose that in the beer and ale experiment Jones wishes the probability to be less than .1 that Smith will be paid if, in fact, he guesses. How many of ten trials must he insist that Smith get correct to achieve this?

3. In the analysis of the beer and ale experiment, we assume that the various trials were independent. Discuss several ways that error can enter, because of the nonindependence of the trials, and how this error can be eliminated. (For example, the glasses in which the beer and ale were served might be distinguishable.)

4. Consider the following two procedures for testing Smith's ability to distinguish beer from ale.
   (a) Four glasses are given at each trial, three containing beer and one ale, and he is asked to pick out the one containing ale. This procedure is repeated ten times. He must guess correctly seven or more times.
   (b) Ten glasses are given him, and he is told that five contain beer and five ale, and he is asked to name the five which he believes contain ale. He must choose all five correctly.

   In each case, find the probability that Smith establishes his claim by guessing. Is there any reason to prefer one test over the other?
   [*Ans.* (a) .003; (b) .004.]

5. A testing service claims to have a method for predicting the order in which a group of freshmen will finish in their scholastic record at the end of college. The college agrees to try the method on a group of five students, and says that it will adopt the method if, for these five students, the prediction is either exactly correct or can be changed into the correct order by interchanging one pair of *adjacent* men in the predicted order. If the method is equivalent to simply guessing, what is the probability that it will be accepted? [*Ans.* $\frac{1}{24}$.]

6. The standard treatment for a certain disease leads to a cure in $\frac{1}{4}$ of the cases. It is claimed that a new treatment will result in a cure in $\frac{3}{4}$ of the cases. The new treatment is to be tested on ten people having the disease. If seven or more are cured the new treatment will be adopted. If three or fewer people are cured, the treatment will not be considered further. If the number cured is four, five, or six, the results will be called inconclusive, and a further study will be made. Find the probabilities for each of these three alternatives under the assumption first, that the new treatment has the same effectiveness as the old, and second, under the assumption that the claim made for the treatment is correct.

7. Three students debate the intelligence of blonde dates. One claims that blondes are mostly (say 90 per cent of them) intelligent. A second claims that very few (say ten per cent) blondes are intelligent, while a third one claims that a blonde is just as likely to be intelligent as not. They administer an intelligence test to ten blondes, classifying them as intelligent or not. They agree that the first man wins the bet if eight or more are intelligent, the second if two or fewer, the third in all other cases. For each man, calculate the probability that he wins the bet, if he is right. [*Ans.* .930, .930, .890.]

8. Ten men take a test with ten problems. Each man on each question has probability $\frac{1}{2}$ of being right, if he does not cheat. The instructor determines the number of students who get each problem correct. If

he finds on four or more problems there are fewer than three or more than seven correct, he considers this convincing evidence of communication between the students. Give a justification for the procedure. [*Hint:* The table in Figure 28 must be used twice, once for the probability of fewer than three or more than seven correct answers on a given problem, and the second time to find the probability of this happening on four or more problems.]

9. In Example 1, assume that the manufacturer wishes the probability of error of each type to be less than .01. Devise a test to satisfy this criterion. [*Ans.* $n = 78$ and $K = 14$.]

10. In Example 1, let $\mathbf{A}(p)$ be the probability of accepting the lot when in fact the true proportion of defectives is p. Find $\mathbf{A}(p)$ for enough values of p to enable a sketch of the graph of $\mathbf{A}$ to be made.

11. For the test devised in Example 1, find, using the central limit theorem, the probabilities for errors of each kind, that is, the probabilities $\mathbf{Pr}_{.1}[\mathbf{s}_{58} > 10]$ and $\mathbf{Pr}_{.3}[\mathbf{s}_{58} \leq 10]$.

SUGGESTED READING

The Commission on Mathematics, College Entrance Examination Board, *Introductory Probability and Statistical Inference for Secondary Schools*, published by the Commission, New York, 1957.

Cramer, Harold, *The Elements of Probability Theory*, Wiley, New York, 1955.

Feller, W., *An Introduction to Probability Theory and its Applications*, Wiley, New York, 2nd edition, 1957.

Bizley, M. T. L., *Probability, An Intermediate Textbook*, Cambridge University Press, Cambridge, 1957.

Neyman, J., *First Course in Probability and Statistics*, Holt, New York, 1950.

CHAPTER 4

Elementary Linear Algebra

1. MATRICES, COLUMN VECTORS, ROW VECTORS

A *matrix* is a rectangular array of numbers, such as

$$\begin{pmatrix} 0 & 5 \\ -1 & \frac{1}{2} \\ 0 & 4 \end{pmatrix}, \quad \begin{pmatrix} 1 & .7 & 3 \\ .9 & 0 & 2.8 \end{pmatrix}, \quad \begin{pmatrix} 1 & 0 \\ 0 & -1 \end{pmatrix}, \quad (\tfrac{1}{2} \ \tfrac{1}{3} \ \tfrac{1}{4}), \quad \begin{pmatrix} 2 \\ 1 \\ 5 \\ -9 \end{pmatrix}.$$

The horizontal lines of numbers in a matrix are called *rows* and the vertical lines of numbers are called *columns*. For instance, the first matrix above has three rows, of which the first is $(0 \ \ 5)$. And it has two columns, of which the first is $\begin{pmatrix} 0 \\ -1 \\ 0 \end{pmatrix}$. We say that this matrix is a "3-by-2" matrix, *always writing the number of rows before the number of columns.* The 1-by-n matrices are called *n-dimensional row vectors*, and the n-by-1 matrices are called *n-dimensional column vectors*. For instance, the fourth matrix above is a 3-dimensional row vector and the fifth matrix is a 4-dimensional column vector. An n-by-n matrix is said to be a *square* matrix. Of course a 1-by-1 matrix is simply a number.

The number that appears in the ith row and jth column of a given matrix is called the i,jth *component* of that matrix. When we use letters to stand for the numbers in the matrix we will often use one fixed letter with appropriate numerical subscripts. Thus

$$A = \begin{pmatrix} a_{11} & a_{12} & a_{13} & a_{14} \\ a_{21} & a_{22} & a_{23} & a_{24} \\ a_{31} & a_{32} & a_{33} & a_{34} \end{pmatrix}.$$

Observe that the first subscript is the row index and the second is the column index.

In general we will use capital letters A or B or C for matrices, with corresponding small letters a_{ij} or b_{ij} or c_{ij} for their respective components. For row vectors, however, we will use E or F or G or H and corresponding small letters e_i or f_i or g_i or h_i for their respective components. For instance,

$$F = (f_1\ f_2\ f_3).$$

And for column vectors we will use W or X or Y or Z. For instance,

$$X = \begin{pmatrix} x_1 \\ x_2 \\ x_3 \\ x_4 \end{pmatrix}.$$

We write $A = B$ only when the matrices have the same shape (i.e., if A is m-by-n, then so is B) and when corresponding components are identical (i.e., $a_{ij} = b_{ij}$ for each possible i,j).

When A and B have the same shape, we can form a new matrix $A + B$ by adding *corresponding components*. For instance,

$$\begin{pmatrix} 2 & 3 \\ -2 & \frac{1}{2} \\ 0 & 4 \end{pmatrix} + \begin{pmatrix} 1 & -1 \\ 2 & \frac{3}{2} \\ 0 & 0 \end{pmatrix} = \begin{pmatrix} 3 & 2 \\ 0 & 2 \\ 0 & 4 \end{pmatrix}.$$

When A and B do not have the same shape, the operation of addition is not defined. In particular, the sum of two row vectors (or of two column vectors) is defined only when they have the same dimension.

When c is a number and A is a matrix we define a new matrix cA, called a *numerical multiple* of A, whose shape is the same as that of A and each of whose components is c times the corresponding component of A. For instance,

$$2\begin{pmatrix} 3 & 4 \\ 5 & 6 \end{pmatrix} = \begin{pmatrix} 6 & 8 \\ 10 & 12 \end{pmatrix}$$

$$-3\begin{pmatrix} -1 \\ 0 \end{pmatrix} = \begin{pmatrix} 3 \\ 0 \end{pmatrix}.$$

And we use the notation $-A$ as an abbreviation for $(-1)A$. For instance,

$$-\begin{pmatrix}-1\\0\\\frac{3}{2}\end{pmatrix}=\begin{pmatrix}1\\0\\-\frac{3}{2}\end{pmatrix}$$

$$-\begin{pmatrix}1&2\\3&4\end{pmatrix}=\begin{pmatrix}-1&-2\\-3&-4\end{pmatrix}.$$

We use the symbol O for a matrix all of whose components are 0. To be completely clear we should perhaps append a subscript to specify the shape of the matrix. For instance,

$$O_{2\times 3}=\begin{pmatrix}0&0&0\\0&0&0\end{pmatrix}$$

$$O_{1\times 4}=(0\ \ 0\ \ 0\ \ 0)$$

$$O_{4\times 1}=\begin{pmatrix}0\\0\\0\\0\end{pmatrix}.$$

But in actual computation no confusion results from using the same symbol O for all of these, since we can tell from context which particular shape the matrix must have.

The first obvious advantage of the matrix notation is that we can manipulate a whole collection of numbers as if it were a single mathematical quantity, and hence can state complicated relationships in a simple manner. Examples 1 and 2 below illustrate how this is done.

Example 1. Consider an oversimplified economy that has three industries that we call coal, electricity, and steel, and three consumers 1, 2, and 3. Suppose that each consumer uses some of the output of each industry and also that each industry uses some of the output of each other industry. We assume that the amounts used are positive or zero, since using a negative quantity has no immediate interpretation. We can represent the needs of each consumer and industry by a three-component demand (row) vector, the first component measuring the amount of coal needed by the consumer or industry; the second component the amount of electricity needed; and the third component the amount of steel needed. All these quantities will be expressed in some convenient units. For example, the demand vectors of the three consumers might be

$$D_1=(3\ \ 2\ \ 5),\quad D_2=(0\ \ 17\ \ 1),\quad D_3=(4\ \ 6\ \ 12);$$

and the demand vectors of each of the industries might be

$$D_C=(0\ \ 1\ \ 4),\quad D_E=(20\ \ 0\ \ 8),\quad D_S=(30\ \ 5\ \ 0),$$

where the subscript C stands for coal; the subscript E, for electricity; and the subscript S, for steel. Then the total demand by the consumers for these goods is given by the sum

$$\begin{aligned} D_1 + D_2 + D_3 &= (3\ \ 2\ \ 5) + (0\ \ 17\ \ 1) + (4\ \ 6\ \ 12) \\ &= (7\ \ 25\ \ 18). \end{aligned}$$

Also, the total industrial demand for the goods is given by the sum

$$\begin{aligned} D_C + D_E + D_S &= (0\ \ 1\ \ 4) + (20\ \ 0\ \ 8) + (30\ \ 5\ \ 0) \\ &= (50\ \ 6\ \ 12). \end{aligned}$$

Therefore, the total over-all demand is given by the sum

$$(7\ \ 25\ \ 18) + (50\ \ 6\ \ 12) = (57\ \ 31\ \ 30).$$

Example 2. Suppose that a building contractor has accepted orders for five ranch style houses, seven Cape Cod houses, and twelve Colonial style houses. We can represent his orders by means of a row vector $F = (5\ \ 7\ \ 12)$. The contractor is familiar, of course, with the kinds of "raw materials" that go into each type of house. Let us suppose that these raw materials are steel, wood, glass, paint, and labor. The numbers in the matrix below give the amounts of each raw material going into each type of house, expressed in convenient units. (The numbers are put in arbitrarily, and are not meant to be realistic.)

$$\begin{array}{l} \\ \text{Ranch:} \\ \text{Cape Cod:} \\ \text{Colonial:} \end{array} \begin{array}{c} \begin{array}{ccccc} \textit{Steel} & \textit{Wood} & \textit{Glass} & \textit{Paint} & \textit{Labor} \end{array} \\ \begin{pmatrix} 5 & 20 & 16 & 7 & 17 \\ 7 & 18 & 12 & 9 & 21 \\ 6 & 25 & 8 & 5 & 13 \end{pmatrix} \end{array} = A$$

Clearly the matrix A is the most convenient way of summarizing these raw material requirements. Observe that each row of the matrix is a 5-component row vector that gives the amounts of each raw material needed for a given kind of house. Similarly, each column of the matrix is a 3-component column vector that gives the amounts of a given raw material needed for each kind of house. This example is pursued further in the next section.

The second major reason for introducing vectors is that they have an important geometric interpretation.

Example 3. From analytic geometry you are familiar with the fact that points in the plane can be represented as number-couples, and hence, if we wish, as 2-dimensional column vectors. This representation is usually carried out by means of a *cartesian coordinate system*, that is, by drawing a horizontal axis and a perpendicular axis, and choosing the same unit of length on each. We assign to each point X the column vector $\begin{pmatrix} x_1 \\ x_2 \end{pmatrix}$

whose first component x_1 is the perpendicular distance of X from the vertical axis (or the negative of that distance if X lies to the left of the vertical axis), and whose second component x_2 is the perpendicular distance of X from the horizontal axis (or the negative of that distance if X lies below the horizontal axis).

Thus, for instance, to find the first coordinate of the point X pictured in Figure 1 we draw a horizontal line segment from X to the vertical axis and measure the length of this segment. Although the segment is drawn

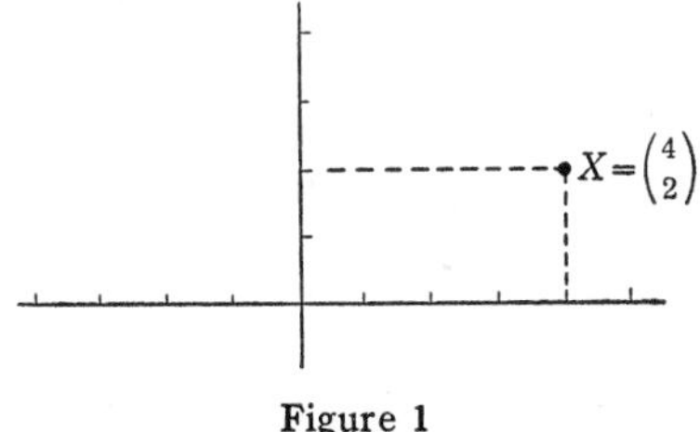

Figure 1

perpendicular to the vertical axis, it is also drawn *parallel* to the horizontal axis; and we will see below that the latter way of looking at it is in general more useful.

Let us now describe a more general kind of coordinate system, called an *oblique coordinate system*. To set up such a system we draw any two intersecting lines as axes, labeling one the "first axis" and the other the "second axis," and choose perhaps different units on them. In choosing the units on a given axis we choose one end of the axis as the plus end and the other end as the minus end. Now given a point X, we draw line segments from X parallel to each axis, and then measure the length of each segment in the appropriate scale, prefixing a minus sign to that length when it is appropriate. The 2-dimensional column vector corresponding to the point X has, for instance, as its first component the length (plus or minus) that was measured parallel to the first axis. See Figures 2 and 3.

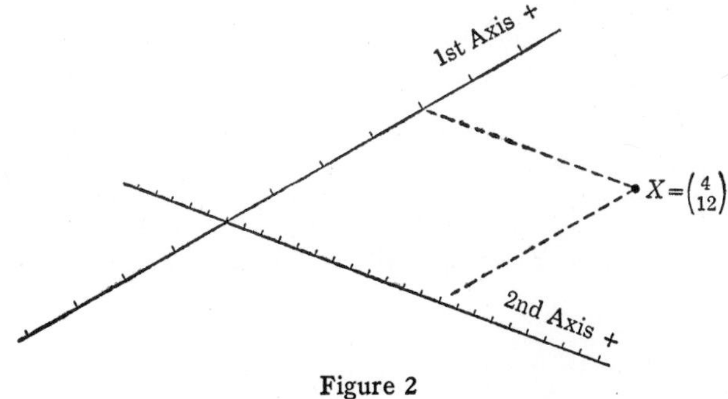

Figure 2

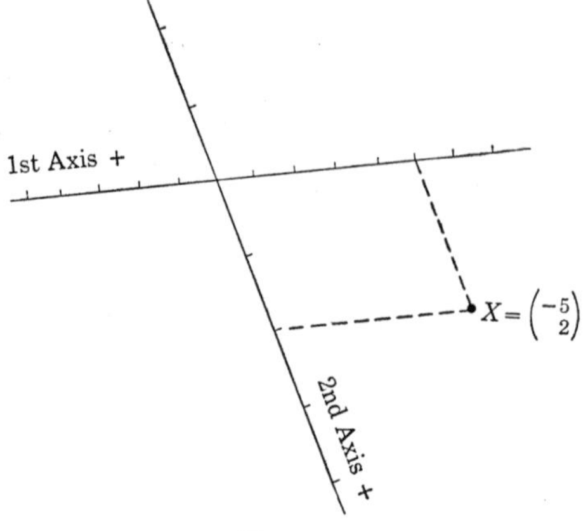

Figure 3

Standard graph paper, which covers the plane with squares, is meant to be used for a cartesian coordinate system. The appropriate graph paper for an oblique coordinate system covers the plane with parallelograms. See Figure 4.

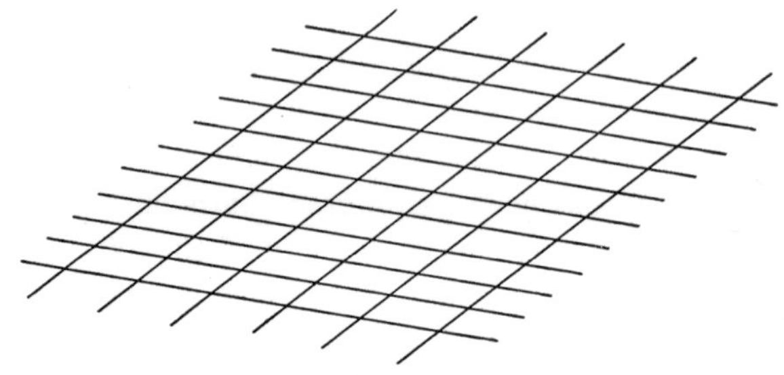

Figure 4

It is often useful to think of a geometric vector as not simply a point $\begin{pmatrix} x_1 \\ x_2 \end{pmatrix}$ in the plane but rather as an arrow from the origin $\begin{pmatrix} 0 \\ 0 \end{pmatrix}$ to the point $\begin{pmatrix} x_1 \\ x_2 \end{pmatrix}$. The most important fact about geometric vectors, a fact we will explain and verify in later sections of this chapter, is that addition and numerical multiplication have a *direct geometric interpretation*, independent of the coordinate system. If you have taken a course in physics, you are already familiar with this interpretation. Otherwise you may infer the geometric interpretation by looking closely at Exercises 12–16.

EXERCISES

1. Given the 3-by-2 matrices

$$A = \begin{pmatrix} 1 & 2 \\ 3 & 4 \\ 5 & 6 \end{pmatrix}, \quad B = \begin{pmatrix} 0 & 3 \\ -1 & 1 \\ 1 & -1 \end{pmatrix}, \quad C = \begin{pmatrix} 0 & 0 \\ 0 & 0 \\ 0 & 0 \end{pmatrix},$$

compute each of the following:

(a) $2A$. [*Ans.* $\begin{pmatrix} 2 & 4 \\ 6 & 8 \\ 10 & 12 \end{pmatrix}$.]

(b) $-B$.
(c) $2A - B$.
(d) $B + C$.
(e) $A + B - C$.

(f) $2A - 3B - C$. [*Ans.* $\begin{pmatrix} 2 & -5 \\ 9 & 5 \\ 7 & 15 \end{pmatrix}$.]

(g) $3A - B + 2C$.

2. Given the 3-dimensional row vectors

$$F = (7 \;\; 0 \;\; -3), \quad G = (2 \;\; 1 \;\; -5), \quad H = (1 \;\; -1 \;\; 0),$$

compute each of the following:
(a) $2F$.
(b) $-G$.
(c) $2F - G$.
(d) $G + H$.
(e) $F + G - H$.
(f) $2F - 3G - H$.
(g) $3F - G + 2H$.

3. Given the 3-dimensional column vectors

$$X = \begin{pmatrix} 3 \\ 1 \\ 2 \end{pmatrix}, \quad Y = \begin{pmatrix} -2 \\ 3 \\ 0 \end{pmatrix}, \quad Z = \begin{pmatrix} -1 \\ -1 \\ 1 \end{pmatrix},$$

compute each of the following:
(a) $2X$.

(b) $-Y$. [*Ans.* $\begin{pmatrix} 2 \\ -3 \\ 0 \end{pmatrix}$.]

(c) $2X - Y$.
(d) $Y + Z$.
(e) $X + Y + Z$.

(f) $2X - 3Y - Z$. [*Ans.* $\begin{pmatrix} 13 \\ -6 \\ 3 \end{pmatrix}$.]

(g) $3X - Y + 2Z$.

4. If $A, B, C, F, G, H, X, Y, Z$ are as in Exercises 1, 2, 3, what are the following components: a_{12}, b_{31}, c_{22}, f_2, g_1, h_3, x_2, y_1, z_3?

5. Under the operations of addition and numerical multiplication, matrices and vectors act in very much the same way as ordinary numbers do. We list below seven important algebraic rules that they obey. In each rule, of course, we assume that all the matrices involved have the same shape.
(1) $(A + B) + C = A + (B + C)$ (associative law for addition).
(2) $O + A = A$.
(3) $-A + A = O$.
(4) $A + B = B + A$ (commutative law for addition).
(5) $(ab)C = a(bC)$.
(6) $(a + b)C = aC + bC$.
(7) $a(B + C) = aB + aC$.
Illustrate each of these rules with the specific 3-by-2 matrices A, B, and C of Exercise 1 and the numbers $a = \frac{1}{2}$, $b = -3$.

6. Show that $OA = O$ for any matrix A. And show also that $aO = O$ for any number a. These two rules establish the connection between the ordinary number 0 and the matrix O.

7. If $\begin{pmatrix} 1 \\ 1 \\ 2 \end{pmatrix} + \begin{pmatrix} x_1 \\ x_2 \\ x_3 \end{pmatrix} = \begin{pmatrix} 1 \\ -1 \\ 0 \end{pmatrix}$, find $\begin{pmatrix} x_1 \\ x_2 \\ x_3 \end{pmatrix}$. [*Ans.* $\begin{pmatrix} 0 \\ -2 \\ -2 \end{pmatrix}$.]

8. If $2\begin{pmatrix} x_1 \\ x_2 \\ x_3 \end{pmatrix} = \begin{pmatrix} 0 \\ 1 \\ 3 \end{pmatrix}$, then $\begin{pmatrix} x_1 \\ x_2 \\ x_3 \end{pmatrix} = ?$

9. The symbol $I_{n\times n}$, or more briefly I, is used for the n-by-n matrix whose ijth component is 1 when $i = j$ and whose ijth component is 0 when $i \neq j$. Write down the matrix $I_{4\times 4}$.

10. What are the column vectors $\begin{pmatrix} x_1 \\ x_2 \end{pmatrix}$ and $\begin{pmatrix} y_1 \\ y_2 \end{pmatrix}$ corresponding to the points X and Y in the oblique coordinate system pictured in Figure 5?
[*Ans.* $X = \begin{pmatrix} -2 \\ 5 \end{pmatrix}$, $Y = \begin{pmatrix} -3 \\ -2 \end{pmatrix}$.]

11. What are the column vectors $\begin{pmatrix} x_1 \\ x_2 \end{pmatrix}$ and $\begin{pmatrix} y_1 \\ y_2 \end{pmatrix}$ corresponding to the points X and Y in the oblique coordinate system pictured in Figure 6?

12. Draw the vectors $2X$, $-\frac{3}{4}X$, and $-5X$ on a coordinate system with axes like those of Figure 5.

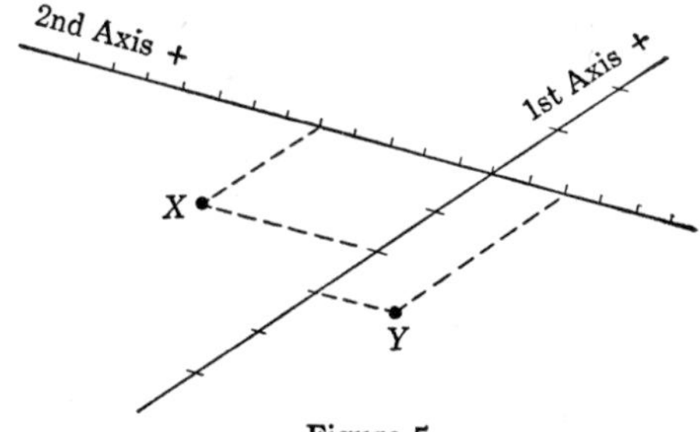

Figure 5

13. Draw the vectors $2X$, $-\frac{3}{4}X$, and $-5X$ on a coordinate system like that in Figure 6.

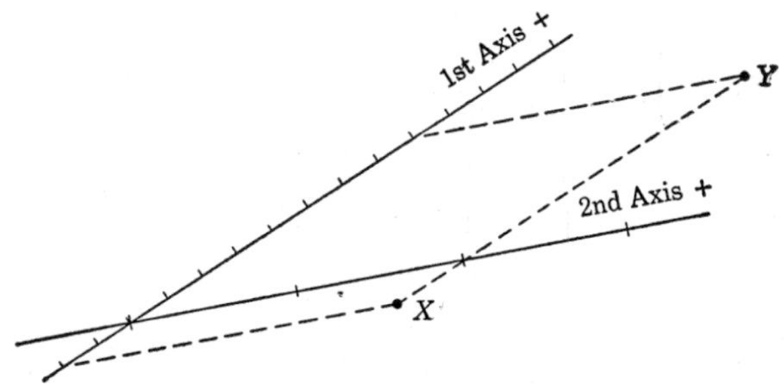

Figure 6

14. Draw the vectors $X + Y$, $-2X + 3Y$, $2X + 3Y$ on a coordinate system like that of Figure 5.

15. Draw the vectors $X + Y$, $-2X + 3Y$, $2X + 3Y$ on a coordinate system like that of Figure 6.

16. Consider an oblique coordinate system such as that of Figure 5 or Figure 6. Discuss the general problem of how to construct the vector kX for k a positive or negative number or zero. Discuss the problem of how to construct the vector $hX + kY$ for h and k positive or negative numbers or zero. Do your constructions hold good in case the axes are perpendicular?

17. Suppose we associate with each person a 3-component row vector having the following entries: age, height, and weight. Would it make sense to add together the vectors associated with two different persons? Would it make sense to multiply one of these vectors by a constant?

18. Suppose that we associate with each person leaving a grocery store a row vector whose components give the quantities of each available

item that he has purchased. Answer the same questions as those in Exercise 17.

19. Let us associate with each grocery store a column vector whose entries give the prices of each item in the store. Would it make sense to add together the vectors associated with two different grocery stores? Would it make sense to multiply one of these vectors by a number? Discuss the differences in the situations given in Exercises 17, 18, and 19.

20. In Example 1 suppose that consumer 1 doubles his requirements, consumer 2 quadruples his requirements, and consumer 3 halves his requirements. Suppose also that the coal industry keeps its requirements the same but the steel and electricity industries triple their requirements. Find the new total-demand vector under these conditions. [*Ans.* (158 91 48).]

21. In Example 2 suppose that the contractor is going to build 5 ranch style houses, 7 Cape Cod houses, and 12 Colonial style houses. What quantities of steel, wood, glass, paint, and labor should he order to fill these orders?

2. MATRIX MULTIPLICATION

Let F be a row vector and X a column vector *of the same dimension*. Then we define the *inner product* FX to be $f_1x_1 + f_2x_2 + \ldots + f_nx_n$. Notice that we always write the row vector on the left and the column vector on the right. And notice that the result is not a vector but an ordinary number. Here are some numerical examples.

$$(1\ \ 2)\begin{pmatrix}-4\\2\end{pmatrix} = 1\cdot(-4) + 2\cdot 2 = 0$$

$$(1\ \ 2\ \ 3\ \ 4\ \ 5)\begin{pmatrix}\frac{1}{5}\\\frac{1}{5}\\\frac{1}{5}\\\frac{1}{5}\\\frac{1}{5}\end{pmatrix} = 1\cdot\tfrac{1}{5} + 2\cdot\tfrac{1}{5} + 3\cdot\tfrac{1}{5} + 4\cdot\tfrac{1}{5} + 5\cdot\tfrac{1}{5} = 3.$$

The first product shows that it is possible for FX to be 0 even though $F \neq O$ and $X \neq O$.

Example 1. Suppose a man goes into a grocery store to buy a dozen each of eggs and oranges, a half dozen each of apples and pears, and three lemons. Let us represent his purchases by means of the following row vector:

$$\begin{aligned} F &= [6 \text{ (apples)}, 12 \text{ (eggs)}, 3 \text{ (lemons)}, 12 \text{ (oranges)}, 6 \text{ (pears)}] \\ &= (6\ \ 12\ \ 3\ \ 12\ \ 6). \end{aligned}$$

Suppose that apples are 4 cents each, eggs are 6 cents each, lemons are 9 cents each, oranges are 5 cents each, and pears are 7 cents each. We can then represent the prices of these items as a column vector

$$X = \begin{pmatrix} 4 \\ 6 \\ 9 \\ 5 \\ 7 \end{pmatrix} \begin{matrix} \text{cents per apple} \\ \text{cents per egg} \\ \text{cents per lemon} \\ \text{cents per orange} \\ \text{cents per pear} \end{matrix}$$

The obvious question to ask now is, what is the total amount that Smith must pay for his purchases? A little reflection shows that the inner product is the correct kind of multiplication to answer this question. Thus

$$\begin{aligned} FX &= (6 \ 12 \ 3 \ 12 \ 6) \begin{pmatrix} 4 \\ 6 \\ 9 \\ 5 \\ 7 \end{pmatrix} \\ &= 24 + 72 + 27 + 60 + 42 \\ &= 225 \text{ cents, or } \$2.25. \end{aligned}$$

This is, of course, the computation that the cashier performs in figuring Smith's bill.

By using inner products of rows and columns we can now define a useful notion of multiplication of matrices. The product AB is defined only when there are *exactly* as many columns in A as there are rows in B, in other words, only when the dimension of each row in A equals the dimension of each column in B. Thus, if A is m-by-k, then B must be k-by-n. (It may well happen that AB makes sense and yet BA does not make sense; for instance when A is a 2-by-2 matrix, and X is a 2-dimensional column vector, then AX always is defined, and XA never.) The result of the multiplication AB is defined to be a certain m-by-n matrix C, whose ijth component c_{ij} is the inner product of the ith row of A by the jth column of B. Here is a numerical example:

$$\begin{pmatrix} 3 & 1 & 4 \\ 2 & 0 & 5 \end{pmatrix} \begin{pmatrix} 1 & 3 & 0 & 0 \\ 1 & 1 & 0 & 0 \\ 0 & 0 & 1 & 1 \end{pmatrix} =$$

$$\begin{pmatrix} 3\cdot1 + 1\cdot1 + 4\cdot0 & 3\cdot3 + 1\cdot1 + 4\cdot0 & 3\cdot0 + 1\cdot0 + 4\cdot1 & 3\cdot0 + 1\cdot0 + 4\cdot1 \\ 2\cdot1 + 0\cdot1 + 5\cdot0 & 2\cdot3 + 0\cdot1 + 5\cdot0 & 2\cdot0 + 0\cdot0 + 5\cdot1 & 2\cdot0 + 0\cdot0 + 5\cdot1 \end{pmatrix}$$

$$= \begin{pmatrix} 4 & 10 & 4 & 4 \\ 2 & 6 & 5 & 5 \end{pmatrix}$$

Notice the following two special cases: m-dimensional row vector times m-by-n matrix:

$$(3\ \ 2\ \ -1)\begin{pmatrix}0 & 1\\ 1 & 0\\ 1 & 1\end{pmatrix} = (3\cdot 0 + 2\cdot 1 - 1\cdot 1\quad 3\cdot 1 + 2\cdot 0 - 1\cdot 1)$$
$$= (1\ \ 2);$$

m-by-n matrix times n-dimensional column vector:

$$\begin{pmatrix}0 & 1\\ 1 & 0\\ 1 & 1\end{pmatrix}\begin{pmatrix}3\\ -3\end{pmatrix} = \begin{pmatrix}0\cdot 3 + 1\cdot(-3)\\ 1\cdot 3 + 0\cdot(-3)\\ 1\cdot 3 + 1\cdot(-3)\end{pmatrix} = \begin{pmatrix}-3\\ 3\\ 0\end{pmatrix}$$

Notice also that an inner product FX itself can be looked at as the matrix product of a 1-by-n matrix with an n-by-1 matrix.

The n-by-n matrix

$$I = \begin{pmatrix}1 & 0 & \dots & 0 & 0\\ 0 & 1 & \dots & 0 & 0\\ & & \dots & & \\ 0 & 0 & \dots & 0 & 1\end{pmatrix}$$

which has 1's for its "main diagonal" components a_{ii}, and 0's elsewhere, has the property that

$$IA = A \text{ for every } n\text{-by-}m \text{ matrix } A$$

and $$AI = A \text{ for every } m\text{-by-}n \text{ matrix } A.$$

In particular $AI = IA = A$ for every n-by-n matrix A, and $FI = F$ for every n-dimensional row vector F, and $IX = X$ for every n-dimensional column vector X. Thus I behaves for products of matrices the way 1 behaves for products of numbers. We call I the *identity matrix.*

Similarly the (not necessarily square) matrix O which has all components 0 (introduced in Section 1) has the property that $AO = O$ or $OA = O$ or both whenever the products make sense. For instance, when A is 2-by-3 and O the 3-by-4 zero matrix, then AO is the 2-by-4 zero matrix.

Another fact which makes matrix multiplication more complicated than multiplication of numbers is the fact that sometimes $AB \neq BA$. See Exercise 16.

Example 2. Here we continue Example 2 of Section 1.

Suppose that the contractor wishes to compute how much of each raw material to obtain in order to fulfill his contracts. Let us continue to denote the matrix by A; then the product FA would tell him what orders to make out.

$$FA = (5\ 7\ 12)\begin{pmatrix} 5 & 20 & 16 & 7 & 17 \\ 7 & 18 & 12 & 9 & 21 \\ 6 & 25 & 8 & 5 & 13 \end{pmatrix}$$

$$= (146\ 526\ 260\ 158\ 388).$$

Thus we see that the contractor should order 146 units of steel, 526 units of wood, 260 units of glass, 158 units of paint, and 388 units of labor. Observe that the answer we get is a five-component row vector and that each entry in this vector is obtained by taking the vector product of F times the corresponding column of the matrix A.

The contractor is also interested in the prices that he will have to pay for these materials. Suppose that steel costs \$15 per unit, wood costs \$8 per unit, glass costs \$5 per unit, paint costs \$1 per unit, and labor costs \$10 per unit. Then we can write the cost as a column vector as follows:

$$Y = \begin{pmatrix} 15 \\ 8 \\ 5 \\ 1 \\ 10 \end{pmatrix}.$$

Here the product AY gives the costs of each type of house.

$$AY = \begin{pmatrix} 5 & 20 & 16 & 7 & 17 \\ 7 & 18 & 12 & 9 & 21 \\ 6 & 25 & 8 & 5 & 13 \end{pmatrix}\begin{pmatrix} 15 \\ 8 \\ 5 \\ 1 \\ 10 \end{pmatrix}$$

$$= \begin{pmatrix} 492 \\ 528 \\ 465 \end{pmatrix}.$$

Thus the cost of materials for the ranch style house is \$492, for the Cape Cod house is \$528, and for the Colonial house \$465.

The final question which the contractor might ask is what is the total cost of raw materials for all the houses he will build. It is easy to see that this is given by the vector FAY. We can find it in two ways as shown below.

$$FAY = (FA)Y = (146\ 526\ 260\ 158\ 388)\cdot\begin{pmatrix} 15 \\ 8 \\ 5 \\ 1 \\ 10 \end{pmatrix} = 11{,}736$$

$$FAY = F(AY) = (5\ 7\ 12)\cdot\begin{pmatrix} 492 \\ 528 \\ 465 \end{pmatrix} = 11{,}736.$$

The total cost is then \$11,736.

Example 3. The quantity $Y = AX$, where A is a square matrix and X is a vector, always has a geometric interpretation that will be explained in detail in later sections of this chapter. We give here one specific example. Suppose that the plane has the usual cartesian coordinate system (explained in Example 3 of the preceding section), and let X be the point in the plane whose coordinates are $\begin{pmatrix} x_1 \\ x_2 \end{pmatrix}$. Suppose that we rotate the plane (but not the coordinate axes) through an angle of 30° counterclockwise, with the origin of coordinates as the center of rotation. Then X will move to a new point $Y = \begin{pmatrix} y_1 \\ y_2 \end{pmatrix}$. How are the coordinates of Y related to those of X? In Figure 7 we have drawn the points X and Y. If d is the distance

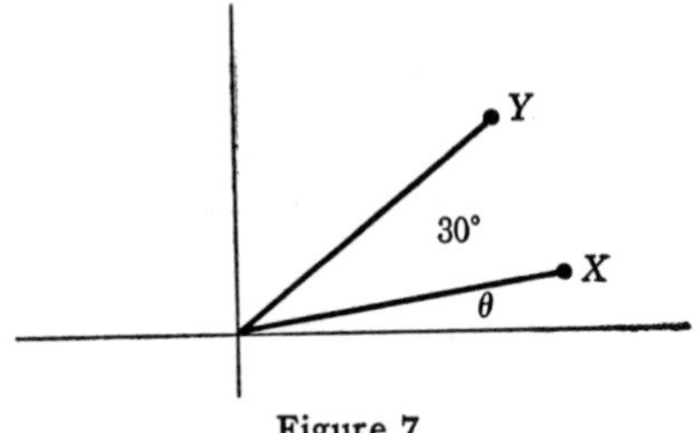

Figure 7

from X to the origin (which may be found using the Pythagorean formula) and θ is the angle indicated, then it is easy to see that

$$\begin{aligned} y_1 = d\cos(\theta + 30°) &= d\cos\theta\cos 30° - d\sin\theta\sin 30° \\ &= \frac{\sqrt{3}}{2}x_1 - \frac{1}{2}x_2 \\ y_2 = d\sin(\theta + 30°) &= d\cos\theta\sin 30° + d\sin\theta\cos 30° \\ &= \frac{1}{2}x_1 + \frac{\sqrt{3}}{2}x_2 \end{aligned}$$

But now we see that we can write these two equations as a single matrix equation as follows:

$$\begin{pmatrix} y_1 \\ y_2 \end{pmatrix} = \begin{pmatrix} \sqrt{3}/2 & -\frac{1}{2} \\ \frac{1}{2} & \sqrt{3}/2 \end{pmatrix} \begin{pmatrix} x_1 \\ x_2 \end{pmatrix}.$$

Or, if we call the matrix

$$A = \begin{pmatrix} \sqrt{3}/2 & -\frac{1}{2} \\ \frac{1}{2} & \sqrt{3}/2 \end{pmatrix},$$

we can simply write this equation as $Y = AX$.

In general, if we rotate the plane through α degrees counterclockwise, then the coordinates of the new point Y are related to the coordinates of the old point X by the formula $Y = AX$, where

$$A = \begin{pmatrix} \cos\alpha & -\sin\alpha \\ \sin\alpha & \cos\alpha \end{pmatrix}.$$

EXERCISES

1. Let $F = (1 \ \ -1 \ \ 4)$

$G = (0 \ \ 1 \ \ 2)$

$$X = \begin{pmatrix} 5 \\ 0 \\ 1 \end{pmatrix}, \quad Y = \begin{pmatrix} -1 \\ -1 \\ 2 \end{pmatrix}.$$

Compute the following:

(a) $FX + GY$. [*Ans.* 12.]

(b) $(-F + 5G)(3X - 2Y)$.

(c) $5FX + 10G(2X - Y)$.

(d) $2(F - G)(X + Y)$. [*Ans.* 24.]

2. Perform the following multiplications:

(a) $\begin{pmatrix} 1 & -1 \\ -2 & 2 \end{pmatrix}\begin{pmatrix} 7 \\ 2 \end{pmatrix} = ?$

(b) $(3 \ \ -4)\begin{pmatrix} 1 & -1 \\ -2 & 2 \end{pmatrix} = ?$ [*Ans.* $(11 \ \ -11)$.]

(c) $\begin{pmatrix} 1 & 3 & 0 \\ 7 & -1 & 3 \\ -8 & 14 & -5 \\ 9 & 2 & 7 \\ 10 & -6 & 0 \end{pmatrix} \cdot \begin{pmatrix} 3 \\ -1 \\ 1 \end{pmatrix} = ?$

(d) $(2 \ \ 2)\begin{pmatrix} 1 & -1 \\ -1 & 1 \end{pmatrix} = ?$ [*Ans.* $(0 \ \ 0)$.]

(e) $\begin{pmatrix} 1 & -1 \\ -1 & 1 \end{pmatrix}\begin{pmatrix} 5 \\ 5 \end{pmatrix} = ?$

(f) $(0 \ \ 2 \ \ -3)\begin{pmatrix} 1 & 7 & -8 & 9 & 10 \\ 3 & -1 & 14 & 2 & -6 \\ 0 & 3 & -5 & 7 & 0 \end{pmatrix} = ?$

(g) $\begin{pmatrix} 6 & 1 \\ 0 & -3 \end{pmatrix}\begin{pmatrix} 4 & 0 & -4 \\ 2 & 1 & -1 \end{pmatrix} = ?$

(h) $\begin{pmatrix} 6 & 0 & -1 \\ 1 & -3 & 2 \end{pmatrix}\begin{pmatrix} 4 & 2 \\ 0 & 1 \\ -5 & -1 \end{pmatrix} = ?$ [*Ans.* $\begin{pmatrix} 29 & 13 \\ -6 & -3 \end{pmatrix}$.]

(i) $\begin{pmatrix} 1 & -1 \\ -1 & 1 \end{pmatrix}\begin{pmatrix} 1 & -1 \\ -1 & 1 \end{pmatrix} = ?$

(j) $\begin{pmatrix} 4 & 1 & 4 \\ -1 & -2 & -1 \\ 2 & -1 & -2 \end{pmatrix}\begin{pmatrix} 3 & 0 & 1 \\ -1 & 2 & 0 \\ 0 & 0 & 2 \end{pmatrix} = ?$ [*Ans.* $\begin{pmatrix} 11 & 2 & 12 \\ -1 & -4 & -3 \\ 7 & -2 & -2 \end{pmatrix}$.]

(k) $\begin{pmatrix} 1 & -2 \\ 0 & 0 \\ 7 & 5 \\ -4 & 8 \\ 0 & -2 \end{pmatrix}\begin{pmatrix} -7 & 9 & -5 & 6 & 0 \\ -1 & 0 & 3 & -4 & 1 \end{pmatrix} = ?$

3. Consider the matrices

$$A = \begin{pmatrix} 1 & 0 & 1 \\ -1 & 17 & 57 \end{pmatrix}, \quad B = \begin{pmatrix} 1 & 1 & 1 \\ 2 & 2 & 2 \\ 3 & 3 & 3 \\ 0 & 0 & 0 \end{pmatrix}, \quad C = \begin{pmatrix} 1 & 0 & -1 \\ 0 & -1 & 1 \\ -1 & 1 & 0 \end{pmatrix},$$

$$D = \begin{pmatrix} -1 & -1 \\ 2 & 2 \\ 1 & 1 \end{pmatrix}.$$

The shapes of these are 2 by 3, 4 by 3, 3 by 3, and 3 by 2, respectively. What is the shape of

(a) AC.
(b) DA.
(c) AD.
(d) BC.
(e) CD.
(f) DAC.
(g) $BCDA$. [*Ans.* 4 by 3.]

4. In Exercise 3 find:

(a) The component in the second row and second column of AC. [*Ans.* 40.]
(b) The component in the fourth row and first column of BC.
(c) The component in the last row and last column of DA. [*Ans.* 58.]
(d) The component in the first row and first column of $BCDA$.

5. The matrix product obeys the following algebraic rules. We assume that in each rule the shapes of the matrices are such that the operations make sense.

(1) $(A + B)C = AC + BC$.
(2) $A(B + C) = AB + AC$.
(3) $(cA)B = c(AB) = A(cB)$.
(4) $A(BC) = (AB)C$ (associative law for multiplication).

Verify each of these rules for the 2-by-2 matrices

$$A = \begin{pmatrix} 1 & 2 \\ 3 & 4 \end{pmatrix}, \quad B = \begin{pmatrix} 7 & -3 \\ 4 & 0 \end{pmatrix}, \quad C = \begin{pmatrix} 1 & 0 \\ 0 & -1 \end{pmatrix},$$

and the number $c = \frac{1}{2}$.

6. If we restate the first three rules given in Exercise 5 for the important special case of the inner product of two vectors, we obtain
(1′) $(F + G)X = FX + GX$.
(2′) $F(X + Y) = FX + FY$.
(3′) $(cF)X = c(FX) = F(cX)$.
Verify these rules for the following row and column vectors:

$$F = (1 \;\; 2 \;\; 3), \quad G = (3 \;\; -1 \;\; 0), \quad X = \begin{pmatrix} -1 \\ 0 \\ \frac{1}{2} \end{pmatrix}, \quad Y = \begin{pmatrix} 0 \\ 0 \\ 5 \end{pmatrix},$$

and the number $c = -1$.

7. Prove that $IA = AI = A$ for the 3-by-3 identity matrix I and all 3-by-3 matrices A.

8. Find a 3-by-3 matrix C such that for every 3-by-3 matrix A we have $CA = 3A$.

9. Prove that $IX = X$ for the 3-by-3 identity matrix I and all 3-dimensional column vectors X.

10. Prove that $FI = F$ for the 3-by-3 identity matrix I and all 3-dimensional row vectors F.

11. Prove that $OA = AO = O$ for the 3-by-3 zero matrix O and all 3-by-3 matrices A.

12. Prove that

$$\begin{pmatrix} 0 & 0 & 0 \\ 0 & 0 & 0 \\ 0 & 0 & 0 \end{pmatrix} X = \begin{pmatrix} 0 \\ 0 \\ 0 \end{pmatrix}$$

for all 3-dimensional column vectors X.

13. Prove that

$$F \begin{pmatrix} 0 & 0 & 0 \\ 0 & 0 & 0 \\ 0 & 0 & 0 \end{pmatrix} = (0 \;\; 0 \;\; 0)$$

for all 3-dimensional row vectors F.

14. (a) Show that $AB = O$ where

$$A = \begin{pmatrix} 1 & 0 \\ 0 & 0 \end{pmatrix}, \quad B = \begin{pmatrix} 0 & 0 \\ 1 & 1 \end{pmatrix}.$$

(b) Find another example of two matrices A and B such that $A \neq O$ and $B \neq O$ but $AB = O$.

15. (a) Show that $BA \neq O$ for the matrices of Exercise 14(a).
(b) Find another example of two matrices A and B such that $AB = O$ but $BA \neq O$.

16. (a) Show that $AB \neq BA$ and neither product is the zero matrix where

$$A = \begin{pmatrix} 1 & 0 \\ 1 & 0 \end{pmatrix}, \qquad B = \begin{pmatrix} 0 & 1 \\ 0 & 1 \end{pmatrix}.$$

(b) Find another example of matrices A and B such that $AB \neq BA$ and neither product is the zero matrix.

17. Prove that if one row of the 2-by-2 matrix A is a numerical multiple of the other row, then there exists a 2-by-2 matrix $B \neq O$ such that $AB = O$.

18. Prove the converse of Exercise 17.

19. Prove that if one row of the 2-by-2 matrix A is a numerical multiple of the other row, then the same fact is true for the columns.

20. If A is a square matrix, it can be multiplied by itself; hence we can define (using the associative law)

$$A^2 = A \cdot A$$
$$A^3 = A^2 \cdot A = A \cdot A \cdot A$$
$$\cdots$$
$$A^n = A^{n-1} \cdot A = A \cdot A \cdot \ldots A \ (n \text{ factors})$$

These are naturally called "powers" of a matrix—the first one being called the square; the second, the cube; etc. Compute the indicated powers of the following matrices.

(a) If $A = \begin{pmatrix} 1 & 0 \\ 3 & 4 \end{pmatrix}$, find A^2, A^3, and A^4.

[*Ans.* $\begin{pmatrix} 1 & 0 \\ 15 & 16 \end{pmatrix}$; $\begin{pmatrix} 1 & 0 \\ 63 & 64 \end{pmatrix}$; $\begin{pmatrix} 1 & 0 \\ 255 & 256 \end{pmatrix}$.]

(b) If I and O are the identity and zero matrices, respectively, find I^2, I^3, I^n, O^2, O^3, and O^n.

(c) If $A = \begin{pmatrix} 0 & 0 & 0 \\ 1 & 0 & 0 \\ 2 & -1 & 0 \end{pmatrix}$, find A^2, A^3, and A^n.

(d) If $A = \begin{pmatrix} 1 & 1 \\ 1 & 1 \end{pmatrix}$, find A^n.

21. Suppose that Brown, Jones, and Smith go to the grocery store and purchase the following items:

Brown: two apples, six lemons, and five pears;
Jones: two dozen eggs, two lemons, and two dozen oranges;
Smith: ten apples, one dozen eggs, two dozen oranges, and a half dozen pears.

(a) How many different kinds of items did they purchase?

[*Ans.* 5.]

(b) Write each of their purchases as row vectors with as many components as the answer found in (a).

(c) Using the price vector given in Example 1, compute each man's grocery bill. [*Ans.* \$0.97; \$2.82; \$2.74.]

(d) By means of vector addition, find the total amount of their purchases as a row vector.

(e) Compute in two different ways the total amount spent by the three men at the grocery store. [*Ans.* \$6.53.]

22. In Exercise 21 construct the 3-by-5 matrix whose rows give the various purchases of Brown, Jones, and Smith. Multiply on the right by the five-component price (column) vector to find the three-component column vector whose entries give each person's grocery bill. Multiply on the left by the row vector $F = (1 \quad 1 \quad 1)$ and on the right by the price vector to find the total amount that they spent in the store.

23. The following matrix gives the vitamin contents of three food items, in conveniently chosen units:

$$\begin{array}{r c} \text{Vitamin:} & \begin{matrix} \text{A} & \text{B} & \text{C} & \text{D} \end{matrix} \\ \begin{array}{r} \text{Food I:} \\ \text{Food II:} \\ \text{Food III:} \end{array} & \begin{pmatrix} .5 & .5 & 0 & 0 \\ .3 & 0 & .2 & .1 \\ .1 & .1 & .2 & .5 \end{pmatrix} \end{array}$$

If we eat 5 units of food I, 10 units of food II, and 8 units of food III, how much of each type of vitamin have we consumed? If we pay only for the vitamin content of each food, paying 10 cents, 20 cents, 25 cents, and 50 cents, respectively, for units of the four vitamins, how much does a unit of each type of food cost? Compute in two ways the total cost of the food we ate.

[*Ans.* $(6.3 \;\; 3.3 \;\; 3.6 \;\; 5.0)$; $\begin{pmatrix} 15 \\ 13 \\ 33 \end{pmatrix}$; \$4.69.

24. In Example 2 of this section, assume that the contractor is to build seven ranch style, three Cape Cod, and five Colonial type houses. Recompute, using matrix multiplication, the total cost of raw materials, in two different ways as in the example.

3. SIMULTANEOUS LINEAR EQUATIONS

In the present section we will develop an effective general method for determining whether or not a given set of linear equations has at least one (simultaneous) solution, and for writing down all possible solutions when there are such. The method we are going to describe is one that will always work for any system of simultaneous linear equations. It is suitable for use either by hand or by machine computation.

When we write a linear equation

$$a_1x_1 + \ldots + a_nx_n = w$$

in the form

$$(a_1 \ldots a_n)X = w$$

or more briefly, using F for the row vector $(a_1 \ldots a_n)$ as

$$FX = w, \tag{1}$$

then the equation is an *open statement* in the sense of Section 4 of Chapter 2. The possibility set for this statement is the set of all n-dimensional column vectors and the truth set (which in geometry is sometimes called the *locus*) of equation (1) is exactly the set of all solutions to the equation. The set of all solutions to (1) is called a *line* if $n = 2$, is called a *plane* if $n = 3$ and is called a *hyperplane* if $n > 3$.

Consider a set of simultaneous linear equations of the form

$$\begin{aligned} F_1X &= w_1 \\ F_2X &= w_2 \\ &\vdots \\ F_mX &= w_m. \end{aligned} \tag{2}$$

Here we have a set of m open statements. Let the truth sets of these statements be $S_1, \ldots, S_m$, respectively. If we now seek simultaneous solutions to all these equations, we are merely seeking the truth set of the conjunction of these open statements. As seen in Chapter 2, we are then seeking the intersection

$$S = S_1 \cap S_2 \cap \ldots \cap S_m$$

of the truth sets of the individual statements.

Since we want only the truth set of the conjunction of the statements (equations) in (2), it is permissible to replace these statements by other statements whose conjunction is equivalent, that is, by other statements whose conjunction has the same truth set. The method that we are about to outline for solving simultaneous equations does just that. By a step by step procedure we proceed from one set of statements to another equivalent set of statements, and after a finite number of steps, we arrive at a set of statements whose truth set is easily discernible. This final truth set is exactly the truth set of the original equations and may (a) be empty if the equations have no solution, or (b) consist of a single element in case the solution is unique, or (c) consist of infinitely many solutions. The examples below illustrate each of these possibilities.

We shall introduce the method first by solving a number of examples. Example 1 has exactly one solution, Example 2 has infinitely many, and Example 3 has none. These three situations are the only possible ones since (as we will see later) whenever there are at least two distinct solutions there are infinitely many.

Example 1.

$$\begin{aligned} 3x_1 + 12x_2 + 9x_3 &= 3 \\ 2x_1 + 5x_2 + 4x_3 &= 4 \\ -x_1 + 3x_2 + 2x_3 &= -5. \end{aligned}$$

Divide the first equation by 3.

$$\begin{aligned} x_1 + 4x_2 + 3x_3 &= 1 \\ 2x_1 + 5x_2 + 4x_3 &= 4 \\ -x_1 + 3x_2 + 2x_3 &= -5. \end{aligned}$$

Subtract 2 times the first equation from the second, and add the first equation to the third.

$$\begin{aligned} x_1 + 4x_2 + 3x_3 &= 1 \\ 0x_1 - 3x_2 - 2x_3 &= 2 \\ 0x_1 + 7x_2 + 5x_3 &= -4. \end{aligned}$$

Divide the second equation by -3.

$$\begin{aligned} x_1 + 4x_2 + 3x_3 &= 1 \\ 0x_1 + x_2 + \tfrac{2}{3}x_3 &= -\tfrac{2}{3} \\ 0x_1 + 7x_2 + 5x_3 &= -4. \end{aligned}$$

Subtract 4 times the second equation from the first. And subtract 7 times the second equation from the third.

$$\begin{aligned} x_1 + 0x_2 + \tfrac{1}{3}x_3 &= \tfrac{11}{3} \\ 0x_1 + x_2 + \tfrac{2}{3}x_3 &= -\tfrac{2}{3} \\ 0x_1 + 0x_2 + \tfrac{1}{3}x_3 &= \tfrac{2}{3}. \end{aligned}$$

Divide the third equation by $\frac{1}{3}$.

$$\begin{aligned} x_1 + 0x_2 + \tfrac{1}{3}x_3 &= \tfrac{11}{3} \\ 0x_1 + x_2 + \tfrac{2}{3}x_3 &= -\tfrac{2}{3} \\ 0x_1 + 0x_2 + x_3 &= 2. \end{aligned}$$

Subtract $\frac{1}{3}$ times the third equation from the first. And subtract $\frac{2}{3}$ times the third equation from the second.

$$\begin{aligned} x_1 + 0x_2 + 0x_3 &= 3 \\ 0x_1 + x_2 + 0x_3 &= -2 \\ 0x_1 + 0x_2 + x_3 &= 2. \end{aligned}$$

Hence the original set of equations has exactly one solution:

$$x_1 = 3, \quad x_2 = -2, \quad x_3 = 2.$$

Notice that "one solution" means a triple of numbers, in other words a single 3-dimensional column vector $\begin{pmatrix} 3 \\ -2 \\ 2 \end{pmatrix}$.

The mechanics of computation is somewhat simplified if we write each equation in row vector times column vector form. In this notation, and with $X = \begin{pmatrix} x_1 \\ x_2 \\ x_3 \end{pmatrix}$ the successive steps of Example 1 become

$$\begin{aligned} (\ \ 3 \ \ 12 \ \ 9)X &= \ \ 3 \\ (\ \ 2 \ \ 5 \ \ 4)X &= \ \ 4 \\ (-1 \ \ 3 \ \ 2)X &= -5 \end{aligned}$$

$$\begin{aligned} (\ \ 1 \ \ 4 \ \ 3)X &= \ \ 1 \\ (\ \ 2 \ \ 5 \ \ 4)X &= \ \ 4 \\ (-1 \ \ 3 \ \ 2)X &= -5 \end{aligned}$$

$$\begin{aligned} (1 \ \ \ \ 4 \ \ \ \ 3)X &= \ \ 1 \\ (0 \ \ -3 \ \ -2)X &= \ \ 2 \\ (0 \ \ \ \ 7 \ \ \ \ 5)X &= -4 \end{aligned}$$

et cetera.

The operations that we perform on a set of equations are legitimate only if every solution to the old set of equations remains a solution to the new set, and conversely. Two basic operations were used. In the first we divided an equation by a number, and in the second we subtracted a multiple of one equation from another equation. That these operations are legitimate will be shown in Section 4.

Example 2. Suppose we are given the equations

$$\begin{aligned} (\ \ 1 \ \ -2 \ \ -3)X &= 2 \\ (\ \ 1 \ \ -4 \ \ -13)X &= 14 \\ (-3 \ \ \ \ 5 \ \ \ \ 4)X &= 0. \end{aligned}$$

We proceed as in Example 1, using the first equation to annihilate the first component in the other two rows by subtracting suitable multiples of this first equation.

$$\begin{aligned} (1 \ \ -2 \ \ -3)X &= 2 \\ (0 \ \ -2 \ \ -10)X &= 12 \\ (0 \ \ -1 \ \ -5)X &= 6. \end{aligned}$$

Divide the second equation by -2 and then operate with this new equation $(0\ 1\ 5)X = -6$ on the other two, to annihilate their second components.

$$\begin{aligned}(1\ 0\ 7)X &= -10\\(0\ 1\ 5)X &= \ \ -6\\(0\ 0\ 0)X &= \quad\ 0.\end{aligned}$$

Or in the other notation:

$$\begin{aligned}x_1 + 0x_2 + 7x_3 &= -10\\0x_1 + \ \ x_2 + 5x_3 &= \ \ -6\\0x_1 + 0x_2 + 0x_3 &= \quad\ 0.\end{aligned}$$

The set of solutions to the third equation is the universal set of all 3-dimensional column vectors, that is, the third equation is *logically true.* Hence we need consider only the other two equations. We transpose terms involving x_3 to the other side of the equations

$$\begin{aligned}x_1 &= -7x_3 - 10\\x_2 &= -5x_3 - \ \ 6.\end{aligned}$$

Then we can assign any value whatsoever to x_3, and produce a corresponding solution $\begin{pmatrix}-7x_3 - 10\\-5x_3 - \ \ 6\\x_3\end{pmatrix}$. Or we can equally well say that the set of solutions consists of all $X = X_0 + \begin{pmatrix}-10\\-6\\0\end{pmatrix}$, where X_0 is some numerical multiple of the column vector $\begin{pmatrix}-7\\-5\\1\end{pmatrix}$. In any event it is clear now that the original set of equations has infinitely many solutions. When we learn to interpret vectors geometrically, we will see that this set of solutions is a certain line through the point $\begin{pmatrix}-10\\-6\\0\end{pmatrix}$ in 3-dimensional space.

Example 3. We take a set of equations whose left-hand sides are the same as in Example 2.

$$\begin{aligned}(\ \ 1\ -2\ \ -3)X &= \ \ 2\\(\ \ 1\ -4\ -13)X &= 14\\(-3\ \ \ 5\ \ \ \ \ \ 4)X &= \ \ 2.\end{aligned}$$

Perform exactly the same sequence of operations as in Example 2, being careful to perform divisions and subtractions on the right-hand side at the same time as on the left-hand side. The successive steps for the right-hand side are these:

$$\begin{array}{lll}= \ \ 2 & = \ \ 2 & = -10\\= 14 & = 12 & = \ \ -6\\= \ \ 2 & = \ \ 8 & = \quad\ 2.\end{array}$$

The successive steps for the left-hand side are, of course, the same as in Example 2. Hence the final equations become

$$\begin{aligned}(1\ 0\ 7)X &= -10\\ (0\ 1\ 5)X &= -6\\ (0\ 0\ 0)X &= 2.\end{aligned}$$

In contrast with Example 2, here the truth set for the third equation is the empty set; that is, the third statement is *logically false.* Hence the truth set for the conjunction of all three equations, and for the three original equations, is the empty set. Therefore the statements indicated by the original equations are inconsistent and these equations have no solution.

The technique used for solving each of the above examples consists in replacing the given set of equations by an equivalent set of equations whose solutions are obvious. Let us spell out the form of the final set of equations in more detail. If we put at the bottom whatever equations have all 0 coefficients,

$$\begin{aligned}F_1X &= w_1\\ &\ \vdots\\ F_rX &= w_r\\ OX &= w_{r+1}\\ &\ \vdots\\ OX &= w_m,\end{aligned}$$

and then the nonzero coefficient rows $F_1, \ldots, F_r$ have two simple properties:

(I) Each row F_i *begins* with a 1. (That is, the first nonzero component is a 1.)

(II) Each row F_i has 0's at all the components where other rows begin.

Such a set of rows is called a ***reduced*** set. To avoid complicating our terminology, we will also sometimes call the whole above set of m equations a reduced set even though some of the rows of coefficients are all zero. In writing down the set of solutions to a reduced set of equations it will be useful to call a component x_k of X a *beginner* variable if some row F_i of the reduced set begins at the kth component. It is an easy consequence of properties (I) and (II) that

(III) Each row F_i begins at a different component.

The order in which the nonzero equations $F_iX = w_i$ appear is not specified, but it is usually convenient to rearrange them to have F_1 *begin* before F_2, and F_2 *begin* before F_3, etc.

If the reduced set contains any logically false statements of the form $OX = w_i \neq 0$, then the truth set of the original equations is empty and there is no solution. The converse of this statement is also true (see Section 4). Hence a set of simultaneous equations has a solution if and only if its reduced set has no equations that are self-contradictions.

Let us make a survey of all possible reduced forms that can arise, for example, from three equations in four unknowns. If we care only about the positions of the beginner components, then it turns out that there are 14 logical possibilities for the left-hand sides. We list six of these below, writing * for the components that are not required to be either 0 or 1.

$$\begin{pmatrix} 1 & 0 & 0 & * \\ 0 & 1 & 0 & * \\ 0 & 0 & 1 & * \end{pmatrix} \quad \begin{pmatrix} 1 & 0 & * & 0 \\ 0 & 1 & * & 0 \\ 0 & 0 & 0 & 1 \end{pmatrix} \quad \begin{pmatrix} 1 & * & 0 & 0 \\ 0 & 0 & 1 & 0 \\ 0 & 0 & 0 & 1 \end{pmatrix}$$

$$\begin{pmatrix} 0 & 1 & 0 & 0 \\ 0 & 0 & 1 & 0 \\ 0 & 0 & 0 & 1 \end{pmatrix} \quad \begin{pmatrix} 1 & 0 & * & * \\ 0 & 1 & * & * \\ 0 & 0 & 0 & 0 \end{pmatrix} \quad \begin{pmatrix} 1 & * & 0 & * \\ 0 & 0 & 1 & * \\ 0 & 0 & 0 & 0 \end{pmatrix}.$$

In Exercise 2 of Section 4 you are asked to list the remaining eight logical possibilities for this example.

Example 4. We again take a set of equations whose left-hand sides are the same as in Example 2, but whose right-hand sides are all 0's. Such equations are called *homogeneous*.

$$\begin{aligned} (\ \ 1 \ \ -2 \ \ \ -3)X &= 0 \\ (\ \ 1 \ \ -4 \ -13)X &= 0 \\ (-3 \ \ \ \ 5 \ \ \ \ \ \ 4)X &= 0 \end{aligned}$$

In the reduced form,

$$\begin{aligned} (1 \ \ 0 \ \ 7)X &= 0 \\ (0 \ \ 1 \ \ 5)X &= 0 \\ (0 \ \ 0 \ \ 0)X &= 0. \end{aligned}$$

Writing the variables out in full, and transposing x_3 to the right-hand side,

$$x_1 = -7x_3, \qquad x_2 = -5x_3.$$

The set of all solutions here can be written $\begin{pmatrix} -7x_3 \\ -5x_3 \\ x_3 \end{pmatrix}$, letting x_3 take on all numerical values. Hence the solutions to Example 2 are precisely those vectors X that can be written $\begin{pmatrix} -10 \\ -6 \\ 0 \end{pmatrix} + X_0$, where X_0 is a solution of the homogeneous equations in the present example.

Example 5. Suppose that after suitable row operations we arrive at the reduced form

$$\begin{aligned} x_1 \quad\quad\; + 2x_4 - \;\; x_5 &= 0 \\ x_2 \quad - \;\; x_4 + \;\; x_5 &= 0 \\ x_3 + 3x_4 + 6x_5 &= 0. \end{aligned}$$

The beginner variables are x_1, x_2, and x_3. Then we can transpose the non-beginner variables x_4 and x_5 to the right-hand side and let these two variables take on arbitrary numerical values independently. The set of solutions consists of all vectors of the form

$$\begin{pmatrix} -2x_4 + \;\; x_5 \\ x_4 - \;\; x_5 \\ -3x_4 - 6x_5 \\ x_4 \\ x_5 \end{pmatrix}.$$

Equivalently, the set of solutions consists of all vectors that can be written as sums of numerical multiples of the two special vectors

$$\begin{pmatrix} -2 \\ 1 \\ -3 \\ 1 \\ 0 \end{pmatrix} \text{ and } \begin{pmatrix} 1 \\ -1 \\ -6 \\ 0 \\ 1 \end{pmatrix}.$$

Example 6. Suppose that our reduced form has left-hand sides exactly like those of Example 5.

$$\begin{aligned} x_1 \quad\quad\; + 2x_4 - \;\; x_5 &= 1 \\ x_2 \quad - \;\; x_4 + \;\; x_5 &= 2 \\ x_3 + 3x_4 + 6x_5 &= 3. \end{aligned}$$

Transposing x_4 and x_5, and letting them take arbitrary values independently, the most general solution is

$$\begin{pmatrix} 1 - 2x_4 + \;\; x_5 \\ 2 + \;\; x_4 - \;\; x_5 \\ 3 - 3x_4 - 6x_5 \\ x_4 \\ x_5 \end{pmatrix}.$$

Equivalently, the most general solution X can be written

$$X = \begin{pmatrix} 1 \\ 2 \\ 3 \\ 0 \\ 0 \end{pmatrix} + X_0$$

where X_0 is the most general solution to the homogeneous equation of Example 5.

Example 7. There is no reason to suppose that if, say, there are two beginner variables, that these are necessarily x_1 and x_2. Suppose that our reduced form is

$$\begin{aligned} x_1 + 2x_2 \quad + \ x_4 - x_5 &= 7 \\ x_3 + 3x_4 + x_5 &= 9. \end{aligned}$$

Here the beginner variables are x_1 and x_3. Then we transpose the non-beginner variables x_2, x_4, x_5. And the most general solution is

$$\begin{pmatrix} 7 - 2x_2 - x_4 + x_5 \\ x_2 \\ 9 - 3x_4 - x_5 \\ x_4 \\ x_5 \end{pmatrix}$$

where x_2, x_4, x_5 are arbitrary. Equivalently the most general solution can be written

$$\begin{pmatrix} 7 \\ 0 \\ 9 \\ 0 \\ 0 \end{pmatrix} + X_0$$

where X_0 is an arbitrary sum of numerical multiples of the three vectors

$$\begin{pmatrix} -2 \\ 1 \\ 0 \\ 0 \\ 0 \end{pmatrix}, \begin{pmatrix} -1 \\ 0 \\ -3 \\ 1 \\ 0 \end{pmatrix}, \begin{pmatrix} 1 \\ 0 \\ -1 \\ 0 \\ 1 \end{pmatrix}.$$

From these examples we abstract the following rule for expressing the set of all solutions when there are infinitely many solutions. (1) *Bring the set of equations into reduced form.* (2) *Solve for each of the beginner variables in terms of the nonbeginner variables.* (3) *Assign arbitrary values independently to the nonbeginner variables.*

We have seen that a set of equations in reduced form has the empty set of solutions only if at least one of the zero equations $OX = w$ has its right-hand side w not equal to 0. Now if we consider only consistent reduced sets of equations and ignore all the zero equations, then there will be exactly one solution when all variables are beginner variables, and infinitely many solutions otherwise. In the case of exactly one solution, the equations (properly arranged) thus have as matrix of coefficients the identity matrix. In this case the reduced equations show the unique solution explicitly. In the case of infinitely many solutions we transpose the nonbeginner variables and we may choose arbitrary values for them.

EXERCISES

1. Find all the solutions of the following simultaneous equations.

(a)
$$\begin{aligned} 4x_1 + 5x_3 &= 6 \\ x_2 - 6x_3 &= -2 \\ 3x_1 + 4x_3 &= 3. \end{aligned}$$
[*Ans.* $x_1 = 9$, $x_2 = -38$, $x_3 = -6$.]

(b)
$$\begin{aligned} 3x_1 - x_2 - 2x_3 &= 2 \\ 2x_2 - x_3 &= -1 \\ 3x_1 - 5x_2 &= 3. \end{aligned}$$
[*Ans.* No solution.]

(c)
$$\begin{aligned} -x_1 + 2x_2 + 3x_3 &= 0 \\ x_1 - 4x_2 - 13x_3 &= 0 \\ -3x_1 + 5x_2 + 4x_3 &= 0. \end{aligned}$$
[*Ans.* $x_1 = -7x_3$, $x_2 = -5x_3$, x_3 arbitrary.]

2. Find all the solutions of the following simultaneous equations.

(a)
$$\begin{aligned} x_1 + x_2 + x_3 &= 0 \\ 2x_1 + 4x_2 + 3x_3 &= 0 \\ 4x_2 + 4x_3 &= 0. \end{aligned}$$

(b)
$$\begin{aligned} x_1 + x_2 + x_3 &= -2 \\ 2x_1 + 4x_2 + 3x_3 &= 3 \\ 4x_2 + 2x_3 &= 2. \end{aligned}$$

(c)
$$\begin{aligned} 4x_1 + 4x_3 &= 8 \\ x_2 - 6x_3 &= -3 \\ 3x_1 + x_2 - 3x_3 &= 3. \end{aligned}$$

3. Find all solutions of the following equations:

(a)
$$\begin{aligned} 5x_1 - 3x_2 &= -7 \\ -2x_1 + 9x_2 &= 4 \\ 2x_1 + 4x_2 &= -2. \end{aligned}$$
[*Ans.* $x_1 = -\frac{17}{13}$; $x_2 = \frac{2}{13}$.]

(b)
$$\begin{aligned} x_1 + 2x_2 &= 1 \\ -3x_1 + 2x_2 &= -2 \\ 2x_1 + 3x_2 &= 1. \end{aligned}$$
[*Ans.* No solution.]

(c)
$$\begin{aligned} 5x_1 - 3x_2 - 7x_3 + x_4 &= 10 \\ -x_1 + 2x_2 + 6x_3 - 3x_4 &= -3 \\ x_1 + x_2 + 4x_3 - 5x_4 &= 0. \end{aligned}$$

4. Find all solutions of:

$$\begin{aligned} x_1 + 2x_2 + 3x_3 + 4x_4 &= 10 \\ 2x_1 - x_2 + x_3 - x_4 &= 1 \\ 3x_1 + x_2 + 4x_3 + 3x_4 &= 11 \\ -2x_1 + 6x_2 + 4x_3 + 10x_4 &= 18. \end{aligned}$$

[*Ans.* $x_1 = \frac{12}{5} - x_3 - \frac{2}{5}x_4$; $x_2 = \frac{19}{5} - x_3 - \frac{9}{5}x_4$, x_3 and x_4 arbitrary.]

5. We consider buying three kinds of food. Food I has one unit of vitamin A, three units of vitamin B, and four units of vitamin C. Food II has two, three, and five units, respectively. Food III has three units each of vitamin A and vitamin C, none of vitamin B. We need to have 11 units of vitamin A, 9 of vitamin B, and 20 of vitamin C.

(a) Find all possible amounts of the three foods that will provide precisely these amounts of the vitamins.

(b) If Food I costs 60 cents and the others cost 10 cents each per unit, is there a solution costing exactly \$1? [*Ans.* (b) Yes; 1, 2, 2.]

6. (a) Let $H = (h_1\ h_2)$ and $A = \begin{pmatrix} 3 & -4 \\ 2 & -6 \end{pmatrix}$. Find all solutions of the equation $HA = H$. [*Ans.* $H = (0\ 0)$.]

(b) Let $H = (h_1\ h_2)$ and $A = \begin{pmatrix} 3 & 6 \\ -2 & -5 \end{pmatrix}$. Find all solutions of the equation $HA = H$. [*Ans.* $H = (k\ k)$ for any number k.]

7. Let $H = (h_1\ h_2)$ and $P = \begin{pmatrix} \frac{1}{3} & \frac{2}{3} \\ \frac{4}{5} & \frac{1}{5} \end{pmatrix}$.

(a) Find all solutions of the equation $HP = H$.

(b) Choose the solution for which $h_1 + h_2 = 1$.

8. If $H = (h_1\ h_2\ h_3)$ and $A = \begin{pmatrix} 1 & -2 & 0 \\ 0 & 5 & 4 \\ 0 & -6 & -4 \end{pmatrix}$, find all solutions of the equation $HA = H$. [*Ans.* $H = (-k/2\ \ 5k/4\ \ k)$ for any number k.]

9. If $H = (h_1\ h_2\ h_3)$ and $P = \begin{pmatrix} 0 & \frac{1}{2} & \frac{1}{2} \\ \frac{1}{3} & \frac{1}{3} & \frac{1}{3} \\ \frac{1}{5} & 0 & \frac{4}{5} \end{pmatrix}$, find all solutions of the equation $HP = H$. Select the unique solution for which $h_1 + h_2 + h_3 = 1$.

10. Find all column vectors $\begin{pmatrix} x_1 \\ x_2 \\ x_3 \end{pmatrix}$ such that

$$\begin{pmatrix} -1 & 1 & 2 \\ 3 & 0 & 4 \end{pmatrix}\begin{pmatrix} x_1 \\ x_2 \\ x_3 \end{pmatrix} = \begin{pmatrix} 1 \\ 1 \end{pmatrix}$$

$$\left[Ans.\ X = \begin{pmatrix} \frac{1}{3} - \frac{4}{3}x_3 \\ \frac{4}{3} - \frac{10}{3}x_3 \\ x_3 \end{pmatrix}.\right]$$

11. Find all column vectors $\begin{pmatrix} x_1 \\ x_2 \end{pmatrix}$ such that

$$\begin{pmatrix} 1 & 2 \\ 3 & 4 \\ 5 & 6 \end{pmatrix}\begin{pmatrix} x_1 \\ x_2 \end{pmatrix} = \begin{pmatrix} 1 \\ -1 \\ 0 \end{pmatrix}.$$

12. Find all possible ways of writing $\begin{pmatrix} 1 \\ 2 \end{pmatrix}$ as a sum of numerical multiples of $\begin{pmatrix} 1 \\ -1 \end{pmatrix}$ and $\begin{pmatrix} 3 \\ -2 \end{pmatrix}$ and $\begin{pmatrix} 0 \\ 1 \end{pmatrix}$.

*4. SIMULTANEOUS LINEAR EQUATIONS (cont.)

In solving any one of the examples of the last section we use at each step one of two *fundamental row operations.*

Either (1) we replace one of the equations, say $F_1X = w_1$, by some nonzero numerical multiple of itself

$$\begin{array}{cc} \textit{Before} & \textit{After} \\ F_1X = w_1 & (cF_1)X = cw_1 \\ F_2X = w_2 & F_2X = w_2 \\ \cdot & \cdot \\ \cdot & \cdot \\ \cdot & \cdot \\ F_mX = w_m & F_mX = w_m \end{array}$$

where the number c is in fact the reciprocal of one of the components of F_1.

Or else (2) we add to one of the equations, say $F_2X = w_2$, some numerical multiple of another, say $F_1X = w_1$.

$$\begin{array}{cc} \textit{Before} & \textit{After} \\ F_1X = w_1 & F_1X = w_1 \\ F_2X = w_2 & (F_2 + cF_1)X = w_2 + cw_1 \\ F_3X = w_3 & F_3X = w_3 \\ \cdot & \cdot \\ \cdot & \cdot \\ \cdot & \cdot \\ F_mX = w_m & F_mX = w_m \end{array}$$

where the number c is in fact the negative of one of the components of F_2.

Let us see why these two row operations are legitimate. To show that our second fundamental row operation preserves the truth set of the conjunction of all the equations, suppose we replace the equations

$$F_1X = w_1, \qquad F_2X = w_2$$

by the equations

$$F_1X = w_1, \qquad (F_2 + cF_1)X = w_2 + cw_1.$$

It is clear that the conjunction of the two old statements implies the conjunction of the two new statements. For if some particular column vector X_0 satisfies both of the old equations, then it satisfies both of the new equations. On the other hand, if we call the new equations

$$G_1X = v_1, \qquad G_2X = v_2$$

then we can get back from these equations to the old ones by subtracting c times the first from the second hence

$$G_1X = v_1, \qquad (G_2 - cG_1)X = v_2 - cv_1.$$

From this we conclude that the conjunction of the new statements both implies and is implied by, and hence is equivalent to, the conjunction of the old.

Notice, however, that the individual statement $(F_2 + cF_1)X = w_2 + cw_1$ is almost never equivalent to the individual statement $F_2X = w_2$. In the second step of Example 1 of Section 3, for instance, we replace the equation

$$2x_1 + 5x_2 + 4x_3 = 4$$

by the equation

$$-3x_2 - 2x_3 = 2.$$

The vector $\begin{pmatrix} 1 \\ 0 \\ -1 \end{pmatrix}$, for instance, belongs to the truth set of the new equation, but not to the truth set of the old.

On the other hand, our first fundamental row operation does preserve the solution set of a given single equation. And it is the only conceivable operation that will do so. If two different nonzero linear equations have the same solution set, then each is necessarily a nonzero numerical multiple of the other (see Exercise 6).

Having shown that the solutions to a set of equations are not altered by row operations, we must now prove the following theorem.

Theorem. Every set of equations can be brought into reduced form by means of suitable repeated applications of the two fundamental row operations.

Proof: We shall proceed to adjust the components one by one to end up with a reduced form. Properties (I) and (II) of the reduced form (see Section 3) restrict only the nonzero components. If all rows have first component 0, then no adjustment is necessary. On the other hand, if some row has nonzero first component a, select the topmost such row, say F_i, divide the equation $F_iX = w_i$ by a, thereby producing a new equation $F_i^*X = w_i^*$ in which the beginning component of F_i^* is 1. If now there is another row F_j with nonzero first component b, subtract b times the equation $F_i^*X = w_i^*$ from the equation $F_jX = w_j$, thereby producing a new equation $F_j^*X = w_j^*$ in which the first component of F_j^* is 0. And continue to operate in this way with F_i^* on other rows until only F_i^* has its first component nonzero.

Now we have adjusted the first component of our set of equations and will proceed to adjust the second. More generally, suppose that we have already adjusted the first j components. That is, suppose that no row violates properties (I) or (II) at any of these components. To reduce the $(j + 1)$th component we proceed almost exactly as we did with the first component. If all rows begin at components other than the $(j + 1)$th, then the first $j + 1$ components are already adjusted. (Note that this situation at the $(j + 1)$th component may occur as a result of our previous manipulations, and may not have been true for the original set of equations.) On the other hand, if some row F_r begins at the $(j + 1)$th component, and supposing F_r is the topmost such row, the equation $F_rX = w_r$ can be replaced by an equivalent equation that has 1 at the $(j + 1)$th component. Then we can operate with this new equation on all the other equations until all of these others have $(j + 1)$th component 0. Notice that operations with this new equation, since it has 0's in its first j components, cannot alter any previously adjusted component.

Thus we proceed to adjust the components, one by one, from left to right, and eventually bring the whole set of equations into reduced form, completing the proof.

Theorem. A reduced set of equations has the empty set of solutions if and only if some zero equation $OX = w$ has $w \neq 0$ that is, if and only if one of the equations of the reduced set is logically false.

Proof: Let S be the solution set for the nonzero equations

$$F_1X = w_1$$

$$\vdots$$

$$F_rX = w_r,$$

and let T be the solution set for the zero equations

$$OX = w_{r+1}$$

$$\vdots$$

$$OX = w_m.$$

The solution set to all m equations is $S \cap T$. From the reduced form it is clear that S is nonempty. For instance, one can set the nonbeginner variables (if any) equal to zero, and then the solution is displayed. On the other hand, each of the zero equations is either logically true or logically false. If they are all logically true then T is the universal set and $S \cap T = S$ is nonempty. So the only way of getting an empty solution set is to have a logically false equation, that is, $OX = w_r \neq 0$.

The next theorem and its corollary give information about the solution set when there are more unknowns than equations.

Theorem. Consider a set of equations of the form

$$F_1X = w_1$$

$$F_2X = w_2$$

$$\vdots$$

$$F_mX = w_m$$

where X is an n-component column vector. If $n > m$ then either these equations have *no* solution or else they have infinitely many solutions.

Proof: When the equations are put into reduced form either (a) one of them will be a self-contradiction of the form $OX = w_k \neq 0$ or (b) none of them will be self-contradictions.

In case (a) we know that the equations have no solution.

In case (b) we know that there will be at least one solution. Now, in the process of putting the equations into reduced form, not all variables can be beginner variables since there are fewer equations than variables. Hence there is at least one nonbeginner variable and therefore infinitely many solutions.

Corollary. A set of homogeneous equations

$$\begin{aligned} F_1X &= 0 \\ F_2X &= 0 \\ &\vdots \\ F_mX &= 0 \end{aligned}$$

where X is an n-component column vector and $n > m$ always has infinitely many solutions.

Proof: One obvious solution to these equations is

$$X = \begin{pmatrix} 0 \\ 0 \\ \cdot \\ \cdot \\ \cdot \\ 0 \end{pmatrix}.$$

Since the equations have one solution, by the above theorem they have infinitely many.

In Exercise 2 the reader is asked to write all reduced forms for the case of three homogeneous equations in four unknowns. It will be easy to check for these that in every case there is at least one nonbeginner variable, and hence an infinite number of solutions.

1. Show that the equations

$$\begin{aligned} (0\ 1\ 0)X &= 1 \\ (0\ 0\ 1)X &= 2 \end{aligned}$$

have infinitely many solutions. [*Hint.* The nonbeginner variable is x_1.]

2. Consider three homogeneous equations in four unknowns. Write all possible forms that the reduced set of equations equivalent to the original equations can take. Show that for each such form there is at least one nonbeginner variable and hence an infinite number of solutions. [*Hint.* Six of these forms were found in Section 3, page 229.]

3. (a) Show that the following two equations in three unknowns have no simultaneous solution:

$$\begin{aligned} x_1 + 2x_2 + 3x_3 &= -7 \\ x_1 + 2x_2 + 3x_3 &= 3. \end{aligned}$$

(b) Construct another example that shows that it is *not* true in the inhomogeneous case that if there are more unknowns than equations then there always is a solution.

4. Consider three homogeneous equations in three unknowns. Show by examples that there may be either a unique solution or infinitely many solutions.

5. Consider the following three equations:

$$\begin{aligned} x_1 + x_2 + x_3 + 4x_4 + 6x_5 &= w_1 \\ x_1 - x_2 - x_3 \qquad\quad - 8x_5 &= w_2 \\ x_1 - x_2 + x_3 + 6x_4 + 4x_5 &= w_3. \end{aligned}$$

Choose values for w_1, w_2, w_3 so that these equations reduce to

$$\begin{aligned} x_1 \qquad + 2x_4 - x_5 &= 1 \\ x_2 \qquad - x_4 + x_5 &= 2 \\ x_3 + 3x_4 + 6x_5 &= 3. \end{aligned}$$

6. Show that, if two nonzero equations have the same truth set, then each is a nonzero numerical multiple of the other.

7. The following set of equations has a unique solution. Determine which of the equations could be thrown away without altering the solution.

$$\begin{aligned} x_1 + x_2 \qquad\quad &= 5 \\ -x_1 \qquad + 3x_3 &= 2 \\ x_1 + 2x_2 + x_3 &= 1 \\ x_2 + x_3 &= -4. \end{aligned}$$

8. Consider a set of three nonhomogeneous equations in two unknowns. Show that, if there is a solution, then at least one of the equations is superfluous and may be omitted. Show that, if there are infinitely many solutions, then two equations are superfluous and may be omitted.

9. Show that the equations

$$\begin{aligned} -4x_1 + 3x_2 + ax_3 &= c \\ 5x_1 - 4x_2 + bx_3 &= d \end{aligned}$$

always have a solution for all values of a, b, c, and d.

10. Find conditions on a, b, and c in order that the equations

$$\begin{aligned} -4x_1 + 3x_2 &= a \\ 5x_1 - 4x_2 &= b \\ -3x_1 + 2x_2 &= c \end{aligned}$$

have a solution. [*Ans.* $2a + b = c$.]

11. (a) Show that the simultaneous linear equations

$$\begin{aligned} x_1 + x_2 + x_3 &= 1 \\ x_1 + 2x_2 + 3x_3 &= 0 \end{aligned}$$

can be interpreted as a single matrix-times-column-vector equation of the form

$$\begin{pmatrix} 1 & 1 & 1 \\ 1 & 2 & 3 \end{pmatrix} \begin{pmatrix} x_1 \\ x_2 \\ x_3 \end{pmatrix} = \begin{pmatrix} 1 \\ 0 \end{pmatrix}.$$

(b) Show that *any* set of simultaneous linear equations may be interpreted as a matrix equation of the form $AX = B$, where A is an $m \times n$ matrix, X is an n-component column vector, and B is an m-component column vector.

12. (a) Show that the equations of Exercise 11(a) can be interpreted as a row-vector-times-matrix equation of the form

$$(x_1 \ x_2 \ x_3) \begin{pmatrix} 1 & 1 \\ 1 & 2 \\ 1 & 3 \end{pmatrix} = (1 \ 0).$$

(b) Show that *any* set of simultaneous linear equations may be interpreted as a matrix equation of the form $XA = B$, where A is an $m \times n$ matrix, X is an m-component row vector, and B is an n-component row vector.

13. (a) Show that the simultaneous linear equations of Exercise 11(a) can be interpreted as asking for all possible ways of expressing the column vector $\begin{pmatrix} 1 \\ 0 \end{pmatrix}$ in terms of the column vectors $\begin{pmatrix} 1 \\ 1 \end{pmatrix}$, $\begin{pmatrix} 1 \\ 2 \end{pmatrix}$, and $\begin{pmatrix} 1 \\ 3 \end{pmatrix}$.

(b) Show that *any* set of linear equations may be interpreted as asking for all possible ways of expressing a column vector in terms of given column vectors.

5. THE INVERSE OF A SQUARE MATRIX

If A and B are square matrices of the same size and such that $AB = BA = I$ (where I is the identity matrix then we say that A and B are *inverse* to each other and we use the notations $B = A^{-1}$ and $A = B^{-1}$. Here is a numerical example.

$$A = \begin{pmatrix} 4 & 0 & 5 \\ 0 & 1 & -6 \\ 3 & 0 & 4 \end{pmatrix}, \qquad A^{-1} = \begin{pmatrix} 4 & 0 & -5 \\ -18 & 1 & 24 \\ -3 & 0 & 4 \end{pmatrix}.$$

You should verify the fact that the product in both orders gives

$$I = \begin{pmatrix} 1 & 0 & 0 \\ 0 & 1 & 0 \\ 0 & 0 & 1 \end{pmatrix}.$$

No matrix has more than one inverse. For if A has the inverse A^{-1}, and if B is another matrix such that $AB = I$, then $B = IB = (A^{-1}A)B = A^{-1}(AB) = A^{-1}I = A^{-1}$. A matrix that has an inverse is said to be *invertible.*

The notation A^{-1} suggests that the inverse of a matrix might behave much like the reciprocal of a number. But the analogy cannot be pushed too far. Though there is only one number without a reciprocal, namely 0, there are many matrices without inverses. In fact, whenever nonzero matrices A and B are such that their product AB is equal to O—as in Exercise 14 of Section 2—then neither A nor B can have an inverse. For if say A^{-1} did exist, then $B = IB = (A^{-1}A)B = A^{-1}(AB) = A^{-1}O = O$, contradicting the fact that $B \neq O$. It can be proved that the above situation is typical, in the sense that whenever A fails to have an inverse then there exist (infinitely many) nonzero matrices B such that $AB = O$.

In Exercises 9 and 10 you are asked to prove that $(A^{-1})^{-1} = A$, and that $(AB)^{-1} = B^{-1}A^{-1}$.

If you are confronted with a simultaneous set of linear equations involving exactly as many unknowns as there are equations, it makes good sense to ask whether the matrix of coefficients is invertible. If so, there is exactly one solution. For if the column vector X satisfies $AX = W$, then necessarily $X = A^{-1}W$. And on the other hand, this choice of X always works. Hence when we apply our equation-solving process to a set of equations $AX = W$ with invertible coefficient matrix A we must reduce to an equivalent set of equations $IX = W^*$ in which the coefficient matrix is the identity matrix, and in which the right-hand coincides with the unique column-vector solution (see the last paragraph of Section 3).

From the above remarks we can develop a general method for computing the inverse of a matrix. Let us begin, however, by considering a more general situation. Suppose we have several sets of equations to solve, but that these sets differ from one another only on their right-hand sides. Writing the coefficients as a matrix A, we have

$$AX_1 = W_1, \quad AX_2 = W_2, \quad \ldots, \quad AX_n = W_n.$$

Then we need to reduce the left-hand side only once, applying the same sequence of row operations simultaneously to each of the right-hand sides. If we line up the column vectors $W_1, W_2, \ldots, W_n$ side by side to form a matrix C, then we are really solving a matrix equation $AB = C$, where A and C are known matrices and we are asked to find all possible matrices B. These B's are formed by lining up the various column-vector solutions $X_1, X_2, \ldots, X_n$.

Example 1. Let us illustrate this method by solving the following system of two equations for three different right-hand sides, (a), (b), (c).

$$\begin{array}{rrrr} & \text{(a)} & \text{(b)} & \text{(c)} \\ x_1 + 2x_2 = & 1 & 1 & 0 \\ 2x_1 + 3x_2 = & 1 & -3 & 0. \end{array}$$

Subtracting twice the first equation from the second one,

$$\begin{array}{rrrr} x_1 + 2x_2 = & 1 & 1 & 0 \\ -\quad x_2 = & -1 & -5 & 0. \end{array}$$

Multiplying the second equation by -1 and subtracting twice the result from the first equation,

$$\begin{array}{rrrr} x_1 \qquad\quad = & -1 & -9 & 0 \\ x_2 = & 1 & 5 & 0, \end{array}$$

we find that the solution for (a) is $\begin{pmatrix} -1 \\ 1 \end{pmatrix}$, for (b) it is $\begin{pmatrix} -9 \\ 5 \end{pmatrix}$, and for (c) we get $\begin{pmatrix} 0 \\ 0 \end{pmatrix}$.

Let us now consider the particular case in which the matrix of coefficients A is n-by-n and invertible. And let us have n different right-hand sides $W_1, W_2, \ldots, W_n$, corresponding to the various columns of the identity matrix I. In other words W_j, for $j = 1, 2, \ldots, n$, is the column vector that has 1 at the jth component and 0's elsewhere. Then the column-vector solution X_j to the equation $AX_j = W_j$ must be the jth column of A^{-1}. Hence we have the following rule for computing the inverse of an invertible matrix A. *Perform a sequence of row operations on A that reduce it to the identity matrix I. Then the result of performing the same sequence of row operations on the matrix I will be the matrix A^{-1}.*

Example 2. For a numerical example let us again take

$$A = \begin{pmatrix} 4 & 0 & 5 \\ 0 & 1 & -6 \\ 3 & 0 & 4 \end{pmatrix}, \qquad I = \begin{pmatrix} 1 & 0 & 0 \\ 0 & 1 & 0 \\ 0 & 0 & 1 \end{pmatrix}.$$

Subtract third row from first row:

$$\begin{pmatrix} 1 & 0 & 1 \\ 0 & 1 & -6 \\ 3 & 0 & 4 \end{pmatrix}, \qquad \begin{pmatrix} 1 & 0 & -1 \\ 0 & 1 & 0 \\ 0 & 0 & 1 \end{pmatrix}.$$

Subtract three times first row from third row:

$$\begin{pmatrix} 1 & 0 & 1 \\ 0 & 1 & -6 \\ 0 & 0 & 1 \end{pmatrix}, \qquad \begin{pmatrix} 1 & 0 & -1 \\ 0 & 1 & 0 \\ -3 & 0 & 4 \end{pmatrix}.$$

Subtract third row from first row:

$$\begin{pmatrix} 1 & 0 & 0 \\ 0 & 1 & -6 \\ 0 & 0 & 1 \end{pmatrix}, \qquad \begin{pmatrix} 4 & 0 & -5 \\ 0 & 1 & 0 \\ -3 & 0 & 4 \end{pmatrix}.$$

Add six times the third row to the second row:

$$I = \begin{pmatrix} 1 & 0 & 0 \\ 0 & 1 & 0 \\ 0 & 0 & 1 \end{pmatrix}, \qquad A^{-1} = \begin{pmatrix} 4 & 0 & -5 \\ -18 & 1 & 24 \\ -3 & 0 & 4 \end{pmatrix}.$$

And this last matrix agrees with what we already know A^{-1} to be. Notice that it is only twice as hard to compute A^{-1} as it is to solve a set of simultaneous equations that has A as coefficient matrix, although naively we might expect it to be n times as hard in view of the fact that we are solving n sets of equations, one for each column W_k of the identity matrix I.

We have insisted above that, in order to apply the given technique for finding A^{-1}, you must first know that A^{-1} exists. Actually you can attempt to apply the technique without this knowledge. If you are successful (that is, if it is possible to reduce A to the identity matrix I) then you know that A^{-1} does exist.

EXERCISES

1. Compute the inverse of each of the following matrices:

$$A = \begin{pmatrix} 1 & 0 & 0 \\ 3 & 1 & 5 \\ -2 & 0 & 1 \end{pmatrix}, \qquad B = \begin{pmatrix} 4 & 3 & 2 \\ 0 & 1 & -1 \\ 0 & 0 & 7 \end{pmatrix},$$

$$C = \begin{pmatrix} 9 & -1 & 0 & 0 \\ 0 & 8 & -2 & 0 \\ 0 & 0 & 7 & -3 \\ 0 & 0 & 0 & 6 \end{pmatrix}, \qquad D = \begin{pmatrix} 1 & 0 & 0 \\ \frac{1}{3} & 4 & 0 \\ \frac{1}{2} & 3 & 2 \end{pmatrix}.$$

2. Show that each of the following matrices fails to have an inverse.

$$A = \begin{pmatrix} 1 & 2 & 3 \\ -1 & 1 & 0 \\ 0 & 3 & 3 \end{pmatrix}, \qquad B = \begin{pmatrix} 1 & 1 & 0 \\ 2 & 0 & 5 \\ -1 & 1 & -5 \end{pmatrix},$$

$$C = \begin{pmatrix} 1 & 1 & 2 & 3 \\ 0 & 5 & 4 & 2 \\ -1 & -3 & 1 & 0 \\ 0 & 3 & 7 & 5 \end{pmatrix}, \qquad D = \begin{pmatrix} 1 & 1 & 1 \\ 1 & 1 & 1 \\ 1 & 1 & 1 \end{pmatrix}.$$

3. Solve the following four simultaneous sets whose right-hand sides are listed under (a), (b), (c) and (d) below.

$$\begin{array}{rcrrrr} & & \text{(a)} & \text{(b)} & \text{(c)} & \text{(d)} \\ 4x_1 \qquad + 5x_3 & = & 1 & 1 & 0 & 0 \\ x_2 - 6x_3 & = & 2 & 0 & 0 & 1 \\ 3x_1 \qquad + 4x_3 & = & 3 & 0 & 1 & 0. \end{array}$$

[*Ans.* (a) $x_1 = -11$, $x_2 = 56$, $x_3 = 9$.]

4. Solve the following four sets of simultaneous equations, which differ only in their right-hand sides.

$$\begin{array}{rcrrrr} & & \text{(a)} & \text{(b)} & \text{(c)} & \text{(d)} \\ x_1 + x_2 + x_3 & = & 3 & 0 & 12 & 0 \\ x_1 - x_2 + 2x_3 & = & 2 & -1 & 7 & 0 \\ 2x_1 + x_2 - x_3 & = & 2 & 3 & 11 & 0. \end{array}$$

5. Show that the following simultaneous equations have different kinds of truth sets for the different right-hand sides.

$$\begin{array}{rcrrr} & & \text{(a)} & \text{(b)} & \text{(c)} \\ x_1 + x_2 + x_3 & = & 1 & 2 & 0 \\ x_1 - x_2 + 2x_3 & = & -2 & 2 & 0 \\ 3x_1 - x_2 + 5x_3 & = & -3 & 2 & 0. \end{array}$$

6. Solve the following problem by first inverting the matrix. (Assume $ad \neq bc$.) If a Holstein cow is fed x units of grain and y units of hay per day, then she will produce $ax + by$ pounds of skim milk and $cx + dy$ pounds of butterfat per day. In other words her production vector is

$$\begin{pmatrix} a & b \\ c & d \end{pmatrix}\begin{pmatrix} x \\ y \end{pmatrix}.$$

What must you feed her to get 40 lbs of milk and $\frac{1}{2}$ lb of butterfat? In order to get 60 lb of milk and 1 lb of butterfat?

7. For each of the matrices A and D in Exercise 2 find a nonzero vector whose product with the given matrix is O.

8. Show that if A has no inverse, then neither does any of its positive powers A^k.

9. The formula $(A^{-1})^{-1} = A$ really states that if A has an inverse A^{-1}, then A^{-1} itself has an inverse, and this inverse is A. Prove both parts of this statement.

10. Expand the formula $(AB)^{-1} = B^{-1}A^{-1}$ into a two-part statement analogous to the one in the exercise above. Then prove both parts of your statement.

11. (a) Show that $(AB)^{-1} \neq A^{-1}B^{-1}$ for the matrices $A = \begin{pmatrix} 1 & 1 \\ 0 & 1 \end{pmatrix}$ and $B = \begin{pmatrix} 1 & 0 \\ 2 & 1 \end{pmatrix}$.

(b) Find $(AB)^{-1}$ in two different ways. [*Hint.* Use Exercise 10.]

12. Give a criterion for deciding whether the 2×2 matrix $\begin{pmatrix} a & b \\ c & d \end{pmatrix}$ has an inverse. [*Ans.* $ad \neq bc$.]

13. Give a formula for $\begin{pmatrix} a & b \\ c & d \end{pmatrix}^{-1}$, when it exists.

14. If $\begin{pmatrix} a & b \\ c & d \end{pmatrix}$ is invertible and has integer components, what condition must it fulfill in order that $\begin{pmatrix} a & b \\ c & d \end{pmatrix}^{-1}$ have integer components?

15. Prove the identity

$$I + B(I - AB)^{-1}A = (I - BA)^{-1}.$$

[*Hint.* Start with the identity $B(I - AB) = (I - BA)B$.]

6. GEOMETRIC VECTORS

In Section 1 we saw that 2-dimensional column vectors could be interpreted as points in the plane. Let us now see what happens geometrically when we perform the algebraic operations of addition and numerical multiplication. Suppose we are given the origin O and the points X and Y as in Figure 8. Where is the point $X + Y$? So far we know how to add directly only column (or row) vectors, hence to add X and Y we must pick a coordinate system. The simplest choice makes the axes run through X and Y, respectively, with scales such that $X = \begin{pmatrix} 1 \\ 0 \end{pmatrix}$ and $Y = \begin{pmatrix} 0 \\ 1 \end{pmatrix}$ (see Figure 9). Then $X + Y = \begin{pmatrix} 1 \\ 1 \end{pmatrix}$, which can be described (without talking about the coordinate system) as the fourth vertex of a parallelogram whose other three vertices are O and X and Y.

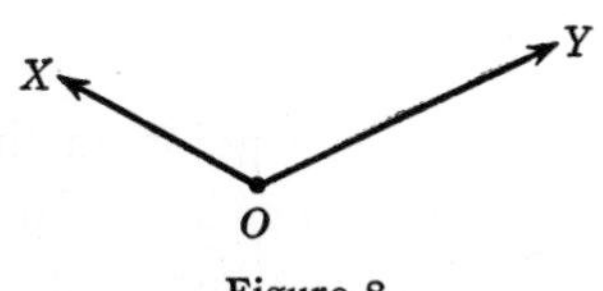

Figure 8

Let us try another coordinate system, for instance the one pictured in Figure 10. Here we manipulate completely different numbers:

$$X = \begin{pmatrix} 2 \\ -\frac{1}{2} \end{pmatrix}, \quad Y = \begin{pmatrix} 1 \\ \frac{1}{2} \end{pmatrix}, \quad X + Y = \begin{pmatrix} 3 \\ 0 \end{pmatrix}.$$

But the net geometric result is the same: $X + Y$ is again the fourth

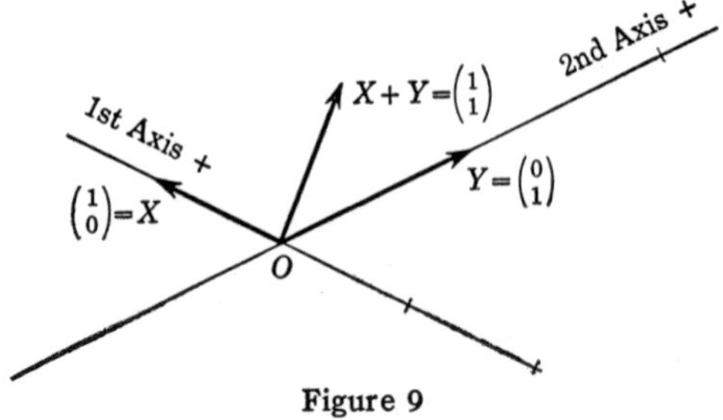

Figure 9

vertex of a parallelogram whose other three vertices are O and X and Y.

Numerical multiplication has an even simpler geometric interpretation. Figures 11 and 12 each illustrate $-2X$ in different coordinate systems. In both cases this vector can be described in coordinate-free

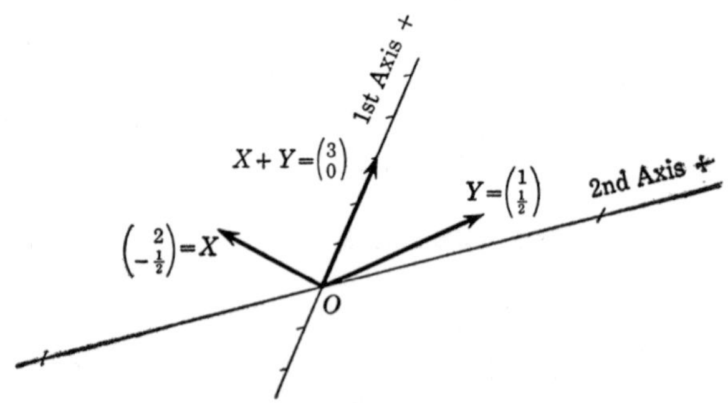

Figure 10

language as a point on the line through O and X, but on the opposite side of O and twice as far from O as X.

From the above examples it would seem that addition and numerical multiplication of vectors have purely geometric interpretations that do not depend on the particular coordinate system. Let us then proceed boldly to define *geometric vectors*, and the operations on them, in a direct coordinate-free way.

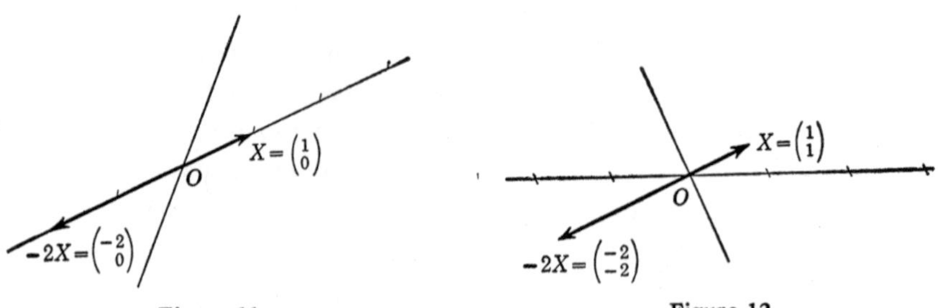

Figure 11

Figure 12

First we must choose one fixed point as *origin*. This point we call the vector O. The other points in the plane are the nonzero vectors. Often it is convenient to draw an arrow from O to a given point X and think of this arrow as the vector X. Since there is an obvious one-to-one correspondence between points other than O and arrows issuing from O, the distinction between points and arrows is unimportant. When it is necessary to emphasize one interpretation and exclude the other, we will write "point" or "arrow." Otherwise we will usually write "vector."

To add X and Y we complete the parallelogram, as described above. In case this is impossible, i.e., when O and X and Y lie on one line, then we have special rules, as follows. If X and Y are on the same side of O,

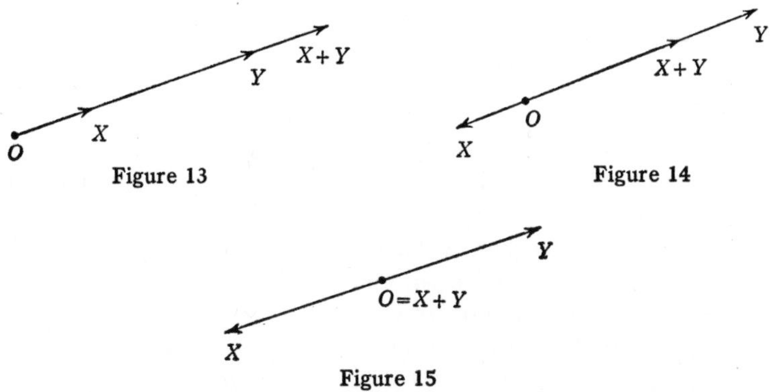

Figure 13

Figure 14

Figure 15

then $X + Y$ is also on that side and the length of the arrow $X + Y$ is the sum of the lengths of the arrows X and Y. If X and Y are on opposite sides of O and have different lengths, then the arrow $X + Y$ is on the side of the longer arrow and has length equal to the difference of the lengths of X and Y. If the arrows X and Y have the same length but opposite directions, then $X + Y$ is O. These three degenerate cases are illustrated in Figures 13, 14, and 15. We define $O + X = X + O = X$ for each vector X.

To multiply the vector X by a positive number c, we draw an arrow pointing in the same direction as X, but having length c times the length of X. To multiply X by a negative number $-c$ we draw an arrow c times the length of X but pointing in the opposite direction. And we define $0X = O$ for any vector X.

We will also have occasion to "subtract" vectors. We do this by defining $X - Y$ to be the same as $X + (-Y)$.

Which notions from high school geometry have we used in defining geometric vectors? Essentially only four:

(1) We can recognize certain special subsets of the plane, called *lines.*
(2) We know when two lines are *parallel.*
(3) Given two points on a line we can recognize the *segment* of points that lies between them.
(4) We can *compare the lengths* of *parallel* segments.

(And, as a matter of fact, only these four notions were used in Section 1 to construct oblique coordinate systems.) Never in the present section (and never in constructing an oblique coordinate system) do we need to compare the lengths of nonparallel segments, and we do not ever consider the angle between intersecting lines. On the other hand, we made use of both these ideas in constructing a cartesian coordinate system.

The notion of angle and the unrestricted notion of length are commonly felt to be part of the structure of the ordinary space we live in. Yet it is easy to invent practical examples in which these two notions must be ignored.

Example 1. Suppose, for instance, that a reconnaissance plane brings back a photograph of enemy fortifications that looks like Figure 16. In the figure, the points labeled X, Y, Z, and W are pillboxes and the lines connecting them are trenches. Assume that the camera is so crude that it shows only a bare ground plan; and assume that we do not know the position from which the picture was taken. Then we can be sure of the following facts: (1) all the trenches are laid out in straight lines, (2) the trench joining pillboxes W and X is parallel to the trench joining pillboxes

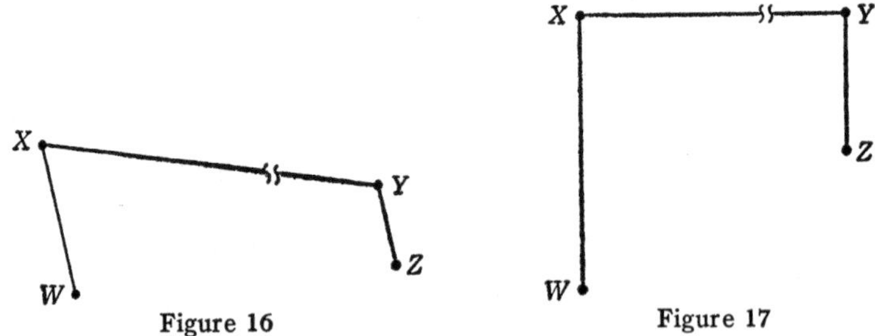

Figure 16 Figure 17

Y and Z, (3) there is a break in the trench between X and Y, (4) the distance between W and X is twice the distance between Y and Z.

Later, having captured the fortifications, we may discover that they really look like Figure 17. In particular, (5) all angles are right angles, (6) X is equidistant from W and Y. But there is no hope of deducing these last two facts from the aerial photograph alone.

It is, of course, also possible to define *three*-dimensional geometric vectors. We choose one particular point in 3-dimensional space as the origin O, and we define the nonzero vectors to be the other points (or arrows issuing from O). Then the definitions of addition and numerical multiplication are exactly what they were for 2-dimensional geometric vectors. In fact we scarcely need to think 3-dimensionally at all. For in adding vectors X and Y not collinear with O we restrict our attention to the plane determined by O and X and Y, and complete the parallelogram in this plane. Similarly, in numerical multiplication, or in the degenerate cases of addition illustrated in Figures 13, 14, and 15, we restrict our attention to a certain line.

EXERCISES

1. Draw a figure like Figure 18 and construct the following vectors.

(a) $X + Y$.
(b) $X + Z$.
(c) $Y + Z$.
(d) $Z + X$.

Figure 18

2. Draw a figure like that of Figure 18 and construct the vectors

(a) $(X + Y) + Z$.
(b) $X + (Y + Z)$.

and compare your results.

3. In a figure like Figure 18, find

(a) $3X$.
(b) $\frac{1}{2}Y$.
(c) $-Z$.
(d) $X - Y$.
(e) $3X - Z$.

4. Prove for any vector X and any pair of numbers c_1, c_2 that $c_2(c_1X) = (c_2c_1)X$. [*Hint.* Divide the problem into cases that depend on the signs of c_1 and c_2.]

5. In a figure like Figure 18, choose a coordinate system whose axes run through X and Z.

(a) Express X and Y in this coordinate system.
(b) Express $X + Y$, as found in Exercise 1(a), in this coordinate system.
(c) Check your answer by numerical vector addition.

6. In a figure like Figure 18 find $3(X + Y)$ and $3X + 3Y$. Present a geometrical argument to prove that these two vectors are the same.

7. In a figure like Figure 18 choose a convenient coordinate system, and use it to prove the result of Exercise 6 numerically.

8. In a figure like Figure 19 find

   (a) $X + Y$.
   (b) $X - Y$.
   (c) $2X + 3Y$.

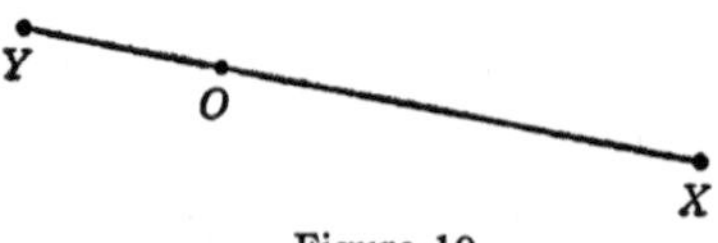

Figure 19

9. In a figure like Figure 19 find $3(X + Y)$ and $3X + 3Y$. Present a geometric argument to prove that the two resulting vectors are the same.

10. In a figure like Figure 19 determine c_1, c_2 so that $O = c_1X + c_2Y$, and $c_1 + c_2 = 1$.

7. ABSTRACT VECTOR SPACES

You may be inclined to ask at this point whether vectors are "really" columns and rows of numbers, or geometrical objects? And what right has a physicist to speak of velocities and forces as vectors? Mathematicians dodge such questions by refusing to consider the nature of the individual vectors and instead concentrating their attention upon how the totality of vectors in a given problem acts with respect to addition and numerical multiplication. The best way to do this is to write down a reasonable set of axioms for an abstract mathematical structure, called a *vector space*, that has all the important algebraic properties common to the various concrete collections of vectors (numerical, geometrical, physical) that we have mentioned.

A *vector space* is any set of objects $X, Y, Z, \ldots$ called *vectors* that can be "added" to each other and "multiplied" by real numbers a, b, $c, \ldots$ — the resulting sums and products being again vectors in the vector space — provided that these abstract operations of addition and multiplication obey certain of the laws of ordinary arithmetic, to wit:

(1) Triple sums can be computed from the left or from the right. That is, $(X + Y) + Z = X + (Y + Z)$.
(2) There is a special vector called O with the property that $O + X = X$, for every vector X.
(3) The numerical multiple $(-1)X$ acts like the "negative" of X. That is, $(-1)X + X = O$. And hence we usually write $(-1)X = -X$.
(4) Sums can be computed in either order. That is, $X + Y = Y + X$.
(5) Repeated numerical multiples can be computed from the left or

from the right. That is, $a(bX) = (ab)X$. Notice the resemblance of this rule to rule (1).

(6) The multiple of a vector by a sum of numbers acts like ordinary multiplication. That is, $(a + b)X = aX + bX$.

(7) The multiple of a sum of vectors by a number acts like ordinary multiplication. That is, $a(X + Y) = aX + aY$.

Other important rules can be derived from the rules (1) through (7). For instance, $-(-X) = X$. For by rule (3), $-(-X) + (-X) = O$. Hence, adding X to both sides,

$$(-(-X) + (-X)) + X = X.$$

Now by rule (1) the left-hand side of this last expression equals $-(-X) + ((-X) + X)$, which by rule (3) equals $-(-X) + O$, and then by rules (2) and (4) equals $-(-X)$.

Let us also prove the fact that the number 1 behaves well as a multiplier, i.e., $1X = X$. It is enough to prove that $((-1)(-1))X = X$. By rule (5), the left-hand side equals $(-1)((-1)X)$, which we have agreed in rule (3) to write $-(-X)$. And we have just proved this last equal to X. To summarize this proof we restate the steps thus:

$$1X = ((-1)(-1))X = (-1)((-1)X) = -(-X) = X.$$

Example 1. The space $\mathfrak{X}_n$ of n-dimensional column vectors. The seven axioms are identical with the seven rules listed in Exercise 5 of Section 1. The proof that column vectors obey these rules is done in two steps: first, the operations of addition and numerical multiplication of column vectors are both performed component by component; second, an individual component is simply a number, and numbers are well known to obey the seven rules.

Example 2. The space of plane geometrical vectors. Before verifying the seven axioms it will be useful to mention a method equivalent to the one discussed in Section 6 for adding Y to X. We draw an auxiliary arrow having the same length and direction as Y but issuing from the tip of X.

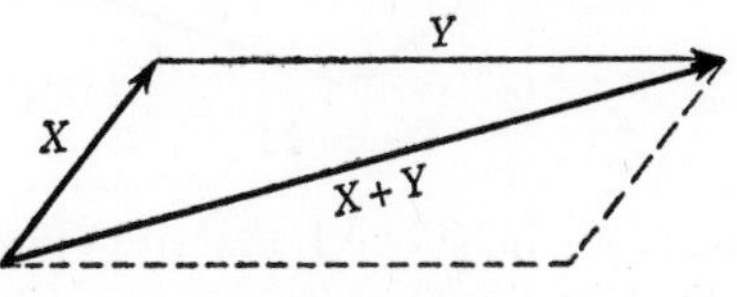

Figure 20

Then $X + Y$ is the arrow from the origin to the tip of this auxiliary arrow. In Figure 20 we have not drawn Y itself, but instead have attached the label Y to the auxiliary arrow.

It is obvious that this method of addition gives the same result as the method discussed in Section 6 because if we complete the parallelogram (see the dotted lines in Figure 20) then the arrow $X + Y$ *is* the diagonal of the parallelogram.

Axiom 1 is now verified in Figure 21. Again, we have attached the labels Y and Z to appropriate auxiliary arrows. Once this axiom is verified we can write $X + Y + Z$ without parentheses. This triple sum has the direct geometrical interpretation pictured in Figure 21.

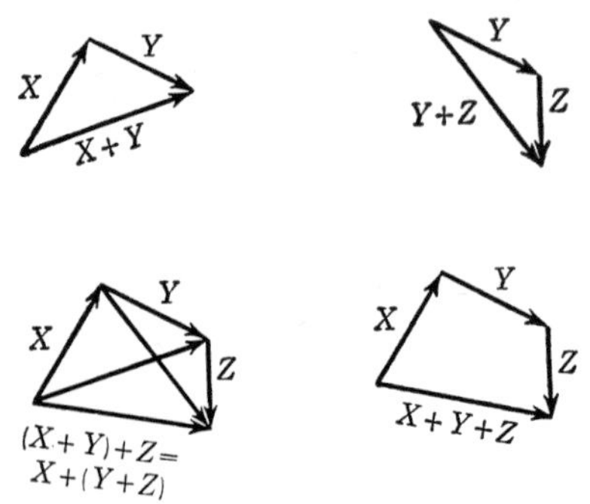

Figure 21

Axiom 2 is true because we have defined $O + X = X + O = X$.

Axiom 3 is a consequence of our definition of $-1X$ (namely, as a vector having the same length as X but pointing in the opposite direction) and of our definition of addition in the degenerate cases where the two vectors do not form a true parallelogram. This axiom states informally that if we walk from one end of a line segment to the other, and then walk back again, the net result is the same as if we had not moved at all.

Axiom 4 corresponds to the situation pictured in Figure 22, and its validity is a consequence of well-known facts about parallelograms.

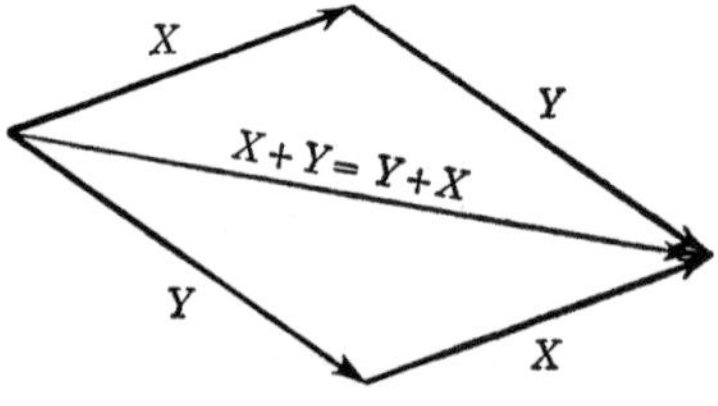

Figure 22

To check Axiom 5 we must check that $a(bX)$ has the same length and direction as $(ab)X$. The directions are the same because they are either both in the same direction as X (in the case when a and b have like sign, i.e., both positive or both negative) or else both in the direction opposite to that of X (in the case where a and b have unlike sign). The lengths, moreover, are both equal to ab times the length of X (when $ab > 0$) or else to $-ab$ times the length of X (when $ab < 0$).

Axiom 6 operates in terms of multiples of one vector X, hence its validity depends on the fact that $(a + b)c = ac + bc$ is true for ordinary numbers, c being interpreted here as the length of X.

Axiom 7 is verified by considering the similar triangles in Figure 23.

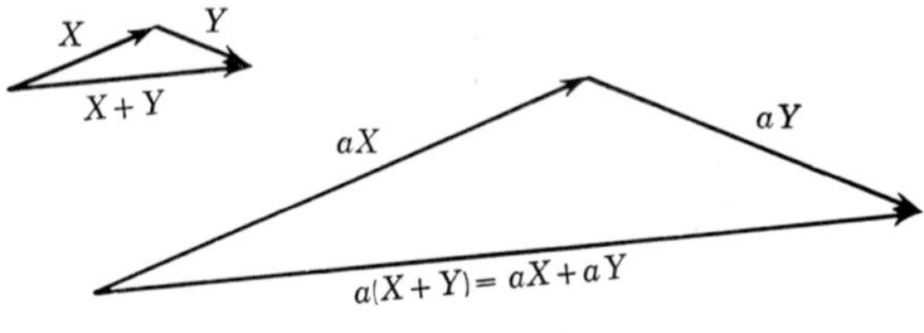

Figure 23

In verifying each of the seven axioms, we should also consider the cases where some or all of the vectors and numbers are zero. These cases are hard to picture geometrically, but it is easy to see that none of them disturbs the validity of the axioms. For instance, in Axiom 5, if either a or b is 0 or if X is O, then both $a(bX)$ and $(ab)X$ are O.

Example 3. Let $\mathcal{U}$ be a finite set, and let $\mathcal{X}$ be all numerical functions that have $\mathcal{U}$ as domain. Define the sum of two functions $\mathbf{X} + \mathbf{Y}$ and the numerical product $c\mathbf{X}$ as in Section 6 of Chapter 2. With these two definitions the set $\mathcal{X}$ becomes a vector space. It is easy to verify the seven axioms directly. But it is even easier to observe that when $\mathcal{U}$ contains n points there is a natural one-one correspondence between numerical functions $\mathbf{X}$ on $\mathcal{U}$ and n-dimensional column vectors. If $\mathbf{X}$ is defined by the table

u	$\mathbf{X}(u)$
u_1	a_1
u_2	a_2
$\cdot$	$\cdot$
$\cdot$	$\cdot$
$\cdot$	$\cdot$
u_n	a_n

then we make correspond to $\mathbf{X}$ the column vector

$$\begin{pmatrix} a_1 \\ a_2 \\ \cdot \\ \cdot \\ \cdot \\ a_n \end{pmatrix}.$$

For instance, that is the way the functions **f** and **g** were defined in Figure 12 of Section 6 of Chapter 2.

From the definition of addition of numerical functions it is clear that if the column vector

$$\begin{pmatrix} a_1 \\ a_2 \\ \cdot \\ \cdot \\ \cdot \\ a_n \end{pmatrix}$$

corresponds to the function **X** and if the column vector

$$\begin{pmatrix} b_1 \\ b_2 \\ \cdot \\ \cdot \\ \cdot \\ b_n \end{pmatrix}$$

corresponds to the function **Y**, then the column vector

$$\begin{pmatrix} a_1 + b_1 \\ \cdot \\ \cdot \\ \cdot \\ a_n + b_n \end{pmatrix}$$

corresponds to the function $\mathbf{X} + \mathbf{Y}$. An example of this kind of addition is given by the function $\mathbf{h} = \mathbf{f} + \mathbf{g}$ in Figure 12 of Chapter 2.

Similarly

corresponds to $c\mathbf{X}$. And since we already know that the set of n-dimensional column vectors satisfies the axioms, then so must the set of numerical functions on $\mathcal{U}$.

EXERCISES

1. Is the following a vector space? Let $\mathcal{X}$ be the set of all positive numbers. Define the abstract "addition" to be the same as ordinary multiplication. And if c is a number and X a "vector," define the abstract numerical product to be the same as the ordinary number X to the cth power. [*Ans.* Yes.]
2. Verify informally that the space of 3-dimensional geometrical vectors obeys the vector space axioms.

3. Show that the vector O described in Axiom 2 is unique. That is, no abstract vector space possesses two different vectors O_1 and O_2 fulfilling the requirements of Axiom 2.

4. Show by using Axiom 6 that $0X = O$.

5. Show by using Axiom 7 that $cO = O$.

6. Show that if $cX = O$, then either $c = 0$ or else $X = O$.

7. Show that the set of ordinary real numbers forms a vector space.

8. Is it possible for a vector space to contain only finitely many vectors, but more than one? [*Ans.* No.]

9. Let $\mathfrak{X}$ be any one-element set. Show how to define addition and numerical multiplication in such a way that $\mathfrak{X}$ becomes a vector space.

10. In Example 3 let us restrict our functions to those having nonnegative values. Is the resulting space a vector space? [*Ans.* No.]

11. Let $\mathfrak{X}$ be the space of all 3 by 2 matrices, with addition and numerical multiplication defined as usual. Is $\mathfrak{X}$ a vector space?

12. Let $\mathfrak{X}$ consist of that subset of $\mathfrak{X}_3$ in which each column vector has the second component equal to 0. Show that $\mathfrak{X}$ is a vector space.

13. Let $\mathfrak{X}$ consist of that subset of $\mathfrak{X}_3$ in which each column vector has second component equal to 1. Show that $\mathfrak{X}$ is *not* a vector space.

8. LINEAR TRANSFORMATIONS

A function $\mathbf{f}$ whose domain and range are vector spaces is *linear* if it satisfies the following two axioms:

(1) $\mathbf{f}(X + Y) = \mathbf{f}(X) + \mathbf{f}(Y)$, for every X and Y in the domain.
(2) $\mathbf{f}(cX) = c\mathbf{f}(X)$, for every X in the domain and every number c.

We will henceforth use the word *transformation* to mean linear function, and will use the word *functional* to mean a numerical linear function. We will use the letters $\mathbf{A}$, $\mathbf{B}$, $\mathbf{C}$ for transformations and the letters $\mathbf{F}$, $\mathbf{G}$, $\mathbf{H}$ for functionals. The choice of these letters is dictated by the fact (proved later) that every transformation on a space of column vectors can be defined by a matrix and every functional by a row vector.

For the value of the transformation $\mathbf{A}$ at the vector X we will write $\mathbf{A}X$ instead of the usual function notation $\mathbf{A}(X)$. Similarly $\mathbf{F}X$. And when $\mathbf{A}X = Y$, we will often write $X \xrightarrow{\mathbf{A}} Y$ or simply $X \to Y$.

Example 1. The following rule defines a linear transformation $\mathbf{A}$ whose domain is the space $\mathfrak{X}_3$ of 3-dimensional column vectors and whose range is the space $\mathfrak{X}_2$ of 2-dimensional column vectors.

$$\begin{pmatrix} x_1 \\ x_2 \\ x_3 \end{pmatrix} \to \begin{pmatrix} x_1 - x_3 \\ 3x_1 + 2x_2 + x_3 \end{pmatrix}.$$

It is easy to see that

$$\mathbf{A}\begin{pmatrix} x_1 + y_1 \\ x_2 + y_2 \\ x_3 + y_3 \end{pmatrix} = \mathbf{A}\begin{pmatrix} x_1 \\ x_2 \\ x_3 \end{pmatrix} + \mathbf{A}\begin{pmatrix} y_1 \\ y_2 \\ y_3 \end{pmatrix}.$$

And it is easy to see that

$$\mathbf{A}\begin{pmatrix} cx_1 \\ cx_2 \\ cx_3 \end{pmatrix} = c\mathbf{A}\begin{pmatrix} x_1 \\ x_2 \\ x_3 \end{pmatrix}.$$

The fact that $\mathbf{A}$ has as range the whole space of 2-dimensional column vectors is equivalent to the fact that the simultaneous equations

$$\begin{aligned} x_1 \qquad\quad - x_3 &= c_1 \\ 3x_1 + 2x_2 + x_3 &= c_2 \end{aligned}$$

have a solution for every choice of numbers c_1 and c_2 on the right-hand side.

Notice that the transformation $\mathbf{A}$ can be defined by means of the matrix

$$A = \begin{pmatrix} 1 & 0 & -1 \\ 3 & 2 & 1 \end{pmatrix}$$

That is, when $X = \begin{pmatrix} x_1 \\ x_2 \\ x_3 \end{pmatrix}$, then

$$\mathbf{A}X = \begin{pmatrix} 1 & 0 & -1 \\ 3 & 2 & 1 \end{pmatrix}\begin{pmatrix} x_1 \\ x_2 \\ x_3 \end{pmatrix}.$$

Example 2. Let $\mathfrak{X}$ be the vector space of vectors in the plane. Let $\mathfrak{L}$ be a fixed line through the origin. Define $\mathbf{A}$ to be the *reflection* of $\mathfrak{X}$ across the line $\mathfrak{L}$. That is, the point X and the image point $\mathbf{A}X$ are the same distance from $\mathfrak{L}$ but on opposite sides, and the line segment joining X and $\mathbf{A}X$ is perpendicular to $\mathfrak{L}$. See Figure 24.

The fact that $\mathbf{A}(X + Y) = \mathbf{A}X + \mathbf{A}Y$ is illustrated in Figure 25.

And the fact that $\mathbf{A}(cX) = c\mathbf{A}X$ is illustrated in Figure 26.

The above example disobeys the strictures against angle and length that we imposed in Section 6. In order to give interesting geometric examples of transformations we are in fact forced to recognize properties of the plane that cannot be stated in pure vector-space terms. It is correct for us to use these nonvector-space properties in giving *examples* of transformations, but it would *not* be correct to use them for proving *theorems* about transformations.

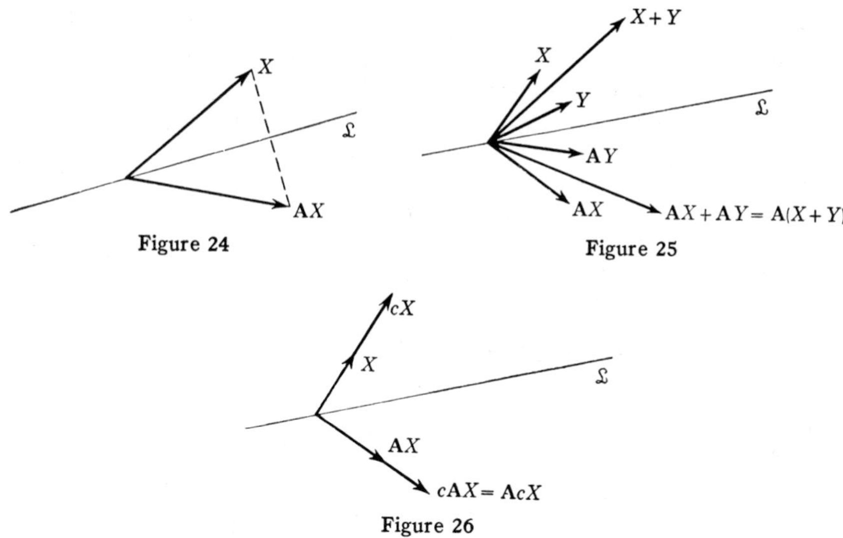

Figure 24

Figure 25

Figure 26

When a transformation $\mathbf{A}$ with domain $\mathcal{X}$ and range $\mathcal{Y}$ is one-one, then it makes the space $\mathcal{X}$ and the space $\mathcal{Y}$ abstractly identical as vector spaces. Each element X of $\mathcal{X}$ corresponds to a unique element Y of $\mathcal{Y}$, and vice versa. And both of the abstract algebraic operations, vector addition and numerical multiplication, are preserved by this correspondence. Hence any statement about vectors in $\mathcal{X}$, provided this statement uses only pure vector space terms, is equivalent, in the obvious way, to a certain statement about vectors in $\mathcal{Y}$.

Example 3. The outstanding example of an abstract identification of two vector spaces is given by the transformation that sends each 2-dimensional column vector $\begin{pmatrix} x \\ y \end{pmatrix}$ onto the point in the plane that has these two numbers as its x and y coordinates. The fact that this identification of number-couples with geometric points is very familiar to you should not obscure the fact that two quite different things are being identified.

Another example of abstract identification of vector spaces is the correspondence between functions and column vectors explained in Example 3 of the previous section.

If $\mathbf{A}$ is a transformation between a space $\mathcal{X}$ and a space $\mathcal{Y}$ then the *kernel* of the transformation is the set of all vectors X in $\mathcal{X}$ such that $\mathbf{A}X = O$. In other words, it is the truth set of the open statement $\mathbf{A}X = O$. The kernel of any transformation always contains the vector O and hence is nonempty.

The kernel of $\mathbf{A}$ is itself a vector space (see Exercise 19 of Section 9).

If the transformation **A** is one-one its kernel consists of the vector O only (see Exercise 2).

Example 4. Let $\mathfrak{X}$ be the set of all 2-component column vectors and $\mathcal{Y}$ be the set of all 1-component column vectors. Let **A** be the transformation that sends the vector $\begin{pmatrix} a \\ b \end{pmatrix}$ onto the vector $(a + b)$ in $\mathcal{Y}$. The kernel of this transformation is the set of all vectors of the form $\begin{pmatrix} a \\ -a \end{pmatrix}$ and it is easy to see that this is a vector space.

EXERCISES

1. Show that for any transformation **A**, $\mathbf{A}(X - Y) = \mathbf{A}X - \mathbf{A}Y$.

2. Show that **A** is one-one if and only if the kernel of **A** consists of the vector O alone.

3. Give a necessary and sufficient condition for a 2-by-2 matrix $\begin{pmatrix} a & b \\ c & d \end{pmatrix}$ to have a nonzero vector in its kernel. [*Ans.* $ad = bc$.]

4. Consider the set of real numbers $\mathfrak{X}_1$ as a vector space. Among the various numerical functions with domain $\mathfrak{X}_1$ that are familiar to you from calculus, which ones are linear transformations? In particular, what constant functions are linear? (*Warning:* the calculus definition of "linear function" is different from ours.) [*Ans.* $\mathbf{f}(x) = ax$; **0**.]

5. Show that the identity function, $X \rightarrow X$ for each vector X in a given space $\mathfrak{X}$, is a transformation.

6. Let **A** be a transformation of ordinary plane vectors. Suppose that there are vectors X and Y such that $\mathbf{A}X = X$ and $\mathbf{A}Y = Y$. And suppose that the line through (the tips of) X and Y does not pass through O. What can we say about the transformation **A**? [*Ans.* **A** is the identity transformation.]

7. Let **A** and **B** be transformations each with domain the space $\mathfrak{X}_3$ of 3-dimensional column vectors. Let

$$W_1 = \begin{pmatrix} 1 \\ 0 \\ 0 \end{pmatrix}, \quad W_2 = \begin{pmatrix} 0 \\ 1 \\ 0 \end{pmatrix}, \quad W_3 = \begin{pmatrix} 0 \\ 0 \\ 1 \end{pmatrix}.$$

Suppose that $\mathbf{A}W_1 = \mathbf{B}W_1$, $\mathbf{A}W_2 = \mathbf{B}W_2$, $\mathbf{A}W_3 = \mathbf{B}W_3$. Show that then $\mathbf{A} = \mathbf{B}$.

8. Let $\mathfrak{X}$ be the set of 2-dimensional column vectors. Show that numerical multiplication by a fixed number $c \neq 0$ is a transformation of $\mathfrak{X}$ into itself.

9. Consider the following transformation with domain and range 2-dimensional column vectors

$$\begin{pmatrix} x_1 \\ x_2 \end{pmatrix} \rightarrow \begin{pmatrix} x_2 \\ -x_1 \end{pmatrix}.$$

When the column vectors are interpreted as points in the plane, what geometric effect does the transformation have?

10. Show that the rotation of the plane defined in Example 3 of Section 2 is a transformation.

11. Given a one-one transformation $\mathbf{A}$ of a space $\mathfrak{X}$ onto a space $\mathfrak{Y}$ let us define the following function $\mathbf{B}$ with domain $\mathfrak{Y}$ and range $\mathfrak{X}$. Since the range of $\mathbf{A}$ is all of $\mathfrak{Y}$, then each Y in $\mathfrak{Y}$ can be written $Y = \mathbf{A}X$ for some X in $\mathfrak{X}$. And since $\mathbf{A}$ is one-one, then Y can be written $\mathbf{A}X$ for only one X. We now define $\mathbf{B}(Y) = X$. Prove that this function is a linear transformation from $\mathfrak{Y}$ onto $\mathfrak{X}$. (We call the transformations $\mathbf{A}$ and $\mathbf{B}$ *inverse* to each other.)

12. Show that if A is an invertible n-by-n matrix, then A defines a one-one transformation with domain and range the space of n-dimensional column vectors.

13. In Exercise 12, show that the matrices A and A^{-1} define transformations inverse to each other.

14. Let $\mathfrak{X}$ be the set of all 3-dimensional column vectors and $\mathfrak{Y}$ be the set of all 2-dimensional column vectors. Find the kernels of the following transformations.

(a) $$\begin{pmatrix} x_1 \\ x_2 \\ x_3 \end{pmatrix} \xrightarrow{\mathbf{A}} \begin{pmatrix} x_1 + x_3 \\ x_2 - x_3 \end{pmatrix}.$$

[*Ans.* The set of vectors of the form $\begin{pmatrix} -a \\ a \\ a \end{pmatrix}$.]

(b) $$\begin{pmatrix} x_1 \\ x_2 \\ x_3 \end{pmatrix} \xrightarrow{\mathbf{A}} \begin{pmatrix} 3x_1 + 7x_2 \\ x_3 \end{pmatrix}.$$

(c) $$\begin{pmatrix} x_1 \\ x_2 \\ x_3 \end{pmatrix} \xrightarrow{\mathbf{A}} \begin{pmatrix} x_2 \\ x_3 \end{pmatrix}.$$

[*Ans.* The set of vectors of the form $\begin{pmatrix} a \\ 0 \\ 0 \end{pmatrix}$.]

(d) $$\begin{pmatrix} x_1 \\ x_2 \\ x_3 \end{pmatrix} \xrightarrow{\mathbf{A}} \begin{pmatrix} 0 \\ 0 \end{pmatrix}.$$

9. MORE EXAMPLES OF VECTOR SPACES AND TRANSFORMATIONS

Once you understand the notion of an abstract vector space, you will discover in mathematics many examples of this structure.

Example 1. The set of all real numbers is itself a vector space. In checking the axioms we must not be confused by the fact that each real number now plays two roles. Let us write each number in **boldface** when it plays the role of a vector. Then the axioms simply coincide with certain familiar rules of elementary arithmetic.

$$
\begin{aligned}
(\mathbf{x} + \mathbf{y}) + \mathbf{z} &= \mathbf{x} + (\mathbf{y} + \mathbf{z})\\
\mathbf{0} + \mathbf{x} &= \mathbf{x}\\
-\mathbf{x} + \mathbf{x} &= \mathbf{0}\\
\mathbf{x} + \mathbf{y} &= \mathbf{y} + \mathbf{x}\\
a(b\mathbf{x}) &= (ab)\mathbf{x}\\
(a + b)\mathbf{x} &= a\mathbf{x} + b\mathbf{x}\\
a(\mathbf{x} + \mathbf{y}) &= a\mathbf{x} + a\mathbf{y}.
\end{aligned}
$$

Example 2. For fixed m and n, say $m = 3$ and $n = 7$, the set of all m-by-n matrices constitutes a vector space. In checking the axioms we consider only addition and numerical multiplication, and ignore matrix multiplication.

Example 3. In Example 3 of Section 7 we took the set $\mathcal{U}$ to be finite. Actually this example is valid for an infinite set $\mathcal{U}$; for instance, suppose that $\mathcal{U}$ is the "unit interval" of all real numbers between 0 and 1. We again take $\mathcal{X}$ to be the set of all numerical functions with domain $\mathcal{U}$, defining addition and numerical multiplication as usual. There is now, of course, no question of making a column vector correspond to each function unless we are willing to contemplate an infinite-dimensional column vector that has a "component" for each real number between 0 and 1.

When a subset $\mathcal{Y}$ of a vector space $\mathcal{X}$ is itself a vector space, then $\mathcal{Y}$ is called a *subspace* of $\mathcal{X}$. It is understood that the operations of addition and numerical multiplication for vectors in $\mathcal{Y}$ are identical with the operations already defined for vectors in $\mathcal{X}$.

Theorem. In order that a subset $\mathcal{Y}$ of a vector space $\mathcal{X}$ be a subspace it is necessary and sufficient that $\mathcal{Y}$ have the following two properties:
(1) if X and Y belong to $\mathcal{Y}$, then so does $X + Y$;
(2) if X belongs to $\mathcal{Y}$, then so do all numerical multiples cX.

Proof: Suppose $\mathcal{Y}$ is a subspace. Then it is a vector space. Hence when X and Y belong to $\mathcal{Y}$, then $X + Y$ and cX are defined and belong to $\mathcal{Y}$. But these operations in $\mathcal{Y}$ are assumed to be the same as those defined for the vector space $\mathcal{X}$. Hence $\mathcal{Y}$ has properties (1) and (2). Conversely, suppose that the subset $\mathcal{Y}$ has the properties (1) and (2). Then for each pair of vectors X and Y in $\mathcal{Y}$ we have an operation of addition already defined, and $X + Y$ is in $\mathcal{Y}$. Similarly for numerical multiplication. And these two operations, looked at as operations on $\mathcal{Y}$, surely satisfy the axioms for a vector space, since the axioms are satisfied on $\mathcal{X}$.

Example 4. Let $\mathcal{U}$ be the unit interval and let $\mathcal{Y}$ be the set of all numerical functions with domain $\mathcal{U}$ that are defined by polynomial formulas. Then $\mathcal{Y}$ is the subspace of the space $\mathcal{X}$ of all numerical functions with domain $\mathcal{U}$. For instance, if $\mathbf{X}$ has the polynomial formula $\mathbf{X}(t) = 5 - 2t + 3t^2$ and $\mathbf{Y}$ has the formula $\mathbf{Y}(t) = 1 + 2t - t^2 + t^3$, then $\mathbf{X} + \mathbf{Y}$ has the formula $(\mathbf{X} + \mathbf{Y})(t) = 6 + 2t^2 + t^3$.

Example 5. Let $\mathcal{U}$ and $\mathcal{X}$ be as in Example 4 and let $\mathcal{Y}$ be the set of all functions with domain $\mathcal{U}$ that are solutions of the homogeneous differential equation

$$\mathbf{X}'''' - 5\mathbf{X}''' + 5\mathbf{X}'' + 5\mathbf{X}' - 6\mathbf{X} = \mathbf{0}.$$

Then $\mathcal{Y}$ is a subspace of $\mathcal{X}$. For instance, if the functions $\mathbf{W}(t) = e^{-t}$ and $\mathbf{Y}(t) = e^{3t}$ are solutions (and they are), then the function $\mathbf{Z}(t) = e^{-t} + e^{3t}$ must be a solution, since $\mathbf{Z}(t) = \mathbf{W}(t) + \mathbf{Y}(t)$, $\mathbf{Z}'(t) = \mathbf{W}'(t) + \mathbf{Y}'(t)$, $\mathbf{Z}''(t) = \mathbf{W}''(t) + \mathbf{Y}''(t)$, etc. Hence substitution of $\mathbf{Z}$ in the differential equation yields $0 + 0 = 0$.

Example 6. Every vector space $\mathcal{X}$ has two trivial subspaces: the space $\mathcal{X}$ itself, and the space consisting of the vector O alone.

Example 7. Let $\mathcal{Y}$ be a subspace of the space $\mathcal{X}$ of 2-dimensional geometrical vectors, not one of the two trivial subspaces mentioned in Example 6. Then $\mathcal{Y}$ must be a line through the origin. For, because $\mathcal{Y}$ does not consist of O alone, it must contain some nonzero vector Y. Because $\mathcal{Y}$ is a subspace it must then contain all numerical multiples of Y. These form a line through the origin. If $\mathcal{Y}$ contains no other vectors, well and good. If $\mathcal{Y}$ contains some Z that is not a numerical multiple of Y, then it is not hard to prove that every vector X in $\mathcal{X}$ can be written as a sum of numerical multiples of Y and Z, and hence that $\mathcal{Y}$ would then be the same as the whole space $\mathcal{X}$. The details of the last assertion will be verified in Section 10.

With the above additions to our vector space repertory it is possible to give new interesting examples of transformations.

Example 8. Let $\mathcal{X}$ be the vector space of all polynomials. To avoid confusion of letters we will write t for the unknown in the polynomial. For each "vector"

$$X = a_0 + a_1t + a_2t^2 + a_3t^3 + \ldots + a_nt^n$$

define $\mathbf{A}X$ to be derivative

$$\mathbf{A}X = a_1 + 2a_2t + 3a_3t^2 + 4a_4t^3 + \ldots + na_nt^{n-1}.$$

Then it is easy to show that $\mathbf{A}$ is a transformation.

Example 9. Let $\mathfrak{X}$ be the vector space of polynomials, let X be a polynomial in $\mathfrak{X}$, and let $\mathbf{A}X$ be the result of substituting $t + 1$ for t in X. For instance, if $X = 3 + t - 2t^2$, then

$$\mathbf{A}X = 3 + (t + 1) - 2(t + 1)^2 = 2 - 3t - 2t^2.$$

Example 10. If $\mathfrak{X}$ is the space of 3 by 7 matrices, and A is some fixed 2 by 3 matrix, and B is some fixed 7 by 5 matrix, then the following transformation has domain $\mathfrak{X}$ and range some subspace of the vector space of 2 by 5 matrices.

$$C \to ACB.$$

Example 11. Let the components of a 3-dimensional column vector represent the profits a business man makes on three transactions. The space of such vectors forms a vector space if we represent losses as negative profits and we allow arbitrarily large profits and losses.

Example 12. Let $X_1, \ldots, X_n$ be vectors in an abstract vector space $\mathfrak{X}$. Define a transformation $\mathbf{A}$ from column vectors onto a subspace of $\mathfrak{X}$ by the rule

$$\begin{pmatrix} c_1 \\ \cdot \\ \cdot \\ \cdot \\ c_n \end{pmatrix} \to c_1X_1 + \ldots + c_nX_n.$$

Example 13. Let $\mathbf{F}_1, \ldots, \mathbf{F}_n$ be functionals on an abstract space $\mathfrak{X}$. Define a transformation $\mathbf{A}$ from $\mathfrak{X}$ onto a subspace of column vectors by the rule

$$X \to \begin{pmatrix} \mathbf{F}_1X \\ \cdot \\ \cdot \\ \cdot \\ \mathbf{F}_nX \end{pmatrix}.$$

We also include below two new examples of transformations on the space $\mathfrak{X}$ of plane geometric vectors. In defining these we again take the point of view that in this illustration it is legitimate to use all the familiar notions of high-school geometry even though some of these notions make no sense in an abstract vector space.

Example 14. Let $\mathfrak{X}$ be provided with cartesian horizontal and vertical axes. Let $\mathbf{A}$ send every point into the point on the x-axis that is directly above it or directly below it. This kind of transformation is called a *projection*.

Example 15. Let **A** move each point in the upper half-plane horizontally to the right, and in the lower half-plane horizontally to the left, a distance equal to the distance of the point from the x-axis. This kind of transformation is called a *shear*.

EXERCISES

1. Verify that the transformation in Example 8 is really a linear function.
2. Verify that the transformation in Example 10 is really a linear function.
3. Verify geometrically that the transformations in Examples 14 and 15 are really linear functions.
4. Let $\mathcal{U}$ be the unit interval, that is, the set of real numbers between 0 and 1, and let $\mathcal{X}$ be the vector space of all numerical functions with domain $\mathcal{U}$. Verify that each of the following sets of functions is a subspace of $\mathcal{X}$.
   (a) All continuous numerical functions with domain $\mathcal{U}$.
   (b) All differentiable functions with domain $\mathcal{U}$.
   (c) All numerical functions **X** on $\mathcal{U}$ such that
   $$\int_0^1 \mathbf{X}(t)\, dt = 0.$$
   (d) All differentiable functions **X** with domain $\mathcal{U}$ that have $\mathbf{X}'(0) = \mathbf{X}'(1) = 0$.
   (e) All numerical functions on $\mathcal{U}$ that have straight-line graphs. (These are called "linear" functions in elementary calculus, but not in this book.)
   (*Hint.* Use the theorem of this section.)
5. Prove that the set of polynomials of degree ≤ 5 constitutes a subspace of the vector space of all polynomials. Prove also that the set of polynomials of degree exactly 5 does not constitute a subspace.
6. Prove that the set of functions that are solutions to the nonhomogeneous linear differential equation
   $$\mathbf{X}''''(t) - 5\mathbf{X}'''(t) + 5\mathbf{X}''(t) + 5\mathbf{X}'(t) - 6\mathbf{X}(t) = e^t$$
   does *not* form a vector space.
7. Describe geometrically all the subspaces of the space of 3-dimensional geometric vectors. [*Hint.* There are four types of subspaces.]
8. Which of the following are subspaces of the space $\mathcal{X}_4$ of 4-dimensional column vectors?
   (a) All $X = \begin{pmatrix} x_1 \\ x_2 \\ x_3 \\ x_4 \end{pmatrix}$ such that $x_4 = 2x_1$.

(b) All numerical multiples of $\begin{pmatrix} 1 \\ -1 \\ 0 \\ 2 \end{pmatrix}$.

(c) All X that have all components positive.

(d) The vector $\begin{pmatrix} 0 \\ 0 \\ 0 \\ 0 \end{pmatrix}$ alone.

(e) All sums of numerical multiples of $\begin{pmatrix} 1 \\ -1 \\ 0 \\ 2 \end{pmatrix}$ and $\begin{pmatrix} 1 \\ 2 \\ 3 \\ 4 \end{pmatrix}$.

(f) All numerical multiples of the sum of $\begin{pmatrix} 1 \\ -1 \\ 0 \\ 2 \end{pmatrix}$ and $\begin{pmatrix} 1 \\ 2 \\ 3 \\ 4 \end{pmatrix}$

(g) All X such that $x_1 = 0$.
(h) All X such that $x_1 \geq x_2$.
(i) All X such that $x_2 = 1$.
(j) All X such that $FX = 0$, where $F = (1 \ -1 \ 2 \ 3)$.

[*Ans.* (a), (b), (d), (e), (f), (g), (j) are subspaces.]

9. Show that the set of solutions to a set of simultaneous *homogeneous* equations in variables $x_1, \ldots, x_n$ constitutes a subspace of the space $\mathfrak{X}_n$ of n-dimensional column vectors. Show also that if one or more of the equations were nonhomogeneous, then the set of solutions would not be a subspace.

10. In Example 1 consider the integers (positive and negative) as a subset of all real numbers. Show that if Y_1 and Y_2 are in this subset, then $Y_1 - Y_2$ is also in the subset. Show also that the set of integers does not form a subspace of the vector space of real numbers.

11. In Example 9, what is the relationship between the graph of the function $3 + t - 2t^2$ and the graph of the function $3 + (t + 1) - 2(t^2 + 2t + 1)$?

12. A vector X such that $\mathbf{A}X = X$ is called a "fixed point" of the transformation $\mathbf{A}$. The vector O is always a fixed point. In which of the Examples 8–15 of this section do there exist nonzero fixed points?

[*Ans.* 9, 14, 15.]

13. Show that the set of solutions to equations

$$F_1X = w_1$$
$$\vdots$$
$$F_1X = w_m$$

can be expressed as follows: Let $\mathfrak{X}_0$ be the subspace of solutions to

$$F_1X = 0$$
$$\vdots$$
$$F_mX = 0$$

and $Z = \begin{pmatrix} z_1 \\ \vdots \\ z_m \end{pmatrix}$ be any one fixed solution to the original set of equations. Then the set of all solutions to the original equations is the set of all $Z + X_0$, with X_0 in $\mathfrak{X}_0$.

14. In which of the examples of transformations in this section is it true that $\mathbf{A}^2 = \mathbf{A}$, i.e., that the result of transforming X into $\mathbf{A}(\mathbf{A}X)$ is the same as that of transforming X into $\mathbf{A}X$? [*Ans.* Example 14.]

15. Show that the intersection of subspaces is a subspace.

16. Show that the complement of a subspace is never a subspace.

17. Show that the union of two subspaces is never a subspace unless one is contained in the other.

18. Prove that the kernels of the transformations given in Exercise 14 of the preceding section are subspaces of $\mathfrak{X}$.

19. If $\mathbf{A}$ is a transformation of a space $\mathfrak{X}$ onto a space $\mathfrak{Y}$ show that the kernel of $\mathbf{A}$ is a subspace of $\mathfrak{X}$.

10. LINEAR INDEPENDENCE AND BASES

Let $\mathfrak{X}$ be a vector space and let $X_1, \ldots, X_n$ be vectors in $\mathfrak{X}$. What vectors do we get when we perform additions and numerical multiplications using only these vectors? First of all, for each X_i we get all its (infinitely many) multiples cX_i. And then taking sums of such, we get expressions of the form $c_1X_1 + c_2X_2 + \ldots + c_nX_n$. For instance, $2X_1 - 1X_2 + 1X_3 - 1X_4$ or $1X_1 + 0X_2 + 0X_3 + 1X_4$ or for that matter $0X_1 + 0X_2 + 0X_3 + 0X_4$. Such an expression is called a *linear combination* of $X_1, \ldots, X_n$. Sums and numerical multiples can themselves be looked at as linear combinations. For instance, $X_1 + X_3 = 1X_1 + 0X_2 + 1X_3 + 0X_4$; and $-5X_2 = 0X_1 - 5X_2 + 0X_3 + 0X_4$. Furthermore, sums and numerical multiples of linear combinations are again linear combinations. For instance $(2X_1 - 1X_2 + 1X_3 - 3X_4) + (-2X_1 + 2X_2 - 3X_3 - 1X_4) = 0X_1 + 1X_2 - 2X_3 - 4X_4$; and $3(2X_1 - 1X_2 + 1X_3 - 3X_4) = 6X_1 - 3X_2 + 3X_3 - 9X_4$. Hence when we perform additions and numerical multiplications starting with $X_1, \ldots, X_n$ we get all linear combinations $c_1X_1 + \ldots + c_nX_n$, and we get nothing else.

DEFINITION. The set of all linear combinations of $X_1, \ldots, X_n$, which is clearly a subspace of $\mathfrak{X}$, is called the *subspace spanned by* $X_1, \ldots, X_n$.

Any subspace of $\mathfrak{X}$ that contains $X_1, \ldots, X_n$ must contain all linear combinations of them. Hence the subspace of $\mathfrak{X}$ spanned by $X_1, \ldots, X_n$ is the *smallest subspace of* $\mathfrak{X}$ *that contains them all.*

Note that it is perfectly possible for two different linear combinations of $X_1, \ldots, X_n$ to represent the same vector X. For instance if we know that X_2 is really the same as $\frac{1}{3}X_1$, then the linear combination $-1X_1 + 3X_2$ represents the same vector as the linear combination $0X_1 + 0X_2$. However, there exist sets of vectors $X_1, \ldots, X_n$ having the agreeable property that $a_1X_1 + \ldots + a_nX_n$ never equals $b_1X_1 + \ldots + b_nX_n$ unless $a_1 = b_1$ and $a_2 = b_2$ and ... and $a_n = b_n$. Such a set of vectors $X_1, \ldots, X_n$ is called *linearly independent.*

It is profitable to look at the notions of *spanning* and *linear independence* from the standpoint of transformations. The following transformation has as domain the space $\mathfrak{X}_n$ of n-dimensional column vectors and as range the subspace of the abstract space $\mathfrak{X}$ that is spanned by $X_1, \ldots, X_n$.

$$\begin{pmatrix} c_1 \\ \cdot \\ \cdot \\ \cdot \\ c_n \end{pmatrix} \rightarrow c_1X_1 + \ldots + c_nX_n.$$

Furthermore, this transformation is one-one if and only if $X_1, \ldots, X_n$ are linearly independent. In Exercise 2 of Section 8 we have proved that a transformation is one-one if and only if its kernel consists of the O vector alone. Hence to check that $X_1, \ldots, X_n$ are linearly independent we need only check to see that O cannot be written as a linear combination $c_1X_1 + \ldots + c_nX_n$ except in the trivial way $0X_1 + \ldots + 0X_n$. We can also prove this condition for linear independence directly, as follows: Suppose two different linear combinations $a_1X_1 + \ldots + a_nX_n$ and

$b_1X_1 + \ldots + b_nX_n$ were both equal to the same vector X. Then the vector O could be written as the linear combination $(a_1 - b_1)X_1 + \ldots + (a_n - b_n)X_n$. And since at least one a_k is different from the corresponding b_k, then this last linear combination is not the same as $0X_1 + \ldots + 0X_n$.

The last result gives an equivalent definition of linear independence which we shall take as the formal definition for this concept.

DEFINITION. The vectors $X_1, \ldots, X_n$ are said to be *linearly independent* if a relation of the form

$$a_1X_1 + \ldots + a_nX_n = O$$

can hold only when $a_1 = \ldots = a_n = 0$. Vectors that are not independent are said to be *dependent.*

It is easy to show that if a set of vectors is linearly dependent then some one of them is a linear combination of the others, and conversely (see Exercise 6).

Let us illustrate these notions with vectors from the space $\mathfrak{X}_4$ of 4-dimensional column vectors.

Example 1. The following three vectors

$$X_1 = \begin{pmatrix}1\\1\\1\\1\end{pmatrix}, \quad X_2 = \begin{pmatrix}0\\1\\1\\1\end{pmatrix}, \quad X_3 = \begin{pmatrix}0\\0\\1\\1\end{pmatrix}$$

are linearly independent. We must show that

$$y_1\begin{pmatrix}1\\1\\1\\1\end{pmatrix} + y_2\begin{pmatrix}0\\1\\1\\1\end{pmatrix} + y_3\begin{pmatrix}0\\0\\1\\1\end{pmatrix} = \begin{pmatrix}0\\0\\0\\0\end{pmatrix}$$

only if

$$\begin{pmatrix}y_1\\y_2\\y_3\end{pmatrix} = \begin{pmatrix}0\\0\\0\end{pmatrix}.$$

In other words, that

$$\begin{aligned}(1\ 0\ 0)Y &= 0\\(1\ 1\ 0)Y &= 0\\(1\ 1\ 1)Y &= 0\\(1\ 1\ 1)Y &= 0\end{aligned}$$

only if $Y = 0$, a fact that is true if this set of equations has a unique solution. And uniqueness can be established by our standard equation-solving techniques for the reduced form of these equations is

$$\begin{aligned}(1\ 0\ 0)Y &= 0\\(0\ 1\ 0)Y &= 0\\(0\ 0\ 1)Y &= 0\\(0\ 0\ 0)Y &= 0.\end{aligned}$$

Example 2. The vectors X_1, X_2, X_3 above, together with

$$X_4 = \begin{pmatrix}0\\0\\0\\1\end{pmatrix}, \qquad X_5 = \begin{pmatrix}1\\1\\0\\0\end{pmatrix},$$

span the space $\mathfrak{X}_4$ of 4-dimensional column vectors. To see this we must show that for any vector

$$\begin{pmatrix}w_1\\w_2\\w_3\\w_4\end{pmatrix} = W$$

the following equations can be solved.

$$y_1\begin{pmatrix}1\\1\\1\\1\end{pmatrix} + y_2\begin{pmatrix}0\\1\\1\\1\end{pmatrix} + y_3\begin{pmatrix}0\\0\\1\\1\end{pmatrix} + y_4\begin{pmatrix}0\\0\\0\\1\end{pmatrix} + y_5\begin{pmatrix}1\\1\\0\\0\end{pmatrix} = \begin{pmatrix}w_1\\w_2\\w_3\\w_4\end{pmatrix}.$$

Written in row vector form, the equations are

$$\begin{aligned}(1\ 0\ 0\ 0\ 1)Y &= w_1\\(1\ 1\ 0\ 0\ 1)Y &= w_2\\(1\ 1\ 1\ 0\ 0)Y &= w_3\\(1\ 1\ 1\ 1\ 0)Y &= w_4.\end{aligned}$$

If we put these equations in reduced form we have

$$\begin{aligned}(1\ \ 0\ \ 0\ \ 0\ \ \ \ 1)Y &= w_1\\(0\ \ 1\ \ 0\ \ 0\ \ \ \ 0)Y &= w_2 - w_1\\(0\ \ 0\ \ 1\ \ 0\ \ -1)Y &= w_3 - w_2\\(0\ \ 0\ \ 0\ \ 1\ \ \ \ 0)Y &= w_4 - w_3.\end{aligned}$$

We see that y_5 is a nonbeginner variable so that there are an infinite number of solutions to this set of equations.

If we choose the solution for which $y_5 = 0$ we obtain

$$\begin{aligned}y_1 &= w_1\\y_2 &= w_2 - w_1\\y_3 &= w_3 - w_2\\y_4 &= w_4 - w_5\\y_5 &= 0\end{aligned}$$

as suitable components for the vector Y. Other solutions of these equations are asked for in Exercise 4.

DEFINITION. If the vectors $X_1, \ldots, X_n$ span the whole space $\mathfrak{X}$ and are also linearly independent, they are said to form a *basis* for the space $\mathfrak{X}$.

It follows from the definitions of spanning and linear independence that if $X_1, \ldots, X_n$ are a basis for $\mathfrak{X}$ then each vector X in $\mathfrak{X}$ can be written in exactly one way as a linear combination $X = c_1X_1 + \ldots + c_nX_n$.

Once we have a basis, the transformation

$$\begin{pmatrix} c_1 \\ \cdot \\ \cdot \\ \cdot \\ c_n \end{pmatrix} \to c_1X_1 + \ldots + c_nX_n$$

completely identifies the space $\mathfrak{X}_n$ of column vectors with the abstract space $\mathfrak{X}$. Thus every problem concerning the vectors in $\mathfrak{X}$ becomes a problem concerning n-dimensional column vectors. We call the numbers $c_1, \ldots, c_n$ the *components* (or *coordinates*) *of* X *with respect to the basis* $X_1, \ldots, X_n$.

Example 3. The vectors X_1, X_2, X_3, X_4 in Examples 1 and 2 constitute a basis for the space of 4-dimensional column vectors. To show this, one must check that they are linearly independent, and that they span the whole space.

Example 4. The most obvious basis for the space $\mathfrak{X}_n$ of n-dimensional column vectors consists of

$$W_1 = \begin{pmatrix} 1 \\ 0 \\ \cdot \\ \cdot \\ \cdot \\ 0 \\ 0 \end{pmatrix}, \quad W_2 = \begin{pmatrix} 0 \\ 1 \\ \cdot \\ \cdot \\ \cdot \\ 0 \\ 0 \end{pmatrix}, \quad \ldots, \quad W_n = \begin{pmatrix} 0 \\ 0 \\ \cdot \\ \cdot \\ \cdot \\ 0 \\ 1 \end{pmatrix}.$$

These are in fact the columns of the n-by-n identity matrix. We will call this the *natural basis* for the space $\mathfrak{X}_n$. Obviously there is a similar natural basis $E_1, \ldots, E_n$ for the space $\mathfrak{F}_n$ of n-dimensional row vectors.

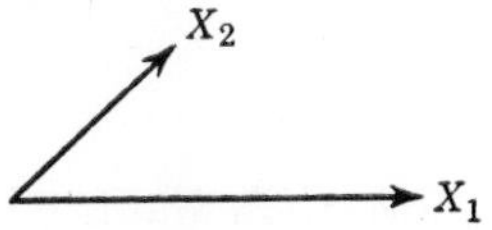

Example 5. Let $\mathfrak{X}$ be the geometrical plane. Then the vectors in Figure 27 constitute a basis for $\mathfrak{X}$. It is important to establish this fact geometrically, without using coordinates. For we can identify the plane with the space of number-couples only after we know that X_1, X_2 constitute a basis. The

X_2

X_1

Figure 27

linear independence of X_1 and X_2 amounts to the assertion that if you first walk a certain distance east (or a distance west) and then walk a distance northeast (or a distance southwest) you will certainly not find yourself at the origin O unless both distances were zero. The fact that X_1 and X_2 span the plane amounts to the assertion that every point in the plane can be reached by first walking a certain distance (possibly 0) east or west, and then walking a distance northeast or southwest.

Example 6. The vector spaces that occur in the nonphysical sciences, such as the space of cost vectors in Example 2 of Section 2, often have the property that the natural basis for column vectors does not have a natural interpretation in terms of the problem. For instance in the space of idealized house-cost vectors, this basis consists of

$$Z_1 = \begin{pmatrix} 1 \\ 0 \\ 0 \end{pmatrix},$$

which represents an economic situation in which the materials for a ranch-style house cost 1 and the materials for Cape Cod and Colonial houses are free; and

$$Z_2 = \begin{pmatrix} 0 \\ 1 \\ 0 \end{pmatrix}; \quad \text{and} \quad Z_3 = \begin{pmatrix} 0 \\ 0 \\ 1 \end{pmatrix};$$

which have analogous interpretations. Since negative prices are not permitted, none of these three basis vectors is included in the range of our particular transformation **A**. And in fact the vectors that make economic sense may not constitute a subspace, but only a "convex" subset. Such subsets of a vector space will be studied in detail in Chapter 5.

Example 7. We have seen in Exercise 9 of Section 9 that the set of solutions to a set of simultaneous homogeneous equations constitutes a subspace of the space of column vectors. From the reduced form of the equations it is possible to write down a basis for the solution space in a mechanical way. For instance in Example 5 of Section 3 the basis for the solution subspace consists of the vectors

$$\begin{pmatrix} -2 \\ 1 \\ -3 \\ 1 \\ 0 \end{pmatrix} \quad \text{and} \quad \begin{pmatrix} 1 \\ -1 \\ -6 \\ 0 \\ 1 \end{pmatrix}.$$

We now want to introduce an important notation. We have just seen that if an abstract vector space $\mathfrak{X}$ possesses a basis we can identify $\mathfrak{X}$ with some space $\mathfrak{X}_n$ of column vectors. The particular way in which we identify the abstract vector space $\mathfrak{X}$ with the column-vector space $\mathfrak{X}_n$

depends on the particular basis we choose for $\mathfrak{X}$. It will be convenient to let a single capital Greek letter Γ or Δ or Ω stand for a basis. Suppose that the basis $\Gamma = \{X_1, X_2, X_3, X_4\}$ is chosen, and $X = 3X_1 + X_3 - X_4$. Then the abstract vector X is expressed by a column vector with respect to the basis Γ, and for this we write

$$\binom{X}{\Gamma} = \begin{pmatrix} 3 \\ 0 \\ 1 \\ -1 \end{pmatrix}.$$

This notation emphasizes the fact that the abstract vector X can be identified with a column vector only after a basis for the abstract space $\mathfrak{X}$ has been chosen. In terms of this notation the one-one transformation of the "abstract" space $\mathfrak{X}$ onto the "concrete" space $\mathfrak{X}_n$ can be written

$$X \to \binom{X}{\Gamma}.$$

Example 8. Let Γ be the basis for the geometrical plane illustrated in Example 5. Given an arbitrary point X in the plane, here is a general procedure for writing down $\binom{X}{\Gamma}\cdot$ We first draw the subspaces spanned by X_1 and X_2. These are lines through O. Then we draw lines parallel to these subspaces through (the tip of) X. Now X will be one vertex of a parallelogram whose diagonally opposite vertex is O. The sides of this parallelogram adjacent to the vertex O are (positive or negative) numerical multiples of X_1 and X_2. In Figure 28, for instance, we might estimate these

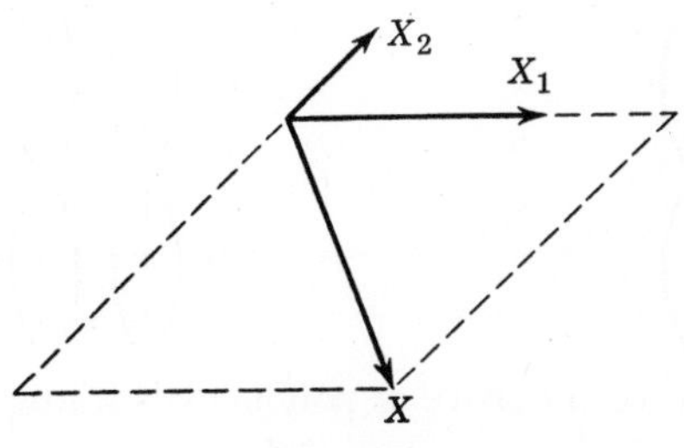

Figure 28

sides to be $\frac{3}{2}X_1$ and $-3X_2$, respectively. And then $X = \frac{3}{2}X_1 - 3X_2$, so that

$$\binom{X}{\Gamma} = \binom{\frac{3}{2}}{-3}.$$

It is clear then that the *basis* X_1, X_2 serves the same purpose as the *oblique coordinate system* introduced in Section 1.

If we are given the coordinate system directly we can easily discover the relevant basis. Simply choose vectors X_1 and X_2 pointing in the positive direction on the first and second axes, respectively, and each having length 1 relative to the scale of its own axis.

A vector space $\mathfrak{X}$ that possesses a basis is called *finite-dimensional.* In this book we restrict our attention almost exclusively to finite-dimensional spaces. All the vector spaces in Sections 7 and 9 are finite-dimensional except for those spaces which are defined in Examples 3 and 4 of Section 9. In Section 11 we will prove that if $X_1, \ldots, X_n$ is a basis for $\mathfrak{X}$, then *every* basis for $\mathfrak{X}$ contains exactly n vectors. This integer n is called the *dimension* of $\mathfrak{X}$. Each abstract finite-dimensional vector space can be identified with exactly one of the column vector spaces $\mathfrak{X}_n$, namely the one having the right dimension.

EXERCISES

1. In $\mathfrak{X}_2$ show that none of the following sets of vectors are linearly independent.

(a) $\begin{pmatrix}2\\6\end{pmatrix}, \begin{pmatrix}3\\9\end{pmatrix}.$ (b) $\begin{pmatrix}1\\2\end{pmatrix}, \begin{pmatrix}2\\3\end{pmatrix}, \begin{pmatrix}3\\4\end{pmatrix}.$

(c) $\begin{pmatrix}1\\2\end{pmatrix}, \begin{pmatrix}2\\1\end{pmatrix}, \begin{pmatrix}5\\5\end{pmatrix}.$ (d) $\begin{pmatrix}0\\0\end{pmatrix}, \begin{pmatrix}6\\11\end{pmatrix}.$

2. We choose ordinary (cartesian) coordinates in 3-dimensional space. Describe geometrically the subspaces spanned by the following sets of vectors.

(a) $\begin{pmatrix}1\\0\\0\end{pmatrix}, \begin{pmatrix}0\\1\\0\end{pmatrix}.$ (b) $\begin{pmatrix}1\\1\\1\end{pmatrix}, \begin{pmatrix}3\\3\\3\end{pmatrix}.$

(c) $\begin{pmatrix}1\\2\\3\end{pmatrix}, \begin{pmatrix}2\\5\\7\end{pmatrix}.$ (d) $\begin{pmatrix}1\\1\\1\end{pmatrix}, \begin{pmatrix}1\\2\\3\end{pmatrix}, \begin{pmatrix}0\\0\\1\end{pmatrix}.$

3. Let $\mathfrak{X}$ be the vector space of polynomials whose degree is at most 2. Let $X = 3x^2 - 2x + 7$. Write $\begin{pmatrix}X\\\Gamma\end{pmatrix}$ where Γ is

(a) $x^2, x, 1$.

(b) $x^2 - x, x - 1, 1$. [*Ans.* (b) $\begin{pmatrix}3\\1\\8\end{pmatrix}$.]

(c) $(x-2)^2, (x-2)^1, (x-2)^0$.

4. In Example 2 show that the reduced set of equations is correct. Then find solutions of the equations corresponding to $y_5 = 3$ and to $y_5 = -5$.

5. Show that the vectors X_1, X_2, X_3, X_4, X_5 of Example 2 are *not* linearly independent.

6. Show that a set of vectors is linearly independent if and only if no one of them is in the subspace spanned by the others.

7. Verify that the vectors

$$X_1 = \begin{pmatrix}1\\1\\1\end{pmatrix},\quad X_2 = \begin{pmatrix}1\\2\\3\end{pmatrix},\quad X_3 = \begin{pmatrix}0\\1\\0\end{pmatrix}$$

form a basis for $\mathfrak{X}_3$.

8. Express each of the following vectors in terms of the basis in Exercise 7.

(a) $\begin{pmatrix}3\\2\\1\end{pmatrix}$ [*Ans.* $4X_1 - X_2$.]

(b) $\begin{pmatrix}-1\\-2\\-3\end{pmatrix}$

(c) $\begin{pmatrix}-3\\2\\5\end{pmatrix}$

9. Show that the three vectors in Exercise 8 form a basis by expressing the vectors of Exercise 7 in terms of them.

10. Show that the effect of a transformation $\mathbf{A}$ on a space $\mathfrak{X}$ is completely determined by what it does to the vectors $X_1, \ldots, X_n$ of a basis.

11. For the basis $\{W_1, W_2\} = \Gamma$ pictured in Figure 29, and the vectors X and Y and Z, write (approximately) the corresponding column vectors

$$\begin{pmatrix}X\\\Gamma\end{pmatrix} \text{ and } \begin{pmatrix}Y\\\Gamma\end{pmatrix} \text{ and } \begin{pmatrix}Z\\\Gamma\end{pmatrix}.$$

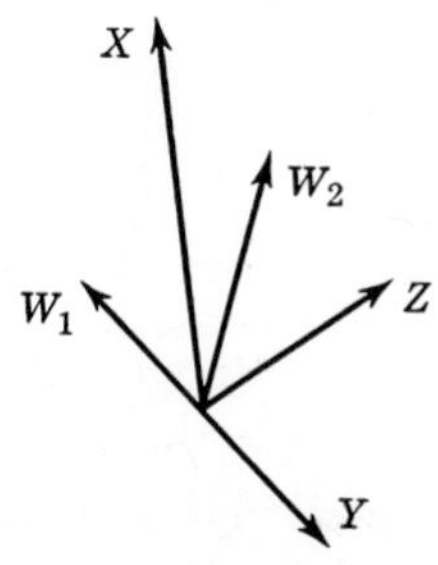

Figure 29

12. Let $\mathfrak{U}$ be the interval $0 \le t \le 2$. Let $\mathfrak{X}$ be the vector space of functions on $\mathfrak{U}$ spanned by the functions $\mathbf{X}_1(t) \equiv 1$, $\mathbf{X}_2(t) = \sin t$, $\mathbf{X}_3(t) = \sin 2t$. Prove that these functions are linearly independent and hence form a basis for $\mathfrak{X}$.

13. Prove that the function $\mathbf{Y}(t) = (\sin t + \cos t)^2$ belongs to the space $\mathfrak{X}$ Exercise 12 and find $\begin{pmatrix}\mathbf{Y}\\\Gamma\end{pmatrix}$, Γ being the basis $\mathbf{X}_1$, $\mathbf{X}_2$, $\mathbf{X}_3$ of Exercise 12.

[*Ans.* $\begin{pmatrix}1\\0\\1\end{pmatrix}$.]

14. Show that the vector space $\mathfrak{X}$ of polynomials of degree ≤ 5 has a basis consisting of the six "monomials" $X_1 = 1$, $X_2 = t$, $X_3 = t^2$, $X_4 = t^3$, $X_5 = t^4$, $X_6 = t^5$.

15. Prove that three fixed vectors X_1, X_2, X_2 constitute a basis for ordinary 3-dimensional space if no single plane through the origin contains all three.

16. Show that the set of all linear combinations of vectors $X_1, \ldots, X_n$ in $\mathfrak{X}$ does constitute a subspace of $\mathfrak{X}$.

17. Show that the vector O can never belong to a linearly independent set of vectors.

18. Show that any subset of a linearly independent set of vectors is still linearly independent.

19. Show that any set containing a set of vectors that spans $\mathfrak{X}$ still spans $\mathfrak{X}$.

20. Verify the fact that if $\mathbf{A}$ is a one-one transformation of $\mathfrak{X}_n$ onto $\mathfrak{X}$, and $W_1, \ldots, W_n$ is a basis for $\mathfrak{X}_n$, then $\mathbf{A}W_1, \ldots, \mathbf{A}W_n$ is a basis for $\mathfrak{X}$.

21. Let $\mathfrak{X}$ be the vector space of all polynomials. Show that no finite set of polynomials $X_1, \ldots, X_n$ can be a basis for $\mathfrak{X}$. (In other words, $\mathfrak{X}$ is not finite-dimensional.)

22. Show that if a finite set $\mathcal{S}$ of vectors span the vector space $\mathfrak{X}$, then some subset of $\mathcal{S}$ is a basis for $\mathfrak{X}$.

23. If $X_1, \ldots, X_n$ is a basis Γ for the space $\mathfrak{X}$, and if $W_1, \ldots, W_n$ is the natural basis for n-dimensional column vectors, show that $\begin{pmatrix} X_j \\ \Gamma \end{pmatrix} = W_j$.

11. UNIQUENESS OF DIMENSION

Suppose the abstract vector space $\mathfrak{X}$ is finite-dimensional. By definition this means that $\mathfrak{X}$ contains at least one finite subset of vectors $W_1, \ldots, W_n$ that span all of $\mathfrak{X}$ and are at the same time linearly independent. Our principal object in this section is to prove that then $\mathfrak{X}$ cannot contain another spanning and independent set $X_1, \ldots, X_r$ with $r \neq n$.

There is no loss of generality in taking $r > n$, for otherwise we could interchange the roles of the W's and the X's. Now to show that $X_1, \ldots, X_r$ cannot be a basis it is enough to show that they cannot be linearly independent. (And in fact it would be folly to try to show more, since it is clearly possible for very large sets of vectors to span $\mathfrak{X}$.)

Theorem 1. If the vector space $\mathfrak{X}$ has a basis of n vectors, then no set of more than n vectors can be linearly independent.

Proof: We consider first the case where $n = 3$, that is, where $\mathfrak{X}$ has a basis consisting of three vectors, say W_1, W_2, and W_3. We can identify $\mathfrak{X}$ with the column vector space $\mathfrak{X}_3$ and carry out our argument with 3-dimensional column vectors. We want to prove that every set of four 3-dimensional column vectors, say X_1, X_2, X_3 and X_4, is linearly independent. Suppose the components of the vectors X_i are

$$X_1 = \begin{pmatrix} a_{11} \\ a_{21} \\ a_{31} \end{pmatrix}, \quad X_2 = \begin{pmatrix} a_{12} \\ a_{22} \\ a_{32} \end{pmatrix}, \quad X_3 = \begin{pmatrix} a_{13} \\ a_{23} \\ a_{33} \end{pmatrix}, \quad \text{and} \quad X_4 = \begin{pmatrix} a_{14} \\ a_{24} \\ a_{34} \end{pmatrix}.$$

In order to show that these vectors are linearly dependent we must find numbers y_1, y_2, y_3, y_4, not all 0, such that

$$y_1X_1 + y_2X_2 + y_3X_3 + y_4X_4 = O.$$

In other words we must find a nonzero solution

$$\begin{pmatrix} y_1 \\ y_2 \\ y_3 \\ y_4 \end{pmatrix}$$

to the simultaneous homogeneous equations

$$\begin{aligned} a_{11}y_1 + a_{12}y_2 + a_{13}y_3 + a_{14}y_4 &= 0 \\ a_{21}y_1 + a_{22}y_2 + a_{23}y_3 + a_{24}y_4 &= 0 \\ a_{31}y_1 + a_{32}y_2 + a_{33}y_3 + a_{34}y_4 &= 0 \end{aligned}$$

And we have seen in Section 4 that a homogeneous system with more unknowns than equations has infinitely many solutions. Hence the theorem is proved, at least for the case $n = 3$ and for any four vectors X_1, X_2, X_3, X_4.

The proof that any set of $n + k$ vectors is linearly dependent when the space $\mathfrak{X}$ has a basis consisting of n vectors follows the same pattern as the special case ($n = 3$) treated above.

As a corollary we can now state the main theorem about finite-dimensional vector spaces. It is this theorem that allows us to attach a unique dimension to each finite-dimensional space.

Theorem 2. If $\mathfrak{X}$ is finite-dimensional and one of its bases contains exactly n vectors, then each of its bases contains exactly n vectors.

We should mention at this point that a vector space containing only one vector is, by definition, said to have dimension 0. (See Exercise 6.)

A theorem that complements Theorem 1 is the following.

Theorem 3. If $\mathfrak{X}$ has a basis of n vectors, then no set of fewer than n vectors can span $\mathfrak{X}$.

Proof: Suppose a set of r vectors $X_1, \ldots, X_r$ spans $\mathfrak{X}$. It may happen that certain subsets of this set also span $\mathfrak{X}$. Let us take the smallest such subset. Then we have a set that spans $\mathfrak{X}$ but which has no proper subset spanning $\mathfrak{X}$. Such a set is a basis for $\mathfrak{X}$ (see Exercise 2), and must have exactly n elements; hence we must have had $r \geq n$.

In the course of proving Theorem 3 we have also proved another result.

Theorem 4. If the set $X_1, \ldots, X_r$ spans $\mathfrak{X}$ then some subset of this set is a basis for $\mathfrak{X}$.

As a parallel fact we have

Theorem 5. If the set $X_1, \ldots, X_r$ is linearly independent but not a basis for $\mathfrak{X}$, then some larger set $X_1, \ldots, X_r, X_r, X_{r+1}, \ldots, X_n$ is a basis for $\mathfrak{X}$ (provided that $\mathfrak{X}$ possesses a finite basis).

Theorem 6. If $\mathbf{A}$ is a linear transformation with n-dimensional domain, r-dimensional range, and k-dimensional kernel, then $r + k = n$.

Proof: Let $X_1, \ldots, X_k$ be a basis for the kernel of $\mathbf{A}$. If the kernel of $\mathbf{A}$ is not all of the domain, use Theorem 4 to adjoin vectors $X_{k+1}, \ldots, X_n$ so that $X_1, \ldots, X_n$ form a basis for the domain of $\mathbf{A}$. Then we will prove that the $n - k$ vectors $\mathbf{A}X_{k+1}, \ldots, \mathbf{A}X_n$ form a basis for the range of $\mathbf{A}$, which will prove the theorem, since $(n - k) + k = n$.

First: $\mathbf{A}X_{k+1}, \ldots, \mathbf{A}X_n$ span the range. For let Y belong to the range. Then $Y = \mathbf{A}X$ for some X in the domain. And X is some linear combination of the basis vectors $X_1, \ldots, X_n$. That is, $X = c_1X_1 + \ldots + c_kX_k + c_{k+1}X_{k+1} + \ldots + c_nX_n$. Hence $Y = \mathbf{A}X = \mathbf{A}(c_1X_1 + \ldots + c_kX_k) + \mathbf{A}(c_{k+1}X_{k+1} + \ldots + c_nX_n)$. The first summand is O, because $c_1X_1 + \ldots + c_kX_k$ belongs to the kernel of $\mathbf{A}$. And the second summand is a linear combination $c_{k+1}(\mathbf{A}X_{k+1}) + \ldots + c_n(\mathbf{A}X_n)$.

Second: $\mathbf{A}X_{k+1}, \ldots, \mathbf{A}X_n$ are linearly independent. For suppose $z_{k+1}(\mathbf{A}X_{k+1}) + \ldots + z_n(\mathbf{A}X_n) = O$. Then $\mathbf{A}(z_{k+1}X_{k+1} + \ldots + z_nX_n) = O$, that is, $Z = z_{k+1}X_{k+1} + \ldots + z_nX_n$ belongs to the kernel of $\mathbf{A}$. But then Z is also some linear combination $z_1X_1 + \ldots + z_kX_k$. And we have $z_1X_1 + \ldots + z_kX_k - z_{k+1}X_{k+1} - \ldots - z_nX_n = O$. Since the X's are independent we are forced to conclude that $z_1 = \ldots = z_k = z_{k+1} = \ldots = z_n = 0$.

As a corollary we have the following theorem.

Theorem 7. Let $\mathbf{A}$ be a transformation whose range is a subspace of its domain. Then $\mathbf{A}$ is one-one if and only if its range is all of its domain.

Proof: Let the domain $\mathfrak{X}$ have dimension n, and suppose that **A** is one-one. Then the dimension of its kernel is 0, and by Theorem 6 the dimension of its range is then n. In Exercise 4 of this section you will prove that $\mathfrak{X}$ contains no n-dimensional proper subspace. Hence the range of **A** must be all of $\mathfrak{X}$.

Conversely suppose that **A** has range of all of $\mathfrak{X}$. Then again by Theorem 6, the dimension of its kernel is 0, that is, its kernel is the 1-element subspace consisting of O alone. And by a now familiar principle, **A** is one-one.

EXERCISES

1. Suppose that $X_1, \ldots, X_n$ are linearly independent, but that it is impossible to choose any vector X_{n+1} in $\mathfrak{X}$ such that $X_1, \ldots, X_n, X_{n+1}$ are linearly independent. Prove that then $X_1, \ldots, X_n$ form a basis for $\mathfrak{X}$.

2. Suppose that $X_1, \ldots, X_n$ span the vector space $\mathfrak{X}$ but that if any X_i is deleted from this set, then $X_1, \ldots, X_{i-1}, X_{i+1}, \ldots, X_n$ fail to span $\mathfrak{X}$. Prove that then $X_1, \ldots, X_n$ form a basis for $\mathfrak{X}$.

3. Prove that if $\mathfrak{X}$ is finite-dimensional of dimension n, and if $X_1, \ldots, X_r$ are linearly independent vectors in $\mathfrak{X}$, then there exist vectors $X_{r+1}, \ldots, X_n$ such that $X_1, \ldots, X_n$ form a basis for $\mathfrak{X}$. (*Hint.* Use Exercise 1.)

4. Let $\mathfrak{X}$ be n-dimensional. Show that any linearly independent set of n vectors forms a basis. Show that any set of n vectors that span $\mathfrak{X}$ forms a basis.

5. Show that if $\mathfrak{X}$ is n-dimensional and $\mathfrak{Y}$ is a subspace of $\mathfrak{X}$ not equal to $\mathfrak{X}$ then $\mathfrak{Y}$ is finite-dimensional of dimension $r < n$. (*Hint.* Use Exercise 13 of Section 9.)

6. Prove that the set of vectors consisting of the zero vector alone is not linearly independent. Use this result to motivate the dimensionality of a vector space consisting of a single vector.

7. Use Theorem 7 to decide which of the following transformations are one-one.
   (a) Section 8 Example 2. [*Ans.* One-one.]
   (b) Section 8 Exercise 9.
   (c) Section 8 Exercise 10.
   (d) The transformation on 3-dimensional vectors that projects them on a given plane.
   (e) The transformation on 3-dimensional vectors that transforms every vector into the O vector.

8. For the transformations in Exercise 7 that were not one-one find the dimension of the range and of the kernel, and check your results by Theorem 6.

9. For the transformation in Example 14 of Section 9 find the dimension of the range and of the kernel. Check your answers by means of Theorem 6.

10. Prove that the transformation in Example 15 of Section 9 is one-one, using the theorems of this section.

11. Consider the vector space $\mathfrak{X}$ of all polynomials $X = a_0 + a_1t + \ldots + a_nt^n + \ldots$. (This is not a finite dimensional space.) Let **A** be the transformation that sends X onto its derivative X'. Show that **A** has as range all of $\mathfrak{X}$ but still has a kernel that contains more than one element. Find the kernel.

12. Let $\mathfrak{X}$ be the vector space of all polynomials of degree at most 5, and let **A** be the transformation that sends X onto X'. Show that **A** maps $\mathfrak{X}$ onto a proper subspace of itself and find the kernel of **A**.

13. Use Theorem 6 to show that if **A** is a transformation with domain a vector space $\mathfrak{X}$ and range the same space $\mathfrak{X}$, and if **A** has a kernel containing at least two distinct elements, then $\mathfrak{X}$ cannot be a finite-dimensional space. [*Hint:* Use Exercises 11 and 12 as a guide.]

14. Prove that if $m \neq n$ then there is no one-one transformation of $\mathfrak{X}_m$ onto $\mathfrak{X}_n$.

12. THE MATRIX OF A TRANSFORMATION

Suppose that **A** is a transformation with domain the column-vector space $\mathfrak{X}_3$ and range the column-vector space $\mathfrak{X}_2$ (or possibly some subspace of $\mathfrak{X}_2$). Apply the transformation **A** to each of the natural basis vectors

$$W_1 = \begin{pmatrix} 1 \\ 0 \\ 0 \end{pmatrix}, \quad W_2 = \begin{pmatrix} 0 \\ 1 \\ 0 \end{pmatrix}, \quad W_3 = \begin{pmatrix} 0 \\ 0 \\ 1 \end{pmatrix}$$

and line up the resulting 2-dimensional column vectors

$$\mathbf{A}W_1 = \begin{pmatrix} a_{11} \\ a_{21} \end{pmatrix}, \quad \mathbf{A}W_2 = \begin{pmatrix} a_{12} \\ a_{22} \end{pmatrix}, \quad \mathbf{A}W_3 = \begin{pmatrix} a_{13} \\ a_{23} \end{pmatrix}$$

in a matrix

$$\begin{pmatrix} a_{11} & a_{12} & a_{13} \\ a_{21} & a_{22} & a_{23} \end{pmatrix}.$$

Call this matrix A. The result of multiplying

$$A \text{ times } \begin{pmatrix} 1 \\ 0 \\ 0 \end{pmatrix} \text{ is } \begin{pmatrix} a_{11} \\ a_{21} \end{pmatrix};$$

the result of multiplying

$$A \text{ times } \begin{pmatrix} 0 \\ 1 \\ 0 \end{pmatrix} \text{ is } \begin{pmatrix} a_{12} \\ a_{22} \end{pmatrix};$$

and the result of multiplying

$$A \text{ times } \begin{pmatrix} 0 \\ 0 \\ 1 \end{pmatrix} \text{ is } \begin{pmatrix} a_{13} \\ a_{23} \end{pmatrix}.$$

Hence the transformation **A** has the same effect as the matrix A on the three basis vectors W_1, W_2, W_3. Then **A** and A must agree on every X (see Exercise 7 of Section 8). We have just proved a special case of the following important theorem.

Theorem 1. Every linear transformation with domain $\mathfrak{X}_n$ and with range some subspace of $\mathfrak{X}_r$ can be defined by an r-by-n matrix.

The above theorem is applicable, of course, to any transformation with finite-dimensional domain and range. For suppose that **A** is a transformation with domain an n-dimensional abstract vector space $\mathfrak{X}$ and with range some subspace of an r-dimensional abstract vector space $\mathfrak{Y}$. Let $\Gamma = \{X_1, \ldots, X_n\}$ be a basis for $\mathfrak{X}$, and let $\Delta = \{Y_1, \ldots, Y_r\}$ be a basis for $\mathfrak{Y}$. Then if we identify each vector X with its corresponding column vector $\begin{pmatrix} X \\ \Gamma \end{pmatrix}$ and each vector Y with its corresponding column vector $\begin{pmatrix} Y \\ \Delta \end{pmatrix}$, **A** becomes a transformation from $\mathfrak{X}_n$ onto a subspace of $\mathfrak{X}_r$. Let us write $\begin{pmatrix} \mathbf{A} \\ \Delta\Gamma \end{pmatrix}$ for the matrix corresponding to this transformation. Notice that the domain basis Γ is written to the right of the range basis Δ.

To compute the matrix $\begin{pmatrix} \mathbf{A} \\ \Delta\Gamma \end{pmatrix}$ we proceed as follows:

(1) Apply **A** to each of the vectors $X_1, \ldots, X_n$ in the domain basis Γ. We then have produced n vectors $\mathbf{A}X_1, \ldots, \mathbf{A}X_n$ in the range.

(2) Compute the components of $\mathbf{A}X_1$ with respect to the range basis Δ; that is, express $\mathbf{A}X_1$ as a linear combination of $Y_1, \ldots, Y_r$, and write

the numerical coefficients as an r-dimensional column vector. According to the notation introduced in Section 10, this column vector is called $\begin{pmatrix} \mathbf{A}X_1 \\ \Delta \end{pmatrix}$. Do the same for $\mathbf{A}X_2$, for $\mathbf{A}X_3$, etc.

(3) Line up the above n columns to form an m-by-n matrix.

To sum up the process briefly: If Γ is the domain basis and Δ is the range basis, then the jth column of $\begin{pmatrix} \mathbf{A} \\ \Delta\Gamma \end{pmatrix}$ is $\begin{pmatrix} \mathbf{A}X_j \\ \Delta \end{pmatrix}$, X_j being the jth vector of the domain basis Γ.

When the range $\mathcal{Y}$ of the transformation $\mathbf{A}$ happens to be a subspace of the domain $\mathcal{X}$ it is often natural to use the same basis for the domain and range. But in some situations, particularly when $\mathbf{A}$ is the identity transformation, it is useful to take different domain and range bases even in the same vector space.

Let us make a list of matrices corresponding to some of the examples of transformations in Sections 8 and 9.

Example 1. Let $\mathbf{A}$ be the transformation defined in Example 1 of Section 8. If Γ is the natural basis in $\mathcal{X}_3$ consisting of the vectors

$$\begin{pmatrix} 1 \\ 0 \\ 0 \end{pmatrix}, \quad \begin{pmatrix} 0 \\ 1 \\ 0 \end{pmatrix}, \quad \begin{pmatrix} 0 \\ 0 \\ 1 \end{pmatrix},$$

and if Δ is the natural basis

$$\begin{pmatrix} 1 \\ 0 \end{pmatrix}, \quad \begin{pmatrix} 0 \\ 1 \end{pmatrix}$$

in $\mathcal{X}_2$, then we can compute $\begin{pmatrix} \mathbf{A} \\ \Delta\Gamma \end{pmatrix}$, as follows:

$$\mathbf{A}\begin{pmatrix} 1 \\ 0 \\ 0 \end{pmatrix} = \begin{pmatrix} 1 \\ 3 \end{pmatrix}, \quad \mathbf{A}\begin{pmatrix} 0 \\ 1 \\ 0 \end{pmatrix} = \begin{pmatrix} 0 \\ 2 \end{pmatrix}, \quad \mathbf{A}\begin{pmatrix} 0 \\ 0 \\ 1 \end{pmatrix} = \begin{pmatrix} -1 \\ 1 \end{pmatrix}.$$

The results of these computations are already expressed with respect to the natural basis in $\mathcal{X}_2$, so that we need only line up the results to obtain the desired matrix. It is

$$\begin{pmatrix} \mathbf{A} \\ \Delta\Gamma \end{pmatrix} = \begin{pmatrix} 1 & 0 & -1 \\ 3 & 2 & 1 \end{pmatrix}.$$

Example 2. Let $\mathbf{A}$ be the reflection transformation defined in Example 2 of Section 8, and let Γ be the two vectors X_1 and X_2 in Figure 30. Then, since $\mathbf{A}$ is the reflection transformation, we have $\mathbf{A}X_1 = X_1$ and $\mathbf{A}X_2 = -X_2$. Since the components of X_1, X_2, and $-X_2$ are

$$\begin{pmatrix} 1 \\ 0 \end{pmatrix}, \quad \begin{pmatrix} 0 \\ 1 \end{pmatrix}, \quad \text{and} \quad \begin{pmatrix} 0 \\ -1 \end{pmatrix},$$

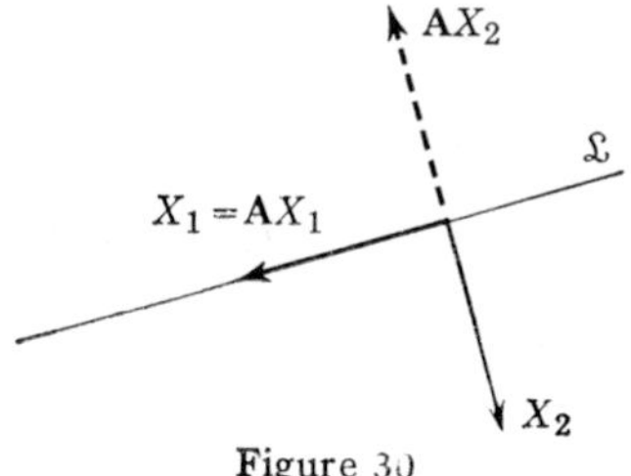

Figure 30

respectively, we see that

$$\begin{pmatrix} \mathbf{A} \\ \Gamma\Gamma \end{pmatrix} = \begin{pmatrix} 1 & 0 \\ 0 & -1 \end{pmatrix}.$$

On the other hand, let Δ be the basis consisting of the vectors Y_1 and Y_2 in Figure 31. In that figure each of these vectors makes an angle of 45°

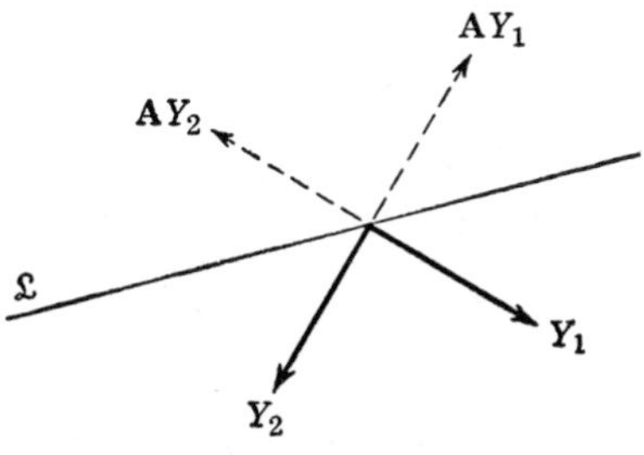

Figure 31

with line $\mathfrak{L}$. In Figure 31 we have drawn the vectors $\mathbf{A}Y_1$ and $\mathbf{A}Y_2$. Then, if each of the vectors X_1, X_2, Y_1, and Y_2 has unit length we can easily compute that

$$\begin{pmatrix} \mathbf{A}Y_1 \\ \Gamma \end{pmatrix} = \begin{pmatrix} -\dfrac{1}{\sqrt{2}} \\ -\dfrac{1}{\sqrt{2}} \end{pmatrix} \quad \text{and} \quad \begin{pmatrix} \mathbf{A}Y_2 \\ \Gamma \end{pmatrix} = \begin{pmatrix} \dfrac{1}{\sqrt{2}} \\ -\dfrac{1}{\sqrt{2}} \end{pmatrix}.$$

Lining these vectors up side by side, we obtain

$$\begin{pmatrix} \mathbf{A} \\ \Gamma\Delta \end{pmatrix} = \begin{pmatrix} -\dfrac{1}{\sqrt{2}} & \dfrac{1}{\sqrt{2}} \\ -\dfrac{1}{\sqrt{2}} & -\dfrac{1}{\sqrt{2}} \end{pmatrix}.$$

Similarly, we can compute that

$$\begin{pmatrix} \mathbf{A}X_1 \\ \Delta \end{pmatrix} = \begin{pmatrix} -\dfrac{1}{\sqrt{2}} \\ \dfrac{1}{\sqrt{2}} \end{pmatrix} \quad \text{and} \quad \begin{pmatrix} \mathbf{A}X_2 \\ \Delta \end{pmatrix} = \begin{pmatrix} -\dfrac{1}{\sqrt{2}} \\ -\dfrac{1}{\sqrt{2}} \end{pmatrix}.$$

And by lining up these vectors, we obtain

$$\begin{pmatrix} \mathbf{A} \\ \Delta\Gamma \end{pmatrix} = \begin{pmatrix} -\frac{1}{\sqrt{2}} & -\frac{1}{\sqrt{2}} \\ \frac{1}{\sqrt{2}} & -\frac{1}{\sqrt{2}} \end{pmatrix}.$$

In each of these cases the basic transformation is the same; but the matrix that gives the transformation changes as the bases are changed.

Example 3. Let $\mathbf{A}$ be the *projection* transformation defined in Example 14 of Section 9. And let Γ consist of a vector X_1 along the x-axis and a vector X_2 along the y-axis. Then

$$\begin{pmatrix} \mathbf{A} \\ \Gamma\Gamma \end{pmatrix} = \begin{pmatrix} 1 & 0 \\ 0 & 0 \end{pmatrix}.$$

Example 4. Let $\mathbf{A}$ be the *shear* transformation defined in Example 15 of Section 9. And let Γ be a basis like that in Example 3, but with both vectors of length 1. Then

$$\begin{pmatrix} \mathbf{A} \\ \Gamma\Gamma \end{pmatrix} = \begin{pmatrix} 1 & 1 \\ 0 & 1 \end{pmatrix}$$

In calculating with the notations defined above, the following two rules are fundamental.

Rule 1. $$\begin{pmatrix} \mathbf{A} \\ \Delta\Gamma \end{pmatrix}\begin{pmatrix} X \\ \Gamma \end{pmatrix} = \begin{pmatrix} \mathbf{A}X \\ \Delta \end{pmatrix};$$

Rule 2. $$\begin{pmatrix} \mathbf{B} \\ \Omega\Delta \end{pmatrix}\begin{pmatrix} \mathbf{A} \\ \Delta\Gamma \end{pmatrix} = \begin{pmatrix} \mathbf{BA} \\ \Omega\Gamma \end{pmatrix}.$$

Notice that in each rule, adjacent basis symbols (Γ in Rule 1, Δ in Rule 2) must be the same.

To establish the validity of Rule 1 we first try it for X equal to one of the basis vectors, say X_2. Then

$$\begin{pmatrix} X_2 \\ \Gamma \end{pmatrix} = \begin{pmatrix} 0 \\ 1 \\ 0 \\ \cdot \\ \cdot \\ \cdot \\ 0 \end{pmatrix}.$$

The reader should show that the result of multiplying this column vector by any matrix A is simply the second column of A. Hence in particular $\begin{pmatrix} \mathbf{A} \\ \Delta\Gamma \end{pmatrix}\begin{pmatrix} X_2 \\ \Gamma \end{pmatrix}$ is the second column of $\begin{pmatrix} \mathbf{A} \\ \Delta\Gamma \end{pmatrix}$, which we know to be $\begin{pmatrix} \mathbf{A}X_2 \\ \Delta \end{pmatrix}$.

Hence our rule works for $X = X_2$; and parallel reasoning shows that it works for each of the other basis vectors. Since a transformation is completely determined by its effect on basis vectors (see Exercise 10 of Section 10), Rule 1 follows.

Rule 2 asserts that if **BA** is the *composite* transformation resulting from performing first **A** then **B**, then the matrix $\binom{\mathbf{BA}}{\Omega\Gamma}$ is the product of $\binom{\mathbf{B}}{\Omega\Delta}$ and $\binom{\mathbf{A}}{\Delta\Gamma}$ in that order. It is enough to check the equality

$$\binom{\mathbf{BA}}{\Omega\Gamma} W = \binom{\mathbf{B}}{\Omega\Delta}\binom{\mathbf{A}}{\Delta\Gamma} W$$

for each n-dimensional column vector W, since W could be any one of the basis vectors in Γ, and a transformation is completely determined by its effect on the basis vectors. We know that any such W can be written $\binom{X}{\Gamma}$ for some uniquely determined vector X in $\mathfrak{X}$. Hence we must verify that

$$\binom{\mathbf{BA}}{\Omega\Gamma}\binom{X}{\Gamma} = \binom{\mathbf{B}}{\Omega\Delta}\binom{\mathbf{A}}{\Delta\Gamma}\binom{X}{\Gamma}$$

But by applying Rule 1 to each side we can simplify the above equality to read

$$\binom{\mathbf{BA}X}{\Omega} = \binom{\mathbf{B}}{\Omega\Delta}\binom{\mathbf{A}X}{\Delta}.$$

This equation follows from Rule 1. Hence Rule 2 is proved.

Rule 2 is most often applied to the case where all three spaces and all three bases are the same. In other words,

$$\binom{\mathbf{B}}{\Gamma\Gamma}\binom{\mathbf{A}}{\Gamma\Gamma} = \binom{\mathbf{BA}}{\Gamma\Gamma}.$$

This says that, if we have fixed our basis once and for all, then we can obtain the matrix of the composite of several transformations by multiplying together their respective matrices.

You will recall (Exercise 11 of Section 8) that a one-one transformation **A** of a vector space $\mathfrak{X}$ onto itself always possesses a unique inverse transformation $\mathbf{A}^{-1}$ with the property that $\mathbf{AA}^{-1} = \mathbf{A}^{-1}\mathbf{A}$ = the identity transformation. The following theorem tells us that the matrix for the inverse transformation coincides with the inverse of the matrix for the original transformation **A**.

Theorem. If **A** is an invertible transformation with domain and $\mathfrak{X}$ range, and if Γ is a basis for $\mathfrak{X}$, then

$$\begin{pmatrix} \mathbf{A}^{-1} \\ \Gamma\Gamma \end{pmatrix} = \begin{pmatrix} \mathbf{A} \\ \Gamma\Gamma \end{pmatrix}^{-1}.$$

Proof. To show that the matrix $\begin{pmatrix} \mathbf{A}^{-1} \\ \Gamma\Gamma \end{pmatrix}$ is the inverse of the matrix $\begin{pmatrix} \mathbf{A} \\ \Gamma\Gamma \end{pmatrix}$ we multiply them together, hoping to get the identity matrix. And we do, since by Rule 2

$$\begin{pmatrix} \mathbf{A}^{-1} \\ \Gamma\Gamma \end{pmatrix}\begin{pmatrix} \mathbf{A} \\ \Gamma\Gamma \end{pmatrix} = \begin{pmatrix} \mathbf{A}^{-1}\mathbf{A} \\ \Gamma\Gamma \end{pmatrix} = \begin{pmatrix} \mathbf{I} \\ \Gamma\Gamma \end{pmatrix} = I.$$

The opposite order of multiplication, of course, gives the same answer. The first **I** in the formula above stands for the identity transformation and the second I stands for the identity matrix.

Corollary. If A and B are matrices such that $BA = I$ then $AB = I$ also.

Proof. A and B both define linear transformations with domain $\mathfrak{X}_n$ and range some subspace of $\mathfrak{X}_n$. The fact that $BA = I$ shows that A has only O in its kernel; for if $AX = O$, then $BAX = IX = X = O$. Hence A is one-one, and by Theorem 7 of Section 11 has range all of $\mathfrak{X}_n$. Hence as a transformation A possesses an inverse, which must be defined by the matrix A^{-1}, and $AA^{-1} = I$. But we have seen in the second paragraph of Section 5 that if the matrix A^{-1} exists then B coincides with A^{-1}. Hence $AB = I$.

It is this result that entitles us to speak of "the inverse" of a matrix, rather than just a "right inverse" or a "left inverse."

When **I** is the identity transformation (that is, the transformation that does not move any vector X in $\mathfrak{X}$), then for every basis Γ we have $\begin{pmatrix} \mathbf{I} \\ \Gamma\Gamma \end{pmatrix}$ equal to the identity matrix I. For different bases Γ and Δ, $\begin{pmatrix} \mathbf{I} \\ \Delta\Gamma \end{pmatrix}$ will never be the identity matrix. But it is at least an invertible matrix, and its inverse is $\begin{pmatrix} \mathbf{I} \\ \Gamma\Delta \end{pmatrix}$. To see this, we compute by Rule 2,

$$\begin{pmatrix} \mathbf{I} \\ \Delta\Gamma \end{pmatrix}\begin{pmatrix} \mathbf{I} \\ \Gamma\Delta \end{pmatrix} = \begin{pmatrix} \mathbf{I} \\ \Delta\Delta \end{pmatrix} = \text{identity matrix},$$

and

$$\begin{pmatrix} \mathbf{I} \\ \Gamma\Delta \end{pmatrix}\begin{pmatrix} \mathbf{I} \\ \Delta\Gamma \end{pmatrix} = \begin{pmatrix} \mathbf{I} \\ \Gamma\Gamma \end{pmatrix} = \text{identity matrix}.$$

A matrix like $\begin{pmatrix} \mathbf{I} \\ \Delta\Gamma \end{pmatrix}$ is useful for "change of basis." If we know the column-vector that corresponds to a vector X with respect to a basis Γ, then we can find the column-vector that corresponds to X with respect to Δ by multiplying

$$\binom{X}{\Gamma} \text{ by } \binom{\mathbf{I}}{\Delta\Gamma}.$$

For in fact by Rule 1

$$\binom{\mathbf{I}}{\Delta\Gamma}\binom{X}{\Gamma} = \binom{\mathbf{I}X}{\Delta} = \binom{X}{\Delta}.$$

Example 5. Suppose that Γ consists of the vectors X_1 and X_2 in Figure 32 below. Then with respect to this basis the geometric vectors W and Y and Z determine the column vectors

$$\begin{pmatrix}1\\2\end{pmatrix} \text{ and } \begin{pmatrix}-2\\0\end{pmatrix} \text{ and } \begin{pmatrix}\frac{1}{2}\\-\frac{1}{2}\end{pmatrix}.$$

But what column vectors do they determine if we use instead a new basis Δ consisting of the vectors X_1^* and X_2^*? To answer this question we first compute the matrix

$$\binom{\mathbf{I}}{\Delta\Gamma} = \begin{pmatrix}\frac{1}{2} & \frac{1}{2}\\-\frac{1}{2} & \frac{1}{2}\end{pmatrix}$$

Then we multiply this matrix

$$\text{times } \begin{pmatrix}1\\2\end{pmatrix} \text{ and times } \begin{pmatrix}-2\\0\end{pmatrix} \text{ and times } \begin{pmatrix}\frac{1}{2}\\-\frac{1}{2}\end{pmatrix}.$$

You should check to see that the answers

$$\begin{pmatrix}\frac{3}{2}\\\frac{1}{2}\end{pmatrix} \text{ and } \begin{pmatrix}-1\\1\end{pmatrix} \text{ and } \begin{pmatrix}0\\-\frac{1}{2}\end{pmatrix}$$

are the same as you would obtain by computing

$$\binom{W}{\Delta} \text{ and } \binom{Y}{\Delta} \text{ and } \binom{Z}{\Delta} \text{ directly.}$$

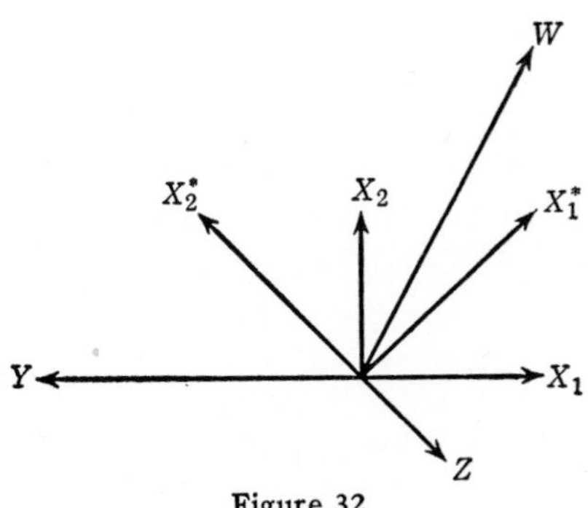

Figure 32

Finally, let us note that all the formulas of the present section can be rephrased in terms of simultaneous linear equations. For concreteness, suppose we have the pair of equations

$$y_1 = x_1 - 2x_2, \qquad y_2 = x_1 + x_2.$$

Then these equations have two distinct geometric interpretations. Under the first interpretation they describe a transformation **A** that distorts the plane in a certain way: it moves the vector $\rightarrow$ into the vector $\nearrow$, it moves the vector $\uparrow$ into the vector $\nwarrow$, and in general moves

$$\text{a vector } \begin{pmatrix} x_1 \\ x_2 \end{pmatrix} \text{ into a vector } \begin{pmatrix} x_1 - 2x_2 \\ x_1 + x_2 \end{pmatrix}.$$

Under the second interpretation, nothing moves at all: all the points in the plane are simply given new names according to a certain system described by the equations; for instance, if a vector has the old name $\begin{pmatrix} 2 \\ 1 \end{pmatrix}$ then it has the new name $\begin{pmatrix} 0 \\ 3 \end{pmatrix}$. One well-known textbook on modern algebra uses the felicitous adjectives *alibi* and *alias* to describe the first and second interpretations, respectively. It is important to notice that every set of simultaneous equations has an alibi interpretation; but the alias interpretation is possible only when (1) there are exactly as many unknowns as equations and (2) the matrix formed from the coefficients is invertible.

EXERCISES

1. Let Γ be a basis for the abstract vector space $\mathfrak{X}$, and let the transformation **A** simply multiply each vector X by the number $\frac{3}{2}$. What is $\begin{pmatrix} \mathbf{A} \\ \Gamma\Gamma \end{pmatrix}$? [*Ans.* $\frac{3}{2}I$.]

2. Let Γ be the natural cartesian basis for the space of plane geometrical fixed vectors. Let **A** be rotation counterclockwise through 45°, and let **B** be rotation clockwise through 30°. Compute $\begin{pmatrix} \mathbf{A} \\ \Gamma\Gamma \end{pmatrix}$ and $\begin{pmatrix} \mathbf{B} \\ \Gamma\Gamma \end{pmatrix}$.

3. By multiplying the matrices in Exercise 2 compute the matrix with respect to Γ of rotation counterclockwise through 15°.

4. Let $\mathfrak{X}$ be the (4-dimensional) space of polynomials of degree ≤ 3. Let **A** be the transformation defined by differentiation. (See Example 8 of Section 9.) Let Γ be the basis of monomials 1, t, t^2, t^3. (See Exercise 14 of Section 10.) What is $\begin{pmatrix} \mathbf{A} \\ \Gamma\Gamma \end{pmatrix}$?

[*Ans.* $\begin{pmatrix} 0 & 1 & 0 & 0 \\ 0 & 0 & 2 & 0 \\ 0 & 0 & 0 & 3 \\ 0 & 0 & 0 & 0 \end{pmatrix}$.]

5. In Exercise 4 compute $\begin{pmatrix} \mathbf{A} \\ \Gamma\Gamma \end{pmatrix}^2$, and interpret it.

6. Let $\mathfrak{X}$ and Γ be as in Exercise 4 above and let $\mathbf{A}$ be the transformation defined by the translation $t \to t + 1$, as in Example 9 of Section 9. What is $\begin{pmatrix} \mathbf{A} \\ \Gamma\Gamma \end{pmatrix}$?

7. Prove that a square matrix A is invertible if and only if its columns are linearly independent. (*Hint.* A defines a linear transformation on the space of column vectors.)

8. Prove that a square matrix A is invertible if and only if its rows are linearly independent.

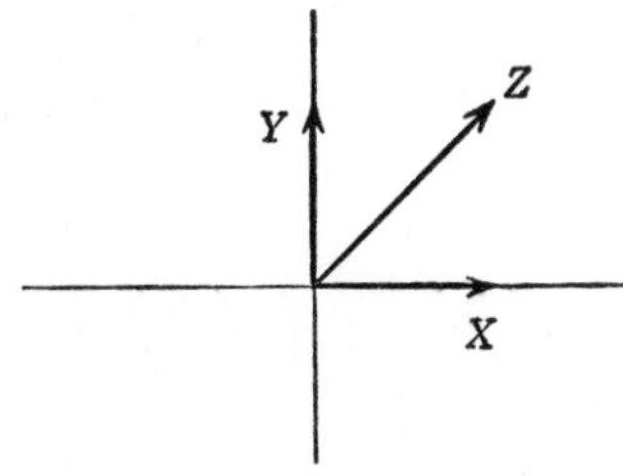

Figure 33

In the remaining exercises $\mathfrak{X}$ will be the space of plane geometric vectors. X, Y, Z are as in Figure 33. Γ consists of X, Y; Δ of Y, X; and Ω of X, Z.

9. Find $\begin{pmatrix} \mathbf{I} \\ \Delta\Gamma \end{pmatrix}$. [*Ans.* $\begin{pmatrix} 0 & 1 \\ 1 & 0 \end{pmatrix}$.]

10. Find $\begin{pmatrix} \mathbf{I} \\ \Omega\Delta \end{pmatrix}$.

11. Find $\begin{pmatrix} \mathbf{I} \\ \Omega\Gamma \end{pmatrix}$ both from its definition and from Exercises 9 and 10.

[*Ans.* $\begin{pmatrix} 1 & -1 \\ 0 & 1 \end{pmatrix}$.]

12. Find $\begin{pmatrix} Z \\ \Gamma \end{pmatrix}$. Use the results of Exercises 9 and 11 to find $\begin{pmatrix} Z \\ \Delta \end{pmatrix}$ and $\begin{pmatrix} Z \\ \Omega \end{pmatrix}$. Verify your answers geometrically.

13. Let $\mathbf{B}$ be a rotation clockwise through 30°. Find

$$\begin{pmatrix} \mathbf{B} \\ \Delta\Gamma \end{pmatrix}, \begin{pmatrix} \mathbf{B} \\ \Omega\Delta \end{pmatrix}, \begin{pmatrix} \mathbf{B} \\ \Omega\Gamma \end{pmatrix}, \begin{pmatrix} \mathbf{B} \\ \Gamma\Delta \end{pmatrix}.$$

14. Find $\begin{pmatrix} \mathbf{I} \\ \Gamma\Delta \end{pmatrix}$. What is the relation of this matrix to the matrix of Exercise 9?

15. Find $\begin{pmatrix} X - 2Y \\ \Delta \end{pmatrix}$. Use the results of Exercises 10 and 14 to express $X - 2Y$ with respect to the bases Γ and Ω.

[*Ans.* $\begin{pmatrix} -2 \\ 1 \end{pmatrix}, \begin{pmatrix} 1 \\ -2 \end{pmatrix}, \begin{pmatrix} 3 \\ -2 \end{pmatrix}$.]

16. Let **A** be the transformation of Example 14 in Section 9. Find $\begin{pmatrix} \mathbf{A} \\ \Delta\Gamma \end{pmatrix}$ and $\begin{pmatrix} \mathbf{A} \\ \Omega\Delta \end{pmatrix}$.

[*Ans.* $\begin{pmatrix} 0 & 0 \\ 1 & 0 \end{pmatrix}, \begin{pmatrix} 0 & 1 \\ 0 & 0 \end{pmatrix}$.]

17. If **A** and **B** are as in Exercises 13 and 16, compute

$$\begin{pmatrix} \mathbf{BA} \\ \Omega\Gamma \end{pmatrix} \quad \text{and} \quad \begin{pmatrix} \mathbf{AB} \\ \Omega\Gamma \end{pmatrix}.$$

What is the geometric significance of the fact that these two matrices differ?

18. From Exercise 13 find

$$\begin{pmatrix} \mathbf{B} \\ \Gamma\Gamma \end{pmatrix} \quad \text{and} \quad \begin{pmatrix} \mathbf{B} \\ \Delta\Delta \end{pmatrix}.$$

[*Ans.* $\begin{pmatrix} \sqrt{3}/2 & \frac{1}{2} \\ -\frac{1}{2} & \sqrt{3}/2 \end{pmatrix}, \begin{pmatrix} \sqrt{3}/2 & -\frac{1}{2} \\ \frac{1}{2} & \sqrt{3}/2 \end{pmatrix}$.]

19. Suppose that

$$\begin{pmatrix} \mathbf{C} \\ \Delta\Gamma \end{pmatrix} = \begin{pmatrix} 1 & 0 \\ 0 & 1 \end{pmatrix}.$$

Interpret **C** geometrically.

20. Prove that if **A** is a one-one transformation of $\mathfrak{X}$ onto $\mathfrak{Y}$ then we can find a basis Γ' such that $\begin{pmatrix} \mathbf{A} \\ \Gamma'\Gamma \end{pmatrix} = \begin{pmatrix} 1 & 0 \\ 0 & 1 \end{pmatrix}$.

*13. FUNCTIONALS

A functional, you will recall, is a particularly simple kind of linear transformation, since its range is a set of numbers. Here are some important examples of functionals, defined on various vector spaces.

Example 1. Let F be some fixed n-dimensional row vector. Then the rule $X \to FX$ defines a functional on the space $\mathfrak{X}_n$ of n-dimensional column vectors. This is, of course, nothing more than a special case of a matrix defining a transformation. Hence conversely, as we have seen in Section 12, every functional on $\mathfrak{X}_n$ is defined by one of the row vectors in the space $\mathfrak{F}_n$. In particular, the collection of all functionals that have domain $\mathfrak{X}_n$ is itself a vector space of dimension n.

Example 2. Assign to each column vector in the space $\mathfrak{X}_n$ its first coordinate. This defines a functional on $\mathfrak{X}_n$. The same functional is of course defined by the row vector $(1 \ 0 \ \ldots \ 0)$.

Example 3. Let F be a 3-dimensional row vector and let X be a fixed 5-dimensional column vector. Let $\mathfrak{X}$ be the vector space of 3-by-5 matrices. Then the following rule defines a functional on $\mathfrak{X}$: $A \to FAX$.

Example 4. Let $\mathfrak{X}$ be the vector space of polynomials. Let t_0 be some fixed real number. Then we define a functional by assigning to each polynomial X its value $X(t_0)$ for $t = t_0$. For instance, if $t_0 = -1$, then $(t^3 + t + 3) \to 1$, $(t^2 + 5) \to 6$, $(t^2 - 1) \to 0$.

Example 5. Let $\mathfrak{X}$ be the space of polynomials. Let a and b be numbers, $a < b$. Then the following integral defines a functional.

$$X \to \int_a^b X(t)\, dt.$$

For instance if $a = 0$ and $b = 1$, then $(t^3 + t + 3) \to \frac{15}{4}$, $(t^2 + 5) \to \frac{16}{3}$, $(t^2 - 1) \to -\frac{2}{3}$.

In each of the following three geometrical examples (and especially in Example 8) it will be tedious to check directly by geometry and trigonometry that the function defined is actually a functional. The sensible way to proceed is to pick a convenient basis in the vector space and then show that the function coincides with some functional defined by a row vector.

Example 6. In the space $\mathfrak{X}$ of 3-dimensional geometrical vectors, let $\mathcal{Y}$ be a plane through the origin. Let us suppose that one side of $\mathcal{Y}$ is labeled "plus" and the other side "minus." Now assign to each vector X in $\mathfrak{X}$ the number which equals the perpendicular distance of (the tip of) X from the plane $\mathcal{Y}$, putting a minus sign in front of this number if X is on the minus side of $\mathcal{Y}$. To see that this rule defines a functional on $\mathfrak{X}$ pick a basis W_1, W_2, W_3 for $\mathfrak{X}$ in which W_2 and W_3 lie in the plane $\mathcal{Y}$ while W_1 is perpendicular to $\mathcal{Y}$ and of length 1. Then the (plus or minus) distance of X from $\mathcal{Y}$ is by elementary geometry equal to the first coordinate of X with respect to the basis W_1, W_2, W_3.

Example 7. Imagine the space $\mathfrak{X}$ of 2-dimensional geometrical vectors as a horizontal plane in ordinary 3-dimensional space. Let $\mathcal{Y}$ be some other plane (but not a vertical one) that intersects the horizontal plane $\mathfrak{X}$ in a line through the origin of $\mathfrak{X}$. Assign to each vector X in $\mathfrak{X}$ the vertical distance of (the tip of) X from the plane $\mathcal{Y}$ if $\mathcal{Y}$ lies above X, and minus that vertical distance if $\mathcal{Y}$ lies below X.

Example 8. Let $\mathfrak{X}$ be the space of 2-dimensional geometric vectors and let W be some fixed vector in $\mathfrak{X}$. Assign to each vector X the product (length of W)(length of X) (cosine of angle between W and X).

Let $\mathfrak{X}$ be an n-dimensional vector space. It is easy to prove that the set $\mathfrak{F}$ of all functionals with domain $\mathfrak{X}$ forms a subspace of the space of all numerical functions with domain $\mathfrak{X}$. (See Exercise 6.)

It is natural then to try to find a set of *functionals* that form a basis on $\mathfrak{X}$ in the sense of Chapter 2, and to investigate the relation between the notion of basis in the sense of logic (which we will call a *functional basis on* $\mathfrak{X}$) and the notion of basis in the sense of linear algebra (which we will call simply a *basis for* $\mathfrak{X}$).

The two conditions on a basis expressed in Chapter 2 were that the functions be logically independent and that they describe $\mathfrak{X}$. In this case the two conditions mean that: (I) Every combination of functional values must be possible on $\mathfrak{X}$. That is, for any set of values of the functions we have an X in $\mathfrak{X}$ for which the functionals take on these values. (II) A vector in $\mathfrak{X}$ must be uniquely identified by the values of the functionals. That is, the functionals cannot have exactly the same values for two different vectors.

Theorem. If $\mathbf{F}_1, \mathbf{F}_2, \ldots, \mathbf{F}_n$ form a functional basis on a vector space $\mathfrak{X}$, then n is the dimension of $\mathfrak{X}$. And we have a unique basis for $\mathfrak{X}$ such that the ith coordinate of any vector X is $\mathbf{F}_iX$.

Proof. $\mathbf{F}_1X = 1$, $\mathbf{F}_2X = 0, \ldots, \mathbf{F}_nX = 0$ is a possible set of values for the functionals; hence there must be a vector X for which precisely these values occur, by (I). Let X_1 be such a vector. Similarly we find a vector for which $\mathbf{F}_2X = 1$ and $\mathbf{F}_1X = \mathbf{F}_3X = \ldots = \mathbf{F}_nX = 0$, and call it X_2. And so on. Let Y be any vector in $\mathfrak{X}$ and let $\mathbf{F}_1Y = c_1$, $\mathbf{F}_2Y = c_2, \ldots, \mathbf{F}_nY = c_n$. The vector Y is uniquely determined by these values, by (II). Let us construct the vector $Z = c_1X_1 + \ldots + c_nX_n$.

$$\mathbf{F}_1Z = c_1\mathbf{F}_1X_1 + c_2\mathbf{F}_1X_2 + \ldots + c_n\mathbf{F}_1X_n = c_1.$$

Similarly, $\mathbf{F}_2Z = c_2$, etc. Hence $Y = Z$. Thus any vector can be expressed as a linear combination of the X_i's. Furthermore, this representation is unique, since the coordinates are the values of the functionals. Thus the X_i's form a basis for $\mathfrak{X}$, of the type required. And since those n vectors form a basis, n is the dimension of $\mathfrak{X}$. If $Y_1, \ldots, Y_n$ is a basis of the required type, then

$$X_1 = 1 \cdot Y_1 + 0 \cdot Y_2 + \ldots + 0 \cdot Y_n = Y_1, \text{ etc.}$$

Hence the basis is unique.

Theorem. For any basis of $\mathfrak{X}$ we can find a unique functional basis $\mathbf{F}_1, \ldots, \mathbf{F}_n$ such that $\mathbf{F}_iX$ is the ith coordinate of X in the basis.

Proof. Let $X_1, \ldots, X_n$ be the basis. Let $\mathbf{F}_i$ be a function whose value for X_i is 1, and for the other basis vectors is 0. Define $\mathbf{F}_i$ for arbitrary X by the condition $\mathbf{F}_i(c_1X_1 + \ldots + c_nX_n) = c_i$. Then it is easy to check that $\mathbf{F}_i$ is a functional. Conditions (I) and (II) for the functionals $\mathbf{F}_i$ to be a basis are a direct consequence of the fact that the X_i's form a basis. The fact that this functional basis is unique follows from the fact that a functional is determined by its values on the basis.

We thus see that there is a one-one correspondence between bases and functional bases. The coordinates of a vector in a given basis are the values of the functionals in the corresponding functional basis, which is usually called the *dual* of the original basis.

The set of all numerical functions on a given space forms a vector space. The functionals on an abstract n-dimensional space $\mathfrak{X}$ clearly form a subspace of the space of all numerical functions on $\mathfrak{X}$. Let us call this vector space $\mathfrak{F}$.

Theorem. Every functional basis on $\mathfrak{X}$ is a basis of $\mathfrak{F}$, and conversely. Hence if $\mathfrak{X}$ is n-dimensional, then so is $\mathfrak{F}$.

Proof. Let $\mathbf{F}_1, \ldots, \mathbf{F}_n$ be a functional basis on $\mathfrak{X}$. Let $X_1, \ldots, X_n$ be the corresponding basis of $\mathfrak{X}$. Let $\mathbf{F}$ be any functional on $\mathfrak{X}$. Then the values $\mathbf{F}X_1 = c_1, \ldots, \mathbf{F}X_n = c_n$ determine $\mathbf{F}$ uniquely. But $c_1\mathbf{F}_1 + \ldots + c_n\mathbf{F}_n$ has the same values on the basis, hence $\mathbf{F} = c_1\mathbf{F}_1 + \ldots + c_n\mathbf{F}_n$ is a representation of $\mathbf{F}$ as a linear combination of the $\mathbf{F}_i$'s. Furthermore, for an arbitrary linear combination $b_1\mathbf{F}_1 + \ldots + b_n\mathbf{F}_n = \mathbf{G}$, the coefficient b_i must equal $\mathbf{G}X_i$. Hence the representation $\mathbf{F} = c_1\mathbf{F}_1 + \ldots + c_n\mathbf{F}_n$ is unique. We have thus shown that the functional basis $\mathbf{F}_1, \ldots, \mathbf{F}_n$ on $\mathfrak{X}$ is also a basis for the vector space $\mathfrak{F}$. This shows also that $\mathfrak{F}$ is n-dimensional.

Conversely, let us suppose that $\mathbf{G}_1, \ldots, \mathbf{G}_n$ is a basis of $\mathfrak{F}$. Then we can show that the functionals satisfy conditions (I) and (II), and hence that they form a functional basis on $\mathfrak{X}$. We will show that if we specify arbitrary values $\mathbf{G}_1X = k_1, \ldots, \mathbf{G}_nX = k_n$, there is always a unique X yielding these values. Let $X_1, \ldots, X_n$ be any basis of $\mathfrak{X}$, and let $\mathbf{F}_1, \ldots, \mathbf{F}_n$ be its dual functional basis. We know that $\mathbf{F}_1, \ldots, \mathbf{F}_n$ is also a basis of $\mathfrak{F}$. Hence each $\mathbf{G}_i$ can be written as a linear combination of $\mathbf{F}_1, \ldots, \mathbf{F}_n$, say $\mathbf{G}_i = a_{i1}\mathbf{F}_1 + \ldots + a_{in}\mathbf{F}_n$. An arbitrary vector X can be written as $X = c_1X_1 + \ldots + c_nX_n$, uniquely. Hence $\mathbf{G}_iX = a_{i1}c_1 + \ldots + a_{in}c_n$. To find an X yielding the desired values we must solve the simultaneous equations

$$\begin{aligned} a_{11}c_1 + \ldots + a_{1n}c_n &= k_1 \\ &\cdots \\ a_{n1}c_1 + \ldots + a_{nn}c_n &= k_n. \end{aligned}$$

The matrix $A = (a_{ij})$ determines a one-one transformation (since it carries a basis into a basis); hence it has an inverse. Thus the set of equations always has a unique solution, giving a unique X with the specified values. This completes the proof.

We now see that the functional bases on $\mathfrak{X}$ are precisely the bases of $\mathfrak{F}$. The duality relation, discussed above, pairs in a natural way the bases of the two vector spaces. Thus we may introduce coordinates in a vector space either by choosing a basis and letting the coordinates of X be the coefficients of the basis vectors in expressing X, or by choosing the dual basis, and letting the coordinates be the values for X on the basis functionals.

As an application of these ideas we will consider the space of all functions on a finite set. Let $\mathfrak{U}$ be a possibility set of n elements, $\mathfrak{U} = \{u_1, \ldots, u_n\}$. Let $\mathfrak{Z}$ be the set of all numerical functions on the possibility space. We know that this is an n-dimensional vector space (see Example 3 of Section 7). What interpretation can we give to the functionals on $\mathfrak{Z}$?

Let us first choose the natural basis for $\mathfrak{Z}$. The "vector" $\mathbf{Z}_i$ is simply the function on $\mathfrak{U}$ that assigns 1 to possibility u_i and 0 to the other possibilities. This may be thought of as the characteristic function of the unit set $\{u_i\}$. Thus these n characteristic functions form a basis for $\mathfrak{Z}$, that is, every numerical function on $\mathfrak{U}$ can be written as a linear combination of the n characteristic functions of unit sets. Once we have the basis chosen, we can write an arbitrary function as

$$\mathbf{Z} = a_1\mathbf{Z}_1 + \ldots + a_n\mathbf{Z}_n. \tag{1}$$

Clearly, this is a function that assigns value a_i to the possibility u_i. If we write the coordinates of this "vector" as a column vector, the components of the column vector are simply the values of the function at the various points of $\mathfrak{U}$. This is the natural representation of a numerical function on a finite space as a column vector. Thus the function

$$\mathbf{Z}(u_1) = a_1, \ldots, \mathbf{Z}(u_n) = a_n, \quad \text{is represented as} \quad \begin{pmatrix} a_1 \\ \cdot \\ \cdot \\ \cdot \\ a_n \end{pmatrix}.$$

Let us next construct the dual of this natural basis. It will consist of functionals $\mathbf{F}_1, \ldots, \mathbf{F}_n$ such that $\mathbf{F}_i\mathbf{Z}_i = 1$, but $\mathbf{F}_i\mathbf{Z}_j = 0$ otherwise. The most general functional can then be written as

$$\mathbf{F} = w_1\mathbf{F}_1 + \ldots + w_n\mathbf{F}_n. \tag{2}$$

Let us combine the results we have for the representation of an arbitrary **Z** and an arbitrary **F**. Using (1), we have $\mathbf{F}_i\mathbf{Z} = a_1\mathbf{F}_i\mathbf{Z}_1 + \ldots + a_n\mathbf{F}_i\mathbf{Z}_n$. All but the ith term are zero, hence $\mathbf{F}_i\mathbf{Z} = a_i$. We already know this from previous considerations, since in the dual basis $\mathbf{F}_i$ assigns to a vector its ith coordinate. Using (2) we then have that

$$\mathbf{FZ} = w_1\mathbf{F}_1\mathbf{Z} + \ldots + w_n\mathbf{F}_n\mathbf{Z} = w_1a_1 + \ldots + w_na_n. \tag{3}$$

This expression is just like the formula for the mean of a function. Indeed, if the w_i are the weights of a measure, then this is the mean of **Z**. Hence we see that **M**(**Z**) is a functional for every measure defined on $\mathcal{U}$. We further see that the most general functional (3) is obtained as a "generalized mean" in which we allow weights to be arbitrary real numbers.

It is also worth while comparing the two dual natural bases. We have noted that the function $\mathbf{Z}_i$ is the characteristic function of the unit set $\{u_i\}$. The functional $\mathbf{F}_i$, thought of as a weight function, assigns weight 1 to u_i, and 0 elsewhere. Hence it may be thought of as asserting that u_i is certain to happen.

EXERCISES

1. Show that if two nonzero functionals **F** and **G** have the same kernel, then $\mathbf{F} = c\mathbf{G}$ for some number c.
2. Show that the kernel of a nonzero functional is a subspace of $\mathcal{X}$ of dimension $n - 1$ (assuming that $\mathcal{X}$ has dimension n).
3. Check that Examples 1–5 are indeed functionals.
4. Find an appropriate basis for the vector space in Example 7, and write the functional of that example as a row vector.
5. Repeat Exercise 4 for Example 8.
6. Show that the set $\mathcal{F}$ of functionals on a vector space is a subspace of the space of all numerical functions on $\mathcal{X}$.
7. Let $\mathcal{X}$ be the space of polynomials $\mathbf{X}(t) = at^2 + bt + c$. Verify that each of the following is a functional on $\mathcal{X}$.
   (a) $\mathbf{G}_1\mathbf{X} = \mathbf{X}(1)$ [the value of the polynomial for $t = 1$].
   (b) $\mathbf{G}_2\mathbf{X} = \int_0^1 \mathbf{X}(t)\,dt$.
   (c) $\mathbf{G}_3\mathbf{X} = b$.
8. Prove that the three functionals in Exercise 7 form a functional basis.
9. In Exercise 7 choose 1, t, t^2, as a basis. Express the dual basis in terms of $\mathbf{G}_1$, $\mathbf{G}_2$, $\mathbf{G}_3$.
10. In Exercise 7 find the dual of the basis $\mathbf{G}_1$, $\mathbf{G}_2$, $\mathbf{G}_3$, of $\mathcal{F}$.

11. Let Γ be a basis for the space $\mathfrak{X}_n$ of column vectors. Let Δ be its dual basis in the space $\mathfrak{F}_n$ of row vectors. Show that also Γ is the basis dual to Δ.

*14. APPLICATION OF VECTOR SPACE IDEAS TO DIFFERENTIAL EQUATIONS

One useful application of vector space ideas arises in the theory of linear differential equations. We shall discuss here the simplest case: to wit, the nth order linear homogeneous differential equation with constant coefficients. The general form of this equation may be written (using the letter $\mathbf{D}$ to indicate differentiation with respect to the variable t) as follows:

$$\mathbf{D}^n\mathbf{Y} + a_1\mathbf{D}^{n-1}\mathbf{Y} + \ldots + a_{n-1}\mathbf{D}\mathbf{Y} + a_n\mathbf{Y} = 0. \tag{1}$$

In equation (1) the quantities a_i are numbers and $\mathbf{Y}$ is the unknown function of t that we want to find. Frequently *initial conditions* are also specified with the problem. These are commonly given by specifying the value of $\mathbf{Y}$ and its first $n - 1$ derivatives at a point. For example,

$$\mathbf{Y} = b_1, \mathbf{D}\mathbf{Y} = b_2, \ldots, \mathbf{D}^{n-1}\mathbf{Y} = b_n, \quad \text{when } t = 0, \tag{2}$$

is a suitable set of initial conditions.

We first observe that the set of all solutions to (1) forms a vector space. To see this we observe that if $\mathbf{Y}$ is a solution then by direct substitution into (1), the function $k\mathbf{Y}$ is also a solution for any number k; and if $\mathbf{Y}_1$ and $\mathbf{Y}_2$ are two different solutions to (1), then the function $\mathbf{Y} = \mathbf{Y}_1 + \mathbf{Y}_2$ is also a solution, as can be seen by direct substitution. This proves that the solutions to (1) form a vector space, since they constitute a subspace of the space of all numerical functions of t.

Knowing that we have a vector space, we can immediately ask two important questions: (i) What is its dimension? and (ii) What is a convenient basis for it? We shall give the answers to these questions and prove the validity of the answers under certain assumptions concerning the coefficients of (1).

Suppose we try as a solution to (1) the function e^{rt}, where r is a constant to be determined. Using the rule $\mathbf{D}^m e^{rt} = r^m e^{rt}$, we have

$$[r^n + a_1 r^{n-1} + \ldots + a_{n-1} r + a_n]e^{rt} = 0. \tag{3}$$

Since the exponential function e^{rt} is never zero, the product in (3) is zero only if the factor in brackets is zero, that is,

$$r^n + a_1 r^{n-1} + \ldots + a_{n-1} r + a_n = 0. \tag{4}$$

Equation (4) is sometimes called the *characteristic equation* of the differential equation (1). Equation (4) is an nth degree polynomial in r and, by a well-known theorem, has n roots (if both real and complex roots are counted, and multiple roots are counted according to their multiplicity). In order to simplify the discussion we shall assume that (4) has *n distinct real* roots.

Let $r_1, r_2, \ldots, r_n$ be the n distinct real roots of (4) and consider the functions $e^{r_1t}, e^{r_2t}, \ldots, e^{r_nt}$. Our first assertion is that these functions are linearly independent; for suppose the roots are written in ascending order of size (by relabeling, if necessary) so that $r_1 < r_2 < \ldots < r_n$, and suppose that we have a linear relation the form

$$(5) \qquad c_1e^{r_1t} + c_2e^{r_2t} + \ldots + c_ke^{r_kt} = 0 \quad \text{and} \quad c_k \neq 0,$$

for all values of t. We have selected our notation here so that k is the largest index of the nonzero coefficients. Now divide (5) by e^{r_kt} and let $t \to \infty$. Since e^{-t} tends to 0 as $t \to \infty$ we obtain $c_k = 0$, contrary to assumption. Hence the functions are linearly independent and the dimension of the vector space of solutions is at least n.

To show that the dimension of the vector space of solutions to (1) is exactly n we must show that the functions $e^{r_1t}, e^{r_2t}, \ldots, e^{r_nt}$ span the space. This will then prove that the "most general solution" is

$$(6) \qquad \mathbf{Y} = c_1e^{r_1t} + c_2e^{r_2t} + \ldots + c_ne^{r_nt}.$$

Theorem. Consider a differential equation of the form (1) such that the characteristic equation has n distinct real roots $r_1, r_2, \ldots, r_n$. Then any solution $\mathbf{Y}$ of the equation is a linear combination of the solutions e^{r_1t}, $e^{r_2t}, \ldots, e^{r_nt}$.

Proof: We shall give the proof only for the case of a second-degree equation. The general proof is similar. Let us write the equation in the form

$$\mathbf{Y}'' + a\mathbf{Y}' + b\mathbf{Y} = 0.$$

Let $\mathbf{Y}$ be any solution of this equation. Consider the equations

$$(7) \qquad \mathbf{Y}(t) = \mathbf{c}(t)e^{rt} + \mathbf{d}(t)e^{st}$$

$$(8) \qquad \mathbf{Y}'(t) = \mathbf{c}(t)re^{rt} + \mathbf{d}(t)se^{st}.$$

For every value of t, there is a unique solution to these equations. (See Exercise 11.) These solutions determine functions $\mathbf{c}$ and $\mathbf{d}$. We would like to prove that these are, in fact, constant functions. If we differentiate (7) we obtain

$$\mathbf{Y}'(t) = \mathbf{c}'(t)e^{rt} + \mathbf{c}(t)re^{rt} + \mathbf{d}'(t)e^{st} + \mathbf{d}(t)se^{st}$$

(The differentiability of functions $\mathbf{c}$ and $\mathbf{d}$ is easy to prove. See Exercise 11.)

Combining this equation with (8) gives

$$0 = \mathbf{c}'(t)e^{rt} + \mathbf{d}'(t)e^{st}. \tag{9}$$

Differentiating (8), we have

$$\mathbf{Y}''(t) = \mathbf{c}'(t)re^{rt} + \mathbf{c}(t)r^2e^{rt} + \mathbf{d}'(t)se^{st} + \mathbf{d}(t)s^2e^{st}. \tag{10}$$

Multiplying (7) by b, (8) by a, and adding the results to (10) gives

$$\mathbf{Y}''(t) + a\mathbf{Y}'(t) + b\mathbf{Y}(t) = \mathbf{c}(t)e^{rt}(r^2 + ar + b)$$
$$+ \mathbf{d}(t)e^{st}(s^2 + as + b) + \mathbf{c}'(t)re^{rt} + \mathbf{d}'(t)se^{st}.$$

Making use of the fact that $\mathbf{Y}$ satisfies the differential equation and that r and s satisfy the characteristic equation, we have

$$0 = \mathbf{c}'(t)re^{rt} + \mathbf{d}'(t)se^{st}. \tag{11}$$

Multiplying (9) by r and subtracting the result from (11) gives

$$0 = \mathbf{d}'(t)(s - r)e^{st}.$$

Since $s \neq r$ and e^{st} is never zero, we must have $\mathbf{d}'(t) = 0$ for every t. Hence $\mathbf{d}$ is a constant function. But then from (11) we also have that $\mathbf{c}'(t)$ must be zero. Hence $\mathbf{c}$ is also a constant function, completing the proof.

Example 1. Consider the differential equation

$$\mathbf{D}^2\mathbf{Y} - 3\mathbf{D}\mathbf{Y} + 2\mathbf{Y} = 0.$$

Its characteristic equation is $r^2 - 3r + 2 = 0$, which has roots $r_1 = 1$ and $r_2 = 2$. Hence the most general solution is $\mathbf{Y}(t) = c_1e^t + c_2e^{2t}$. The reader may verify that this function is a solution to the equation by taking its first and second derivatives and substituting them into the equation.

Next we shall prove that given an equation of the form (1) whose characteristic equation has n distinct real roots, there is one and only one solution of (1) that satisfies initial conditions of the form (2). Consider the following transformation $\mathbf{A}$ that has as domain the space $\mathcal{Y}$ of all solutions $\mathbf{Y}$ to the homogeneous differential equation (1) and range contained in the space $\mathfrak{X}_n$ of n-dimensional column vectors.

$$\mathbf{Y} \xrightarrow{\mathbf{A}} \begin{pmatrix} \mathbf{Y}(0) \\ \mathbf{Y}'(0) \\ \cdot \\ \cdot \\ \cdot \\ \mathbf{Y}^{(n-1)}(0) \end{pmatrix}. \tag{12}$$

What we want to prove about the existence and uniqueness of solutions to (1) amounts to proving that the transformation $\mathbf{A}$ is one-one.

If we let Γ be the basis $e^{r_1 t}, \ldots, e^{r_n t}$ for $\mathcal{Y}$ and Δ the natural basis for $\mathcal{X}_n$, then (see Exercise 7)

$$\binom{\mathrm{A}}{\Delta\Gamma} = \begin{pmatrix} 1 & 1 & \ldots & 1 \\ r_1 & r_2 & \ldots & r_n \\ r_1^2 & r_2^2 & \ldots & r_n^2 \\ \cdot & \cdot & \cdot\cdot\cdot & \cdot \\ r_1^{n-1} & r_2^{n-1} & \ldots & r_n^{n-1} \end{pmatrix}. \tag{13}$$

We must prove that this matrix is invertible. It will be so unless (say) the rows are linearly dependent. Hence suppose there exist n numbers $c_0, \ldots, c_{n-1}$ such that

$$c_0(1\ 1\ \ldots\ 1) + c_1(r_1\ r_2\ \ldots\ r_n) + \ldots + c_{n-1}(r_1^{n-1}\ r_2^{n-1}\ \ldots\ r_n^{n-1}) = 0.$$

We have then really n simultaneous equations

$$\begin{aligned} c_0 + c_1 r_1 + \ldots + c_{n-1} r_1^{n-1} &= 0 \\ c_0 + c_1 r_2 + \ldots + c_{n-1} r_2^{n-1} &= 0 \\ \ldots\quad & \\ c_0 + c_1 r_n + \ldots + c_{n-1} r_n^{n-1} &= 0. \end{aligned}$$

Or equivalently we have n distinct "roots" of the polynomial

$$c_0 + c_1 x + \ldots + c_{n-1} x^{n-1}.$$

But you are familiar with the fact that a polynomial of degree $n - 1$ cannot have n different roots. Hence our supposition that the rows of the matrix were dependent is impossible, and we have the following theorem.

Theorem. Suppose that the polynomial $a_n + a_{n-1}x + \ldots + a_1 x^{n-1} + x^n$ has n distinct real roots. Then the vector space $\mathcal{Y}$ of solutions $\mathbf{Y}$ to the homogeneous differential equation

$$(\mathbf{D}^n + a_1\mathbf{D}^{n-1} + \ldots + a_{n-1}\mathbf{D} + a_n)\mathbf{Y} = 0$$

is n-dimensional. And the transformation

$$\mathbf{Y} \to \begin{pmatrix} \mathbf{Y}(0) \\ \mathbf{Y}'(0) \\ \cdot \\ \cdot \\ \cdot \\ \mathbf{Y}^{(n-1)}(0) \end{pmatrix}$$

is one-one.

Example 1 (Cont.). For the differential equation of Example 1 suppose that the following initial conditions have been specified:

$$\mathbf{Y} = -2 \quad \text{and} \quad \mathbf{DY} = 3 \quad \text{when} \quad t = 0.$$

Then we must solve the equations

$$c_1 + c_2 = -2, \qquad c_1 + 2c_2 = 3.$$

The matrix of coefficients and its inverse are

$$M = \begin{pmatrix} 1 & 1 \\ 1 & 2 \end{pmatrix} \quad \text{and} \quad M^{-1} = \begin{pmatrix} 2 & -1 \\ -1 & 1 \end{pmatrix}.$$

Hence we have

$$\begin{pmatrix} c_1 \\ c_2 \end{pmatrix} = \begin{pmatrix} 2 & -1 \\ -1 & 1 \end{pmatrix}\begin{pmatrix} -2 \\ 3 \end{pmatrix} = \begin{pmatrix} -7 \\ 5 \end{pmatrix}.$$

The reader may easily check that the solution $\mathbf{Y}(t) = -7e^t + 5e^{2t}$ does solve the differential equation and also satisfies the initial conditions.

EXERCISES

Find the general solutions to the following differential equations:

1. $\mathbf{D}^2\mathbf{Y} - \mathbf{DY} - 6\mathbf{Y} = 0.$
2. $\mathbf{D}^3\mathbf{Y} - 5\mathbf{D}^2\mathbf{Y} - 2\mathbf{DY} + 24\mathbf{Y} = 0.$

   [*Ans.* $\mathbf{Y}(t) = a_1e^{3t} + a_2e^{4t} + a_3e^{-2t}$.]
3. $2\mathbf{D}^2\mathbf{Y} + 13\mathbf{DY} + 6\mathbf{Y} = 0.$
4. For the differential equation in Exercise 1 find the particular solution **Y** such that
$$\mathbf{Y}(0) = 1, \qquad \mathbf{Y}'(0) = 2.$$
5. For the differential equation in Exercise 2 find the particular solution **Y** such that
$$\mathbf{Y}(0) = 0, \qquad \mathbf{Y}'(0) = 1, \qquad \mathbf{Y}''(0) = -1.$$
   [*Ans.* $a_1 = \frac{3}{5}$, $a_2 = -\frac{1}{3}$, $a_3 = -\frac{4}{15}$.]
6. For the differential equation in Exercise 3 find the particular solution Y such that
$$\mathbf{Y}(0) = -2, \qquad \mathbf{Y}'(0) = 3.$$
7. If **A** is the transformation in (12) show that $\begin{pmatrix} \mathbf{A} \\ \Delta\Gamma \end{pmatrix}$ has the form shown in (13), when Γ consists of the functions $e^{r_1t}, \ldots, e^{r_nt}$ and Δ is the natural basis in $\mathfrak{X}_n$.
8. Given initial conditions (2) and the general solution to the nth order equation (1), use the theorem of this section to show that a particular solution can always be found that satisfies these initial conditions.
9. A differential equation of the form

   (*) $\quad \mathbf{D}^n\mathbf{Y} + a_1\mathbf{D}^{n-1}\mathbf{Y} + \ldots + a_{n-1}\mathbf{DY} + a_n\mathbf{Y} = \mathbf{W},$

   where **W** is a given function and **Y** is the unknown function, is called *nonhomogeneous*. Show that if $\mathbf{Y}_1$ and $\mathbf{Y}_2$ are solutions to this equation, then the function $\mathbf{Y}_1 - \mathbf{Y}_2$ is a solution to the homogeneous equation

(**) $\mathbf{D}^n\mathbf{Y} + a_1\mathbf{D}^{n-1}\mathbf{Y} + \ldots + a_{n-1}\mathbf{D}\mathbf{Y} + a_n\mathbf{Y} = 0.$

10. Show that if $\mathbf{Y}_0$ is one solution to the nonhomogeneous differential equation (*) of Exercise 9, then the general solution to this nonhomogeneous equation is of the form $\mathbf{Y} + \mathbf{Y}_0$, where $\mathbf{Y}$ is the general solution to the homogeneous equation (**).

11. Solve equations (7) and (8) for $\mathbf{c}(t)$ and $\mathbf{d}(t)$. Show that the resulting functions are differentiable.

15. THREE-DIMENSIONAL VECTOR GEOMETRY

The concepts of ordinary 2- and 3-dimensional geometry may be divided into two main categories. The first category would contain such concepts as point, plane, between, parallel, and parallel comparative length. Only these concepts of the first category were used in Section 1 for defining (oblique) coordinate systems and in Section 6 for defining geometric vectors. The second category would contain angle, distance, perpendicular, and cartesian coordinate system. The significant difference between the two categories is that concepts in the first category can be explained purely in terms of vectors, while the second category requires something additional. We will discuss the pure vector concepts in this section and the next section, and will take up concepts of the second category in Section 17. Our discussion will focus at first on three-dimensional space, but we will eventually point out the generalization of our methods to fewer and more dimensions.

It will be convenient to adopt a conventional notation for variables and for constants. In analytic geometry it is customary to use (x, y, z) as the coordinates of a variable point, while subscripts are added if we think of the point as fixed. Similarly in the geometry sections of the present chapter we will write X, $\mathbf{F}$, t for variable vectors, functionals, and numbers, respectively, while X_1, $\mathbf{F}_1$, and t_1 will be thought of as fixed.

As our first problem we consider the vector representation of a line in three dimensions. If the line $\mathcal{L}$ passes through the origin, then it forms a 1-dimensional subspace, and hence must consist of all multiples of some given vector. Hence a line through the origin may be written in the form

$$tX_1, \qquad X_1 \neq 0, \tag{1}$$

where t may take on any real number as a value. This is known as a *parametric representation* of $\mathcal{L}$, and t is called a *parameter*. Suppose that we now add the vector X_2 to every point on $\mathcal{L}$. Then the resulting set of points

$$(2) \qquad tX_1 + X_2, \qquad X_1 \neq 0,$$

will be a line $\mathcal{L}'$ parallel to $\mathcal{L}$ (see Figure 34). We also say that $\mathcal{L}'$ results from $\mathcal{L}$ through *translation* by X_2. (And more generally we say that any subset $\mathcal{S}_1$ of a vector space is a *translate* of some other subset $\mathcal{S}$ if there is some fixed vector Y such that when we add Y to each of the points in $\mathcal{S}$ we obtain precisely the points in $\mathcal{S}_1$.)

But given any line $\mathcal{L}'$ in 3-dimensional space, it always is parallel to some line $\mathcal{L}$ through the origin, and can be obtained from $\mathcal{L}$ through translation. Hence any line can be represented parametrically in the form (2), as all points of the form $tX_1 + X_2$, where t is any real number.

If in (2) we set t equal to 0, we note that X_2 is a point on our line. And conversely, it is easily seen that X_2 may be chosen as any point on the line (see Exercise 1).

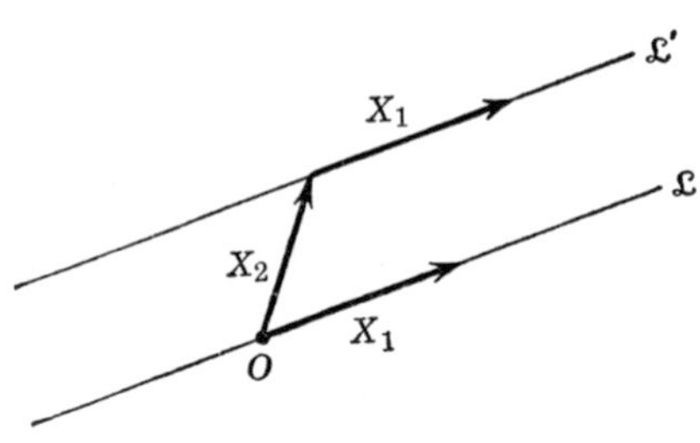

Figure 34

From Figure 34 we see that the vector X_1 may be thought of as determining the "direction" of the line. Since X_1 and kX_1 are in the same direction for $k \neq 0$, we may choose any nonzero multiple of X_1 (see Exercise 2), in place of X_1.

Thus we see that while any line may be represented parametrically in the form (2), this representation is not unique. The vector X_1 may be replaced by a nonzero multiple, and X_2 may be any point on the line. This representation of a line may be thought of as corresponding to the determination of a line in two dimensions by specifying a point on it and the slope of the line.

Example 1. The expression $t\begin{pmatrix}1\\0\\2\end{pmatrix}$ is a parametric representation of a line $\mathcal{L}$ through the origin. This line contains all points of the form $\begin{pmatrix}t\\0\\2t\end{pmatrix}$. The line $\mathcal{L}'$ represented by $t\begin{pmatrix}1\\0\\2\end{pmatrix} + \begin{pmatrix}-1\\5\\3\end{pmatrix}$ results from the former by translation, and hence it is a parallel line, through $\begin{pmatrix} -1 \\ 5 \\ 3 \end{pmatrix}$. It contains all points of the form $\begin{pmatrix} t-1 \\ 5 \\ 2t+3 \end{pmatrix}$.

The numerical vectors that appear in the above example, and in subsequent examples, should be interpreted geometrically, but relative to an *oblique* coordinate system, since perpendicularity of the axes plays no role in sections 15–16.

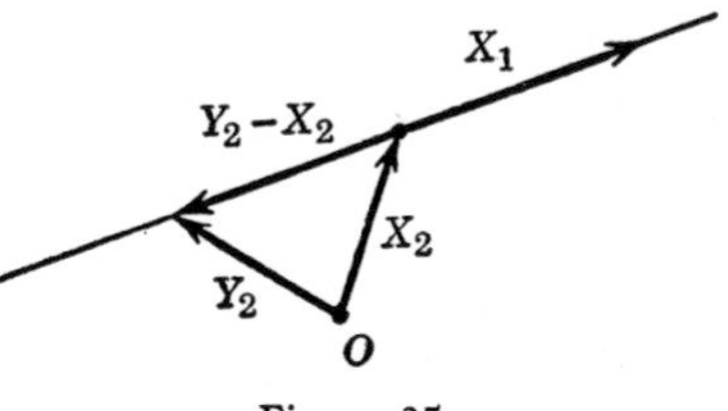

Figure 35

Suppose that we are given a line $tX_1 + X_2$, and a point Y_2. We are asked to determine whether Y_2 lies on the given line. This means that for some value of the parameter, $tX_1 + X_2 = Y_2$, or $tX_1 = Y_2 - X_2$. Hence we have to test only whether $Y_2 - X_2$ is a multiple of X_1. This can also be seen easily from Figure 35.

Example 2. Let us ask whether $Y_2 = \begin{pmatrix} 2 \\ 5 \\ 9 \end{pmatrix}$ lies on either line in Example 1. For $\mathcal{L}$ we have $X_2 = 0$, and hence Y_2 itself would have to be a multiple of $X_1 = \begin{pmatrix} 1 \\ 0 \\ 2 \end{pmatrix}$. But since Y_2 does not have 0 as its second component, this is clearly not so. For $\mathcal{L}'$, $Y_2 - X_2 = \begin{pmatrix} 3 \\ 0 \\ 6 \end{pmatrix} = 3X_1$. Hence Y_2 lies on $\mathcal{L}'$ and corresponds to the parameter value $t = 3$.

Two lines $tX_1 + X_2$ and $tY_1 + Y_2$ are parallel if and only if they are translated from the same line through the origin. This would be the case if $X_1 = Y_1$. But since we may replace X_1 by any nonzero multiple, the two lines will be parallel if and only if $Y_1 = kX_1$.

Example 3. Let us find a line parallel to $t\begin{pmatrix} 1 \\ 2 \\ 3 \end{pmatrix} + \begin{pmatrix} 1 \\ 1 \\ 1 \end{pmatrix}$ which goes through the point $\begin{pmatrix} 1 \\ 0 \\ -1 \end{pmatrix}$. Obviously, the line $t\begin{pmatrix} 1 \\ 2 \\ 3 \end{pmatrix} + \begin{pmatrix} 1 \\ 0 \\ -1 \end{pmatrix}$ will have both of these properties.

Let us now turn to planes in three dimensions. A plane $\mathcal{P}$ through the origin is a 2-dimensional subspace of 3-dimensional space, and hence it must be the kernel of some functional. Hence the plane is the truth set of an open statement of the form

$$(3) \qquad \mathbf{F}_1X = 0, \qquad \mathbf{F}_1 \neq 0.$$

This is known as an *implicit* representation of $\mathcal{P}$. Let us now consider a plane $\mathcal{P}'$ not through the origin. It can be obtained from some plane $\mathcal{P}$ through the origin by adding some X_1 to each point, that is, through translation by X_1 (see Figure 36). Thus Y is in $\mathcal{P}'$ if and only if it is of the form $Y = X + X_1$, where X is in $\mathcal{P}$. But then $\mathbf{F}_1Y = \mathbf{F}_1X + \mathbf{F}_1X_1 = \mathbf{F}_1X_1 = c_1$, where c_1 is a number. Hence the points on $\mathcal{P}'$ are the truth set of an equation

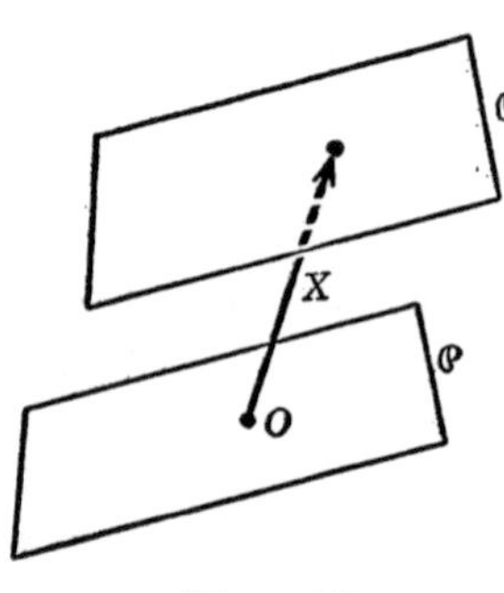

Figure 36

$$(4) \qquad \mathbf{F}_1X = c_1.$$

This implicit representation is again not unique, since we can multiply through by a number, that is, $\mathbf{F}_1$ and c_1 may be replaced by $k\mathbf{F}_1$ and kc_1, for any nonzero k. For a given functional $\mathbf{F}_1$ the various planes obtained by taking various values for c_1 in the equation $\mathbf{F}_1X = c_1$ are known as the *level planes* of the functional $\mathbf{F}_1$. All these level planes are parallel. And conversely, any two parallel planes can be represented as different level planes of the same functional.

To test whether a given point X_1 lies in the plane given by (4), we merely test whether it lies in the truth set of the equation, that is, whether $\mathbf{F}_1X_1 = c_1$ is true.

Example 4. Does the point $\begin{pmatrix} 1 \\ 2 \\ 3 \end{pmatrix}$ lie in $(5 \quad 3 \quad -1)X = 2$? Since

$$(5 \quad 3 \quad -1)\begin{pmatrix} 1 \\ 2 \\ 3 \end{pmatrix} = 8,$$

the point is not in the plane. And since

$$(5 \quad 3 \quad -1)\begin{pmatrix} 1 \\ -1 \\ 0 \end{pmatrix} = 2,$$

the point $\begin{pmatrix} 1 \\ -1 \\ 0 \end{pmatrix}$ is in the plane.

Let us ask how one finds the intersection of the line $tX_1 + X_2$ with the plane $\mathbf{F}_1X = c_1$. The point(s) of intersection would have to be of the form $tX_1 + X_2$ and would have to lie in the truth set of the equation. Hence we look for one or more parameter values for which

$$\mathbf{F}_1(tX_1 + X_2) = t\mathbf{F}_1X_1 + \mathbf{F}_1X_2 = c_1, \tag{5}$$

where $\mathbf{F}_1X_1$ and $\mathbf{F}_1X_2$ are numbers. If $\mathbf{F}_1X_1 \neq 0$, we have a unique solution for (5), namely,

$$t_0 = (c_1 - \mathbf{F}_1X_2)/\mathbf{F}_1X_1 \quad \text{and} \quad X_0 = t_0X_1 + X_2. \tag{6}$$

Thus t_0 is the parameter value of the point of intersection, and X_0 is the unique intersection point.

But the solution is entirely different if $\mathbf{F}_1X_1 = 0$. Then (5) reduces to $\mathbf{F}_1X_2 = c_1$, an expression that does not contain t. If this equation is true, then any value of t yields an intersection point; but if it is false, then no value of t will serve. Another way of putting it is to say that an equality between two numbers is either logically true or logically false, hence its set is either the set of all real numbers or the empty set.

From these considerations we deduce that $\mathbf{F}_1X_1 = 0$ is the necessary and sufficient condition for the line $tX_1 + X_2$ to be parallel to the plane $\mathbf{F}_1X = c_1$. If in addition $\mathbf{F}_1X_2 = c_1$, then the line lies entirely in the plane.

Example 5. Consider the plane $(1, 2, 3)X = 6$, and lines $\mathcal{L}_1$, $\mathcal{L}_2$, $\mathcal{L}_3$ given parametrically as

$$t\begin{pmatrix}1\\2\\1\end{pmatrix} + \begin{pmatrix}-1\\0\\1\end{pmatrix}, \quad t\begin{pmatrix}1\\1\\-1\end{pmatrix} + \begin{pmatrix}-1\\0\\1\end{pmatrix}, \quad t\begin{pmatrix}1\\1\\-1\end{pmatrix} + \begin{pmatrix}1\\1\\1\end{pmatrix},$$

respectively. For $\mathcal{L}_1$,

$$(1 \quad 2 \quad 3)\begin{pmatrix}1\\2\\1\end{pmatrix} = 8 \neq 0,$$

hence we have a unique intersection;

$$t_0 = \frac{6-2}{8} = \frac{1}{2} \quad \text{and} \quad X_0 = \frac{1}{2}\begin{pmatrix}1\\2\\1\end{pmatrix} + \begin{pmatrix}-1\\0\\1\end{pmatrix} = \begin{pmatrix}-\frac{1}{2}\\1\\\frac{3}{2}\end{pmatrix}.$$

For $\mathcal{L}_2$ and $\mathcal{L}_3$,

$$(1 \quad 2 \quad 3)\begin{pmatrix}1\\1\\-1\end{pmatrix} = 0,$$

hence they are parallel to the plane. For $\mathcal{L}_3$ we also find

$$(1 \quad 2 \quad 3)\begin{pmatrix}1\\1\\1\end{pmatrix} = 6 = c_1,$$

hence it lies in the plane.

Next let us raise the question as to whether the lines $tX_1 + X_2$ and $tY_1 + Y_2$ are *coplanar*, that is whether there is a plane containing both of them. In general, one expects a negative answer, but under special conditions on X_1, X_2, Y_1, Y_2 such a plane may exist. Here we are searching for a nonzero **F** and a c such that the plane they determine contains both lines. This leads to five conditions:

$$\mathbf{F} \neq 0, \quad \mathbf{F}X_1 = 0, \quad \mathbf{F}Y_1 = 0, \quad \mathbf{F}X_2 = c, \quad \text{and} \quad \mathbf{F}Y_2 = c.$$

But we do not really care what the value of c is, as long as it exists. Hence the last two conditions reduce to $\mathbf{F}X_2 = \mathbf{F}Y_2$. Thus the conditions for the two lines to be coplanar may be written as:

(7) There is nonzero functional **F** such that $\mathbf{F}X_1 = 0$, $\mathbf{F}Y_1 = 0$, and $\mathbf{F}(X_2 - Y_2) = 0$.

If these three equations for **F** have a common nonzero solution, then the lines are coplanar. If one solution is $\mathbf{F} = \mathbf{F}_0$, and we let $\mathbf{F}_0X_2 = c_0$, then the plane $\mathbf{F}_0X = c_0$ contains both lines.

Example 6. Are the lines $t\begin{pmatrix}1\\1\\-1\end{pmatrix} + \begin{pmatrix}1\\1\\1\end{pmatrix}$ and $t\begin{pmatrix}1\\-2\\1\end{pmatrix} + \begin{pmatrix}2\\5\\-2\end{pmatrix}$ coplanar?

Letting $\mathbf{F} = (f_1 f_2 f_3)$, the conditions (7) become

$$\begin{aligned} f_1 + f_2 - f_3 &= 0, \\ f_1 - 2f_2 + f_3 &= 0, \\ -f_1 - 4f_2 + 3f_3 &= 0. \end{aligned}$$

These equations are consistent, hence the lines are coplanar. Letting $\mathbf{F}_0 = (1 \quad 2 \quad 3)$, and hence $c_0 = 6$, we have $(1 \quad 2 \quad 3)X = 6$ as an equation for the plane containing both lines. (We have already seen in Example 5 that the first line lies in this plane.)

EXERCISES

1. In representing the line $\mathcal{L}$ by the parametric expression

$$tX_1 + X_2,$$

show that X_2 may be chosen as any point on $\mathcal{L}$.

2. Show that in representing the line $\mathcal{L}$ by the parametric expression

$$tX_1 + X_2,$$

that X_1 may be replaced by any of its nonzero numerical multiples kX_1.

3. Give a geometric interpretation for the equations (7) for two lines to be coplanar.

4. Show that the following two parametric expressions represent the same line:

$$t\begin{pmatrix}1\\0\\-2\end{pmatrix}+\begin{pmatrix}1\\2\\3\end{pmatrix}, \qquad t\begin{pmatrix}-2\\0\\4\end{pmatrix}+\begin{pmatrix}2\\2\\1\end{pmatrix}.$$

5. Is the line through $\begin{pmatrix}1\\2\\3\end{pmatrix}$ and $\begin{pmatrix}3\\-1\\0\end{pmatrix}$ parallel to the vector $\begin{pmatrix}5\\-2\\3\end{pmatrix}$?

6. Represent parametrically the line through $\begin{pmatrix}1\\2\\5\end{pmatrix}$ parallel to the line through $\begin{pmatrix}1\\0\\3\end{pmatrix}$ and $\begin{pmatrix}0\\1\\2\end{pmatrix}$.

7. Find an equation for the plane through

$$\begin{pmatrix}1\\2\\3\end{pmatrix}, \quad \begin{pmatrix}0\\0\\1\end{pmatrix}, \quad \begin{pmatrix}0\\1\\0\end{pmatrix}.$$

8. Which of the following points lie on the plane in Exercise 7 above?

$$\begin{pmatrix}1\\3\\2\end{pmatrix}, \quad \begin{pmatrix}1\\1\\4\end{pmatrix}, \quad \begin{pmatrix}0\\0\\0\end{pmatrix}, \quad \begin{pmatrix}4\\-1\\2\end{pmatrix}.$$

9. Write an equation for a plane parallel to the plane in Exercise 7 and passing through $\begin{pmatrix}5\\-2\\0\end{pmatrix}$.

10. For each of the following lines and planes find the point(s) of intersection of the line with plane.

(a) $t\begin{pmatrix}1\\1\\1\end{pmatrix}+\begin{pmatrix}1\\0\\-1\end{pmatrix}$; $(1\ 1\ 1)X = 3$. [*Ans.* $\begin{pmatrix}2\\1\\0\end{pmatrix}$.]

(b) $t\begin{pmatrix}1\\1\\1\end{pmatrix}+\begin{pmatrix}1\\0\\-1\end{pmatrix}$; $(3\ 2\ 1)X = 6$.

(c) $t\begin{pmatrix}1\\0\\-1\end{pmatrix}+\begin{pmatrix}3\\2\\1\end{pmatrix}$; $(1\ 1\ 1)X = 3$. [*Ans.* None.]

(d) $t\begin{pmatrix}1\\0\\-1\end{pmatrix}+\begin{pmatrix}2\\1\\0\end{pmatrix}$; $(1\ 1\ 1)X = 3$.

11. Which of the following pairs of lines are coplanar? For the coplanar pairs write an equation for the plane in which they lie.

(a) $t\begin{pmatrix}1\\0\\-1\end{pmatrix}+\begin{pmatrix}1\\1\\1\end{pmatrix}$; $t\begin{pmatrix}1\\-2\\1\end{pmatrix}+\begin{pmatrix}3\\0\\0\end{pmatrix}$.

[*Ans.* Coplanar; $(1\ 1\ 1)X = 3$.]

(b) $t\begin{pmatrix}1\\0\\0\end{pmatrix}+\begin{pmatrix}1\\1\\2\end{pmatrix}$; $t\begin{pmatrix}0\\1\\0\end{pmatrix}+\begin{pmatrix}1\\1\\1\end{pmatrix}$. [*Ans.* Not coplanar.]

(c) $t\begin{pmatrix}1\\1\\1\end{pmatrix}+\begin{pmatrix}1\\2\\3\end{pmatrix}$; $t\begin{pmatrix}-1\\1\\-1\end{pmatrix}$.

(d) $t\begin{pmatrix}-1\\1\\1\end{pmatrix}+\begin{pmatrix}1\\1\\1\end{pmatrix}$; $t\begin{pmatrix}1\\-2\\1\end{pmatrix}+\begin{pmatrix}2\\0\\0\end{pmatrix}$.

12. Let a line $\mathcal{L}$ be given by the parametric expression $Y_0 + tW_0$. Let Z_0 be some point not on $\mathcal{L}$. Write an equation for the plane that contains $\mathcal{L}$ and Z_0.

13. Given different level planes $\mathcal{P}_1$ and $\mathcal{P}_2$ of the same functional **F**, how can we recognize from c_1 and c_2 whether the planes are on the same or opposite sides of the origin?

16. FURTHER TOPICS IN VECTOR GEOMETRY

We know that any two points will determine a line and any three points not on a line will determine a plane in three dimensions. Let us see how we find the line and plane so determined.

Let Y_1 and Y_2 be any two points on $\mathcal{L}$, and let us look for a parametric representation of $\mathcal{L}$. From Figure 37 we see that $Y_1 - Y_2$ will serve as X_1 in the parametric representation, and either point will serve as X_2.

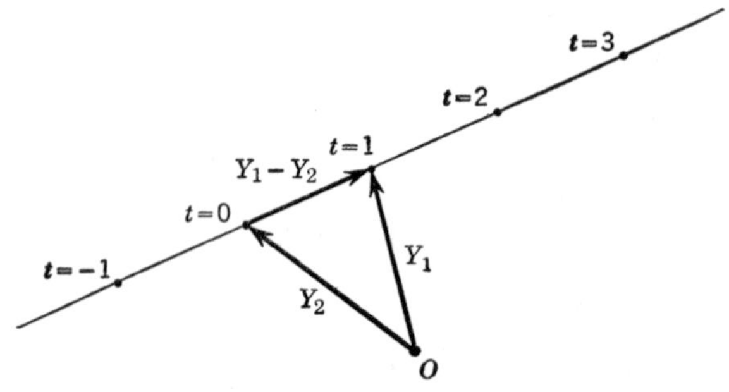

Figure 37

Thus one easy way of writing down the parametric representation of $\mathcal{L}$ is

$$t(Y_1 - Y_2) + Y_2. \tag{1}$$

We can also see from (1) directly that this is the desired line. If $t = 0$ we obtain Y_2, and if $t = 1$ we obtain Y_1, hence (1) represents a line containing both Y_1 and Y_2. It is also clear from (1) that Y_1 and Y_2 had to be distinct, otherwise t would disappear from the representation.

Let Y_1, Y_2, and Y_3 be three points which do not lie on a line. To find the plane containing them, we search for a nonzero $\mathbf{F}$ and a c such that

$$\mathbf{F}Y_1 = c, \quad \mathbf{F}Y_2 = c, \quad \text{and} \quad \mathbf{F}Y_3 = c. \tag{2}$$

We know from the nature of the problem that (2) determines a unique plane. Hence the equations will determine $\mathbf{F}$, up to a constant factor; that is, if $\mathbf{F} = \mathbf{F}_1$ is one solution, then the general solution is of the form $\mathbf{F} = k\mathbf{F}_1$, and then $c = k\mathbf{F}_1Y_1$. Hence an equation of the plane will be $\mathbf{F}_1X = \mathbf{F}_1Y_1$.

Example 1. Find the plane through the points

$$\begin{pmatrix}1\\1\\1\end{pmatrix}, \begin{pmatrix}0\\0\\2\end{pmatrix}, \text{ and } \begin{pmatrix}10\\-2\\0\end{pmatrix}.$$

The conditions (2) become

$$\begin{aligned} f_1 + f_2 + f_3 &= c,\\ 2f_3 &= c,\\ 10f_1 - 2f_2 \qquad &= c. \end{aligned}$$

The general solution of these equations is $\mathbf{F} = c(\frac{1}{6}\ \frac{1}{3}\ \frac{1}{2})$. Choosing $c = 6$, we obtain the equation $(1\ \ 2\ \ 3)X = 6$.

Equations (2) can also be used when Y_1, Y_2, Y_3 lie on a line. In this case equations (2) will yield implicit equations for *all* planes through Y_1, Y_2, Y_3. Thus solving (2) automatically tells us whether Y_1, Y_2, Y_3 lie on a line; they do if and only if (2) does not determine $\mathbf{F}$ (up to a constant factor).

There is an alternative way of testing whether three points lie on a line. We know that the line through Y_1 and Y_2 has the equation (1). We then have to decide whether Y_3 lies on this line. This will happen if and only if $Y_3 - Y_2$ is a multiple of $Y_1 - Y_2$.

Example 2. Do $\begin{pmatrix}1\\1\\1\end{pmatrix}, \begin{pmatrix}1\\0\\-1\end{pmatrix}, \begin{pmatrix}1\\3\\5\end{pmatrix}$ lie on a line? The conditions (2) become

$$\begin{aligned} f_1 + f_2 + f_3 &= c, \\ f_1 \qquad - f_3 &= c, \\ f_1 + 3f_2 + 5f_3 &= c. \end{aligned}$$

The general solutions to these equations can be written as

$$\mathbf{F} = (c + k \quad -2k \quad k).$$

Since $\mathbf{F}$ is not determined up to a constant factor by these points, we know that the given points lie on a line $\mathcal{L}$. Note that we have also found the equations of *all* planes through $\mathcal{L}$. They are of the form $(c + k \quad -2k \quad k)X = c$. For each k this is the equation of a plane through $\mathcal{L}$. By the alternate method we have to test whether $Y_3 - Y_2 = \begin{pmatrix} 0 \\ 3 \\ 6 \end{pmatrix}$ is a multiple of $Y_1 - Y_2 = \begin{pmatrix} 0 \\ 1 \\ 2 \end{pmatrix}$, which it clearly is.

Let us next suppose that we are given the planes $\mathbf{F}_1X = c_1$ and $\mathbf{F}_2X = c_2$, and we are asked to find their line of intersection. (A line represented as the intersection of two planes is said to be represented *implicitly*.) If Y is any point on their line of intersection, then it lies in both planes, and hence

$$\mathbf{F}_1Y = c_1 \quad \text{and} \quad \mathbf{F}_2Y = c_2. \tag{3}$$

If $\mathbf{F}_2 \neq k\mathbf{F}_1$, then we know that the general solution of these two simultaneous equations is $Y = tX_1 + X_2$, where X_1 is a solution of the homogeneous equations, and X_2 is any one solution of the equations. And this solution is the parametric representation of the line of intersection.

If $\mathbf{F}_2 = k\mathbf{F}_1$, then (3) will have no solution unless $c_2 = kc_1$. And in the latter case the solution contains two parameters, and hence represents more than one line. Thus we may conclude that the necessary and sufficient condition for the two planes to be parallel is that $\mathbf{F}_2$ is a multiple of $\mathbf{F}_1$. If in addition c_2 is the same multiple of c_1, then the planes coincide. Since we can always divide the second equation by k, we may write parallel planes in the form $\mathbf{F}_1X = c_1$ and $\mathbf{F}_1X = c_2$, with the same $\mathbf{F}_1$. Then the planes coincide if and only if $c_1 = c_2$.

Example 3. Find the line of intersection of $(1\ 2\ 3)X = 6$ with $(1\ 3\ 5)X = 9$. The equations (3) become

$$\begin{aligned} y_1 + 2y_2 + 3y_3 &= 6, \\ y_1 + 3y_2 + 5y_3 &= 9. \end{aligned}$$

The general solution is $Y = t\begin{pmatrix} 1 \\ -2 \\ 1 \end{pmatrix} + \begin{pmatrix} 1 \\ 1 \\ 1 \end{pmatrix}$, hence this is the parametric representation of the line of intersection.

One concept of the first category not yet discussed is the relation that Y lies *between* Y_1 and Y_2, that is, on the line segment connecting them. We know that (1) gives the entire line $\mathcal{L}$ in Figure 37, and that for $t = 0$ we obtain Y_2, while for $t = 1$ we obtain Y_1. It is easily seen from Figure 37 that the other points between Y_1 and Y_2 are given by intermediate values of t. Hence the parametric representation of the segment between Y_1 and Y_2 is

$$t(Y_1 - Y_2) + Y_2 = tY_1 + (1 - t)Y_2 \qquad 0 \leq t \leq 1. \tag{4}$$

Example 4. To find the points that trisect the segment joining $\begin{pmatrix} 1 \\ 2 \\ 3 \end{pmatrix}$ to $\begin{pmatrix} 1 \\ -1 \\ 0 \end{pmatrix}$, we take $t = \frac{1}{3}$ and $t = \frac{2}{3}$ in the parametric formula for the segment.

The trisecting point close to $\begin{pmatrix} 1 \\ 2 \\ 3 \end{pmatrix}$ is

$$\frac{2}{3}\begin{pmatrix} 1 \\ 2 \\ 3 \end{pmatrix} + \frac{1}{3}\begin{pmatrix} 1 \\ -1 \\ 0 \end{pmatrix} = \begin{pmatrix} 1 \\ 1 \\ 2 \end{pmatrix}.$$

And the trisecting point close to $\begin{pmatrix} 1 \\ -1 \\ 0 \end{pmatrix}$ is

$$\frac{1}{3}\begin{pmatrix} 1 \\ 2 \\ 3 \end{pmatrix} + \frac{2}{3}\begin{pmatrix} 1 \\ -1 \\ 0 \end{pmatrix} = \begin{pmatrix} 1 \\ 0 \\ 1 \end{pmatrix}.$$

Notice that the coefficients $\frac{1}{3}$ and $\frac{2}{3}$ of the end-point vectors have sum 1, as they should, and that the "heavier" of the two coefficients goes with the nearer of the two end points.

All applications of vector methods that we have considered so far were carried out without the introduction of a coordinate system. Even in proving geometric theorems it may happen that these coordinate-free methods give a quick proof.

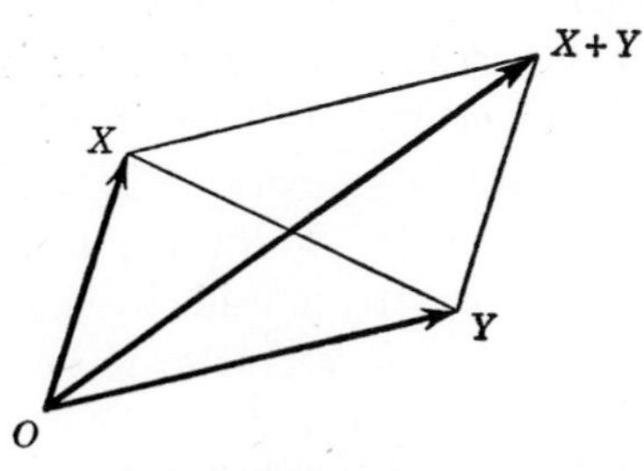

Figure 38

Example 5. Suppose we want to show that the diagonals of a parallelogram bisect each other. Let us put the origin O at one vertex and vectors X and Y at the two adjacent vertices (see Figure 38). Then the fourth vertex is $X + Y$. The intersection of the two diagonals is some numerical multiple $w(X + Y)$ of the vector $X + Y$. Hence we have

$$w(X + Y) = (1 - t)X + tY,$$
$$wX + wY = (1 - t)X + tY.$$

Since X and Y are linearly independent, the coefficients of X must be equal, and the coefficients of Y must be equal.

$$w = 1 - t,$$
$$w = t.$$

Hence $t = 1 - t = w = \frac{1}{2}$, and we have proved that the intersection of the diagonals is the mid-point of each.

We thus see that a great many geometrical problems can be solved without introducing such concepts as length and angles. Actually, we can even introduce a limited concept of length by purely vector methods.

We know that the choice of a coordinate system is equivalent to the choice of a basis for the vector space. It is only when we require that the axes be perpendicular and that we have the "same" unit of length on all axes that we need concepts of the second category. These problems will be discussed in the next section.

While with vector methods alone we cannot compare the lengths of two vectors, we can compare their components. If we have a basis X_1, X_2, X_3 chosen for our 3-dimensional space, then all vectors are represented as numerical column vectors, and we can compare corresponding components. More generally, if two vectors are parallel, then one is a numerical multiple of the other, and hence we can compare their lengths.

It is important to note that in the vast majority of the applications of the calculus, angles and (absolute) lengths are not defined. Suppose that in an economic example $\begin{pmatrix} a \\ b \end{pmatrix}$ represents a shoes and b hats. What sense can we make of the length of this vector, or of the angle between two such vectors? Similarly, in physics if one component represents pressure and the other volume, we can make no sense of lengths and of angles. The only area of application of the calculus in which concepts of the second category enter is the application of the calculus to euclidean geometry. Therefore it is very important to keep concepts of the two types separated in the calculus. This is not always easy if the calculus is taught in the usual manner. For example, tangents and normals are treated side by side, even though tangents can be defined by means of pure vector concepts, while normals require the introduction of perpendicularity.

Let us consider briefly how our basic tools generalize to n-dimensional geometry. In any number of dimensions a line through the origin is a 1-dimensional subspace, and hence can be represented as tX_1. Since any line is obtained from a line through the origin by translation, the parametric representation $tX_1 + X_2$ will be applicable in any number of dimensions.

The equation $F_1X = 0$ in n-dimensional space must represent an $(n - 1)$-dimensional subspace. This follows from the fact that F_1 is a transformation with a 1-dimensional range (assuming $F_1 \neq 0$), and hence its kernel must have dimension $n - 1$. (See Theorem 6 of Section 11.) Such a subspace, whose dimension is 1 less than the dimension of the entire space, is generally known as a *hyperplane*. Notice that the concept of line does not depend on the dimension of the space that contains it, while the concept of hyperplane does. It can be shown, using methods exactly analogous to those used in Section 15, that a hyperplane not through the origin is the truth set of an equation $F_1X = c_1$, with $c_1 \neq 0$.

Nearly all that we did in these last two sections carries over to n dimensions if for "line" we still read "line" and for "plane" we read "hyperplane."

It is interesting to "step down" from 3-dimensional space to 2-dimensional space. Here a coincidence occurs. Since a hyperplane is $(n - 1)$-dimensional, and since $n - 1 = 1$, hyperplanes are simply lines. This is the reason why in plane analytic geometry lines may be represented either parametrically or by equations. This leaves us with a great deal of freedom as to whether we think of a line as a line or as a hyperplane. But it also makes it hard to conjecture the proper n-dimensional generalizations of 2-dimensional theorems. The smallest "typical" space is 3-dimensional.

In higher dimensional spaces there are, of course, nontrivial subspaces of all dimensions r between 1 and $n - 1$. Translates of these are sometimes called *flats*. Each r-dimensional flat can be represented either parametrically or implicitly. (In particular, a plane in 3-space can be represented parametrically and a line in 3-space can be represented implicitly, though both of these representations are less natural than the ones presented in Section 15.) Parametrically, an r-dimensional flat is written

$$X_0 + t^{(1)}X_1 + \ldots + t^{(r)}X_r,$$

where X_0 is any fixed point on the flat, and $X_1, \ldots, X_r$ are any r linearly independent vectors parallel to the flat, and the parameters $t^{(1)}, \ldots, t^{(r)}$ run independently over all real numbers. Implicitly, an r-dimensional flat is written as the truth set of the conjunction of $n - r$ equations.

$$\begin{aligned} \mathbf{F}_1 X &= c_1, \\ &\vdots \\ \mathbf{F}_{n-r} X &= c_{n-r}, \end{aligned} \tag{5}$$

where the functionals $\mathbf{F}_1, \ldots, \mathbf{F}_{n-r}$ are linearly independent. That is, the flat is represented as the intersection of hyperplanes.

EXERCISES

1. Write a parametric expression for the line through

$$\begin{pmatrix} 1 \\ 2 \\ -3 \end{pmatrix} \text{ and } \begin{pmatrix} 0 \\ 1 \\ 5 \end{pmatrix}.$$

2. Write another parametric expression for the line in Exercise 1.

3. Write an equation for the plane through

$$\begin{pmatrix} 2 \\ 2 \\ 3 \end{pmatrix}, \begin{pmatrix} 2 \\ 3 \\ 3 \end{pmatrix}, \begin{pmatrix} 2 \\ 3 \\ 4 \end{pmatrix}.$$

[*Ans.* $(1, 0, 0)X = 2.$]

4. Show that the points

$$\begin{pmatrix} 0 \\ -2 \\ -1 \end{pmatrix}, \begin{pmatrix} 1 \\ 4 \\ 0 \end{pmatrix}, \begin{pmatrix} 2 \\ 10 \\ 1 \end{pmatrix}$$

do not determine a unique plane.

5. Find a parametric expression for the line of intersection of the plane $(5\ 2\ 1)X = 0$ with the plane $(1\ {-1}\ 0)X = 1$.

6. Find the plane parallel to $(5\ 2\ 1)X = 1$ that contains the point $\begin{pmatrix} 100 \\ 200 \\ 300 \end{pmatrix}$. [*Ans.* $(5\ 2\ 1)X = 1200.$]

7. Find the three points that divide the segment between $\begin{pmatrix} 1 \\ 9 \\ -2 \end{pmatrix}$ and $\begin{pmatrix} 0 \\ 1 \\ 1 \end{pmatrix}$ into four equal parts. [*Ans.* $\begin{pmatrix} \frac{1}{4} \\ 3 \\ \frac{1}{4} \end{pmatrix}, \begin{pmatrix} \frac{1}{2} \\ 5 \\ -\frac{1}{2} \end{pmatrix}, \begin{pmatrix} \frac{3}{4} \\ 7 \\ -\frac{5}{4} \end{pmatrix}.$]

8. Check that each of the following points lies on the line through $Y_0 = \begin{pmatrix} 1 \\ 2 \\ 3 \end{pmatrix}$ and $Z_0 = \begin{pmatrix} -1 \\ 0 \\ 2 \end{pmatrix}$. Which of them lie between Y_0 and Z_0?

$$\begin{pmatrix} 0 \\ 1 \\ \frac{5}{2} \end{pmatrix}, \begin{pmatrix} -\frac{1}{2} \\ \frac{1}{2} \\ \frac{9}{4} \end{pmatrix}, \begin{pmatrix} 2 \\ 3 \\ \frac{7}{2} \end{pmatrix}, \begin{pmatrix} -3 \\ -2 \\ 1 \end{pmatrix}.$$

9. Check that all the following segments are parallel, and compare their lengths.

$$\mathcal{S}_1 = \text{the segment joining} \begin{pmatrix} 1 \\ 2 \\ 0 \end{pmatrix} \quad \text{and} \quad \begin{pmatrix} 2 \\ 3 \\ -1 \end{pmatrix}.$$

$$\mathcal{S}_2 = \text{the segment joining} \begin{pmatrix} 4 \\ 5 \\ -2 \end{pmatrix} \quad \text{and} \quad \begin{pmatrix} 6 \\ 7 \\ -4 \end{pmatrix}.$$

$$\mathcal{S}_3 = \text{the segment joining} \begin{pmatrix} \frac{1}{2} \\ \frac{1}{2} \\ \frac{1}{2} \end{pmatrix} \quad \text{and} \quad \begin{pmatrix} 1 \\ 1 \\ 0 \end{pmatrix}.$$

[*Ans.* The length of $\mathcal{S}_2$ is twice that of $\mathcal{S}_1$ and the length of $\mathcal{S}_3$ is $\frac{1}{2}$ that of $\mathcal{S}_1$.]

10. Which of the following points lie in the plane determined by $\begin{pmatrix} 1 \\ 0 \\ 0 \end{pmatrix}$, $\begin{pmatrix} 0 \\ 1 \\ 0 \end{pmatrix}$, $\begin{pmatrix} 0 \\ 0 \\ 1 \end{pmatrix}$?

$$\begin{pmatrix} 5 \\ -2 \\ -3 \end{pmatrix}, \begin{pmatrix} 4 \\ -2 \\ -1 \end{pmatrix}, \begin{pmatrix} \frac{1}{2} \\ \frac{1}{2} \\ \frac{1}{2} \end{pmatrix}, \begin{pmatrix} \frac{1}{3} \\ \frac{1}{3} \\ \frac{1}{3} \end{pmatrix}, \begin{pmatrix} \frac{1}{2} \\ \frac{1}{2} \\ 0 \end{pmatrix}, \begin{pmatrix} 0 \\ 0 \\ 0 \end{pmatrix}.$$

11. If X, Y, Z are linearly independent vectors, interpret geometrically the point $\frac{1}{3}X + \frac{1}{3}Y + \frac{1}{3}Z$.

12. Given a triangle, take one vertex as the origin and take the two adjacent sides as the vectors of a basis. What then are the coordinates of each of the other two vertices? What are the coordinates of the mid-points of each of the sides?

13. Find the points that trisect the segment joining $\begin{pmatrix} 1 \\ 2 \end{pmatrix}$ to $\begin{pmatrix} -3 \\ 0 \end{pmatrix}$.

14. Find a point X_0 on the segment between $Y_0 = \begin{pmatrix} 1 \\ 2 \\ 3 \end{pmatrix}$ and $Z_0 = \begin{pmatrix} \frac{1}{2} \\ \frac{1}{2} \\ \frac{1}{2} \end{pmatrix}$ such that X_0 is five times as far from Y_0 as it is from Z_0.

[*Ans.* $\begin{pmatrix} \frac{7}{12} \\ \frac{3}{4} \\ \frac{11}{12} \end{pmatrix}$.]

15. Let F_0 be the functional that sends each column $\begin{pmatrix} x_1 \\ x_2 \\ x_3 \end{pmatrix}$ into $3x_1 + 2x_2 +$

x_3. What is an equation for the level plane of F_0 that passes through $\begin{pmatrix} 4 \\ -1 \\ 2 \end{pmatrix}$?

16. Let X_1, X_2, X_3 be any three linearly independent points in 3-dimensional space. Let W_1 be the mid-point of the segment from 0 to X_1. Let W_2 be the mid-point of the segment from X_1 to X_2. Let W_3 be the mid-point of the segment from X_2 to X_3. And let W_4 be the mid-point of the segment from X_3 to 0. Prove that a parallelogram is formed by drawing segments between W_1 and W_2, between W_2 and W_3, between W_3 and W_4, and between W_4 and W_1.

17. Write a parametric expression for the line of intersection of the planes

$$(1\ 2\ 3)X = 1 \quad \text{and} \quad (1\ 1\ -1)X = -1.$$

[*Ans.* $t\begin{pmatrix} 5 \\ -4 \\ 1 \end{pmatrix} + \begin{pmatrix} -3 \\ 2 \\ 0 \end{pmatrix}$.]

18. Do the following three points lie on a line?

$$\begin{pmatrix} 2 \\ 3 \\ -4 \end{pmatrix}, \quad \begin{pmatrix} 2 \\ 1 \\ -1 \end{pmatrix}, \quad \begin{pmatrix} 2 \\ 7 \\ -10 \end{pmatrix}.$$

[*Ans.* Yes.]

19. Do the following four points lie on a plane?

$$\begin{pmatrix} 6 \\ 0 \\ -3 \end{pmatrix}, \quad \begin{pmatrix} -1 \\ 6 \\ -11 \end{pmatrix}, \quad \begin{pmatrix} 4 \\ 3 \\ -16 \end{pmatrix}, \quad \begin{pmatrix} 13 \\ -6 \\ 5 \end{pmatrix}.$$

20. The plane $\mathcal{P}$ goes through the points $\begin{pmatrix} 1 \\ 2 \\ 3 \end{pmatrix}$ and $\begin{pmatrix} -1 \\ 0 \\ 1 \end{pmatrix}$ and $\begin{pmatrix} 1 \\ 0 \\ 0 \end{pmatrix}$. Write an equation for $\mathcal{P}$.

[*Ans.* $(1\ -3\ 2)X = 1$.]

21. Write a parametric expression for the line of intersection of the planes determined by the following two equations:

$$\begin{aligned} x_1 - x_2 + x_3 &= 1, \\ x_1 + 2x_2 + 3x_3 &= 1. \end{aligned}$$

22. Write an implicit equation for the plane that contains the line $X = t\begin{pmatrix} 1 \\ 0 \\ 5 \end{pmatrix} + \begin{pmatrix} 1 \\ 2 \\ -1 \end{pmatrix}$ and also contains the point $\begin{pmatrix} 1 \\ 0 \\ 1 \end{pmatrix}$.

[*Ans.* $(5\ -1\ -1)X = 4$.]

23. Show that among all the level planes in 3-dimensional space of the functional F_0, the level plane passing through Y_0 coincides with the truth set of $F_0(X - Y_0) = 0$.

24. Let $\mathcal{L}_1$ and $\mathcal{L}_2$ be lines in the plane. Show that any one of the following three properties is sufficient to make $\mathcal{L}_1$ and $\mathcal{L}_2$ parallel.

(a) The points in $\mathcal{L}_2$ are obtained by adding some fixed vector Y_0 to all the points in $\mathcal{L}_1$.

(b) $\mathcal{L}_1$ and $\mathcal{L}_2$ are different level lines of the same functional F_0.

(c) $\mathcal{L}_1$ and $\mathcal{L}_2$ never intersect.

25. Suppose the plane $\mathcal{P}_0$ goes through the origin and through the points $\begin{pmatrix}1\\2\\3\end{pmatrix}$ and $\begin{pmatrix}-1\\0\\1\end{pmatrix}$. Suppose the plane $\mathcal{P}_1$ is parallel to $\mathcal{P}_0$ and goes through the point $\begin{pmatrix}3\\7\\-9\end{pmatrix}$. Determine whether the point $\begin{pmatrix}5\\8\\-7\end{pmatrix}$ belongs to the plane $\mathcal{P}_1$. [*Ans.* No.]

26. Show that as t varies over all real numbers (not only between 0 and 1) that

$$(*) \qquad tX_1 + (1 - t)X_2$$

represents the line through X_1 and X_2. The above expression can also be written

$$(**) \qquad t^{(1)}X_1 + t^{(2)}X_2$$

with the understanding that $t^{(1)}$ and $t^{(2)}$ are numerical variables subject only to the restriction $t^{(1)} + t^{(2)} = 1$.

27. Show that the following expression represents a plane through X_1 and X_2 and X_3 if the variables $t^{(1)}$ and $t^{(2)}$ and $t^{(3)}$ are subject to the restriction $t^{(1)} + t^{(2)} + t^{(3)} = 1$, and X_1, X_2, X_3 are not on a line

$$(***) \qquad t^{(1)}X_1 + t^{(2)}X_2 + t^{(3)}X_3.$$

28. Show that if the variables $t^{(1)}$ and $t^{(2)}$ and $t^{(3)}$ in the expression (***) above are also required to be nonnegative then we have a representation of the triangular region pictured in Figure 39.

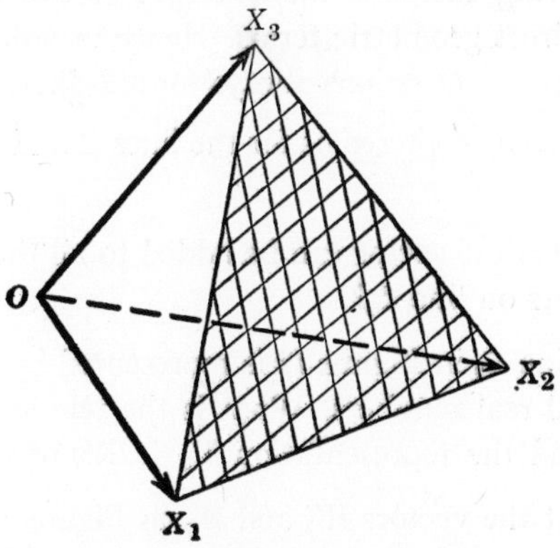

Figure 39

29. Prove by use of vector space ideas, and without setting up a coordinate system, that the three medians of a triangle intersect at a common point. (A "median" of a triangle is the segment joining one vertex to the mid-point of the opposite side.)

30. Prove by use of vector space ideas and without setting up a coordinate system that the point at which the three medians of a triangle intersect (see Exercise 29 above) divides each median in the ratio 2 to 1.

31. Given a parallelogram, take one vertex as the origin O and take the two adjacent sides as the vectors of a basis for the geometric plane. What then are the coordinates of each of the other three vertices? And of the point where the diagonals intersect? Do the same for a square, and compare.

32. In n-dimensional space show that the simultaneous implicit equations (5) define a flat of dimension exactly r if and only if the functionals $\mathbf{F}_1, \ldots, \mathbf{F}_{n-r}$ are linearly independent. (Hence, in particular, if $\mathbf{F}X = 0$ and $\mathbf{G}X = 0$ define the same hyperplane, then $\mathbf{G}$ is a numerical multiple of $\mathbf{F}$ and vice versa.)

33. In the situation of Exercise 32 above, what can we say about the dimension of the flat defined by equations (5) when the functionals $\mathbf{F}_1, \ldots, \mathbf{F}_{n-r}$ are linearly dependent?

[*Ans.* Either the truth set of these simultaneous equations is empty, or else the flat they define has dimension $>r$.]

34. Express the theorems stated in Exercises 32 and 33 above as theorems about simultaneous linear equations.

GRAPHICAL EXERCISES IN 2-DIMENSIONAL VECTOR GEOMETRY

In the following exercises the concepts of the last two sections are interpreted in direct geometric terms. Hence in order to be able to draw pictures, we state the questions always for a 2-dimensional space.

35. Write parametric expressions for the lines $\mathcal{L}$ and $\mathcal{L}_0$ pictured in Figure 40.

36. In Figure 41 what vector can be added to all the points on line $\mathcal{L}_1$ to give all points on line $\mathcal{L}_2$? [*Ans.* $Y_2 - Y_1$.]

37. Show that line $\mathcal{L}_0$ in Figure 42 is represented by $tY_0 + (1 - t)Z_0$, as t runs over all real numbers. What is the relation between this representation and the representation $Y_0 + tW_0$ of line $\mathcal{L}_0$ in Figure 40?

38. Suppose that the vectors W_1 and W_2 in Figure 43 are chosen as basis for the plane, and that coordinates are assigned to every point in the

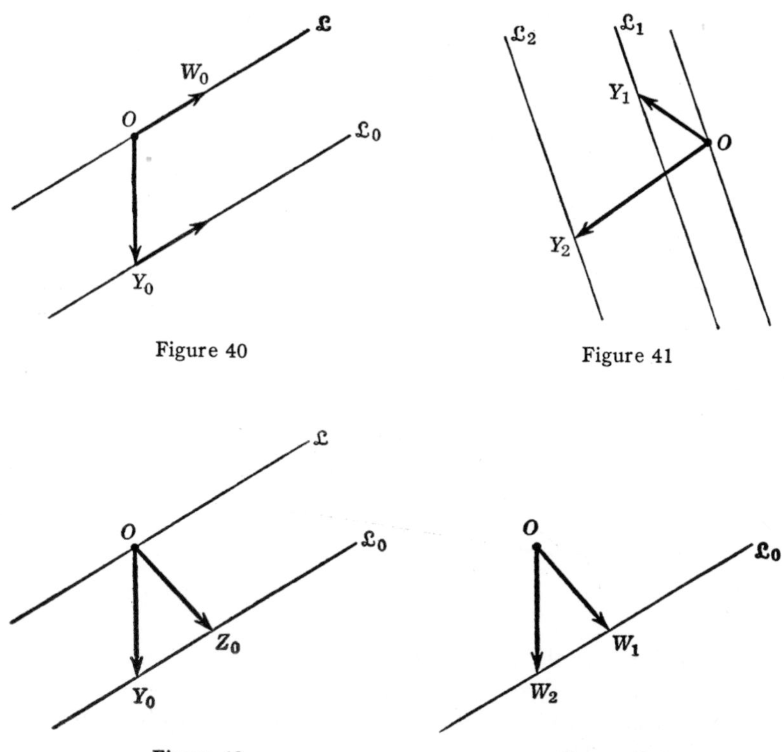

Figure 40

Figure 41

Figure 42

Figure 43

plane relative to this basis. Show that then the line $\mathcal{L}_0$ in Figure 43 consists of all vectors of the form $\begin{pmatrix} t \\ 1-t \end{pmatrix}$.

39. Relative to the basis $\{W_1, W_2\}$ in Exercise 38 above, choose (a_1, a_2) so that $a_1x_1 + a_2x_2 = 1$, or $(a_1, a_2)X = 1$, is an implicit equation for the line $\mathcal{L}$ in Figure 44. [*Ans.* $a_1 = a_2 = 4$.]

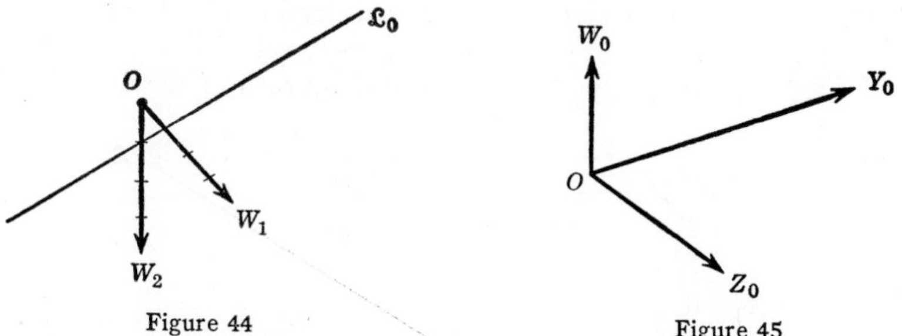

Figure 44

Figure 45

40. If W_0, Y_0, Z_0 are the plane vectors shown in Figure 45, sketch each of the following parametric lines:

$$W_0 + tY_0,$$
$$W_0 + tZ_0,$$
$$Y_0 + tW_0,$$
$$Z_0 + tW_0,$$
$$Z_0 + tZ_0,$$
$$tW_0,$$
$$(W_0 - Y_0) + tZ_0,$$
$$Z_0 + t(W_0 - Y_0).$$

41. Express each of the points X_1, X_2, X_3 pictured below in Figure 46 as a linear combination of Y_0 and Z_0. [*Partial Ans.* $X_3 = \frac{5}{4}Y_0 - \frac{1}{4}Z_0$.]

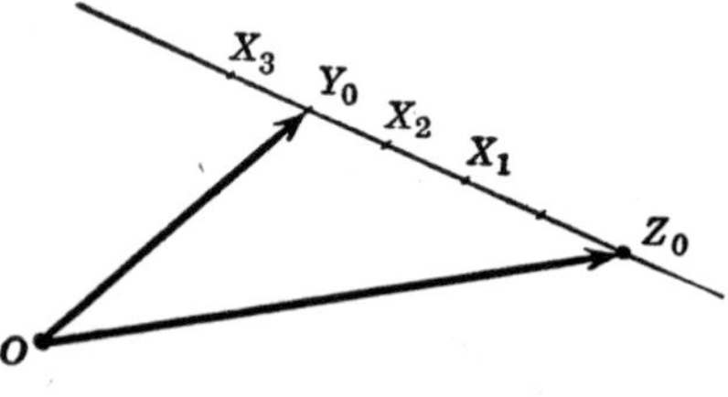

Figure 46

42. Imagine that the page on which these words are printed represents the plane that passes through the (tips of) linearly independent 3-dimensional vectors W, Y, Z. Locate in Figure 47, the points corresponding to

$$\tfrac{1}{2}W + \tfrac{1}{4}Y + \tfrac{1}{4}Z,$$
$$\tfrac{1}{3}W + \tfrac{1}{3}Y + \tfrac{1}{3}Z,$$
$$\tfrac{1}{2}W + \tfrac{1}{3}Y + \tfrac{1}{6}Z,$$
$$\tfrac{1}{2}W + \tfrac{1}{2}Y.$$

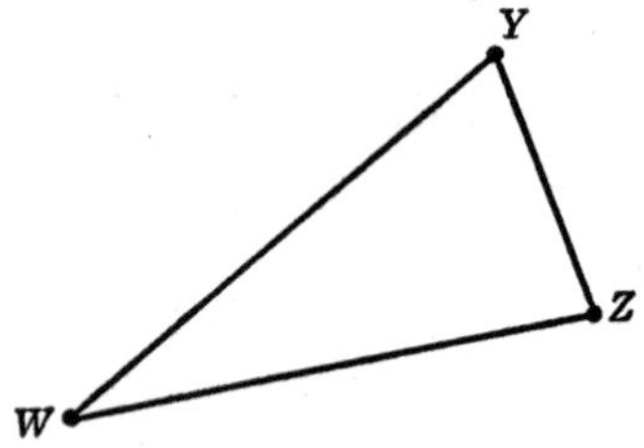

Figure 47

43. In Figure 48 we have drawn the "unit level line" $\mathfrak{L}$ of a certain functional **F**. In other words, $\mathfrak{L}$ is the truth set of the open statement $\mathbf{F}X = 1$. Draw the lines represented by each of the following four equations

$$\mathbf{F}X = 2,$$
$$\mathbf{F}X = \tfrac{1}{2},$$
$$\mathbf{F}X = 0,$$
$$\mathbf{F}X = -1.$$

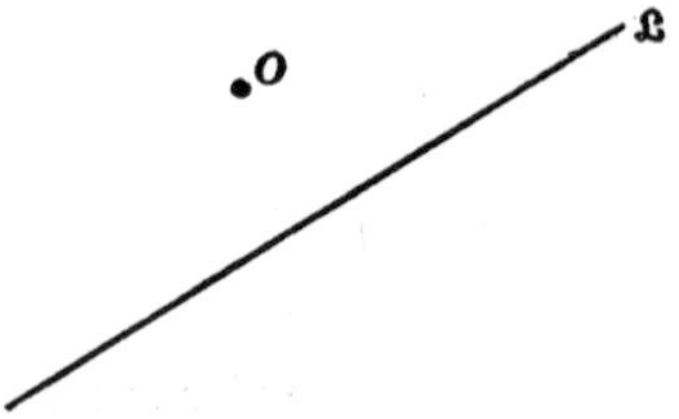

Figure 48

44. For the functional **F** of Exercise 43, pictured in Figure 48 draw the unit level lines of 2**F**, of $\frac{1}{2}$**F**, and of −**F**.

45. In Figure 49 we have drawn the unit level lines $\mathcal{L}_1$ and $\mathcal{L}_2$ of functionals $\mathbf{F}_1$ and $\mathbf{F}_2$. Draw the unit level line of $\mathbf{F}_1 + \mathbf{F}_2$.

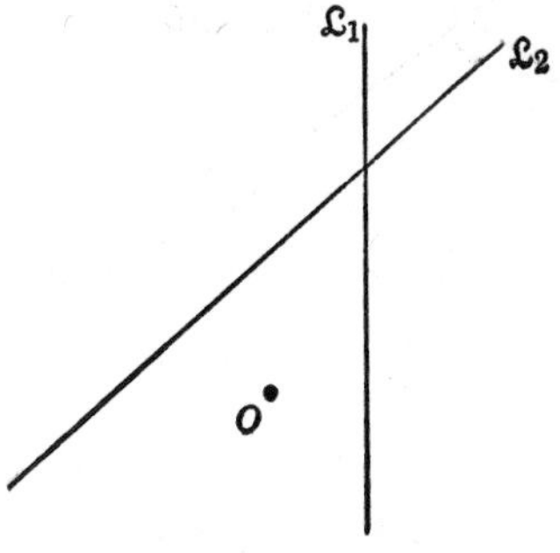

Figure 49

46. Let $\mathbf{F}_1$ and $\mathbf{F}_2$ have the unit level lines $\mathcal{L}_1$ and $\mathcal{L}_2$ in Figure 50 below, and let **F** have the unit level line $\mathcal{L}$. Express **F** as a linear combination of $\mathbf{F}_1$ and $\mathbf{F}_2$ making use of the various lines in Figure 50.

[*Ans.* $\mathbf{F} = -\mathbf{F}_1 + 2\mathbf{F}_2$.]

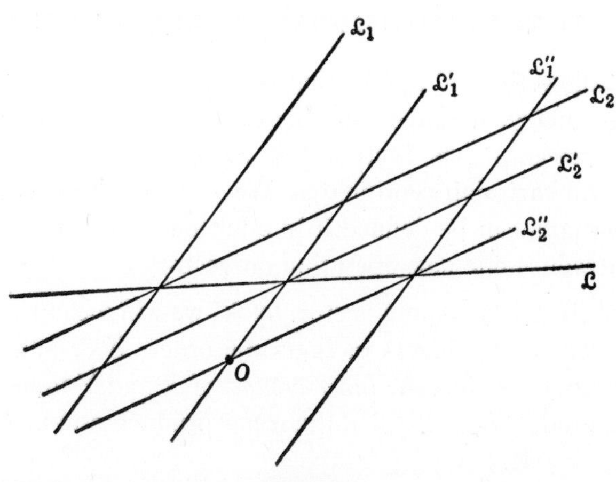

Figure 50

47. In Figure 51 are drawn the unit level lines $\mathcal{L}_1$ and $\mathcal{L}_2$ of functionals $\mathbf{F}_1$ and $\mathbf{F}_2$. Draw the unit level lines of $\frac{1}{2}\mathbf{F}_1 + \frac{1}{2}\mathbf{F}_2$, and of $\frac{1}{3}\mathbf{F}_1 + \frac{2}{3}\mathbf{F}_2$.

48. Given unit level lines $\mathcal{L}_1$ and $\mathcal{L}_2$ like those drawn in Figure 51 above, how can we describe geometrically the set of all unit level lines of linear combinations $c_1\mathbf{F}_1 + c_2\mathbf{F}_2$, $c_1 \geq 0$, $c_2 \geq 0$, $c_1 + c_2 = 1$.

[*Ans.* All the lines passing through *P* and not lying in the sector of the plane that contains the origin.]

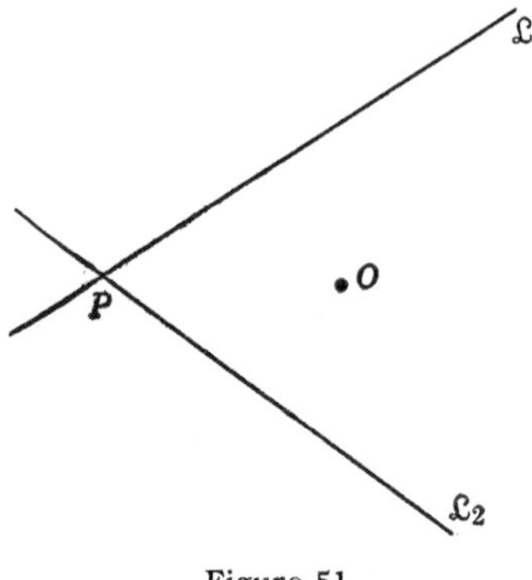

Figure 51

49. In Figure 51 above, draw a basis of vectors W_1 and W_2 "dual" to the functionals $\mathbf{F}_1$ and $\mathbf{F}_2$ of Exercise 47, i.e., such that $\mathbf{F}_1W_1 = 1$, $\mathbf{F}_2W_2 = 1$, $\mathbf{F}_1W_2 = 0$, $\mathbf{F}_2W_1 = 0$.

50. In Figure 50, p. 319, draw a basis of vectors W_1 and W_2 "dual" to the functionals $\mathbf{F}_1$ and $\mathbf{F}_2$ of Exercise 46, and write an implicit equation of the line $\mathfrak{L}$ in coordinate form.

17. THREE-DIMENSIONAL EUCLIDEAN GEOMETRY

To allow the full application of abstract vector space ideas to euclidean geometry, we must find a means of introducing concepts of the second category (see Section 15), such as length, angle, perpendicularity, and cartesian coordinates. We will show in this section that all these concepts can be defined if in addition to our vector space concepts we introduce one new operation on vectors.

Definition. If X is a column vector, by X' we will mean the row vector having the same components in the same order. If X and Y are both column vectors, we define the *inner product* of X and Y to be the number $X'Y$. (This product is also called the *scalar* product, and is often symbolized by $X \cdot Y$.) If

$$X = \begin{pmatrix} x_1 \\ x_2 \\ x_3 \end{pmatrix} \quad \text{and} \quad Y = \begin{pmatrix} y_1 \\ y_2 \\ y_3 \end{pmatrix},$$

then
$$X'Y = x_1y_1 + x_2y_2 + x_3y_3.$$

From this we see immediately that the inner product is *symmetric* in X and Y, that is, $X'Y = Y'X$. Also it is clear that the inner product is *positive-definite*, that is, $X'X > 0$ when $X \neq 0$.

Let us first of all consider the length of a given vector X. If $X = \begin{pmatrix} x_1 \\ x_2 \\ x_3 \end{pmatrix}$ in some coordinate system, we may think of the length of the vector as the distance from the origin to the point with coordinates $\begin{pmatrix} x_1 \\ x_2 \\ x_3 \end{pmatrix}$. In a general coordinate system the formula for this distance would be fairly complicated. But here is where we gain by the introduction of a *cartesian* coordinate system, that is, the choice of perpendicular axes and the same unit of length on each axis. In such a coordinate system the pythagorean theorem gives us a simple formula for the distance (see Figure 52). Letting $|X|$ stand for the length of the vector X, we obtain

(1) $|X|^2 = x_1^2 + x_2^2 + x_3^2 = X'X.$

Thus we see that the *length* of the vector X can be expressed in terms of the inner product as $\sqrt{X'X} = |X|$. Note that we use the same symbol for the length of a vector as for the absolute value of a number. Indeed, if we think of a number as a one-component vector, its length is its absolute value.

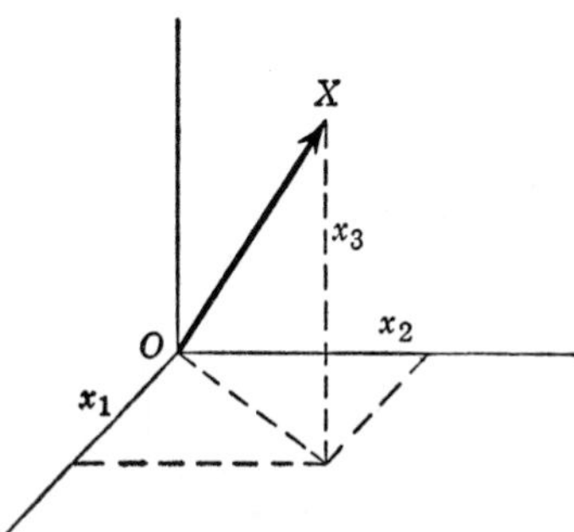

Figure 52

Next we would like to express the angle between two nonzero vectors. The usual convention is to take this angle θ to be in the interval $0 \leq \theta \leq \pi$ (see Exercise 1). The solution of this problem is provided by the following theorem.

Theorem 1. If θ is the angle between X and Y, then $\cos\theta = X'Y/|X||Y|$.

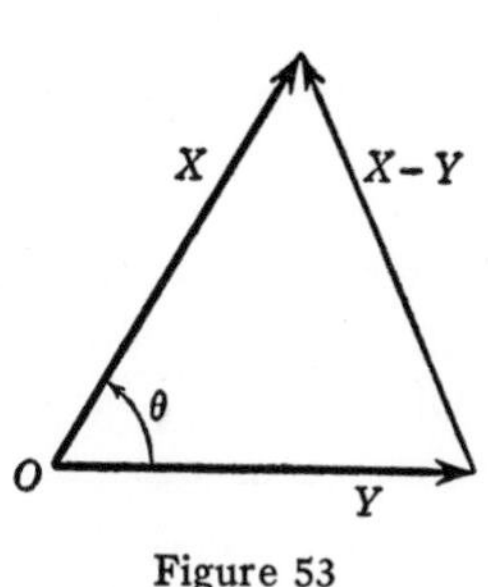

Figure 53

Proof. Let us apply the law of cosines to the triangle shown in Figure 53. It states that

$$|X - Y|^2 = |X|^2 + |Y|^2 - 2|X||Y|\cos\theta,$$

which we can rewrite, using (1) as

$$(X - Y)'(X - Y) = X'X + Y'Y - 2|X||Y|\cos\theta$$

Since $(X - Y)' = X' - Y'$, we obtain

$$X'X - X'Y - Y'X + Y'Y = X'X + Y'Y - 2|X||Y|\cos\theta$$

and

$$2X'Y = 2|X||Y|\cos\theta$$

from which the theorem follows by dividing by $2|X||Y|$.

We see from this theorem that $X'Y$ in absolute value is at most $|X||Y|$, i.e., $|X'Y| \leq |X||Y|$. This is known as the "Cauchy-Schwarz inequality."

Example 1. What is the angle θ between $X = \begin{pmatrix} 1 \\ 2 \\ 3 \end{pmatrix}$ and $Y = \begin{pmatrix} -1 \\ 0 \\ 1 \end{pmatrix}$? We easily compute that $X'X = 1^2 + 2^2 + 3^2 = 14$, $Y'Y = (-1)^2 + 0^2 + 1^2 = 2$, and $X'Y = -1 + 0 + 3 = 2$. Hence $|X| = \sqrt{14}$, $|Y| = \sqrt{2}$, and $\cos\theta = 2/\sqrt{28} = 1/\sqrt{7}$. By consulting a trigonometric table we find that $\theta = 1.18$ radians approximately (or about 68°).

The theorem also provides a simple test for perpendicularity of two vectors. They are perpendicular if and only if $\theta = \pi/2$, and hence $\cos\theta = 0$. Thus the condition for perpendicularity is simply

$$X'Y = 0. \tag{2}$$

Example 2. Let us find a vector X of length 2 perpendicular to $\begin{pmatrix} 1 \\ 2 \\ 3 \end{pmatrix}$ and to $\begin{pmatrix} 1 \\ 0 \\ -1 \end{pmatrix}$. From geometric considerations we see that there will be two solutions, since if X is a solution, so is $-X$. (See Figure 54.) We have to write down three conditions, two for the perpendicularity requirements, using (2), and a third condition to assure length 2:

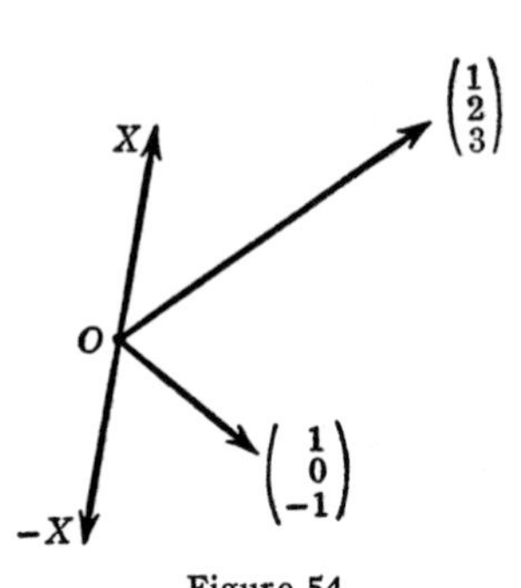

Figure 54

$$\begin{aligned} x_1 + 2x_2 + 3x_3 &= 0, \\ x_1 \qquad - \ x_3 &= 0, \\ x_1^2 + x_2^2 + x_3^2 &= 4. \end{aligned}$$

These equations have the pair of solutions

$$X = \pm \begin{pmatrix} \sqrt{2/3} \\ -2\sqrt{2/3} \\ \sqrt{2/3} \end{pmatrix}.$$

We have thus succeeded in expressing the concepts of length, angle, and perpendicularity in terms of the inner product. Of course, all these formulas are subject to the assumption that the coordinates are cartesian. In vector terminology this means that we have chosen a basis X_1, X_2, X_3 so that each basis vector has length 1 and each basis vector is perpendicular to both of the other basis vectors. Such a basis is called *orthonormal*. The full significance of the choice of an orthonormal basis will be shown in the next section.

The test for the perpendicularity of two vectors may be applied also to test the perpendicularity of two lines. Let $tX_1 + X_2$ and $tY_1 + X_2$ be two lines $\mathcal{L}$, $\mathcal{L}'$ through X_2. We want to decide whether the lines are perpendicular. Clearly, this is equivalent to the question whether X_1 and Y_1 are perpendicular. (See Figure 55.) Hence the condition is given by (2).

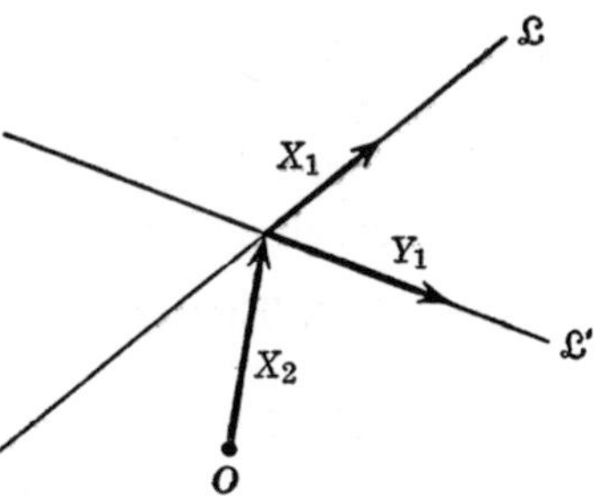

Figure 55

For many purposes it is convenient to "normalize" the vector X_1 in the parametric representation of $tX_1 + X_2$ of a line. Since it may be replaced by any nonzero multiple, we may as well choose it to be of unit length (in which case X_1 is determined up to a minus sign). This can be accomplished by dividing X_1 by its length, $|X_1|$. If the vectors X_1 and Y_1 are both chosen to be of unit length, then the cosine of the acute angle between the lines $\mathcal{L}$ and $\mathcal{L}'$ (see Figure 55) will simply be $|X_1'Y_1|$.

Example 3. Let $\mathcal{L}$ be given by $t\begin{pmatrix}3\\0\\-4\end{pmatrix}+\begin{pmatrix}1\\1\\1\end{pmatrix}$ and $\mathcal{L}'$ by $t\begin{pmatrix}12\\-3\\4\end{pmatrix}+\begin{pmatrix}1\\1\\1\end{pmatrix}$.

In normalized form $\mathcal{L}$ is given by $t\begin{pmatrix}\frac{3}{5}\\0\\-\frac{4}{5}\end{pmatrix}+\begin{pmatrix}1\\1\\1\end{pmatrix}$ and $\mathcal{L}'$ by $t\begin{pmatrix}\frac{12}{13}\\-\frac{3}{13}\\\frac{4}{13}\end{pmatrix}+\begin{pmatrix}1\\1\\1\end{pmatrix}$.

These lines intersect at $\begin{pmatrix}1\\1\\1\end{pmatrix}$. What is the angle between them? The answer is

$$\cos\theta = \left(\tfrac{3}{5} \quad 0 \quad -\tfrac{4}{5}\right)\begin{pmatrix}\frac{12}{13}\\-\frac{3}{13}\\\frac{4}{13}\end{pmatrix} = \tfrac{4}{13}.$$

Hence $\theta = 1.26$ (or about 72°).

In euclidean geometry we have a simple geometric interpretation of the row vector $\mathbf{F}_1$. Since $\mathbf{F}_1$ is a row vector, we may think of it as $\mathbf{F}_1 = X_1'$, where X_1 is the column vector with the same components. We will now show that X_1 is the (common) direction of lines perpendicular to the plane $\mathbf{F}_1X = c_1$. In other words, we wish to show that $tX_1 + X_2$ is perpendicular to the plane, for any X_2. It is a necessary and sufficient condition that this line be perpendicular to every line through X_2 which is parallel to the plane. Such a line has equation $tY_1 + X_2$, where $\mathbf{F}_1Y_1 = X_1'Y_1 = 0$. But this is precisely the condition for the perpendicularity of the two lines.

Thus we will from now on (if we are doing euclidean geometry, and not simply vector geometry) write $X_1'X = c_1$ for the equation of a plane. Then we immediately know that the perpendicular line (or *normal*) passing through a given point X_2 is simply $tX_1 + X_2$.

Example 4. The parametric representation of the normal to the plane $(1 \quad 2 \quad 3) \quad X = 6$ at the point $\begin{pmatrix}1\\1\\1\end{pmatrix}$ is $t\begin{pmatrix}1\\2\\3\end{pmatrix} + \begin{pmatrix}1\\1\\1\end{pmatrix}$.

We recall that the equation $X_1'X = c_1$ for a plane is not unique, since we can multiply through by a number k. This suggests getting a unique representation by normalization, that is, by choosing X_1' to have length 1. Then X_1 will be a unit vector perpendicular to the plane. (Actually this still leaves two possible choices.) Such a choice has many advantages. For example, the normal $tX_1 + X_2$ will also appear in the normalized representation. The formula for the angle between two planes takes on a particularly simple form (see Exercise 5). And it leads to a simple formula for the distance from a point to the plane, as we will now show.

Theorem 2. If $X_1'X = c_1$ is the normalized equation of $\mathcal{P}$, and X_2 is any point, then the distance from X_2 to $\mathcal{P}$ is the absolute value of $c_1 - X_1'X_2$.

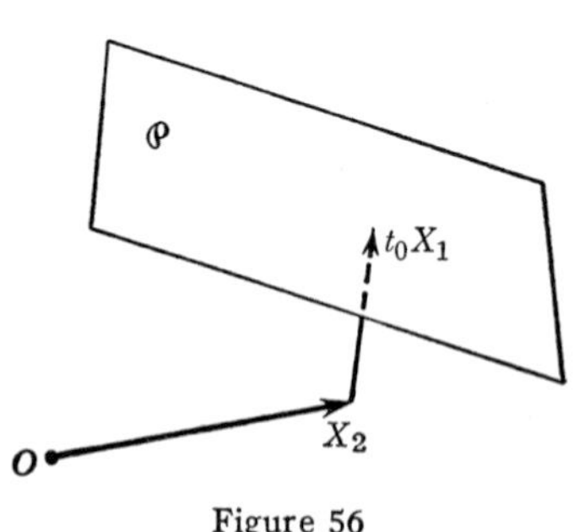

Figure 56

Proof. By definition, the distance is to be measured along a line from X_2 perpendicular to $\mathcal{P}$. This line is represented by $tX_1 + X_2$, and the intersection with $\mathcal{P}$ will occur for some $t = t_0$. The desired distance is then $|t_0X_1|$, which is simply the absolute value of t_0 since X_1 has unit length. (See Figure 56.) If $t_0X_1 + X_2$ lies in $\mathcal{P}$, then $X_1'(t_0X_1 + X_2) = c_1$. Remembering that $X_1'X = 1$, we obtain $t_0 + X_1'X_2 = c_1$, from which the theorem follows.

Example 5. Find the distance from $\begin{pmatrix}1\\1\\1\end{pmatrix}$ to the plane $(3 \quad 0 \quad -4)X = -3$.

The normalized equation of the plane is $(\frac{3}{5} \quad 0 \quad -\frac{4}{5})X = -\frac{3}{5}$. Then

$$c_1 - X_1'X_2 = -\tfrac{3}{5} - \left(\tfrac{3}{5} \quad 0 \quad -\tfrac{4}{5}\right)\begin{pmatrix}1\\1\\1\end{pmatrix} = -\tfrac{2}{5}.$$

Hence the distance is $\frac{2}{5}$.

The following theorem is a special case of a very important theorem for n-dimensional space.

Theorem 3. If $\mathcal{P}$ is any plane and X_0 any vector, X_0 can be written uniquely as $X_0 = Y_0 + Z_0$, where Y_0 is parallel to $\mathcal{P}$ and Z_0 is perpendicular to $\mathcal{P}$.

Proof. Let $X_1'X = c_1$ be the normalized equation of the plane $\mathcal{P}$, and let $k = X_1'X_0$. First we will show that $Y_0 = X_0 - kX_1$ and $Z_0 = kX_1$ have all the desired properties. We see immediately that their sum is X_0, and that Z_0 is perpendicular to $\mathcal{P}$. By computing $X_1'Y_0 = X_1'X_0 - kX_1'X_1 = k - k = 0$, we see that Y_0 is parallel to $\mathcal{P}$.

Conversely, we must show that if $X_0 = Y + Z$, and Y is parallel to $\mathcal{P}$, and Z is perpendicular to $\mathcal{P}$, then $Y = Y_0$ and $Z = Z_0$. Since Y is parallel to $\mathcal{P}$, $X_1'Y = 0$. Then $k = X_1'X_0 = X_1'Z$. But Z is perpendicular to $\mathcal{P}$, hence $Z = cX_1$, $X_1'Z = cX_1'X_1 = c$, and thus $c = k$. Therefore $Z = Z_0$, and $Y = X_0 - Z_0 = Y_0$.

When $\mathcal{P}$ is a plane through the origin, the vector Y_0 is the *projection* of X_0 on $\mathcal{P}$, and Z_0 is the projection of X_0 on the normal to $\mathcal{P}$ through the origin. (See Figure 57.)

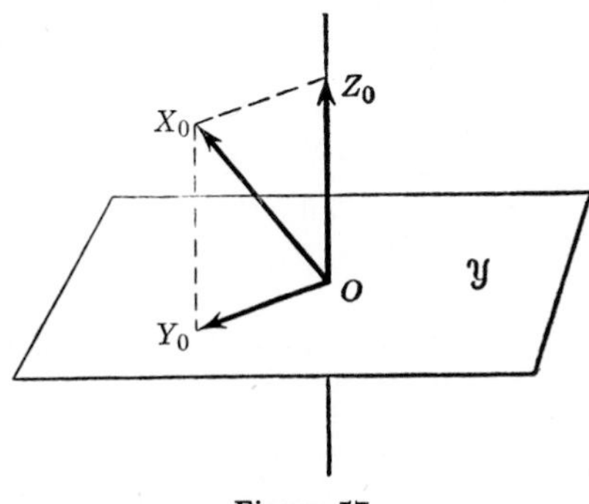

Figure 57

The theorem above allows us to draw the graph in 3 dimensions of a numerical function "of 2 real variables," i.e., a numerical function $\mathbf{f}$ having as domain a 2-dimensional vector space. We identify the domain of $\mathbf{f}$ with the horizontal plane $\mathcal{Y}$ through the origin of 3-dimensional space. And we represent the vertical line $\mathfrak{Z}$ through the origin by the parametric expression tZ_1, where Z_1 has length 1 and points upward. Now for every Y in the domain $\mathcal{Y}$ of $\mathbf{f}$ we plot in 3-space the point $Y + \mathbf{f}(Y)Z_1$. The *graph* of $\mathbf{f}$ consists of all such points. In other words, this graph is the truth set in 3-space of the open statement "$X = Y + Z$, with Y the projection of X on $\mathcal{Y}$, and Z the projection of X on $\mathfrak{Z}$, and $Z = \mathbf{f}(Y)Z_1$." Notice that this open statement depends on X alone, since the vectors Y and Z are uniquely determined by X. Roughly speaking, the graph of $\mathbf{f}$ is a surface in 3-space. And for each point Y in the horizontal plane $\mathcal{Y}$, the corresponding point on the graph of $\mathbf{f}$ is at a height $\mathbf{f}(Y)$ above Y (or $|\mathbf{f}(Y)|$ below Y when $\mathbf{f}(Y)$ is negative).

When $\mathbf{f}$ is a linear functional $\mathbf{F}$, the graph of $\mathbf{F}$ will be a nonvertical plane through the origin. Any nonvertical plane $\mathcal{P}$ through the origin is the graph of some uniquely determined linear functional $\mathbf{F}$. And more generally, any nonvertical plane whatsoever is the graph of a unique sum of a linear functional and a constant function. The equation $Z = \mathbf{F}Y + k$ is known as the *explicit* equation for the nonvertical plane it represents.

EXERCISES

1. Show that each pair of vectors determines a unique angle θ such that $0 \leq \theta \leq \pi$.
2. Find an equation for the plane perpendicular to the line $tX_1 + X_2$ that passes through the point Y_2.
3. Prove that the angle between two planes is equal to the angle between two normals passing through a common point.
4. Use the result of Exercise 3 to find the cosine of the angle between the planes $X_1'X = c_1$ and $Y_1'Y = c_2$.
5. Prove that if $X_1'X = c_1$ and $Y_1'Y = c_2$ are normalized equations of two planes, then the cosine of the angle between them is $X_1'Y_1$.
6. Show from Theorem 2 that distance from a point in $\mathcal{P}$ to $\mathcal{P}$ is 0.
7. Prove that if X_1 is any vector and tY_1 is the normalized equation of a line through the origin, then the length of the projection of X_1 on the line is $X_1'Y_1$.
8. Find the angle between the vectors $\begin{pmatrix}1\\1\\1\end{pmatrix}$ and $\begin{pmatrix}1\\0\\1\end{pmatrix}$. Interpret graphically.
9. Find a vector of unit length perpendicular to both vectors in Exercise 8. [*Ans.* $\begin{pmatrix}1/\sqrt{2}\\0\\-1/\sqrt{2}\end{pmatrix}$.]
10. Find the normalized equation of the plane through $\begin{pmatrix}1\\2\\3\end{pmatrix}$ that is perpendicular to the vector of Exercise 9. Verify that both vectors in Exercise 8 are parallel to this plane.

11. Normalize the equations of the following pairs of planes, and use the result of Exercise 5 to find the angle between them.

(a) $(1\quad 2\quad 3)X = 6$; $(3\quad 2\quad 1)X = 6$.

(b) $(1\quad 2\quad 3)X = 6$; $(1\quad 1\quad -1)X = 1$.

(c) $(1\quad 2\quad 3)X = 6$; $(\frac{1}{6}\quad \frac{1}{2}\quad \frac{1}{3})X = 2$.

12. For each of the points and planes listed below find the distance from the point to the plane.

(a) $\begin{pmatrix} 1 \\ 0 \\ -1 \end{pmatrix}$; $(1\quad 1\quad 1)X = 1$.

(b) $\begin{pmatrix} 1 \\ 0 \\ -1 \end{pmatrix}$; $(1\quad 2\quad 3)X = 1$.

(c) $\begin{pmatrix} 1 \\ 1 \\ 1 \end{pmatrix}$; $(1\quad 2\quad 3)X = 6$.

13. Write $\begin{pmatrix} 1 \\ 1 \\ 1 \end{pmatrix}$ as the sum of vectors perpendicular and parallel to the plane

$(1\quad 2\quad 3)X = 6$. [*Ans.* $\begin{pmatrix} \frac{4}{7} \\ \frac{1}{7} \\ -\frac{2}{7} \end{pmatrix} + \begin{pmatrix} \frac{3}{7} \\ \frac{6}{7} \\ \frac{9}{7} \end{pmatrix}$.]

Certain of the following exercises deal with vectors of dimension other than 3. In all cases the appropriate definitions are the obvious analogues of those used in 3-space. For instance, the length of $\begin{pmatrix} x_1 \\ x_2 \end{pmatrix}$ is $\sqrt{x_1^2 + x_2^2}$. And the inner product of 4-dimensional vectors X and Y is

$$x_1y_1 + x_2y_2 + x_3y_3 + x_4y_4.$$

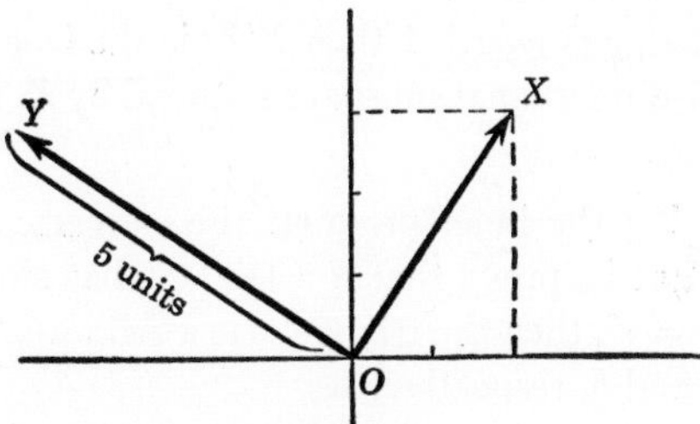

Figure 58

14. In Figure 58 we have drawn perpendicular vectors X and Y. The vector X has coordinates $\begin{pmatrix} 2 \\ 3 \end{pmatrix}$. The vector Y has length 5. What are the coordinates $\begin{pmatrix} y_1 \\ y_2 \end{pmatrix}$ of Y? [*Ans.* $\begin{pmatrix} -15/\sqrt{13} \\ 10/\sqrt{13} \end{pmatrix}$.]

15. Let θ be the angle between $X = \begin{pmatrix} 3 \\ -4 \end{pmatrix}$ and $Y = \begin{pmatrix} -12 \\ -5 \end{pmatrix}$. Show (without recourse to a table of cosines) that θ is between 90° and 120°.

16. Find all vectors Z perpendicular to both $X = \begin{pmatrix} 1 \\ 2 \\ 0 \end{pmatrix}$ and $Y = \begin{pmatrix} 0 \\ -1 \\ 3 \end{pmatrix}$.

[*Ans.* $t\begin{pmatrix} -6 \\ 3 \\ 1 \end{pmatrix}$.]

17. In Figure 59 we have drawn a vector Y_0 in the plane. Suppose that we know this vector to be of length 2. Draw the line $\mathfrak{L}$ having equation $Y_0'X = 2$. Draw also the line $\mathfrak{L}_1$ having equation $Y_0'X = -4$.

Figure 59

18. In each of the figures below, state whether the inner product $X_0'Y_0$ is positive, negative, or zero.

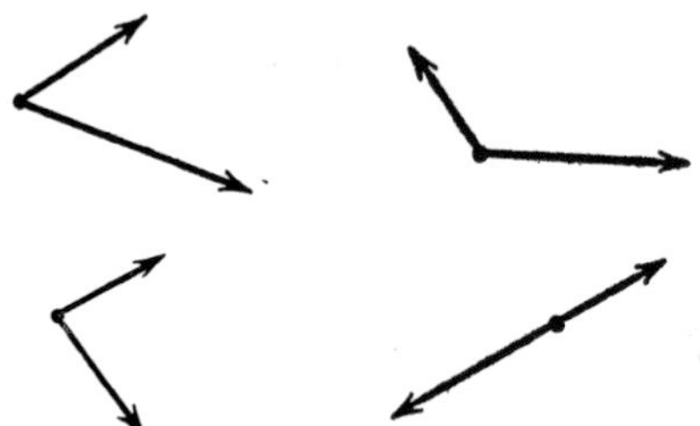

19. Show that if Z_1 has length 1 then $X'Z_1$ is the length of the projection of X on the 1-dimensional subspace spanned by Z_1 (or else the negative of this length).

20. Prove, by using the inner product, the converse of the pythagorean theorem. [That is, prove that if a triangle has sides of lengths a, b, c with $a^2 + b^2 = c^2$, then the triangle has a right angle between the sides of lengths a and b, respectively.]

21. Find the distance between $\begin{pmatrix} 1 \\ 2 \end{pmatrix}$ and $\begin{pmatrix} 0 \\ 5 \end{pmatrix}$. Between $\begin{pmatrix} -1 \\ 2 \end{pmatrix}$ and $\begin{pmatrix} \frac{1}{2} \\ \frac{1}{2} \end{pmatrix}$. Between the origin and $\begin{pmatrix} -1 \\ -3 \end{pmatrix}$. Between $\begin{pmatrix} 1 \\ 2 \\ 3 \end{pmatrix}$ and $\begin{pmatrix} -1 \\ 3 \\ 2 \end{pmatrix}$.

22. In Section 16 we learned that the mid-point $Z = \begin{pmatrix} z_1 \\ z_2 \end{pmatrix}$ of the segment connecting $X = \begin{pmatrix} x_1 \\ x_2 \end{pmatrix}$ and $Y = \begin{pmatrix} y_1 \\ y_2 \end{pmatrix}$ was $Z = \frac{1}{2}X + \frac{1}{2}Y$. Verify this fact now by computing the appropriate distances.

23. Determine x_2 so that $\begin{pmatrix} 1 \\ x_2 \end{pmatrix}$ is perpendicular to $\begin{pmatrix} \frac{1}{2} \\ -\frac{1}{2} \end{pmatrix}$.

24. Determine x_2 and x_3 so that $\begin{pmatrix} 5 \\ x_2 \\ x_3 \end{pmatrix}$ is perpendicular to both $\begin{pmatrix} 1 \\ 2 \\ 3 \end{pmatrix}$ and $\begin{pmatrix} 1 \\ -2 \\ 1 \end{pmatrix}$. [*Ans.* $x_2 = \frac{5}{4}$, $x_3 = -\frac{5}{2}$.]

25. Using tables of trigonometric functions find the angles between

(a) $\begin{pmatrix} 1 \\ 2 \end{pmatrix}$ and $\begin{pmatrix} -1 \\ -1 \end{pmatrix}$. (b) $\begin{pmatrix} 1 \\ 0 \\ 1 \end{pmatrix}$ and $\begin{pmatrix} 1 \\ 2 \\ 0 \end{pmatrix}$.

26. In Figure 60 we have drawn the origin O and the "unit circle," which consists of all points that lie at distance 1 from the origin. Draw the

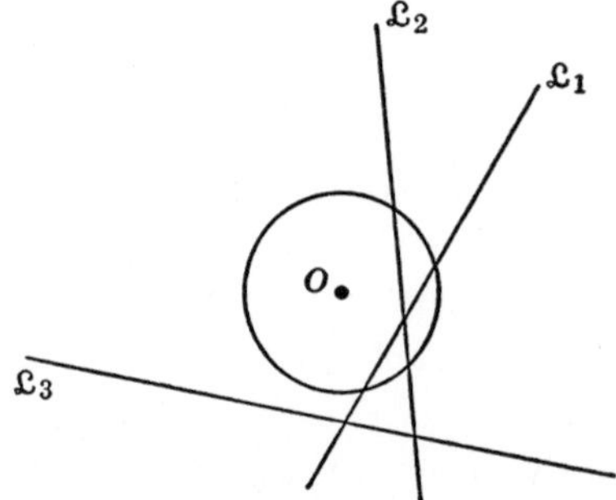

Figure 60

vectors Y_1 and Y_2 and Y_3 such that $\mathfrak{L}_1$ has the equation $Y_1'X = 1$, $\mathfrak{L}_2$ has the equation $Y_2'X = 1$, and $\mathfrak{L}_3$ has the equation $Y_3'X = 1$.

27. What is the distance between the point $\begin{pmatrix} 1 \\ -3 \end{pmatrix}$ and the line whose equation is $\begin{pmatrix} 2 \\ 5 \end{pmatrix}' X = 1$? Between the point $\begin{pmatrix} 1 \\ 0 \\ 2 \end{pmatrix}$ and the plane whose equation is $\begin{pmatrix} 1 \\ -2 \\ 1 \end{pmatrix}' X = 3$? [*Ans.* $\frac{14}{\sqrt{29}}$; 0.]

28. Show that $|X + Y| \leq |X| + |Y|$ for any vectors X and Y. (This inequality is known as the Minkowski inequality or the triangle inequality. Can you supply the motivation behind the latter name?)

29. Show that in any parallelogram the sum of the squares of the lengths of the four sides equals the sum of the squares of the lengths of the diagonals. (*Hint:* Take the corners to be $O, X, Y, X + Y$.)

30. Show that if non-zero vectors X_1, X_2, X_3 are perpendicular to each other, then they are linearly independent.

*18. ABSTRACT EUCLIDEAN VECTOR SPACES

We propose to examine somewhat more closely the geometric foundations of cartesian geometry. You will recall that the only purely vector concept of length was *parallel comparative length.* Let us now decide instead to recognize the stronger idea of absolute length for all segments. Since perpendicularity can be defined in terms of length by using the converse of the pythagorean theorem (see Exercise 20 of the previous section) we will then have what is needed for setting up a cartesian coordinate system.

Length is best thought of as a numerical (in fact, nonnegative-valued) function with domain the set of all vectors. (Here we think of vectors as arrows rather than as points.) This length function has certain important special properties. First, it is consistent with the already established pure vector space notion of comparative parallel length. Second, the length of any one side of a triangle is always less than the sum of the lengths of the other two sides. Third, the sum of the squares of the lengths of the four sides of a parallelogram always equals the sum of the squares of the lengths of the diagonals. It can be shown that all the properties of length we ever use can be derived from the above three. In view of this fact it seems sensible to axiomatize a special kind of vector space, which we will call an (abstract) euclidean vector space, adjoining the following axioms for the length $|X|$ of a vector X to the axioms (1)–(7) listed in Section 7.

$$|X| > 0, \quad \text{except that} \quad |0| = 0. \tag{8}$$

$$|aX| = |a||X|. \tag{9}$$

$$|X + Y| \leq |X| + |Y|. \tag{10}$$

$$2|X|^2 + 2|Y|^2 = |X + Y|^2 + |X - Y|^2. \tag{11}$$

Now, if we want, we can introduce the notion of perpendicularity (via the converse pythagorean theorem) by calling vectors X and Y perpendicular when $|X|^2 + |Y|^2 = |X + Y|^2$. Because of the axioms we have adopted for length, this notion of perpendicularity will behave as we want it to. We can define for any subspace $\mathcal{Y}$ its "perpendicular supplement" $\mathcal{Y}^{\perp}$, defined as the truth set of the open statement "X is perpendicular to every vector in $\mathcal{Y}$." It is then possible to prove that in every case $\mathcal{Y}^{\perp}$ will be another subspace such that (dimension of $\mathcal{Y}$) + (dimension of $\mathcal{Y}^{\perp}$) = dimension of whole space $\mathcal{X}$. And every vector X in $\mathcal{X}$ can be written uniquely as a sum $X = Y + Z$, with Y in $\mathcal{Y}$ and Z in $\mathcal{Y}^{\perp}$.

In particular we now have a natural way of associating with each nonzero vector X in $\mathcal{X}$ a certain functional on $\mathcal{X}$. Namely, take the $(n - 1)$-dimensional subspace $\mathcal{Y}$ that is the perpendicular supplement to the 1-dimensional space spanned by X. This hyperplane $\mathcal{Y}$ is the kernel of many different functionals $\mathbf{F}$, but they are all numerical multiples of each other. Pick the particular $\mathbf{F}$ for which $\mathbf{F}X = |X|^2$. If we call this $\mathbf{F}$ by name X', then we have defined a one-one linear transformation $X \to X'$ from the euclidean space $\mathcal{X}$ onto its dual space $\mathcal{F}$. (To complete the definition, we make $O' = O$.) In the course of the (not altogether trivial) proof of the above facts we would show, incidentally, that $X'Y = Y'X$.

On the other hand, if we know only the transformation $X \to X'$ of $\mathcal{X}$ onto its dual space $\mathcal{F}$, we can define the length $|X|$ as $\sqrt{X'X}$. In order that $|X|$ have the right properties (namely those listed at the beginning of this section) it is necessary and sufficient that the transformation $X \to X'$, in addition to being one-one, obey the restrictions

$$(*) \qquad X'X > 0, \quad \text{except for} \quad O'O = 0$$

and

$$(**) \qquad X'Y = Y'X.$$

Hence an abstract euclidean space can also be defined (and is often defined) as a vector space $\mathcal{X}$ together with a specified one-one transformation of $\mathcal{X}$ onto its dual space, obeying the two rules above. Of course every vector space possesses such a transformation, in fact infinitely many such. But $\mathcal{X}$ does not become euclidean until some particular one of these is singled out for special attention.

The expression $X'Y$ acts algebraically as though the vectors X and Y were being multiplied. Specifically

$$(***) \qquad (X + Y)'Z = X'Z + Y'Z$$

$$(****) \qquad X'(Y + Z) = X'Y + X'Z$$

The identity (***) follows from the definition of addition in the space of functionals. And (****) follows simply from the fact that X' is a functional. Hence the name "inner product" of X and Y.

Example 1. When $\mathfrak{X}$ is the space $\mathfrak{X}_n$ of n-dimensional column vectors, then the space of functionals is $\mathfrak{F} = \mathfrak{F}_n =$ the n-dimensional row vectors. The most obvious transformation from $\mathfrak{X}_n$ onto $\mathfrak{F}_n$ is defined by the rule

$$\begin{pmatrix} c_1 \\ \vdots \\ c_n \end{pmatrix} \to (c_1 \ldots c_n).$$

Or using the prime notation,

$$\begin{pmatrix} c_1 \\ \vdots \\ c_n \end{pmatrix}' = (c_1 \ldots c_n).$$

Proof that $X'Y = Y'X$: Let $X = \begin{pmatrix} x_1 \\ \vdots \\ x_n \end{pmatrix}$ and $Y = \begin{pmatrix} y_1 \\ \vdots \\ y_n \end{pmatrix}$. Then

$$\begin{aligned} X'Y &= (x_1 \ldots x_n)\begin{pmatrix} y_1 \\ \vdots \\ y_n \end{pmatrix} \\ &= x_1y_1 + \ldots + x_ny_n = y_1x_1 + \ldots + y_nx_n \\ &= (y_1 \ldots y_n)\begin{pmatrix} x_1 \\ \vdots \\ x_n \end{pmatrix} = Y'X. \end{aligned}$$

Proof that $X'X > 0$: If $X \neq 0$, then some component x_k is nonzero, and $x_k^2 > 0$. Hence

$$\begin{aligned} X'X &= (x_1 \ldots x_k \ldots x_n)\begin{pmatrix} x_1 \\ \vdots \\ x_k \\ \vdots \\ x_n \end{pmatrix} \\ &= x_1^2 + \ldots + x_k^2 + \ldots + x_n^2 \geq x_k^2 > 0. \end{aligned}$$

Example 2. Let $\mathfrak{X}$ be any abstract vector space and let $\mathfrak{F}$ be the space of functionals on $\mathfrak{X}$. Let $X_1, \ldots, X_n$ be a basis for $\mathfrak{X}$ and let $\mathbf{F}_1, \ldots, \mathbf{F}_n$ be the dual basis (see Section 13) for $\mathfrak{X}$. Suppose now that we define $X_1' = \mathbf{F}_1$, $X_2' = \mathbf{F}_2$, etc. And suppose that for every vector $X = c_1X_1 + \ldots + c_nX_n$ we define $X' = c_1\mathbf{F}_1 + \ldots + c_n\mathbf{F}_n$. Then we have made $\mathfrak{X}$ a Euclidean space. For when we choose the basis $X_1, \ldots, X_n$ in $\mathfrak{X}$, and the basis $\mathbf{F}_1, \ldots, \mathbf{F}_n$ in $\mathfrak{F}$, we make $\mathfrak{X}$ into a column-vector space $\mathfrak{X}_n$ and $\mathfrak{F}$ into a row-vector space $\mathfrak{F}_n$. And then our definition of X' coincides with the definition of X' in Example 1. It is important to realize, however, that the euclidean structure we have imposed on the space $\mathfrak{X}$ depends on the basis $X_1, \ldots, X_n$. If we change the basis we may change the euclidean structure (see Exercise 2).

Example 3. Let $\mathfrak{X}$ be the vector space of polynomials. For two polynomials X and Y let us define

$$X'Y = Y'X = \int_0^1 X(u)Y(u)\,du.$$

The proof that this definition makes $\mathfrak{X}$ a euclidean space is left for Exercise 1.

Example 4. Let $\mathfrak{U}$ be a finite probability space with measure $\mathbf{m}$ defined by some weight function $\mathbf{w}$. Let $\mathfrak{X}$ be the vector space of numerical functions having domain $\mathfrak{U}$ and define $\mathbf{X}'\mathbf{Y}$ to be $\Sigma\, \mathbf{X}(u)\mathbf{Y}(u)\mathbf{w}(u)$.

If we start with the inner product $X'Y$, then we *define* the cosine of the angle between nonzero vectors X and Y to be $\dfrac{X'Y}{|X|\,|Y|}\cdot$ Defining the cosine of θ is more satisfactory than defining θ itself because then we do not have to worry about whether the angle between X and Y is

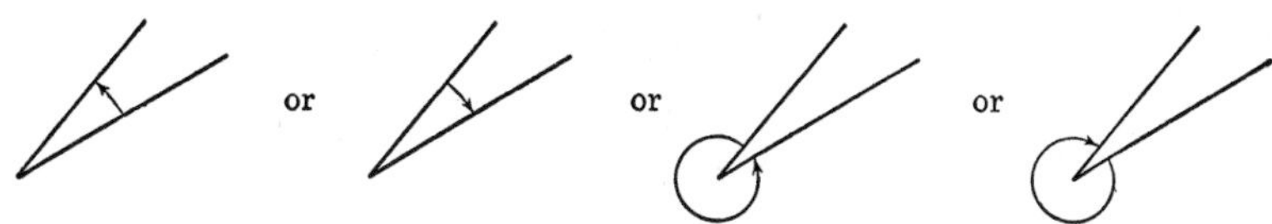

In order that $\dfrac{X'Y}{|X|\,|Y|}$ may be the cosine of an angle it is necessary that it be ≤ 1 in absolute value. That is, the Cauchy-Schwarz inequality

$$|X'Y| \leq |X|\,|Y|$$

must hold. We proceed to prove this fact, using only $X'X > 0$ and $X'Y = Y'X$. If one vector is a numerical multiple of the other, say $Y = cX$, then

$$\begin{aligned} |X'Y| &= X'(cX) = c(X'X) \\ &= c|X|^2 \leq |c|\,|X|^2 = |X|\,|cX| = |X|\,|Y|. \end{aligned}$$

Otherwise X and Y are linearly independent and it is impossible to find a number x such that $xX + Y = 0$. That is, $|xX + Y|^2 > 0$. But $|xX + Y|^2 = |X|^2x^2 + 2(X'Y)x + |Y|^2$. This can be looked at as a polynomial $ax^2 + bx + c$. Since no value of x will make this polynomial zero, i.e., it has no root, then its discriminant $b^2 - 4ac$ is < 0. But

$$b^2 - 4ac = (2X'Y)^2 - 4|X|^2|Y|^2 < 0.$$

That is,
$$4(X'Y)^2 < 4|X|^2|Y|^2$$
and
$$|X'Y| < |X|\,|Y|.$$

It is now easy to prove the "triangle inequality," $|X + Y| \leq |X| + |Y|$, as follows.

$$|X + Y|^2 = |X|^2 + 2X'Y + |Y|^2 \leq |X|^2 + 2|X'Y| + |Y|^2$$
$$\leq |X|^2 + 2|X|\,|Y| + |Y|^2 = (|X| + |Y|)^2.$$

Hence $|X + Y| \leq |X| + |Y|$.

Now we will show that the coordinatized euclidean spaces of Section 17 (and of Examples 1 and 2 of the present section) are not essentially different from abstract euclidean vector spaces. First, let $X_1, \ldots, X_n$ be nonzero vectors in a euclidean space such that each one is perpendicular to all the others. Then $X_1, \ldots, X_n$ are *automatically linearly independent.* For suppose that $c_1X_1 + \ldots + c_nX_n = 0$. We want to prove that each c_k must be zero. To do this we simply apply to this linear combination the functional X_k'. Then

$$0 = X_k'(c_1X_1 + \ldots + c_kX_k + \ldots + c_nX_n)$$
$$= c_1X_k'X_1 + \ldots + c_kX_k'X_k + \ldots + c_nX_k'X_n = c_k|X_k|^2,$$

since X_k is perpendicular to all the others. And then $c_k = 0$ because $|X_k| \neq 0$.

When the whole euclidean space $\mathfrak{X}$ is n-dimensional, then $X_1, \ldots, X_n$ must form a basis for $\mathfrak{X}$. It is natural also to require that each X_k have length 1; for then any inner product $X'Y$ is computed by the formula $x_1y_1 + \ldots + x_ny_n$, which is the natural generalization of the formula in Section 17.

To see this, let $X = a_1X_1 + \ldots + a_nX_n$ and let $Y = b_1X_1 + \ldots + b_nX_n$. Then

$$\begin{aligned} X'Y &= (a_1X_1' + \ldots + a_nX_n')(b_1X_1 + \ldots + b_nX_n) \\ &= a_1b_1X_1'X_1 + a_1b_2X_1'X_2 + \ldots + a_1b_nX_1'X_n + a_2b_1X_2'X_1 \\ &\quad + a_2b_2X_2'X_2 + \ldots + a_2b_nX_2'X_n + \ldots \\ &\quad + a_nb_1X_n'X_1 + \ldots \qquad\qquad + a_nb_nX_n'X_n. \end{aligned}$$

Now all the terms drop out except

$$a_1b_1X_1'X_1 + a_2b_2X_2'X_2 + \ldots + a_nb_nX_n'X_n$$
$$= a_1b_1 + a_2b_2 + \ldots + a_nb_n.$$

Hence we can now identify X and Y with column vectors, and compute lengths and inner products coordinatewise, as in the 3-dimensional case. A basis for a euclidean space $\mathfrak{X}$ in which the basis vectors are perpendicular to each other and of length 1, is called an *orthonormal basis* for $\mathfrak{X}$, as in the 2- and 3-dimensional case. It is easy to prove the existence of such an orthonormal basis in any number of dimensions.

When **A** is a transformation with domain and range a euclidean space $\mathfrak{X}$, it makes sense to ask whether **A** preserves lengths and angles.

Such a transformation is expressed by the identity $(\mathbf{A}X)'\mathbf{A}Y = X'Y$, which says that $\mathbf{A}$ preserves the inner product. If $\{X_1, \ldots, X_n\} = \Gamma$ is an orthonormal basis for $\mathfrak{X}$, then the matrix $\begin{pmatrix} A \\ \Gamma\Gamma \end{pmatrix}$ must be such that each column, considered as a vector in the euclidean space $\mathfrak{X}_n$, has length 1 and is perpendicular to all the other columns. For these columns correspond to the vectors $\mathbf{A}X_1, \ldots, \mathbf{A}X_n$, which are (by the inner-product preserving nature of $\mathbf{A}$) perpendicular to each other and of length 1.

Conversely, if the columns of $\begin{pmatrix} \mathbf{A} \\ \Gamma\Gamma \end{pmatrix}$, Γ being an orthonormal basis for the abstract euclidean space $\mathfrak{X}$, form an orthonormal basis for the euclidean space $\mathfrak{X}_n$ of column vectors, then $\mathbf{A}$ preserves length and angle. For it is clear that $\mathbf{A}$ preserves length and angle at least for the n vectors $X_1, \ldots, X_n$ that constitute the basis Γ. And then we can mechanically check, as in the paragraph above, that $\mathbf{A}$ preserves the inner product between any two vectors

$$X = a_1X_1 + \ldots + a_nX_n \quad \text{and} \quad Y = b_1X_1 + \ldots + b_nX_n.$$

Let us call a matrix whose columns form an orthonormal basis for $\mathfrak{X}_n$ an *orthogonal* matrix. It is very pleasant to compute the inverse of such a matrix. Suppose

$$\mathbf{A} = \begin{pmatrix} a_{11} & a_{12} & \ldots \\ a_{21} & a_{22} & \ldots \\ \vdots & \vdots & \end{pmatrix}$$

is orthogonal. Then its inverse is simply

$$\mathbf{A}^{-1} = \begin{pmatrix} a_{11} & a_{21} & \ldots \\ a_{12} & a_{22} & \ldots \\ \vdots & \vdots & \end{pmatrix}.$$

For when these two matrices are multiplied together in the order $\mathbf{A}^{-1}\mathbf{A}$, the result is the identity matrix I.

EXERCISES

1. Prove that the inner product defined in Example 3 of this section satisfies the requirements

$$X'X > 0, \quad \text{for} \quad X \neq 0$$

and

$$X'Y = Y'X.$$

2. Let $X_1, \ldots, X_n$ constitute a basis Γ for a vector space $\mathfrak{X}$, and let $Y_1, \ldots, Y_n$ constitute a basis Δ for $\mathfrak{X}$. Each of these bases defines (as in Example 2 of this section) a euclidean structure on the space $\mathfrak{X}$.

Suppose that these two structures are the same. That is, suppose that for every vector X, the length $|X|$ is the same whether computed with respect to Γ or with respect to Δ. What then is the relation between Γ and Δ? The answer is most simply stated in terms of the matrix $\begin{pmatrix} I \\ \Delta\Gamma \end{pmatrix}$.

3. Which of the following geometric ideas make sense in an abstract vector space, and which make sense only in a euclidean space?

(a) Bisect line segment.
(b) Bisect angle.
(c) Medians of triangle.
(d) Altitudes of triangle.
(e) Parallelogram.
(f) Rhombus.
(g) Rectangle.
(h) Square.
(i) Trapezoid.
(j) Ellipse.
(k) Circle.
(l) Hyperbola.
(m) Regular polygon.
(n) Isosceles triangle.
(o) Acute angle.
(p) Convex polygon.

[*Ans.* (a), (c), (e), (i), (j), (l), (p) are the ones that make sense in an abstract vector space.]

SUGGESTED READING

Birkhoff, G., and S. MacLane, *A Survey of Modern Algebra*, Macmillan, New York, 1941; rev. ed., 1953.

Johnson, R. E., *First Course in Abstract Algebra*, Prentice-Hall, New York, 1953.

Beaumont, R. A., and R. W. Ball, *Introduction to Modern Algebra and Matrix Theory*, Rinehart, New York, 1954.

Hohn, Franz E., *Elementary Matrix Algebra*, Macmillan, New York, 1958.

Thrall, Robert M. and Leonard Tornheim, *Vector Spaces and Matrices*, Wiley, New York, 1957.

CHAPTER 5*

Convex Sets

1. POLYHEDRAL CONVEX SETS

As background preparation for this chapter the reader should have covered the unstarred sections of Chapters 1, 2, and 4.

The reader will recall that a linear equation of the form $AX = W$ is an *open statement*. (Here A is an m-by-n matrix, X is an n-component variable column vector, and W is an m-component constant column vector.) Thus for some vectors X the statement $AX = W$ is true and for other vectors it is false. The truth set of such an equation consists of all vectors X^0 that satisfy the equation; that is, vectors X^0 for which the equation $AX^0 = W$ is a true statement. In geometry it is traditional to refer to this truth set as the *locus* of the equation, and we may occasionally use that terminology.

Example 1. Suppose that

$$A = (-2\ 3), \quad X = \begin{pmatrix} x_1 \\ x_2 \end{pmatrix}, \quad \text{and} \quad W = (6).$$

Then the equation (a), $AX = W$, is the single equality

(a) $$-2x_1 + 3x_2 = 6,$$

whose locus or truth set is the straight line (a) plotted in Figure 1. Points

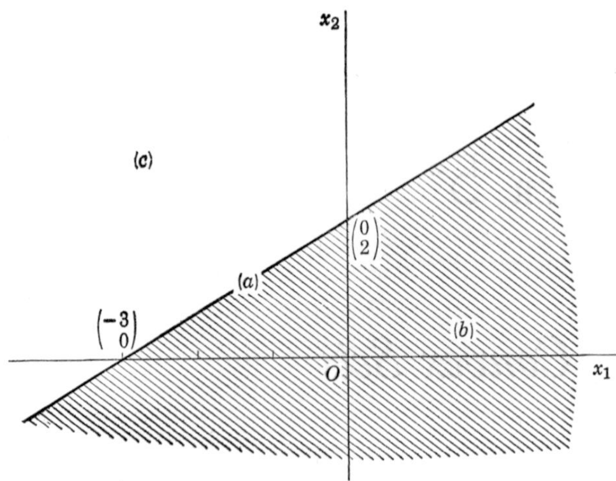

Figure 1

on this line may be obtained by assuming values for one of the variables and computing the corresponding value for the other variable. Thus, setting $x_1 = 0$, we find $x_2 = 2$ so that the point $\begin{pmatrix}0\\2\end{pmatrix}$ lies on the locus, etc.

The linear equation $AX = W$ is equivalent to the assertion of the conjunction of the m statements $A_iX = w_i$ for $i = 1, \ldots, m$, where A_i is the ith row of A and w_i is the ith component of W. In the same way we will define an inequality assertion $AX \leq W$ to be equivalent to the conjunction of the m inequality statements $A_iX \leq w_i$ for $i = 1, \ldots, m$. It is also an open statement and the truth set of $AX \leq W$ is the set of all X^0 for which the statement $AX^0 \leq W$ is true.

Example 2. Consider the inequalities (b) $AX < w$, (c) $AX > w$, (d) $AX \leq w$, and (e) $AX \geq w$ where A, X, and w are as in Example 1. They may be written as

(b) $$-2x_1 + 3x_2 < 6,$$

(c) $$-2x_1 + 3x_2 > 6,$$

(d) $$-2x_1 + 3x_2 \leq 6,$$

(e) $$-2x_1 + 3x_2 \geq 6.$$

Consider (b) first. What points $\begin{pmatrix}x_1\\x_2\end{pmatrix}$ satisfy this inequality? By trial and error we can find many points on the locus. Thus the point $\begin{pmatrix}1\\2\end{pmatrix}$ is on it since $-2 + 6 = 4 < 6$; on the other hand the point $\begin{pmatrix}1\\3\end{pmatrix}$ is not on the locus because $-2\cdot 1 + 3\cdot 3 = -2 + 9 = 7$, which is not less than 6.

In between these two points we find $\begin{pmatrix} 1 \\ \frac{8}{3} \end{pmatrix}$ which lies on the boundary, i.e., on the locus of (a). We note that, starting with $\begin{pmatrix} 1 \\ \frac{8}{3} \end{pmatrix}$ on locus (a), by increasing x_2 we went outside the locus (b); by decreasing x_2 we came into the locus (b) again. This holds in general. Given a point on the locus of (a), by increasing its second coordinate we get more than 6, but by decreasing the second coordinate we get less than 6, and hence the latter gives a point in the truth set of (b). Thus we find that the locus of (b) consists of all points of the plane *below* the line (a), in other words, the shaded area in Figure 1. The area on one side of a straight line is called an *open half plane.*

We can apply exactly the same analysis to show that the locus of (c) is the open half plane above the line (a). This can also be deduced from the fact that the truth sets of statements (a), (b), and (c) are disjoint and have as union the entire plane.

Since (d) is the disjunction of (a) and (b), the truth set of (d) is the union of the truth sets of (a) and (b). Such a set, which consists of an open half plane together with the points on the line that define the half plane, is called a *closed half plane.* Obviously the truth set of (e) consists of the union of (a) and (c) and therefore is also a closed half plane.

If the vector X has n components where $n = 2, 3, \ldots,$ then the truth sets of such equalities or inequalities will be subsets of $\mathfrak{X}_n$. The results of the above examples motivate the following definition.

DEFINITION. Let $\mathbf{F}$ be a functional (see Chapter 4, Section 14) on $\mathfrak{X}_n$ and let w be a number. The truth set of the equation $\mathbf{F}X = w$ is a hyperplane in $\mathfrak{X}_n$. The truth sets of inequalities of the form $\mathbf{F}X < w$ or $\mathbf{F}X > w$ are called *open half spaces* while the truth sets of the inequalities $\mathbf{F}X \leq w$ or $\mathbf{F}X \geq w$ are called *closed half spaces* in $\mathfrak{X}_n$.

Example 3. Consider the following example: $AX \leq W$, where

$$A = \begin{pmatrix} -1 & 0 \\ 0 & -1 \\ 2 & 3 \end{pmatrix}, \quad X = \begin{pmatrix} x_1 \\ x_2 \end{pmatrix}, \quad W = \begin{pmatrix} 0 \\ 0 \\ 6 \end{pmatrix}.$$

If we write the components of the equations $AX \leq W$, we obtain

(f) $-x_1 \leq 0$ which is equivalent to $x_1 \geq 0$,

(g) $-x_2 \leq 0$ which is equivalent to $x_2 \geq 0$,

(h) $2x_1 + 3x_2 \leq 6$.

Here we are simultaneously asserting three different statements; i.e., we assert their conjunction. Therefore the truth set of $AX \leq W$ is the intersection of the three individual truth sets. The truth set of (f) is the upper half plane; the truth set of (g) is the right half plane; and the truth set of (h) is the half plane below the line $2x_1 + 3x_2 = 6$. The intersection of these is the triangle (including the sides) shaded in Figure 2. The area shaded in Figure 2 contains those points which simultaneously satisfy (f), (g), and (h).

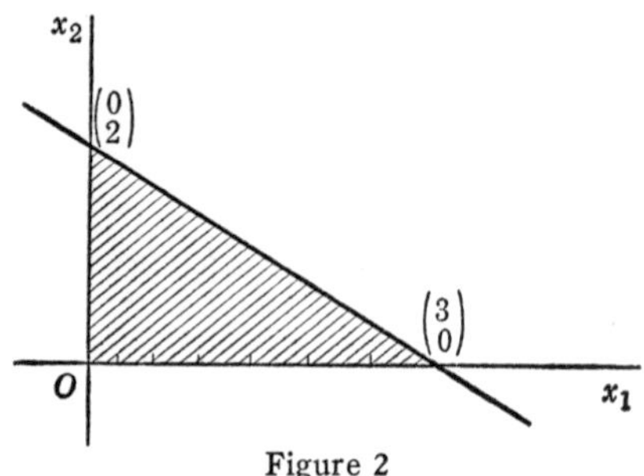

Figure 2

Half spaces and sets that are the intersection of half spaces have the property of being convex. The following series of definitions and theorems elucidate this idea.

DEFINITION. A set C is said to be *convex* if, whenever U and V are points of C, the entire line segment between U and V also belongs to C. In other words, all points of the form $Z = aU + (1 - a)V$ for $0 \leq a \leq 1$ belong to C whenever both U and V do. (The empty set $\mathcal{E}$ and any unit set satisfy this definition vacuously and so are considered to be convex.)

Theorem. The intersection of two or more convex sets is also a convex set.

Proof. Let D and E be convex sets and $C = D \cap E$. If C is empty or a unit set there is nothing to prove. If C has at least two distinct points, choose two, U and V. Then D and E each contain both U and V. Since D and E are convex sets they each also contain the line segment between U and V. Because C contains all the points common to both D and E it also contains the line segment between U and V and therefore is a convex set.

Theorem. A half space (closed or open) is convex.

Proof. Consider $AX < w$ where A is a functional (i.e., row vector) on $\mathfrak{X}_n$, X is a vector in $\mathfrak{X}_n$, and w is a number. Let U and V be two vectors in the truth set of this inequality; then $AU < w$ and $AV < w$ are true statements. Let $Z = aU + (1 - a)V$ where a satisfies $0 \leq a \leq 1$. Then

$$AZ = aAU + (1 - a)AV < aw + (1 - a)w = w,$$

so that Z also belongs to the truth set. Therefore the line segment between U and V is in the truth set and an open half space is convex. The same argument with $<$ replaced by $\leq$ shows that a closed half space is convex. Similarly for $>$, $\geq$.

Theorem. The intersection of half spaces is a convex set.

Proof. Follows directly from the above two theorems.

DEFINITION. We shall call the intersection of a finite number of closed half spaces a *polyhedral convex set.* (In particular, we shall use this terminology even in the 1- and 2-dimensional cases, where polyhedral sets are actually intervals and polygons, respectively.)

Theorem. Any polyhedral convex set is the truth set of an inequality statement of the form $AX \leq W$.

Proof. A closed half space is the locus of an inequality of the form $A_iX \leq w_i$, where A_i is a functional, X is a column vector, and w_i is a number. (An inequality of the form $BX \geq w$ can be converted to one of this form by multiplying by -1.) Now a polyhedral convex set is the truth set of the conjunction of several such statements. And if we let A be the matrix whose ith row is A_i and let W be the column vector with components w_i, then the inequality statement $AX \leq W$ is a succinct way of stating the conjunction of the inequalities $A_1X \leq w_1, \ldots, A_mX \leq w_m$. This completes the proof.

In the next section we shall study other properties of polyhedral convex sets.

EXERCISES

1. Draw pictures of the truth sets of $AX \leq W$, where A and W are as given below. (Construct the truth sets of the individual statements first and then take their intersection.)

(a) $A = \begin{pmatrix} 1 & 0 \\ 0 & 1 \\ -2 & -3 \end{pmatrix}, \quad W = \begin{pmatrix} 3 \\ 2 \\ 0 \end{pmatrix}.$

(b) $A = \begin{pmatrix} -2 & -3 \\ -1 & 1 \\ 1 & 1 \end{pmatrix}, \quad W = \begin{pmatrix} -6 \\ 2 \\ 3 \end{pmatrix}.$

(c) $A = \begin{pmatrix} 2 & 3 \\ -1 & 1 \\ 1 & 1 \end{pmatrix}, \quad W = \begin{pmatrix} 6 \\ 2 \\ 3 \end{pmatrix}.$

(d) $A = \begin{pmatrix} 0 & -1 \\ -1 & 0 \\ 1 & 0 \end{pmatrix}, \quad W = \begin{pmatrix} 0 \\ 0 \\ 2 \end{pmatrix}.$

(e) $A = \begin{pmatrix} 1 & 0 \\ -1 & 0 \\ 0 & 1 \\ 0 & -1 \end{pmatrix}, \quad W = \begin{pmatrix} 2 \\ 2 \\ 3 \\ 3 \end{pmatrix}.$

(f) $A = \begin{pmatrix} 3 & 2 \\ 3 & 2 \end{pmatrix}, \quad W = \begin{pmatrix} -6 \\ 6 \end{pmatrix}.$

(g) $A = \begin{pmatrix} -3 & -2 \\ 3 & 2 \end{pmatrix}, \quad W = \begin{pmatrix} -6 \\ 6 \end{pmatrix}.$

(h) $A = \begin{pmatrix} -1 & 1 \\ 1 & 1 \end{pmatrix}, \quad W = \begin{pmatrix} 0 \\ 0 \end{pmatrix}.$

(i) $A = \begin{pmatrix} 1 & 0 \\ -1 & 0 \end{pmatrix}, \quad W = \begin{pmatrix} 2 \\ -5 \end{pmatrix}.$

(j) $A = \begin{pmatrix} -3 & -2 \\ -2 & -3 \\ -1 & 0 \\ 0 & -1 \end{pmatrix}, \quad W = \begin{pmatrix} -6 \\ -6 \\ 0 \\ 0 \end{pmatrix}.$

(k) $A = \begin{pmatrix} -2 & -1 \\ 1 & 0 \\ 0 & 1 \end{pmatrix}, \quad W = \begin{pmatrix} -7 \\ 0 \\ 0 \end{pmatrix}.$

2. Consider the following sets:
$\mathfrak{U}$ is the whole plane;
A is the half plane which is the locus of $-2x_1 + x_2 < 3$.
B is the half plane which is the locus of $-2x_1 + x_2 > 3$.
C is the half plane which is the locus of $-2x_1 + x_2 \leq 3$.
D is the half plane which is the locus of $-2x_1 + x_2 \geq 3$.
L is the line which is the locus of $-2x_1 + x_2 = 3$.
$\mathcal{E}$ is the empty set.
Show that the following relationships hold among these sets: $\tilde{A} = D$, $\tilde{B} = C$, $\tilde{L} = A \cup B$, $C \cap D = L$, $A \cap B = \mathcal{E}$, $A \cap C = A$, $B \cap D = B$, $A \cup D = \mathfrak{U}$, $B \cup C = \mathfrak{U}$, $A \cup C = C$, $B \cup D = D$, $A \cup L = C$, $B \cup L = D$. Can you find other relationships?

3. Of the polyhedral convex sets constructed in Exercise 1, which have a finite area and which have infinite area?

[*Partial Ans.* (c), (d), (f), (h), and (j) are of infinite area; (g) is a line; (i) and (k) are empty.]

4. For each of the following half planes give an inequality of which it is the truth set.

(a) The open half plane above the x_1-axis. [*Ans.* $x_2 > 0$.]

(b) The closed half plane on and above the straight line making angles of 45° with the positive x_1- and x_2-axis.

Exercises 5–9 refer to a situation in which a family decides to buy x books and y record albums. The books cost \$4 each, and the albums cost \$3 each.

5. One cannot buy a negative number of books or albums. Write these conditions as inequalities, and draw their truth sets.

6. There are only six books and six albums that they like. Modify the set found in Exercise 5 to take this into account.

7. They are not willing to spend more than \$24 altogether. Modify the set found in Exercise 6.

8. They decide to spend at least twice as much on books as on records. Modify the set of Exercise 7.

9. Finally, they decide that they want to spend \$9 on records. What possibilities are left? [*Ans.* None.]

10. Assume that the minimal requirements of human beings are given by the following table:

	Phosphorus	Calcium
Adult	.02	.01
Child	.03	.03
Infant	.01	.02

Plot the amount of phosphorus on the vertical axis and the amount of calcium on the horizontal. Then draw in the convex sets of minimal diet requirements for adults, children (noninfants), and infants. State whether or not the following assertions are true.

(a) If a child's needs are satisfied, so are an adult's.
(b) An infant's needs are satisfied only if a child's needs are.
(c) An adult's needs are satisfied only if an infant's needs are.
(d) Both an adult's and an infant's needs are satisfied only if a child's needs are.
(e) It is possible to satisfy adult needs without satisfying the needs of an infant.

11. Prove that the following sets are convex. Which are polyhedral convex sets?

(a) The interior plus the edges of a triangle.
(b) The interior of a circle.
(c) The interior of a rectangle.
(d) A rectangle surmounted by a semicircle.

12. Consider the plane with a cartesian coordinate system. A rectangle with sides of length a and b ($a \neq b$) is placed with one corner at the origin and two of its sides along the axes. Prove that the interior of the rectangle plus its edges forms a polyhedral convex set and find the statement of the form $AX \leq W$ of which it is the truth set.

13. The following polygons are placed in a plane with a cartesian coordinate system with one corner at the origin and one side along an axis. Find the statements $AX \leq W$ of which they are the truth sets.
(a) A regular pentagon.
(b) A regular hexagon.

2. EXTREME POINTS OF POLYHEDRAL CONVEX SETS

Here we shall discuss the problem of finding the extreme points of a bounded polyhedral convex set. We shall use the following notation: The set C is the truth set of the statement $AX \leq W$, where A is an m-by-n matrix, X is a vector in $\mathfrak{X}_n$, and W is a vector in $\mathfrak{X}_m$. (We may consider A as the matrix of a transformation from $\mathfrak{X}_n$ to $\mathfrak{X}_m$ when the natural bases are used in these spaces.) We shall let $A_1, A_2, \ldots, A_m$ denote the rows of A. Hence A_i is an n-component row vector that may be considered a functional on $\mathfrak{X}_n$, and

$$A = \begin{pmatrix} A_1 \\ A_2 \\ \vdots \\ A_m \end{pmatrix}.$$

The statement $AX \leq W$ is then the conjunction of the statements $A_1X \leq w_1$, $A_2X \leq w_2$, $\ldots$, $A_mX \leq w_m$, and its truth set C is a subset of $\mathfrak{X}_n$.

Sometimes it happens that one of the inequality statements defining a convex set is unnecessary. We shall say that the inequality $A_iX \leq w_i$ is *superfluous* if the truth set of the conjunction of all the statements $A_1X \leq w_1, \ldots, A_mX \leq w_m$ is the same as the conjunction of all these statements except for $A_iX \leq w_i$. For instance, in Example 3 of Section 1, if we add the statement $x_1 \geq -1$ to the statements defining the convex set there, it is superfluous, since the statement $x_1 \geq 0$ implies $x_1 \geq -1$. Other examples of superfluous statements are given in Exercise 1. For convenience, we shall assume that all superfluous inequality statements have been eliminated from those defining convex sets considered in this chapter.

DEFINITION. If A is a row vector, the truth set of the statement $AX = w$ will be called the *bounding hyperplane* of the half space $AX \leq w$. The bounding hyperplanes of a polyhedral convex set will be the bounding hyperplanes of the half spaces that define the set.

In Example 3 of Section 1 the bounding hyperplanes of the convex set given there are the three boundary lines of the triangle shaded in Figure 2.

DEFINITION. Let C be the polyhedral convex set defined by $AX \leq W$. Then a point T is an *extreme point* of C if it

(a) belongs to C, and

(b) is the intersection of n bounding hyperplanes of C, where n is the dimension of the entire space.

Example 1. Find the extreme points of the polyhedal convex set $AX \leq W$ where

$$A = \begin{pmatrix} -2 & -1 \\ 1 & -3 \\ 1 & 2 \end{pmatrix}, \qquad W = \begin{pmatrix} 9 \\ 6 \\ 3 \end{pmatrix}.$$

A sketch of the three half planes, Figure 3, shows that the set is a triangle. Hence we can find the extreme points by changing the inequalities to

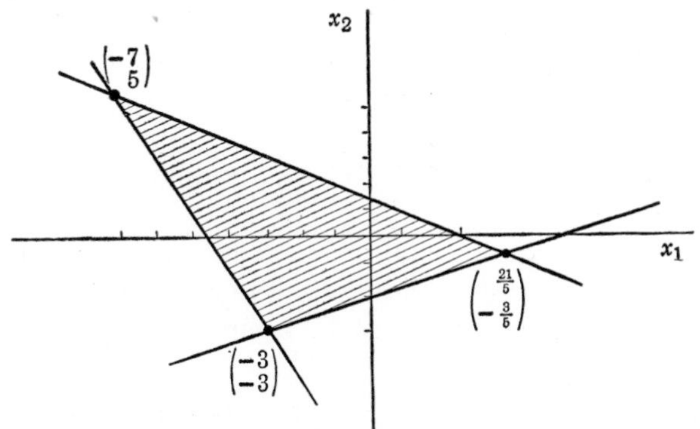

Figure 3

equalities in pairs and solving three sets of simultaneous equations. We obtain in this way the points

$$\begin{pmatrix} -3 \\ -3 \end{pmatrix}, \quad \begin{pmatrix} -7 \\ 5 \end{pmatrix}, \quad \text{and} \quad \begin{pmatrix} \frac{21}{5} \\ -\frac{3}{5} \end{pmatrix}$$

which are the extreme points of the set.

There is a mechanical (but perhaps lengthy) method for finding all the extreme points of a convex set of C defined by $AX \leq W$. Namely, consider the bounding hyperplanes $A_1X = w_1$, $A_2X = w_2$, . . . , $A_mX = w_m$ of the half spaces that determine C. Select a subset of n of these hyperplanes and solve their equations simultaneously. If the result is a *unique* point X^0 (and only then) check to see whether or not X^0 belongs to C. If it does then, by the above definition, X^0 is an extreme point of C. Moreover, all extreme points of C can be found in this way.

Example 2. Let $A = \begin{pmatrix} -1 & 0 \\ 0 & -1 \end{pmatrix}$ and $W = \begin{pmatrix} 0 \\ 0 \end{pmatrix}$. Then the convex set C defined by $AX \leq W$ is the first quadrant of the x_1, x_2 plane, shaded in Figure 4. The only extreme point is the origin, which is the intersection

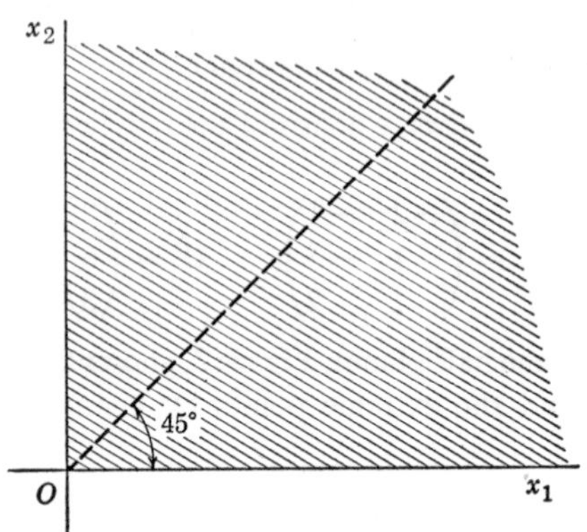

Figure 4

of the lines $x_1 = 0$ and $x_2 = 0$. This is an example of an *unbounded* convex set.

Notice that the set C contains the *ray* or half line that starts at the origin of coordinates and extends upward to the right making a 45° angle with the axes. This ray is dotted in Figure 4. Of course, this set also contains many other rays.

We shall say that a set is *bounded* if it does not contain a ray (i.e., a half line). A set, such as the one in Figure 4 that does contain rays, will be called *unbounded*. For simplicity we shall restrict our discussion to bounded convex sets in most of this chapter. In particular this means that necessarily $m > n$, that is, the convex set must be the intersection of at least $n + 1$ half spaces. This is a necessary but not sufficient condition that the convex set is bounded (see Exercise 14).

DEFINITION. Let $U_1, U_2, \ldots, U_k$ be vectors in $\mathfrak{X}_n$ and let $a_1, a_2, \ldots, a_k$ be nonnegative numbers such that $a_1 + a_2 + \ldots + a_k = 1$. Then the vector

$$Z = a_1U_1 + a_2U_2 + \ldots + a_kU_k$$

is said to be a *convex combination* of $U_1, U_2, \ldots, U_k$.

Notice that a convex combination of vectors is also a linear combination of the same vectors. But a linear combination of vectors is a convex combination only if the coefficients are nonnegative and their sum is one.

Theorem. Let C be a bounded polyhedral convex set and let $T_1, T_2, \ldots,$ T_k be all its extreme points. Then:

(A) Every point Z that is a convex combination of the extreme points of C belongs to C.

(B) Every point in C can be written as a convex combination of the extreme points of C.

Proof. (A) Observe that all the statements $AT_i \leq W$ are true for $i = 1, \ldots, k$ since the extreme points T_i belong to C. If $Z = a_1T_1 + \ldots + a_kT_k$, where the a_i's are nonnegative numbers whose sum is one, then

$$AZ = a_1AT_1 + a_2AT_2 + \ldots + a_kAT_k \leq a_1W + a_2W + \ldots + a_kW = W$$

so that Z belongs to C, completing the proof.

We shall indicate the proof of (B) for the case that C is a plane convex set. The proof for the general case is beyond the scope of this book, but it proceeds in a manner analogous to the following.

Let Z be any point in the convex set C but not on the boundary of C, as in Figure 5. Draw any line through Z and mark the points R and S where the line intersects the boundary lines of C. Clearly there are exactly two such points (see Exercise 15). Suppose that R lies on the boundary line segment between extreme points T_i and T_j while S lies on the boundary line segment between extreme points T_h and T_k. (Actually R or S could be one of these extreme points without affecting the analysis.) As we saw in Chapter 4, Section 16, any point on the line segment between two given points could be written as a convex combination of these two points. Hence we can assume that

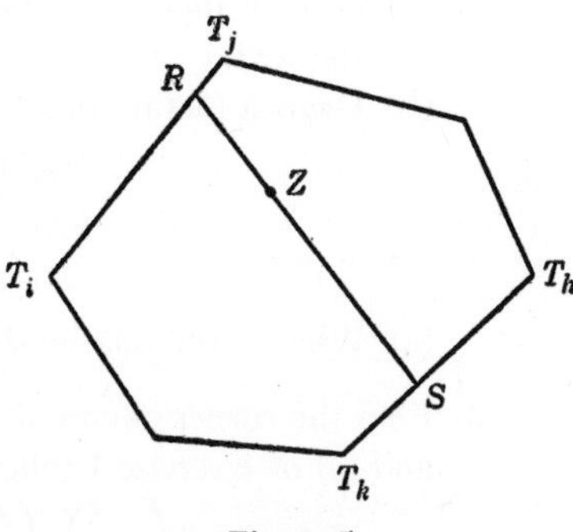

Figure 5

$$R = aT_i + (1 - a)T_j, \quad \text{where} \quad 0 \leq a \leq 1,$$

$$S = bT_h + (1 - b)T_k, \quad \text{where} \quad 0 \leq b \leq 1,$$

and

$$Z = cR + (1 - c)S, \quad \text{where} \quad 0 \leq c \leq 1.$$

Substituting the first two of these equations into the third, we obtain

$$Z = caT_i + c(1 - a)T_j + (1 - c)bT_h + (1 - c)(1 - b)T_k.$$

If we now observe that

$$ca + c(1 - a) + (1 - c)b + (1 - c)(1 - b) = 1,$$

we see that Z is written as a convex combination of extreme points.

If Z is a point on the boundary of C, then it lies on a line segment between two extreme points of C and is therefore a convex combination of these two extreme points. This completes the proof of (B) for the case $n = 2$.

EXERCISES

1. In the following sets of inequalities at least one is superfluous. In each case find the superfluous ones.

(a) $x_1 + x_2 \leq 3,\quad -x_1 - x_2 \geq 0,\quad x_1 \geq -1,\quad -x_2 \leq 2.$

(b) $x_1 + x_2 \geq 0,\quad x_1 - x_2 \leq 0,\quad x_1 \leq 4,\quad x_2 \leq -4.$

(c) $-1 \leq x_1 \leq 1,\quad -2 \leq x_2 \leq 2,\quad x_1 + x_2 \geq 10,\quad 2x_1 - x_2 \leq 2.$

[*Ans.* (a) $x_1 + x_2 \leq 3$.]

2. (a) Draw a picture of the convex polygon obtained in Example 1 of the text.

(b) Draw a picture of the convex set defined by the inequalities

$$\begin{aligned} 2x_1 + x_2 + 9 &\leq 0, \\ -x_1 + 3x_2 + 6 &\leq 0, \\ x_1 + 2x_2 - 3 &\leq 0. \end{aligned}$$

(c) What is the relationship between the two figures?

3. Find the corner points of the convex polygons given in parts (a), (b), and (e) of Exercise 1 following Section 1.

[*Ans.* (a) $\begin{pmatrix} 3 \\ -2 \end{pmatrix}, \begin{pmatrix} 3 \\ 2 \end{pmatrix}, \begin{pmatrix} -3 \\ 2 \end{pmatrix}$; (e) $\begin{pmatrix} 2 \\ 3 \end{pmatrix}, \begin{pmatrix} -2 \\ 3 \end{pmatrix}, \begin{pmatrix} 2 \\ -3 \end{pmatrix}, \begin{pmatrix} -2 \\ -3 \end{pmatrix}$.]

4. (a) Show that the three lines whose equations are

$$\begin{aligned} 2x_1 + x_2 + 9 &= 0, \\ -x_1 + 3x_2 + 6 &= 0, \\ x_1 + 2x_2 - 3 &= 0 \end{aligned}$$

divide the plane into seven convex regions. Mark these regions with Roman numerals I–VII.

(b) For each of the seven regions found in part (a), write a set of three inequalities, having the region as its locus. (*Hint:* Two of these sets of inequalities are considered in Exercise 2.)

(c) There is one more way of putting inequality signs into the three equations given in (a). What is the locus of this last set of inequalities? [*Ans.* The empty set $\mathcal{E}$.]

5. A convex polygon has the points $(-1, 0)$, $(3, 4)$, $(0, -3)$, and $(1, 6)$ as extreme points. Find a set of inequalities which defines the convex polygon having these extreme points.

6. Find the extreme points of the convex polygon given by the equations

$$\begin{aligned} 2x_1 + x_2 + 9 &\geq 0, \\ -x_1 + 3x_2 + 6 &\geq 0, \\ x_1 + 2x_2 - 3 &\leq 0, \\ x_1 + x_2 &\leq 0. \end{aligned}$$

(*Hint:* Use some of the results of Example 1 in the text.)

7. Give an example of a quadrilateral that is not a convex set.

8. Prove that for any three vectors U, V, W, the set of all points $aU + bV + cW$ $(a \geq 0, b \geq 0, c \geq 0, a + b + c = 1)$ is a convex set. What geometric figure is this locus?

[*Ans.* In general, the locus is a triangle.]

9. The owner of an oil truck with a capacity of 500 gallons hauls gasoline and oil products from city to city. On any given trip he wishes to load his truck with at least 200 gallons of regular test gasoline, at least 100 gallons of high test gasoline, and at most 150 gallons of kerosene. Assuming that he always fills his truck to capacity, find the convex set of ways that he can load his truck. Interpret the extreme points of the set. (*Hint:* There are four extreme points.)

10. An advertiser wishes to sponsor a half hour television comedy and must decide on the composition of the show. The advertiser insists that there be at least three minutes of commercials, while the television network requires that the commercial time be limited to at most 15 minutes. The comedian refuses to work more than 22 minutes each half hour show. If a band is added to the show to play during the time that neither the comedian nor the commercials are on, construct the convex set C of possible assignments of time to the comedian, the commercials, and the band that use up the 30 minutes. Find the extreme points of C.

[*Ans.* If x_1 is the comedian time, x_2 the commercial time, and $30 - x_1 - x_2$ the band time, the extreme points are

$$\begin{pmatrix} 0 \\ 3 \end{pmatrix}, \begin{pmatrix} 22 \\ 3 \end{pmatrix}, \begin{pmatrix} 22 \\ 8 \end{pmatrix}, \begin{pmatrix} 15 \\ 15 \end{pmatrix}, \text{ and } \begin{pmatrix} 0 \\ 15 \end{pmatrix}.]$$

11. Let C be any plane polyhedral convex set. Show that if X is a point that lies on three bounding lines of C, then one of the inequalities defining C is superfluous.

12. Let X and Y be two distinct points of a polyhedral convex set C, let c be a number such that $0 < c < 1$, and define $Z = cX + (1 - c)Y$. Show that Z is not an extreme point of C. [*Hint:* Use the indirect method.]

13. Prove that the intersection of two half planes is a bounded convex set only if it is empty.

14. Construct examples that show that the intersection of three half planes either may or may not be a bounded convex set.

15. If C is a closed planar convex set and Z is a point of C that is not a boundary point, show that any line through Z intersects the boundary of C in exactly two points.

*3. BASES FOR POLYHEDRAL CONVEX SETS

In a 1-dimensional vector space the simplest convex set is an interval (line segment). In a 2-dimensional space, the simplest such set is a triangle, and in a 3-dimensional space it is a tetrahedron (i.e., a pyramid with triangular base.) We begin this section by defining the analogous kind of simple convex set in a vector space of n dimensions. Throughout this section we shall always be working in such a vector space.

DEFINITION. In an n-dimensional vector space an *n-simplex* is a bounded convex polyhedral subset that has exactly $n + 1$ extreme points and that is not contained in any hyperplane.

Our first theorem gives an equivalent definition of an n-simplex that depends upon the idea of linear independence discussed in Chapter 4, Section 10.

Theorem 1. A bounded convex polyhedral set S with $n + 1$ extreme points, $T_0, T_1, \ldots, T_n$, is an n-simplex if and only if $T_1 - T_0, T_2 - T_0, \ldots, T_n - T_0$ are linearly independent vectors.

Proof. We must show that S does *not* lie in any hyperplane of our n-space if and only if $T_1 - T_0, \ldots, T_n - T_0$ are linearly independent. We shall, in fact, prove the equivalent statement that $T_1 - T_0, \ldots, T_n - T_0$ are linearly dependent if and only if $T_0, T_1, \ldots, T_n$ lie in a hyperplane. They lie in such a hyperplane if there is a nonzero functional $\mathbf{F}$ and a constant c such that $\mathbf{F}T_i = c$ for all i $(= 0, 1, \ldots, n)$. Setting $c = \mathbf{F}T_0$, we can restate this condition as $\mathbf{F}T_i = \mathbf{F}T_0$, or $\mathbf{F}(T_i - T_0) = 0$ for $i = 1, 2, \ldots, n$. In other words, the vectors $T_i - T_0$ must all lie in the kernel of $\mathbf{F}$. But for this to be true, it is necessary and sufficient that they span a subspace of at most $n - 1$ dimensions, that is, that they be linearly dependent. This completes the proof.

Clearly, the statement and proof of Theorem 1 does not depend on which extreme point is labeled T_0.

Theorem 2. If $T_0, T_1, \ldots, T_n$ are the extreme points of an n-simplex, S, then each point X of S can be uniquely represented as a convex combination of the extreme points, that is, as

$$X = \sum_{i=0}^{n} a_i T_i, \quad \text{where} \quad a_i \geq 0 \quad \text{and} \quad \sum_{i=0}^{n} a_i = 1.$$

Proof. We will first prove the theorem for the special case where $T_0 = 0$. By Theorem 1, the vectors $T_1, T_2, \ldots, T_n$ are linearly independent in this case, and hence they form a basis for the n-dimensional space. Therefore every vector X in the whole space can be expressed uniquely as a linear combination $X = \Sigma\, a_i T_i$. Those particular combinations that have all $a_i \geq 0$ and $\Sigma\, a_i = 1$ clearly belong to vectors X in the simplex S. What is not so obvious is the fact that every X in S has all $a_i \geq 0$ and $\Sigma\, a_i = 1$. But now recall from Section 13 of Chapter 4 that the coefficients a_i depend linearly on X, and, in fact, are the values of n linearly independent functionals $\mathbf{F}_i$ (which constitute the basis for $\mathfrak{F}$ dual to the basis $T_1, \ldots, T_n$ for $\mathfrak{X}$). That is, $X = \Sigma\, a_i T_i = \Sigma\, (\mathbf{F}_i X) T_i$. Each $\mathbf{F}_i$ is 1 on one extreme point and 0 on the others, and, since $\mathbf{F}_i$ is a linear function, it maps the convex set S onto a convex set. Hence the range of each $\mathbf{F}_i$ is necessarily the interval $[0, 1]$. Similarly, the functional $\mathbf{F} = \mathbf{F}_1 + \mathbf{F}_2 + \ldots + \mathbf{F}_n$ is 1 on $T_1, T_2, \ldots, T_n$ and 0 on T_0, so, for the same reasons, it has the same range. Let $a_i = \mathbf{F}_i X$ for $i = 1, 2, \ldots, n$, and let $a_0 = 1 - \sum_{i=1}^{n} \mathbf{F}_i X$. Then $X = \sum_{i=0}^{n} a_i T_i$ satisfies $a_i \geq 0$ and $\sum_{i=1}^{n} a_i = 1$ and is the required representation of X.

The uniqueness of this representation follows from the fact that $T_1, \ldots, T_n$ is a basis for $\mathfrak{X}$.

Now let us extend the result to an arbitrary simplex S. We may now consider S to be gotten from S_0 through translation by T_0 where S_0 has as extreme points the points $T_i - T_0$ (one of which is the origin). Any point X in S has $X - T_0$ in S_0. Hence, applying the previous result,

$$X - T_0 = \sum_{i=0}^{n} a_i (T_i - T_0) = \sum_{i=0}^{n} a_i T_i - T_0,$$

so that
$$X = \sum_{i=0}^{n} a_i T_i$$
is a unique representation of X.

It is worth while interpreting the "coordinates" a_i for the general case. The functionals $\mathbf{F}_i$ are the dual basis to the basis $T_i - T_0$. Letting $k_i = \mathbf{F}_i T_0$, we find that for $i = 1, \ldots, n$,
$$a_i = \mathbf{F}_i(X - T_0) = F_i X - k_i \quad \text{and} \quad a_0 = 1 - \sum_{i=1}^{n} a_i.$$

These numbers, $a_0, a_1, \ldots, a_n$ are called the *barycentric coordinates* of X.

Theorem 3. Let C be a bounded convex polyhedral set in $\mathfrak{X}_n$ (not contained in any hyperplane) with extreme points $T_0, \ldots, T_k$; then C can be divided into n-simplices and every point X in C can be expressed as a convex combination of at most $n + 1$ extreme points, corresponding to the extreme points of one of these simplices.

Proof. We first sketch the proof of this result for convex polygons in the plane. Consider the polygon shown in Figure 6. Choose three consecutive extreme points on the boundary of C, say T_1, T_2, and T_3. Now draw the line segment between T_1 and T_3. We have divided the polygon into two parts, one a 2-simplex (triangle) and the other a polygon C' with $k - 1$ extreme points. Repeat this procedure with C' and continue until C has been divided into triangles. Every point of C, except for the points lying on line segments joining two extreme points, now lies in exactly one triangle whose vertices are extreme points of C, and can be expressed as a linear combination of the three extreme points that are the corners of the triangle. And points on line segments joining two extreme points can be expressed as convex combinations of at most two extreme points. This completes the proof in 2 dimensions.

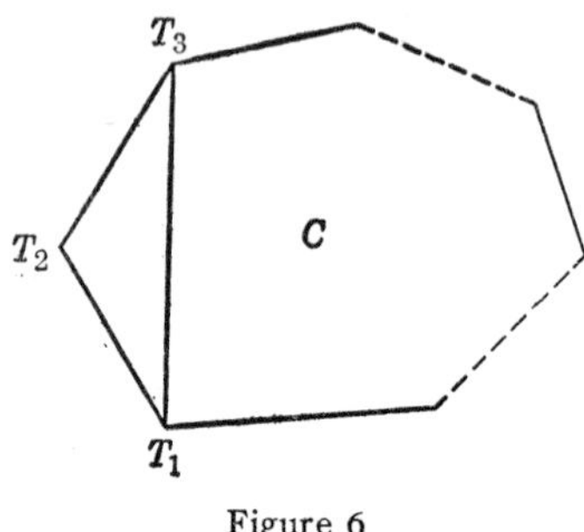

Figure 6

Before we proceed to the proof of the result in n-dimensions we define the concept of an extreme edge of a convex set C. If T and T' are two extreme points of C then every point X on the line segment between them can be written as a convex combination of T and T'. We shall say that T and T' are joined by an *extreme edge* of C if each point X on the line segment between T and T' can be written as a convex combination of the extreme points of C *only* in this way. (For instance, the edges of a square are extreme edges while the diagonals are not.)

The proof of the theorem in n-dimensions now proceeds by mathematical induction. For a convex set with $n + 1$ vertices the theorem is a restatement of Theorem 2. Now suppose that we have proved the result for all convex sets with k or fewer vertices in n-dimensions, where $k \geq n + 1$, and we want to show it true for convex sets with $k + 1$ vertices. Let C be such a convex set with extreme points $T_0, T_1, \ldots, T_k$. There are two cases to consider.

In the first case there is an extreme point of C, say T_0, that is connected by an extreme edge of C to at most $k - 1$ other extreme points, say $T_1, \ldots, T_s$, where $s \leq k - 1$. If we now consider the convex sets spanned by $T_0, T_1, \ldots, T_s$ and $T_1, T_2, \ldots, T_k$, they each have at most k extreme points, and, by the induction assumption, can be subdivided as in the statement of the theorem. These subdivisions give, in turn, the required subdivision of C.

In the second case, every extreme point is connected by an extreme edge to every other extreme point. In two and three dimensions this can happen only if C is a triangle or a tetrahedron, respectively. But from dimension four on up, it is possible to have convex sets with this property having any number of extreme points. (The details of the construction of such sets are omitted.) In the latter case, we fix one extreme point, say T_0, and then choose subsets of n points from the remaining k vertices in all possible ways. Taking T_0 together with such a subset of points gives the extreme points of an n-simplex, and there are $\binom{k}{n}$ of them in all. So this gives a subdivision of C into $\binom{k}{n}$ simplices that overlap in only lower dimensional faces. The proof is then complete.

Example 1. Consider the convex set C defined by

$$0 \leq x_1 \leq 1,$$
$$0 \leq x_2 \leq 1.$$

It is easy to show that C is a square [see Figure 7(a)] in the first quadrant with side length one. There are obviously two ways of dividing C into triangles, one way using one of the diagonals of the square and the other way using the other. [See Figures 7(a) and 7(b).] A way of introducing a basis for the square is to use two sets of three functions, one set for each of the triangles. Observe that there are two essentially different ways of introducing a basis in this way.

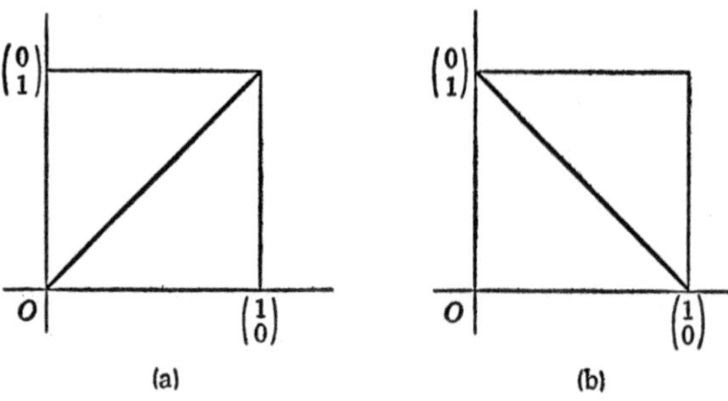

Figure 7

Consider a specific subdivision of a convex set C into simplices. By a *canonical basis* for C we shall mean the set of functionals that give the barycentric coordinates of points in the various simplices of the subdivision. Since there are only a finite number of ways of subdividing C into simplices, it is obvious that there are only a finite number of canonical bases for C. For instance, in Example 1 there were two different canonical bases. The canonical basis of a convex set is unique if and only if the set is a simplex.

EXERCISES

1. How many canonical bases are possible for the following convex sets?
   (a) A rectangle surmounted by an equilateral triangle.
   (b) A rectangle with two equilateral triangles placed on opposite sides.
2. Give an example of a nonconvex planar set which can be subdivided into triangles in such a way that a canonical basis is possible.
3. Consider the triangle whose vertices are the points

$$\begin{pmatrix}0\\0\end{pmatrix}, \quad \begin{pmatrix}a\\0\end{pmatrix}, \quad \text{and} \quad \begin{pmatrix}0\\b\end{pmatrix}.$$

   Call these vertex 1, vertex 2, and vertex 3. Let Z be any point in the triangle, let d_i be the perpendicular distance between Z and the side opposite vertex i, and let c_i be the length of the altitude drawn from vertex i.
   (a) Show that $d_2 = z_1$, $d_3 = z_2$, and $d_1 = [ab - bz_1 - az_2]/\sqrt{a^2 + b^2}$.
   (b) Show that $c_2 = a$, $c_3 = b$, and $c_1 = ab/\sqrt{a^2 + b^2}$.
   (c) Show that $d_1/c_1 + d_2/c_2 + d_3/c_3 = 1$.
   (d) Show that the functions $\mathbf{F}_1(z) = d_1/c_1$, $\mathbf{F}_2(z) = d_2/c_2$, $\mathbf{F}_3(z) = d_3/c_3$ form a linear convex basis for the triangle.
4. Show that the convex set of Example 1 has no linear convex basis.
5. Write in detail the two different canonical bases for the convex set of

Example 1. Hence show that a necessary condition that a convex set have a unique convex basis is that it is an n-simplex.

6. Let P_n be a regular polygon of n sides, $n \geq 3$, in the plane and let $\mathbf{h}(P_n)$ be the number of distinct canonical bases for P_n. Thus $\mathbf{h}(P_3) = 1$. Find $\mathbf{h}(P_4)$. Find $\mathbf{h}(P_5)$. Find $\mathbf{h}(P_6)$. If you can, find a formula for $\mathbf{h}(P_n)$.

7. Write in detail all canonical bases possible for a regular pentagon P_5.

4. EXTREME VALUES OF FUNCTIONALS ON CONVEX SETS

Let $\mathbf{F}$ be a functional on $\mathfrak{X}_n$ and C a bounded convex polyhedral set in $\mathfrak{X}_n$. Let us now pose the problem of finding the extreme values, that is, the maximum and minimum values that $\mathbf{F}X$ takes on, as X ranges over C. Let M be equal to the maximum value of $\mathbf{F}X$ and m be equal to the minimum value of $\mathbf{F}X$ as X ranges over C.

Theorem. If $\mathbf{F}$ is a functional on $\mathfrak{X}_n$ and C is a bounded convex polyhedral set in $\mathfrak{X}_n$, then:

(A) The maximum value M of $\mathbf{F}X$ is taken on at one or more extreme points of C. Similarly the minimum value m of $\mathbf{F}X$ is taken on at one or more extreme points of C.

(B) The truth set of the statement $\mathbf{F}X = M$ is a convex polyhedral set whose extreme points are also extreme points of C. Similarly, the set of all X in C such that $\mathbf{F}X = m$ is a convex polyhedral set whose extreme points are also extreme points of C.

Proof. We shall prove only the parts of the theorem relating to the maximum value of $\mathbf{F}$, since the rest can be proved similarly.

(A) By the theorem of Section 2, a point X is in C if and only if it can be written as

$$(1) \qquad X = a_1T_1 + a_2T_2 + \ldots + a_kT_k,$$

where $T_1, T_2, \ldots, T_k$ are extreme points of C and the numbers $a_1, \ldots, a_k$ satisfy the following conditions:

$$(2) \qquad a_1 \geq 0, \ldots, a_k \geq 0, \quad \text{and} \quad a_1 + a_2 + \ldots + a_k = 1.$$

Let M be the largest value $\mathbf{F}T_i$; then

$$(3) \qquad \begin{aligned} \mathbf{F}X &= \mathbf{F}(a_1T_1 + \ldots + a_kT_k) \\ &= a_1\mathbf{F}T_1 + \ldots + a_k\mathbf{F}T_k \\ &\leq a_1M + \ldots + a_kM = M. \end{aligned}$$

Hence M has the properties stated in part (A) of the theorem.

(B) Let us relabel the extreme points of C so that the maximum value of **F** is taken on at the extreme points $T_1, \ldots, T_j$, where $j \leq k$. Then we have $\mathbf{F}T_1 = M, \ldots, \mathbf{F}T_j = M$, and $\mathbf{F}T_{j+1} < M, \ldots, \mathbf{F}T_k < M$. Then if X is a point in C that is a convex combination of the extreme points $T_1, \ldots, T_j$ only, that is, $X = a_1T_1 + \ldots + a_jT_j$, where $a_1 + \ldots + a_j = 1$, we have

$$\mathbf{F}X = \mathbf{F}(a_1T_1 + \ldots + a_jT_j) = a_1M + \ldots + a_jM = M.$$

On the other hand, if X is a point of C not of the above form, then $j < k$ and X can be written

$$X = a_1T_1 + \ldots + a_jT_j + a_{j+1}T_{j+1} + \ldots + a_kT_k,$$

where $a_i > 0$ for some i between $j + 1$ and k. Then

$$\begin{aligned} \mathbf{F}X &= \mathbf{F}(a_1T_1 + \ldots + a_jT_j + \ldots + a_kT_k) \\ &= a_1\mathbf{F}T_1 + \ldots + a_j\mathbf{F}T_j + \ldots + a_k\mathbf{F}T_k \\ &< a_1M + \ldots + a_jM + \ldots + a_kM = M. \end{aligned}$$

Hence $\mathbf{F}X = M$ if and only if X is a convex combination of $T_1, \ldots, T_j$, completing the proof.

Theorem. If $\mathbf{G}(X) = \mathbf{F}X + c$, where **F** is a linear functional defined on a bounded polyhedral convex set D and c is a number, then the conclusions of the preceding theorem hold for **G**.

Proof. The addition of the constant c merely changes every value of the function **F**, including the maximum and minimum values, by that amount. Hence the analysis of where the extreme values of the function are taken on is unchanged.

These theorems provide a method for finding the extreme values of a function **G** defined by $\mathbf{G}(X) = \mathbf{F}X + c$ where F is a functional on a polyhedral convex set C. First, find all the extreme points of C; there will be a finite number of them, and they may be found as the intersections of bounding hyperplanes of C. Now substitute the coordinates of these extreme points into the function **G** and find the maximum and minimum of the resulting set of numbers. These will also be the extreme values of **G** on C. This procedure is illustrated in the following examples.

Example 1. Find the extreme values of the functional **F** defined by $\mathbf{F}X = 4x_1 + 8x_2$ on the convex set C which is the truth set of the inequalities

$$\begin{aligned} -2x_1 + 3x_2 &\leq 6, \\ -x_1 - 2x_2 &\leq 3, \\ x_1 + x_2 &\leq 2. \end{aligned}$$

The extreme points of C are easily found to be

$$\begin{pmatrix}-3\\0\end{pmatrix},\quad \begin{pmatrix}0\\2\end{pmatrix},\quad \text{and}\quad \begin{pmatrix}7\\-5\end{pmatrix}.$$

(The reader should sketch the convex set C.) Substituting the coordinates of these extreme points into **F**, we find that it has values -12, 16, and -12, respectively. Hence the maximum value of **F** on C is 16 and that is taken on only at the second extreme point. The minimum value of **F** on C is -12 and is taken on at the first and third extreme points, and hence also on the line segment between them.

Example 2. Find the extreme values of the function **G** defined by $\mathbf{G}(X) = -2x_1 + 3x_2 - 9$ on the convex set C of Example 1. Here the values of **G** on the extreme points are -3, -3, and -38, respectively. Hence the maximum value of **G** on C is -3 and is taken on at the first two extreme points and hence also on the entire line segment between them. The minimum value of **G** on C is -38 and is taken on only at the third extreme point.

The method outlined above for finding extreme values works well when the convex set C is a planar set or is a convex set in 3-space. However, for higher-dimensional sets the method is cumbersome and lengthy because the corner positions are hard to find, and more refined methods are needed. One such method (the simplex method) is discussed in Section 7 of this chapter.

EXERCISES

1. Find the extreme values of the function **G** defined by

$$\mathbf{G}(X) = 7x_1 + 5x_2 - 3$$

over the convex polygon of Exercise 6 of Section 2.

2. Find the maximum and minimum of the function

$$\mathbf{G}(X) = -2x_1 + 5x_2 + 17$$

over each of the convex polygons given in parts (a), (b), and (e) of Exercise 1 following Section 1. [*Ans.* (a) 33, 1; (e) 36, -2.]

3. Find the maximum and minimum, when they exist, of the function

$$\mathbf{G}(X) = 5x_1 + 3x_2 - 6$$

over each of the polyhedral convex sets given in parts (h) and (j) of Exercise 1 following Section 1.

[*Ans.* (h) Neither maximum nor minimum; (j) minimum is 3.]

4. Consider the polyhedral convex set P defined by the inequalities

$$-1 \leq x_1 \leq 4,$$
$$0 \leq x_2 \leq 6.$$

Find four different sets of conditions on the constants a and b that the functional $\mathbf{F}X = ax_1 + bx_2$ should have its maximum at one and only one of the four corner points of P. Find conditions that $\mathbf{F}$ should have its minimum at each of these points.

[*Ans.* For example, the maximum is at $\begin{pmatrix}4\\6\end{pmatrix}$ if $a > 0$ and $b > 0$.]

5. Let $\mathbf{H}$ be the quadratic function defined by $\mathbf{H}(X) = (x_1 - \frac{1}{4})^2 + (x_2 - \frac{1}{4})^2$ on the convex set C which is the truth set of the inequalities

$$\begin{aligned} x_1 + x_2 &\leq 1, \\ x_1 &\geq 0, \\ x_2 &\geq 0. \end{aligned}$$

Are the maximum and minimum values of $\mathbf{H}$ taken on at the extreme points of C? Discuss reasons why this problem is essentially harder than that of finding the extreme values of a linear function on a polyhedral convex set.

6. In Exercise 9 of Section 2, suppose that the oil truck operator gets 3 cents per gallon for delivering regular gasoline, 2 cents per gallon for high test, and 1 cent per gallon for kerosene. Write the expression that gives the total amount he will get paid for each possible load that he carries. How should he load his truck in order to earn the maximum amount?

[*Ans.* He should carry 400 gallons of regular gasoline, 100 gallons of high test, and no kerosene.]

7. In Exercise 6, if he gets 3 cents per gallon of regular and 2 cents per gallon of high test gasoline, how high must his payment for kerosene become before he will load it on his truck in order to make a maximum profit?

[*Ans.* He must get paid at least 3 cents per gallon of kerosene.]

8. In Exercise 10 of Section 2, let x_1 be the number of minutes the comedian is on, and x_2 be the number of minutes the commercial is on the program. Suppose the comedian costs \$200 per minute, the commercials cost \$50 per minute, and the band is free. How should the advertiser choose the composition of the show in order that its cost be a minimum?

9. If $\mathbf{F}$ is a functional and $\mathbf{G}$ is a constant function defined on a bounded convex set C, show that $\mathbf{F} + \mathbf{G}$ takes on its maximum and minimum values at extreme points of C.

10. If $\mathbf{F}$ and $\mathbf{G}$ are functionals defined on a bounded convex set C, show that the functions $\mathbf{F} - \mathbf{G}$, and $a\mathbf{F} + b\mathbf{G}$ (where a and b are constants) all take on their maximum and minimum values at extreme points of C.

5. LINEAR PROGRAMMING PROBLEMS

An important class of practical problems are those that require the determination of the maximum or minimum of a vector function of the form $\mathbf{G}(X) = \mathbf{F}X + c$ where $\mathbf{F}$ is a functional, c is a number, and X ranges over a convex polyhedral set of points. In the present section we illustrate these so-called *linear programming problems* by means of examples. In Section 6 we shall discuss more abstractly the theory of linear programming and in Section 7 give a computational method that provides solutions to large-scale problems.

Example 1. A mining company owns two different mines that produce a given kind of ore. The mines are located in different parts of the country and hence have different production capacities. After crushing, the ore is graded into three classes: high-grade, medium-grade, and low-grade ores. There is some demand for each grade of ore. The mining company has contracted to provide a smelting plant with 12 tons of high-grade, 8 tons of medium-grade, and 24 tons of low-grade ore per week. It costs the company \$200 per day to run the first mine and \$160 per day to run the second mine. However, in a day's operation the first mine produces 6 tons of high-grade, 2 tons of medium-grade, and 4 tons of low-grade ore, while the second mine produces 2 tons of high-grade, 2 tons of medium-grade, and 12 tons of low-grade ore each day it operates. How many days a week should each mine be operated in order to fulfill the company's orders most economically?

Before solving the problem it is convenient to summarize the above information as in the tableau of Figure 8. The numbers in the tableau form a 3-by-2 matrix, the requirements form a column vector R and the costs form a row vector C. The entries in the matrix indicate the production of each kind of ore by the mines, the entries in the requirements vector R indicate the quantities that must be produced, and the entries in the cost vector C indicate the daily costs of running each mine.

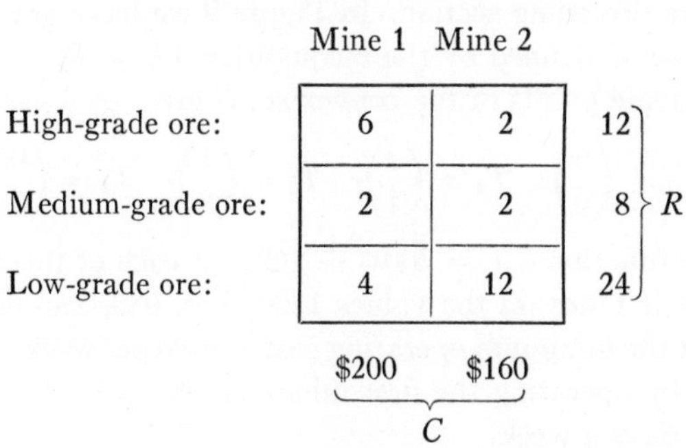

Figure 8

Let $X = \begin{pmatrix} x_1 \\ x_2 \end{pmatrix}$ be the 2-component column vector whose component x_1 gives the number of days per week that mine 1 operates and x_2 gives the number of days per week that mine 2 operates. If we define the quantities

$$A = \begin{pmatrix} 6 & 2 \\ 2 & 2 \\ 4 & 12 \end{pmatrix}, \quad R = \begin{pmatrix} 12 \\ 8 \\ 24 \end{pmatrix}, \quad \text{and} \quad C = (200 \quad 160),$$

we can state the above problem as a minimum problem.

Minimum problem: Determine the vector X so that the weekly operating cost, given by the quantity CX, is a minimum subject to the inequality restraints $AX \geq R$ and $X \geq 0$. The inequality restraints insure that the weekly output requirements are met and the limits on the components of X are not exceeded.

It is clear that this is a minimum problem of the type discussed in

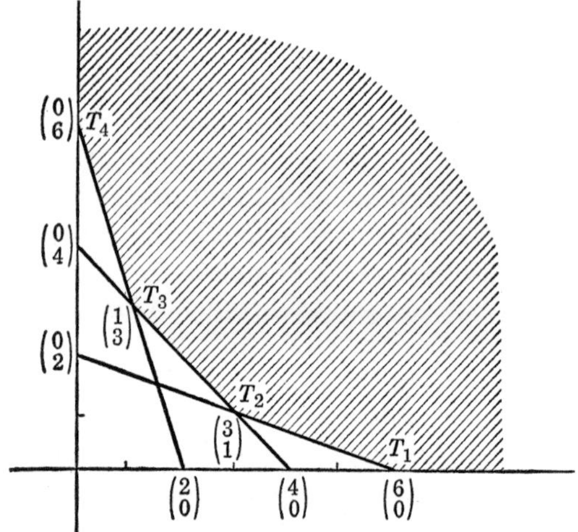

Figure 9

detail in the preceding section. In Figure 9 we have graphed the convex polyhedral set C defined by the inequalities $AX \geq R$.

The extreme points of the convex set C are

$$T_1 = \begin{pmatrix} 6 \\ 0 \end{pmatrix}, \quad T_2 = \begin{pmatrix} 3 \\ 1 \end{pmatrix}, \quad T_3 = \begin{pmatrix} 1 \\ 3 \end{pmatrix}, \quad T_4 = \begin{pmatrix} 0 \\ 6 \end{pmatrix}.$$

Testing the function $CX = 200x_1 + 160x_2$ at each of these extreme points we see that it takes on the values 1200, 760, 680, and 960, respectively. We see that the minimum operating cost is \$680 per week and it is achieved at T_3, i.e., by operating the first mine one day per week and the second mine three days a week.

Observe that if the mines are operated as indicated, then the combined weekly production will be 12 tons of high-grade ore, 8 tons of medium-grade ore, and 40 tons of low-grade ore. In other words, for this solution low-grade ore is overproduced. If the company has no other demand for the low-grade ore, then it must discard 16 tons of it per week in this minimum-cost solution of its production problem. We shall discuss this point further in the next section.

Example 2. As a variant of Example 1, assume that the cost vector is $C = (160, 200)$; in other words the first mine now has a lower daily cost than the second. By the same procedure as above we find that the minimum cost level is again \$680 and is achieved by operating the first mine three days a week and the second mine one day per week. In this solution, 20 tons of high-grade ore, instead of the required 12 tons are produced, while the requirements of medium- and low-grade ores are exactly met. Thus eight tons of high-grade ore must be discarded per week.

Example 3. As another variant of Example 1, assume that the cost vector is $C = (200, 200)$; in other words, both mines have the same production costs. Evaluating the cost function CX at the extreme points of the convex set we find costs of \$1200 on two of the extreme points (T_1 and T_4) and costs of \$800 on the other two extreme points (T_2 and T_3). Thus the minimum cost is attained by operating either one of the mines three days a week and the other one one day a week. But there are other solutions, since if the minimum is taken on at two distinct extreme points it is also taken on at each of the points on the line segment between. Thus any vector X where $1 \leq x_1 \leq 3$, $1 \leq x_2 \leq 3$, and $x_1 + x_2 = 4$ also gives a minimum-cost solution. For example, each mine could operate two days a week.

It can be shown (see Exercise 1) that for any solution X with $1 < x_1 < 3$, $1 < x_2 < 3$, and $x_1 + x_2 = 4$, both high-grade and low-grade ore are overproduced.

EXERCISES

1. In Example 3, show that both high- and low-grade ore are overproduced for solution vectors X with $1 < x_1 < 3$, $1 < x_2 < 3$, and $x_1 + x_2 = 4$.

2. A well-known nursery rhyme says "Jack Sprat could eat no fat. His wife (call her Jill) could eat no lean. . . ." Suppose Jack wishes to have at least one pound of lean meat per day, while Jill needs at least .4 pound of fat per day. Assume they buy only beef having 10 per cent fat and 90 per cent lean, and pork having 40 per cent fat and 60 per cent lean. Jack and Jill want to fulfill their minimal diet requirements at the lowest possible cost.
(a) Let x be the amount of beef and y the amount of pork which they

purchase per day. Construct the convex set of points in the plane representing purchases that fulfill both persons' minimum diet requirements.

(b) Suggest necessary restrictions on the purchases, that will change this set into a convex polygon.

(c) If beef costs $1 per pound, and pork costs 50 cents per pound, show that the diet of least cost has only pork, and find the minimum cost. [*Ans.* $.83.]

(d) If beef costs 75 cents and pork costs 50 cents per pound, show that there is a whole line segment of solution points and find the minimum cost. [*Ans.* $.83.]

(e) If beef and pork each cost $1 a pound, show that the unique minimal cost diet has both beef and pork. Find the minimum cost. [*Ans.* $1.40.]

(f) Show that the restriction made in part (b) did not alter the answers given in (c)-(e).

3. In Exercise 2(d) show that for all but one of the minimal cost diets Jill has more than her minimum requirement of fat, while Jack always gets exactly his minimal requirement of lean. Show that all but one of the minimal cost diets contains some beef.

4. In Exercise 2(e) show that Jack and Jill each get exactly their minimal requirements.

5. In Exercise 2, if the price of pork is fixed at $1 a pound, how low must the price of beef fall before Jack and Jill will eat only beef? [*Ans.* $.25.]

6. In Exercise 2, suppose that Jack decides to reduce his minimal requirement to 0.6 pound of lean meat per day. How does the convex set change? How do the solutions in 2(c), (d), and (e) change?

7. A poultry farmer raises chickens, ducks, and turkeys and has room for 500 birds on his farm. While he is willing to have a total of 500 birds, he does not want more than 300 ducks on his farm at any one time. Suppose that a chicken costs $1.50, a duck $1.00, and a turkey $4.00 to raise to maturity. Assume that the farmer can sell chickens for $3.00, ducks for $2.00, and turkeys for T dollars each. He wants to decide which kind of poultry to raise in order to maximize his profit.

(a) Let x be the number of chickens and y be the number of ducks he will raise. Then $500 - x - y$ is the number of turkeys he raises. What is the convex set of possible values of x and y which satisfy the above restrictions?

(b) Find the expression for the cost of raising x chickens, y ducks, and $(500 - x - y)$ turkeys. Find the expression for the total amount he gets for these birds. Compute the profit which he would make under these circumstances.

(c) If $T = \$6.00$, show that to obtain maximal profit the farmer should raise only turkeys. What is the maximum profit? [*Ans.* \$1000.]

(d) If $T = \$5.00$, show that he should raise only chickens and find his maximum profit. [*Ans.* \$750.]

(e) If $T = \$5.50$, show that he can raise any combination of chickens and turkeys and find his maximum profit. [*Ans.* \$750.]

8. Rework Exercise 7 if the price of chickens drops to \$2.00 and T is (a) \$6.00, (b) \$5.00, (c) \$4.50, and (d) \$4.00.

9. In Exercise 7 show that if the price of turkeys drops below \$5.50, the farmer should raise only chickens. Also show that if the price is above \$5.50, he should raise only turkeys.

10. In Exercise 9 of Section 2, assume that the truck operator gets p cents a gallon for regular gasoline, q cents a gallon for high-test gasoline, and r cents a gallon for kerosene. Show that he will carry kerosene for maximum profit only if $r \geq p$ and $r \geq q$.

11. In Exercise 10 of Section 2, suppose that for each minute the comedian is on the program 70,000 more people will tune in, for each minute the band is on 10,000 more people will tune in, and for each minute the commercial is on 1 more person will tune in. Let N be the function that gives the number of persons that tune in for each point in C. How should the times be alloted in order that N be a maximum?

[*Ans.* There should be 3 minutes of commercials, 22 minutes of the comedian, and 5 minutes of band music.]

12. In Exercise 10 of Section 2, assume that the band and comedian each cost \$200 per minute while the commercials cost \$50 per minute. Write the function that gives the cost of the program. Show that there is a whole line segment of minimum cost solutions.

[*Ans.* The commercials are on for 15 minutes while the band and comedian can share the remaining 15 minutes in any manner.]

6. THE DUAL PROBLEM AND THE DUALITY THEOREM

Along with a given linear programming problem there arises quite naturally another linear programming problem called the *dual* of the original problem. And the dual of the dual problem is the original problem. As we shall see, the dual of a maximizing problem is a minimizing one, and the dual of a minimizing problem is a maximizing one. If the stated linear programming problem has an interpretation then its dual also has an interpretation. All these ideas are best introduced first by means of examples.

Example 1. Let us consider a problem related to that mentioned in Example 1 of Section 5. Suppose that the accounting department of the mining company wishes to assign a value to each of the grades of ore that the company produces. Such an assignment might help it in determining retail prices. These prices will assign, in effect, a share of the cost of running the mine to each product produced.

Economists call these *shadow* prices—they are inferred prices and have no necessary relation to market prices. As we shall see, any product that is produced in surplus will be assigned zero shadow price even though part of it may be sold at a positive market price. Such a product may conveniently be interpreted as a *by-product* of the mine. And we shall see that if the demand for the various products changes, some by-products may change into principal products, and vice versa.

To return to the mine example, let z_1 be the accounting price assigned to high-grade ore, z_2 be the accounting price of medium-grade ore, and z_3 be the accounting price assigned to low-grade ore. We let Z be the three-component row vector with these components. With these prices, the accounting value of weekly sales is simply $ZR = 12z_1 + 8z_2 + 24z_3$. Clearly it is desirable for the company to make this amount as large as possible, since it can then use it as an argument for charging high prices. However, if the accounting value is to have meaning, the total value of ore produced by a mine must not add up to more than it costs to run the mine for a day. We can then write two inequalities that express this fact: for Mine 1 the inequality is $6z_1 + 2z_2 + 4z_3 \leq 200$; and for Mine 2 it is $2z_1 + 2z_2 + 24z_3 \leq 160$. In matrix notation these can be more simply written as: $ZA \leq C$. Since prices are naturally nonnegative we can also add the obvious inequality $Z \geq 0$.

We now state a maximum problem that is called the linear programming problem *dual* to the minimum problem previously considered.

Maximum problem: Determine the accounting price vector Z so that the weekly value of goods sold, which is given by the quantity ZR, is a maximum, subject to the inequality restraints $ZA \leq C$ and $Z \geq 0$. These inequalities assure that prices are nonnegative and that the accounting value of a mine's output does not exceed the cost of operating the mine.

The dual problem is also a linear programming problem. In the case of Example 1, it is a 3-dimensional problem, and cannot be solved graphically as easily as that problem was solved. Here we shall content ourselves with simply stating the solution to the dual problem, and in Section 7 we shall give a computational method that will find this solution, and, indeed, the solution of any other solvable linear programming problem.

It can be shown (see Section 7, Example 1) that the solution to the dual problem of Example 1 is given by the vector $Z^0 = (10, 70, 0)$. This means that high-grade ore has an accounting value of $10 per ton, medium-grade ore has an accounting value of $70 per ton, and low-grade ore is valued at $0 per ton! Observe that the accounting or shadow price of the ore depends more upon the cost of producing it than upon its quality. (Selling prices *would* reflect quality.) Observe also that the overproduced low-grade ore has accounting price zero, i.e., it is a by-product. We will see later that *any* overproduced quantity has zero accounting price. A final important observation is that max ZR = min CX = $680.

Perhaps a word more of discussion concerning the assignment of accounting prices is in order. The mine-owner's problem in assigning these prices is the following: He wants to assign accounting prices to each of the goods he produces in such a way that as much of the value of the total production is assigned to the goods actually desired by consumers and as little as possible to those goods not desired—i.e., to by-products. But he must not assign accounting values in such a way that the value of the goods produced is greater than the cost of producing them. By so doing he can justify to the consumers his assignment of accounting values. The remarkable fact is that he can simultaneously find a solution to both dual linear programming problems, minimizing cost and maximizing accounting values. And, at the solution, the total cost is equal to the total accounting value. This fact is the duality theorem of linear programming that we shall presently state more precisely.

Example 2. The solution of the problem dual to the one in Example 2 of Section 5 is an accounting price vector of $Z = (0 \quad 70 \quad 5)$. Here high-grade ore is overproduced (i.e., is a by-product) and has price zero; medium-grade ore has its previous accounting price of $70 per ton; and low-grade ore has an accounting value of $5 per ton (note that it is no longer a by-product). Again we see that max ZR = min CX = $680.

From these examples we may abstract the ideas of the dual linear programming problems and further study the questions on the relationship that exists between the solutions of the dual problems.

We shall use the following notation: A will be an m-by-n matrix; X will be an n-by-1 variable vector (the quantity vector); Z will be a 1-by-m variable vector (the accounting price vector); R will be an m-by-1 constant vector (the requirements vector); and C will be a 1-by-n constant vector (the cost vector).

Actually the interpretations of X, Z, C, and R need not always be as stated parenthetically above. However, it is convenient to have some interpretation in mind, and we may safely use the ones given.

With this notation we can now state the dual linear programming problems:

The *minimum* problem:	The *maximum* problem:
Find:	Find:
Min CX	Max ZR
Subject to:	Subject to:
(1) $AX \geq R$,	(3) $Z \geq 0$,
(2) $X \geq 0$.	(4) $ZA \leq C$.

Vectors X that satisfy (1) and (2) and vectors Z that satisfy (3) and (4) will be called *feasible vectors*.

The next theorem is the principal theorem of linear programming.

The Duality Theorem. The minimum problem has as a solution a feasible vector X^0, such that $CX^0 = \text{Min}\, CX$, if and only if the maximum problem has a solution that is a feasible vector Z^0, such that $Z^0R = \text{Max}\, ZR$. Moreover, the equality $CX^0 = Z^0R$ holds if and only if X^0 and Z^0 are solutions.

Remark. The duality theorem is extremely powerful for it says that if one of the problems has a solution then the other one necessarily also has a solution, and both problems share a common value. Another consequence of the theorem is that if one of the problems does *not* have a solution then neither does the other one.

Although the proof of the duality theorem is beyond the scope of this book we can prove half of the second statement of the theorem. Namely, we will show that if there are feasible vectors X_1 and Z_1 that satisfy $CX_1 = Z_1R$, then they are solutions to the dual problems. To show that X_1 is a solution we consider any other feasible vector X. Then, using successively (4), (1), and the hypothesis, we have $CX \geq Z_1AX \geq Z_1R = CX_1$, which shows that X_1 solves the minimum problem. The proof that Z_1 solves the maximum problem is similar and is Exercise 1.

The next example illustrates a case for which neither linear programming problem has a solution.

Example 3. Find the minimum of the function $FX = -x_1 + x_2$ subject to the inequalities: $x_1 \geq 0$, $x_2 \geq 0$, and $x_1 - x_2 \geq 1$. Here $A = (1 \quad -1)$ and $R = 1$. A sketch of the set of feasible vectors (an unbounded convex set) for this problem appears in Figure 10. Since we can make x_1 as large

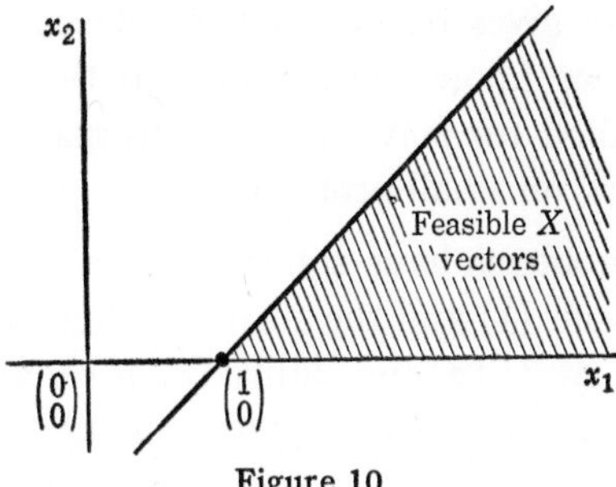

Figure 10

as we please and at the same time keep $x_2 = 0$, we see that there is no minimum value of FX for vectors X in the polyhedron of feasible vectors.

From the duality theorem we know also that the dual maximum problem does not have a solution either. The dual problem is the following: maximize the number $ZR = z_1$, subject to the inequalities $z_1 \leq -1$ and $z_1 \geq 0$. Observe that for the dual problem there are no feasible vectors because no number z simultaneously satisfies $z \leq -1$ and $z \geq 0$. Hence the dual problem has no solution, as expected.

The next theorem gives conditions under which we can be certain that linear programming problems have solutions. These conditions will be satisfied in most practical problems.

Theorem. Either of the following conditions is sufficient that both dual linear programming problems have solutions:

(A) The set of feasible vectors is nonempty and bounded for either of the dual problems.

(B) The matrix A has no zero rows or columns and both $A \geq 0$ and $C \geq 0$.

Proof. (A) By the first theorem of Section 4, a functional defined on a bounded closed set takes on both its maximum and minimum values. Hence if either of the sets of feasible vectors is bounded and nonempty, then that problem, and hence its dual problem, has a solution.

(B) If $C \geq 0$ there is at least one feasible vector, because the vector $Z = 0$ satisfies the inequalities $Z \geq 0$ and $ZA \leq C$. The set of feasible Z vectors is bounded. To see this, let A_j be the jth column of A and consider the inequalities $ZA_j \leq c_j$. Since $A \geq 0$ and has no zero columns, this inequality restricts the size of all variables z_i for which $a_{ij} \neq 0$. And since A has no zero rows, every variable is restricted by one such inequality. Hence, by (A), the maximum problem, and therefore the minimum problem, have solutions.

As will be seen, this theorem insures existence of solutions to most of the examples we shall treat.

The next theorem gives results that enable us to solve the dual of a given problem if we know the solution to the original problem. It also provides a method for solving linear programming problems that works reasonably well on small problems.

Theorem. If both problems have solutions then, of each of the m pairs of inequalities one from (1) and the corresponding one from (3), at least one must hold as an equality, and similarly for each of the n pairs of inequalities one from (2) and the corresponding one from (4).

Proof. Let Z^0 and X^0 be solutions to the maximum and minimum problems, respectively. Then by the duality theorem we know that $Z^0R = Z^0AX^0 = CX^0$. Let A_j be the jth column of the matrix A. Then, if $Z^0A_j < c_j$, we must have $x_j^0 = 0$; for otherwise, from $Z^0A \leq C$, one could show that $Z^0AX^0 < CX^0$, a contradiction. Similarly, if A_i is the ith row of A, then, if $A_iX^0 > R_i$, we must have $z_i^0 = 0$; for otherwise, from $AX^0 \geq R$, one could show $Z^0AX^0 > R$, a contradiction.

Example 4. In Example 3 of Section 5 we found solutions to the problem in which both high-grade and low-grade ore were overproduced. By the theorem just proved we can then conclude that zero accounting prices must be assigned to these grades of ore. From this information it is not hard to show that the solution to the dual problem is $Z^0 = (0, 100, 0)$. Observe that max $ZR =$ min $CX =$ \$800.

The theorem just proved also gives a method for solving linear programming problems. For we know that of the $2(m + n)$ inequalities listed in (1)-(4) at least $m + n$ of them must be equations, one of each pair. There are 2^{m+n} ways of choosing $m + n$ equations, one from each pair, from expressions (1)-(4). If we actually solve all such sets of equations, among the solutions found will be the desired solutions of our linear programming problems. This procedure is illustrated in the next example.

Example 5. Solve the mining problem (Example 1 of Section 5) and its dual by the method of choosing equalities. These problems are:

Find:	Find:
Min $(200x_1 + 160x_2)$	Max $(12z_1 + 8z_2 + 24z_3)$
Subject to:	Subject to:
$6x_1 + 2x_2 \geq 12,$	$z_1 \geq 0,$
$2x_1 + 2x_2 \geq 8,$	$z_2 \geq 0,$
$4x_1 + 12x_2 \geq 24,$	$z_3 \geq 0,$
$x_1 \geq 0,$	$6z_1 + 2z_2 + 4z_3 \leq 200,$
$x_2 \geq 0.$	$2z_1 + 2z_2 + 12z_3 \leq 160.$

Here there are $2^5 = 32$ possible ways of choosing exactly one of each pair to make an equality. If we try to find a solution in which both mines are used, that is, with both x_1 and x_2 positive, then the last two expressions on the right must be equalities. If we then observe that the coefficients of z_3 are generally larger than the coefficients of the other accounting prices, we might try to find a solution with $z_3 = 0$, and the other two accounting prices positive. Solving with the first two expressions on the left and the last three expressions on the right taken as equalities gives (see Exercise 2) the solutions $x_1 = 1$, $x_2 = 3$, $z_1 = 10$, $z_2 = 70$, and $z_3 = 0$.

A more efficient computational method for the solution of dual linear programming problems is discussed in the next section.

EXERCISES

1. If X_1 and Z_1 satisfy $CX_1 = Z_1R$ show that Z_1 solves the maximum problem.
2. In Example 5 make the first two expressions on the left and the last three expressions on the right into equalities and solve to show that the answer stated there is correct.
3. Reconsider the oil truck example of Section 3, Exercise 9 and Section 4, Exercise 6.
   (a) State and interpret the dual problem.
   (b) Solve using the method of choosing equalities.
4. Reconsider the television example of Section 2, Exercise 10 and Section 4, Exercise 8.
   (a) State and interpret the dual problem.
   (b) Solve using the method of choosing equalities.
5. Use the method of choosing equalities to solve Exercises 11 and 12 of Section 5.
6. A nutritionist in a large institution wishes to serve foods that provide the necessary vitamins for the people who eat them. Upon testing three different foods F_1, F_2, and F_3, he finds they contain the following amounts of vitamins A and B:

	F_1	F_2	F_3
Vitamin A:	2	4	3
Vitamin B:	5	2	5

The units of the numbers express the quantity of each vitamin per pound of food eaten. Suppose the nutritionist must provide at least 80 units of vitamin A and at least 60 units of vitamin B. If the costs of the three foods are \$1 per pound for food F_1, 80 cents per pound for F_2, and \$1.50 per pound for F_3, how should he place his orders for the various foods to meet the minimum diet requirements while also minimizing the total cost of the foods purchased?"

(a) Set up this problem as a linear programming problem.
(b) Set up and interpret the dual problem.
(c) Solve both problems by the method of choosing equalities.

Set up and interpret each of the following problems as linear programming problems. Also state and interpret the dual problem. They will be solved by the simplex method as exercises at the end of the next section.

7. A caterer knows that he will need 40 napkins on a given day and 70 napkins the day after. He can purchase napkins at 20 cents each and, after they are purchased, he can have dirty napkins laundered at 5 cents each for use the next day. In order to minimize his costs how many napkins should he purchase initially and how many dirty napkins should he have laundered?

[*Ans.* Let x_1 be the number purchased and x_2 the number laundered. Then the data of the problem is given by the following quantities:

$$A = \begin{pmatrix} 0 & -1 \\ 1 & 1 \end{pmatrix}, \quad R = \begin{pmatrix} -40 \\ 110 \end{pmatrix}, \quad \text{and} \quad C = (20 \quad 5).$$

The interpretation of the dual problem is left to the reader.]

8. A more complicated version of Exercise 7 is the following: A caterer knows he will need 40, 70, and 60 napkins on three successive days. He can purchase napkins at 20 cents each, after which he can have dirty napkins laundered by a fast one-day laundry service at 15 cents each and by a slow two-day laundry service at 8 cents each. How many napkins should he purchase initially and how many dirty napkins should he have laundered on each of the days in order to minimize his costs?

[*Ans.* Let x_1 be the number purchased, x_2 the number of dirty napkins from the first day laundered by the fast service, x_3 the number of dirty napkins from the first day laundered by the slow service, and x_4 the number of dirty napkins from the second day laundered by the fast service. The data of the problem are given by

$$A = \begin{pmatrix} 0 & -1 & -1 & 0 \\ 1 & 1 & 0 & 0 \\ 0 & -1 & -1 & -1 \\ 1 & 1 & 1 & 1 \end{pmatrix}, \quad R = \begin{pmatrix} -40 \\ 110 \\ -110 \\ 170 \end{pmatrix}, \quad \text{and} \quad C = (20 \quad 15 \quad 8 \quad 15).$$

The interpretation of the dual problem is left to the reader.]

9. This example shows that in a maximizing problem the interpretation of the various quantities is different from that of previous problems. A nut manufacturer has on hand 121 pounds of peanuts and 49 pounds of cashews. He can sell two kinds of mixtures of these nuts: a cheap mix that has 80 per cent peanuts and 20 per cent cashews; or a party mix that has 30 per cent peanuts and 70 per cent cashews. If he can sell the party mix at 80 cents a pound and the cheap mix at 50 cents a pound how many pounds of each mix should he make in order to maximize the amount he can obtain?

[*Ans.* Let z_1 be the number of pounds of party mix and z_2 the number of pounds of the cheap mix. Then the data are

$$A = \begin{pmatrix} .3 & .7 \\ .8 & .2 \end{pmatrix}, \quad R = \begin{pmatrix} 80 \\ 50 \end{pmatrix}, \quad \text{and} \quad C = (121 \quad 49).$$

The interpretation of the dual problem is left to the reader.]

10. We consider another example of a maximizing problem. An oil refinery changes crude oil into gasoline, kerosene, and low-grade motor oil. The refinery processes 20,000 barrels of crude oil per day, and from this a total of at most 16,000 barrels of gasoline and kerosene can be produced each day. Moreover the process is such that there is always at least as much kerosene as gasoline produced, and all the remaining crude oil is converted into low-grade motor oil. If the wholesale prices of kerosene, gasoline, and motor oil are \$9, \$16, and \$3 per barrel, respectively, what quantities of each should the manufacturer produce in order to maximize his income? [*Hint.* Let x_1 be the number of barrels of gasoline produced and x_2 the number of barrels of kerosene produced; then $20{,}000 - x_1 - x_2$ is the amount of motor oil produced.]

11. Two very small countries, call them P and Q, decide to join together in their production of food and clothing. Country P has 28,000 man-hours of labor available per month, and for each man-hour applied to food manufacture, produces 1 unit of food, while for each man-hour applied to clothing manufacture it produces 3 units of clothing. Country Q has 15,000 man-hours of labor available and for each man-hour applied to food manufacture produces 2 units of food while for each man-hour applied to clothing manufacture produces $\frac{1}{2}$ unit of clothing. Country P pays its food workers \$2 per hour and its clothing workers \$3 per hour, while country Q pays its food workers \$5 an hour and its clothing workers \$4 an hour. How should the countries divide up the labor if in all they need 10,000 units of food and 15,000 units of clothing and want to minimize total labor cost?

12. A manufacturer of a certain good owns two warehouses and supplies two markets. The first warehouse contains 90 tons of the good and the second contains 120 tons. The first market needs 60 tons of the good while the second market needs 150 tons. From the first warehouse it costs \$6 per ton to ship to the first market and \$10 to ship to the second market. From the second warehouse it costs \$8 per ton to ship to the first market and \$12 per ton to ship to the second market. What quantities should the manufacturer ship from each warehouse to each market in order to minimize shipping costs?

7. THE SIMPLEX METHOD

In the preceding sections we have seen repeatedly that even very simple linear programming problems lead to difficult computations beyond the power of the simple graphical method of solving them. Hence it is necessary to have a routine computational method for handling problems of greater size. Such a method is the so-called *simplex method.* The name is not descriptive of the method but of its early applications. However, we shall continue to use this name.

Before we can describe the simplex method we must make a change in the formulation of the dual programs. What we shall do is to add *dummy* variables to the inequalities stated in expressions (1) and (4) of Section 6 in such a way as to make them into equations. To see how this is done consider as an example the system of inequalities $-u + 2v \leq 5$, $u \geq 0$, and $v \geq 0$. We now add a new dummy variable w and obtain a new system of expressions, $-u + 2v + w = 5$, $u \geq 0$, $v \geq 0$, and $w \geq 0$. Thus we obtain an equation, $-u + 2v + w = 5$, in nonnegative variables. Notice that the new system of expressions is equivalent to the old system since any solution of the new system that has $w = 0$ represents a case for which $-u + 2v = 5$, and a solution of the new system for which $w > 0$ represents a case for which $-u + 2v < 5$. Moreover, it is obvious that any solution of the old system can be written as a solution of the new system by properly choosing a nonnegative value of w. Thus the truth sets of the two systems are identical.

In order to change expressions (1) and (4) on page 366 into equalities we must add $m + n$ dummy variables to the system. For this purpose we define the following vectors of dummy variables: Y is an m-by-1 vector of dummy variables y_i, and W is a 1-by-n vector of dummy variables w_j. We then restate the dual linear programming problems:

The *minimum* problem	The *maximum* problem:
Find:	Find:
Min CX	Max ZR

Subject to:	Subject to:
(1) $AX - Y = R$,	(3) $Z \geq 0$, $W \geq 0$,
(2) $X \geq 0$, $Y \geq 0$.	(4) $ZA + W = C$.

Vectors X and Y that satisfy (1) and (2) and vectors Z and W that satisfy (3) and (4) will be called *feasible vectors.* We shall identify this form of the problem by saying the constraints are in *equality* form.

The proof that the solutions of a linear programming problem stated in equality form are the same as the solutions of the corresponding problem stated as on page 366 follows from the fact that the sets of X and Z vectors in each case are the same and the fact that the dummy variables do not affect the functions being maximized or minimized.

Example 1. Consider again Example 1 of Section 5. There we had the quantities

$$A = \begin{pmatrix} 6 & 2 \\ 2 & 2 \\ 4 & 12 \end{pmatrix}, \quad R = \begin{pmatrix} 12 \\ 8 \\ 24 \end{pmatrix}, \quad C = (200 \quad 160)$$

$$U = \begin{pmatrix} u_1 \\ u_2 \end{pmatrix}, \quad \text{and} \quad Z = (z_1 \quad z_2 \quad z_3).$$

If we define the dummy variable vectors

$$Y = \begin{pmatrix} y_1 \\ y_2 \\ y_3 \end{pmatrix}, \quad \text{and} \quad W = (w_1 \quad w_2),$$

we can state the dual linear programs of that problem with constraints in equality form.

Although the simplex method can be shown to be applicable to any linear programming problem we shall make two assumptions in order to simplify the description of the method. They are:

(I) (The nondegeneracy assumption.) If r is the rank of the matrix A (that is, r is the number of linearly independent rows of A) then it is not possible to write C as a linear combination of fewer than r rows of A, and it is not possible to write R as a linear combination of fewer than r columns of A.

(II) (The positivity assumption.) We shall assume that $C \geq 0$.

The reason for the nondegeneracy assumption (I) is that, without it, the simplex method may fail unless suitable precautions are taken. Actually (see Exercise 2) the simplex method works almost always even when this assumption is not satisfied.

As we shall see, the simplex method gives solutions to both the maximum and the minimum problems simultaneously. But in order to start the method it is necessary to have solutions of equations (1), (3), and (4).

With the positivity assumptions (II) it is easy to obtain such initial solutions since obviously

$$X = 0, \quad Y = -R, \quad Z = 0, \quad \text{and} \quad W = C$$

are solutions of equations (1), (3), and (4). Note that, by hypothesis (II), X, Z, and W are initially nonnegative. But Y is nonnegative only if we already have a solution to the problem. Note also that $CX = ZR = 0$ initially.

The simplex method starts by arranging the data in the form of the initial tableau of Figure 11. The letter A_i indicates the row vector that is the ith row of the matrix A, and the letter B_i indicates the row vector that has an entry of 1 in the jth place and zeros elsewhere.

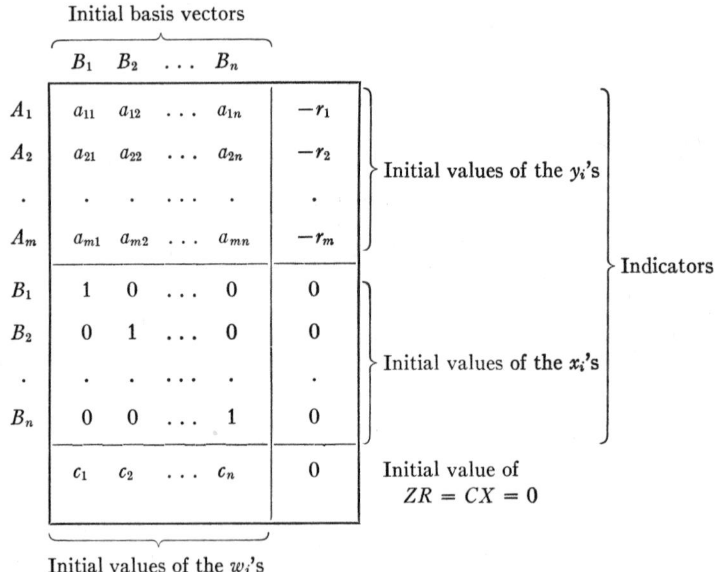

Figure 11. Initial simplex tableau.

Look now at equation (4). Observe that C is written in terms of the vectors A_i and the vectors B_i. In fact, initially we have $C = W = c_1B_1 + c_2B_2 + \ldots + c_nB_n$. We call the basis, $B_1, B_2, \ldots, B_n$, the *initial basis.* The labels of the initial basis vectors appear at the top of the tableau. In the first m rows of the column furthest to the right we have the initial values of the y_i's; recall that initially $Y = -R$. And in the next n rows of the last column appear the initial x_i's; recall that initially $X = 0$. For reasons that will become clear later, the initial values of the x_i's and y_i's are called *indicators.* In the lower right-hand corner we have the initial value of $ZR = CX = 0$; recall that initially both $Z = 0$ and $X = 0$. Finally, in the first n columns of the last row we have the initial w_j's; recall that initially $W = C$.

The first step of the simplex method consists in replacing the initial basis by another basis that differs from it in one vector. Then we replace the new basis by another that differs in another vector, etc. Each time we change basis we make certain that the following conditions hold: (1) $ZR = CX$, (2) the new value of $ZR = CX$ is larger (or at least, no smaller) than its previous value, and (3) an indicator that was previously negative becomes positive.

An intermediate simplex tableau is shown in Figure 12. Here the entries a^*_{ij} are obtained from the entries of A by suitable column opera-

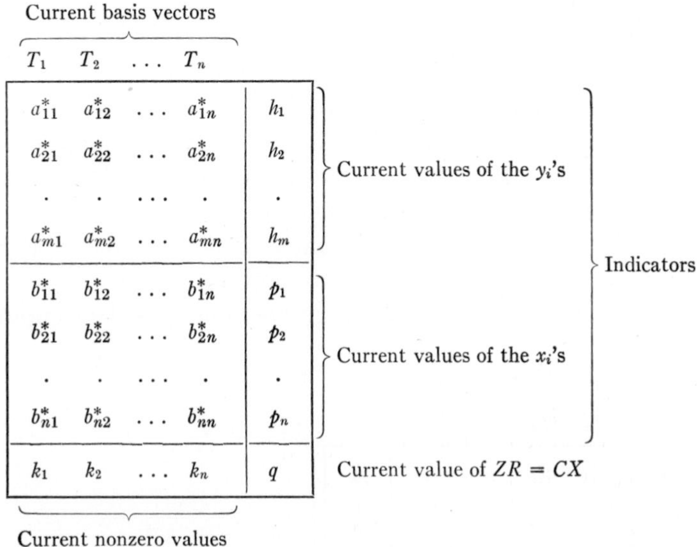

Figure 12. Intermediate simplex tableau.

tions to be described. Similarly, the entries b^*_{ij} are obtained from the entries of the matrix B formed from the vectors B_i. The numbers h_i are the current values of the y_i's; the p_i's are the current values of the x_i's; and the k_j's are the current nonzero values of the z_j's and w_j's. The letters $T_1, T_2, \ldots, T_n$ are the names of the current basis vectors and are either A_i's or B_i's as explained in the rules below. The current values of the x_i's and y_i's are *indicators* as before.

Assuming that a suitable set of basis vectors (initial or current) has been selected, we write the steps involved in changing the basis to a new basis.

Step 1. Select any row that has a negative indicator, suppose it is the ith row.

Step 2. If $i \leq m$, then for each l such that $a^*_{il} > 0$ compute the quantities k_l/a^*_{il} and select the smallest such ratio. If $m < i \leq m + n$ then compute the corresponding quantities for the b^* and again select the smallest such ratio. In either case let j be the index of a column for which this ratio is smallest. We shall call the i,jth entry the *pivot.*

Step 3. Divide through the jth column (which has $m + n + 1$ entries) by the pivot, and write this column in the jth column of the new tableau. Multiply this new jth column by the entry in the ith row of the lth column, and subtract the result from the lth column of the old tableau and enter the resulting numbers in the lth column of the new tableau. Do this for each column (including the $(n + 1)$st column) in the tableau (except, of course, the jth one).

Step 4. If $i \leq m$ write A_i at the top of the jth column of the new tableau (indicating that A_i is the new basis vector annexed). If $m + 1 \leq i \leq m + n$, write B_{i-m} at the top of the jth column of the new tableau (indicating that B_{i-m} is the new vector annexed to the basis). Label the other current basis vectors the same as in the old tableau.

Step 5. If any rows remain with negative indicators go back to Step 1 and repeat the process. Otherwise go to Step 6.

Step 6. When all rows have nonnegative indicators the computation

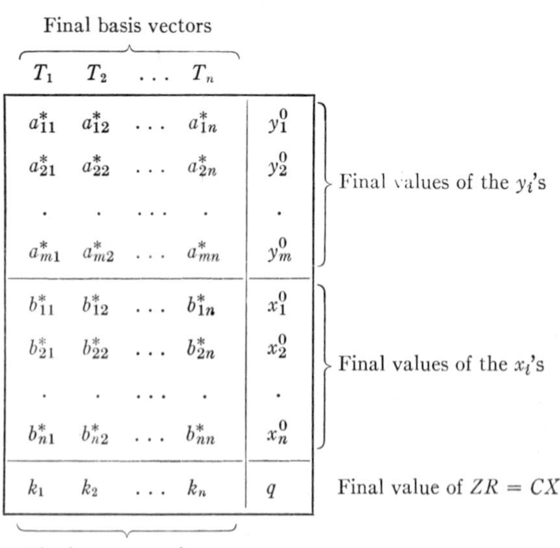

Figure 13. Final simplex tableau.

is finished. (It can be shown that this state will be reached in a finite number of steps if *there is a solution and if* (I) is satisfied.) The results will then be as in the final tableau of Figure 13. The final values of the y_i's appear in the first m entries in the last column; the final values of the x_i's occur in the next n entries of the last column; and the value of $Z^0R = CX^0$, the common values of the maximum and minimum problems, appear in the lower right-hand corner. Lastly, the nonzero components of the vectors W^0 and Z^0 appear in the first n entries of the last row of the final simplex tableau. If the jth column of the tableau is labeled A_i then the ith component of Z^0 is equal to k_j. And if the jth column of the tableau is labeled B_i, then the ith component of W^0 is equal to k_j. All other components of Z^0 and W^0 are equal to zero.

Since this is a rather complicated algorithm we illustrate it by solving the problem of Example 1 and then explain further the reasons behind the various steps.

	B_1	B_2		
A_1	(6)	2	-12	Indicators
A_2	2	2	-8	Indicators
A_3	4	12	-24	Indicators
B_1	1	0	0	Indicators
B_2	0	1	0	Indicators
	200	160	0	

Figure 14

Example 1 (Continued). The initial tableau for the problem is shown in Figure 14. Be sure to compare the quantities in Figure 14 with those in Figure 11 and identify each of them.

Since three of the indicators are negative we can select any one and we arbitrarily choose the first one. We find the pivot (as in Step 2) by dividing the entries of the first row into the corresponding entries of the last row and obtaining the ratios 100/3 and 80. Since the first of these is smaller, the pivot is the 6 entry circled in Figure 14.

We now divide the first column by 6 and carry out the rest of the details of Steps 3 and 4 of the simplex algorithm and obtain the tableau given in Figure 15. Here the two basis vectors are A_1 and B_2. The values of the nonzero variables are $z_1 = 100/3$ and $w_2 = 280/3$ and, as it should be, $C = z_1A_1 + w_2B_2$. With this basis the current value of ZR is 400.

Since there are still rows with negative indicators we are not finished.

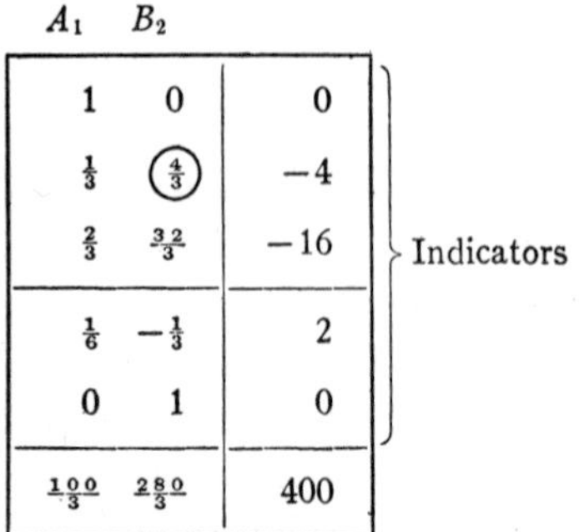

A_1	B_2	
1	0	0
$\frac{1}{3}$	($\frac{4}{3}$)	-4
$\frac{2}{3}$	$\frac{32}{3}$	-16
$\frac{1}{6}$	$-\frac{1}{3}$	2
0	1	0
$\frac{100}{3}$	$\frac{280}{3}$	400

Figure 15

Choosing the second row, we divide its entries into the corresponding entries of the last row and obtain the ratios 100 and 70; hence the $\frac{4}{3}$ entry circled in Figure 15 is the pivot. Carrying out Steps 3 and 4 we obtain the tableau of Figure 16.

A_1	A_2	
1	0	0
0	1	0
-2	8	16
$\frac{1}{4}$	$-\frac{1}{4}$	1
$-\frac{1}{4}$	$\frac{3}{4}$	3
10	70	680

Figure 16

Since there are no more rows with negative indicators we are finished and the solution is given by the following quantities:

$$Z^0 = (10 \quad 70 \quad 0), \quad X^0 = \begin{pmatrix} 1 \\ 3 \end{pmatrix} \quad \text{and} \quad Z^0R = CX^0 = 680.$$

There is one surprising fact about the final tableau given in Figure 16. Observe that the matrices

$$\begin{pmatrix} \frac{1}{4} & -\frac{1}{4} \\ -\frac{1}{4} & \frac{3}{4} \end{pmatrix} \quad \text{and} \quad \begin{pmatrix} 6 & 2 \\ 2 & 2 \end{pmatrix}$$

are inverses of each other. The reader can discover why this is so by working Exercises 4 and 5.

The reasons for the various steps in the algorithms are now clear. In Step 2, the pivot was chosen in order to have the smallest ratio

k_l/a_{il} in order that no current z_j or w_j variable should have a negative value. The reader may verify that if the pivot is chosen not to have this property, then some such variable is made negative (see Exercise 3). The reason that the algorithm was finished when all the indicators were positive is also clear. For we moved from step to step with equations (1), (3), and (4) and $CX = ZR$ continuously satisfied. And when all the indicators are positive we have also $X \geq 0$ and $Y \geq 0$, which means that (2) is satisfied. By the duality theorem if X, Y, Z, and W satisfy equations (1)–(4) and $CX = ZR$, then a solution to the programming problem has been obtained.

Example 2. Solve the dual problem set up in Exercise 6 of Section 6. Figures 17, 18, and 19 give the necessary tableaus. The pivots are circled in Figures 17 and 18. From the tableau of Figure 19 we read off the solutions as

$$X^0 = \begin{pmatrix} 5 \\ 17.5 \\ 0 \end{pmatrix}, \quad Z^0 = (12.5 \quad 15), \quad \text{and} \quad Z^0R = CX^0 = 1900.$$

	B_1	B_2	B_3	
A_1	2	(4)	3	−80
A_2	5	2	5	−60
B_1	1	0	0	0
B_2	0	1	0	0
B_3	0	0	1	0
	100	80	150	0

Figure 17

	B_1	A_1	B_3	
A_1	0	1	0	0
A_2	(4)	$\frac{1}{2}$	$\frac{7}{2}$	−20
B_1	1	0	0	0
B_2	$-\frac{1}{2}$	$\frac{1}{4}$	$-\frac{3}{4}$	20
B_3	0	0	1	0
	60	20	90	1600

Figure 18

	A_2	A_1	B_3	
A_1	0	1	0	0
A_2	1	0	0	0
B_1	$\frac{1}{4}$	$-\frac{1}{8}$	$-\frac{7}{8}$	5
B_2	$-\frac{1}{8}$	$\frac{5}{16}$	$-\frac{5}{16}$	$\frac{35}{2}$
B_3	0	0	1	0
	15	$\frac{25}{2}$	$\frac{75}{2}$	1900

Figure 19

From this we see that the nutritionist should order 5 units of F_1, 17.5 units of F_2, and no units of F_3. The price of the minimum-cost diet is \$19.00. From the solution Z^0 of the dual problem we see that the value or shadow price of the vitamins is 12.5 cents for each unit of vitamin A and 15 cents for each unit of vitamin B. The nutritionist might want to compare these shadow prices for vitamins with the market prices of the same vitamins in other forms.

In the first and last tableaux we find the matrices

$$\begin{pmatrix} 2 & 4 \\ 5 & 2 \end{pmatrix} \quad \text{and} \quad \begin{pmatrix} \frac{1}{4} & -\frac{1}{8} \\ -\frac{1}{8} & \frac{5}{16} \end{pmatrix}$$

which satisfy

$$\begin{pmatrix} 2 & 4 \\ 5 & 2 \end{pmatrix}\begin{pmatrix} \frac{1}{4} & -\frac{1}{8} \\ -\frac{1}{8} & \frac{5}{16} \end{pmatrix} = \begin{pmatrix} 0 & 1 \\ 1 & 0 \end{pmatrix}.$$

The reader is again advised to work Exercises 4 and 5 to see why this is so.

Example 3. Our last example illustrates a case in which some of the x_i indicators become negative. Figures 20–23 give the necessary tableaus

B_1	B_2	
2	3	−17
①	1	−5
1	0	0
0	1	0
3	4	0

Figure 20

B_1	A_1	
2	①	−7
1	0	0
1	−1	5
0	1	0
3	1	15

Figure 21

A_2	A_1	
0	1	0
1	0	0
③	−1	−2
−2	1	7
1	1	22

Figure 22

B_1	A_1	
0	1	0
$\frac{1}{3}$	$\frac{1}{3}$	$\frac{2}{3}$
1	0	0
$-\frac{2}{3}$	$\frac{1}{3}$	$\frac{17}{3}$
$\frac{1}{3}$	$\frac{4}{3}$	$22\frac{2}{3}$

Figure 23

and the pivots are circled there. There is another way of working this problem that requires only two tableaus. It starts with a pivot in the first row instead of the second (see Exercise 6). This illustrates the rule that it usually is best to start the simplex method with a row having the most negative indicator.

EXERCISES

1. Use the simplex method to solve Example 2 of Section 5.

2. Use the simplex method to solve Example 3 of Section 5 even though the nondegeneracy hypothesis is not satisfied. Show that there are two ways to proceed, each one leading to a different solution of the minimum problem.

3. In the tableau of Figure 14 make the pivot be the 2 entry in the first row rather than the circled 6 entry shown. Show that this leads to a negative value of w_1, and hence explain the reasons in Step 2 for the special choice of the pivot.

4. Let a, b, c, and d be positive numbers such that $ad - bc \neq 0$, and consider the matrix

$$\left(\begin{array}{cc|c} a & b & -p \\ c & d & -q \\ \hline 1 & 0 & 0 \\ 0 & 1 & 0 \end{array}\right).$$

By column transformations (i.e., adding a multiple of a column to another column or dividing a column by a number) change this matrix to be one of the form:

$$\left(\begin{array}{cc|c} 1 & 0 & 0 \\ 0 & 1 & 0 \\ \hline e & f & x \\ g & h & y \end{array}\right).$$

Show that

$$\begin{pmatrix} a & b \\ c & d \end{pmatrix}\begin{pmatrix} e & f \\ g & h \end{pmatrix} = \begin{pmatrix} 1 & 0 \\ 0 & 1 \end{pmatrix}$$

and

$$\begin{pmatrix} x \\ y \end{pmatrix} = \begin{pmatrix} e & f \\ g & h \end{pmatrix}\begin{pmatrix} p \\ q \end{pmatrix}.$$

From this example derive an algorithm for solving linear equations of the form

$$\begin{pmatrix} a & b \\ c & d \end{pmatrix}\begin{pmatrix} x \\ y \end{pmatrix} = \begin{pmatrix} p \\ q \end{pmatrix}.$$

5. Let a, b, c, and d be positive numbers such that $ad - bc \neq 0$, and consider the matrix

$$\left(\begin{array}{cc|c} a & b & -p \\ c & d & -q \\ \hline 1 & 0 & 0 \\ 0 & 1 & 0 \\ \hline r & s & 0 \end{array}\right),$$

where p, q, r, and s are arbitrary numbers. By column transformations change this matrix to be one of the form:

$$\left(\begin{array}{cc|c} 1 & 0 & 0 \\ 0 & 1 & 0 \\ \hline e & f & x \\ g & h & y \\ \hline u & v & z \end{array}\right).$$

Show that the following equations hold:

$$\begin{pmatrix} a & b \\ c & d \end{pmatrix}\begin{pmatrix} e & f \\ g & h \end{pmatrix} = \begin{pmatrix} 1 & 0 \\ 0 & 1 \end{pmatrix},$$

$$\begin{pmatrix} x \\ y \end{pmatrix} = \begin{pmatrix} e & f \\ g & h \end{pmatrix}\begin{pmatrix} p \\ q \end{pmatrix},$$

$$(u \quad v) = (r \quad s)\begin{pmatrix} e & f \\ g & h \end{pmatrix},$$

$$(ad - bc)z = (r \quad s)\begin{pmatrix} e & f \\ g & h \end{pmatrix}\begin{pmatrix} p \\ q \end{pmatrix}.$$

Discuss an algorithm for solving simultaneously sets of equations of the form:

$$(u \quad v)\begin{pmatrix} a & b \\ c & d \end{pmatrix} = (r \quad s) \quad \text{and} \quad \begin{pmatrix} a & b \\ c & d \end{pmatrix}\begin{pmatrix} x \\ y \end{pmatrix} = \begin{pmatrix} p \\ q \end{pmatrix}.$$

6. Solve the problem in Example 3 by choosing the first pivot in the first row. Show that the answer can be obtained in one step.

7. Use the simplex method to solve the linear programming problem with data given as

$$A = \begin{pmatrix} 3 & -2 \\ 0 & 1 \end{pmatrix}, \quad R = \begin{pmatrix} -1 \\ 1 \end{pmatrix}, \quad \text{and} \quad C = (1 \quad 0).$$

8. Try the simplex method on the problem with the following data:

$$A = \begin{pmatrix} -3 & -2 \\ 0 & 1 \end{pmatrix}, \quad R = \begin{pmatrix} -1 \\ 1 \end{pmatrix}, \quad \text{and} \quad C = (1 \quad 0).$$

Show that the simplex method breaks down and then prove independently that the problem has no solution.

9. Use the simplex algorithm to solve the linear programming problem whose data is given as

$$A = \begin{pmatrix} 3 & 7 \\ 6 & 2 \\ 3 & 4 \\ 5 & 5 \end{pmatrix}, \quad R = \begin{pmatrix} 8 \\ 3 \\ 4 \\ 2 \end{pmatrix}, \quad \text{and} \quad C = (25 \quad 32).$$

10. Use the simplex method to solve the linear programming problem whose data is given as

$$A = \begin{pmatrix} 10 & 3 & 11 & 8 \\ 4 & 9 & 7 & 3 \\ 12 & 15 & 8 & 11 \end{pmatrix}, \quad R = \begin{pmatrix} 6 \\ 5 \\ 10 \end{pmatrix}, \quad \text{and} \quad C = (35 \quad 48).$$

11. Use the simplex method to solve Exercise 7 of Section 6.

[*Ans.* The caterer should buy 70 napkins and have 40 laundered after the first day.]

12. Use the simplex method to solve Exercise 8 of Section 6.

[*Ans.* The caterer should purchase 110 napkins initially and have 40 laundered by the slow service after the first day. He should not use the fast laundry service.]

13. Solve Exercise 9 of Section 6.

[*Ans.* The manufacturer should make 30 pounds of the party mix and 140 pounds of the cheap mix. His income is \$94.]

14. Solve by the simplex method Exercise 10 of Section 6.

15. Solve by the simplex method Exercise 11 of Section 6.

[*Partial Ans.* All the laborers of country Q rest.]

16. In Exercise 15 suppose country P raises the wages of its food workers to \$4 per hour. What is the new solution?

[*Partial Ans.* The food workers of country P and the clothing workers of country Q rest.]

17. Solve by the simplex method Exercise 12 of Section 6.

18. In Exercise 17 suppose that the first warehouse has 80 tons and the second warehouse has 120 tons. The needs at the first market are 70 tons and at the second market 120 tons. How should the manufacturer now place his shipping orders? Interpret the dual problem.

SUGGESTED READING

Charnes, A., and W. W. Cooper, "Linear Programming," *Scientific American*, **191** (1954), pp. 21–23.

Charnes, A., W. W. Cooper, and A. Henderson, *An Introduction to Linear Programming*, Wiley, New York, 1953.

Kemeny, J. G., J. L. Snell, and G. L. Thompson, *Introduction to Finite Mathematics*, Prentice-Hall, Englewood Cliffs, N. J., 1957, Chapter VI.

Koopmans, T. C. (editor), *Activity Analysis of Production and Allocation*, (Cowles Commission Monograph No. 13), Wiley, New York, 1951.

Kuhn, H. W., and A. W. Tucker (editors), *Linear Inequalities and Related Systems*, Annals of Mathematics Study No. 38, Princeton University Press, Princeton, 1956.

Vajda, S., *The Theory of Games and Linear Programming*, Methuen and Co., London, and Wiley, New York, 1956.

CHAPTER 6

Finite Markov Chains

1. BASIC CONCEPTS AND EXAMPLES

As preparation for this chapter the reader should have covered the unstarred sections from Chapter 1, from Chapter 2, from Chapter 3 Sections 1–10, and from Chapter 4 Sections 1–5. While in Chapter 4 the important vectors were column vectors, in Markov chain theory it is customary to use row vectors as probability vectors.

Let us review the basic concepts of a Markov chain process as defined in Section 7 of Chapter 3. Recall that we may think of a Markov chain as a process that moves successively through a set of states $s_1, s_2, \ldots, s_r$. We shall always assume that $r \geq 2$. Given that it is in state s_i, it moves on the next stop to state s_j with probability p_{ij}. These probabilities can be exhibited in the form of a *transition matrix* P:

$$P = \begin{array}{c} \\ s_1 \\ s_2 \\ \cdot \\ s_r \end{array} \begin{array}{c} \begin{array}{cccc} s_1 & s_2 & \ldots & s_r \end{array} \\ \begin{pmatrix} p_{11} & p_{12} & \ldots & p_{1r} \\ p_{21} & p_{22} & \ldots & p_{2r} \\ \cdot & \cdot & \ldots & \cdot \\ p_{r1} & p_{r2} & \ldots & p_{rr} \end{pmatrix} \end{array}.$$

The entries of P are nonnegative and the sum of the components in any given row is 1. A vector with nonnegative components having sum 1 is called a *probability vector*. Therefore, each row of P is a probability vector.

To determine a Markov chain process completely we must specify the transition matrix and the starting state. From this information we can construct an n-stage tree as a possibility space for the first n steps. We denote by $\mathbf{f}_j$ the jth outcome function. The n outcome functions $\mathbf{f}_1, \ldots, \mathbf{f}_n$ describe the tree.

Assume now that we are interested in questions relating to the outcome of the nth step. Then we could assign to $\mathcal{U} = \{s_1, s_2, \ldots, s_r\}$ a new weight function $\mathbf{w}^{(n)}$ with weight given by

$$\mathbf{w}^{(n)}(s_j) = \mathbf{Pr}[\mathbf{f}_n = s_j].$$

We denote by $W^{(n)}$ the vector

$$W^{(n)} = (\mathbf{w}^{(n)}(s_1), \mathbf{w}^{(n)}(s_2), \ldots, \mathbf{w}^{(n)}(s_r)).$$

Example. In Section 7 of Chapter 3 we described the weather in the Land of Oz as a Markov chain. The states were Rain, Nice and Snow. The transition matrix was,

$$P = \begin{array}{c} \\ \mathrm{R} \\ \mathrm{N} \\ \mathrm{S} \end{array} \begin{array}{c} \begin{array}{ccc} \mathrm{R} & \mathrm{N} & \mathrm{S} \end{array} \\ \begin{pmatrix} \frac{1}{2} & \frac{1}{4} & \frac{1}{4} \\ \frac{1}{2} & 0 & \frac{1}{2} \\ \frac{1}{4} & \frac{1}{4} & \frac{1}{2} \end{pmatrix} \end{array}.$$

Let us assume that we start with a nice day. We consider the process for the first three steps. This determines the tree and tree measure indicated in Figure 1, p. 386.

From this tree and tree measure we can find the components of the vectors $W^{(1)}$, $W^{(2)}$, and $W^{(3)}$. For example, let us find $\mathbf{w}^{(3)}(\mathrm{R})$. That is, the probability of rain on the third day. The paths in the truth set of this statement are indicated in Figure 1 by circling their end points. Adding their weights we have

$$\mathbf{w}^{(3)}(\mathrm{R}) = \mathbf{Pr}[\mathbf{f}_3 = \mathrm{R}] = \tfrac{1}{8} + \tfrac{1}{16} + \tfrac{1}{32} + \tfrac{1}{16} + \tfrac{1}{16} + \tfrac{1}{16} = \tfrac{13}{32}.$$

By the same method we can find from the tree measure the components of each of the vectors $W^{(1)}$, $W^{(2)}$, $W^{(3)}$. We obtain,

$$\begin{aligned} W^{(1)} &= (\tfrac{1}{2} \quad 0 \quad \tfrac{1}{2}), \\ W^{(2)} &= (\tfrac{3}{8} \quad \tfrac{2}{8} \quad \tfrac{3}{8}), \\ W^{(3)} &= (\tfrac{13}{32} \quad \tfrac{6}{32} \quad \tfrac{13}{32}). \end{aligned}$$

In studying independent processes we found it necessary to develop methods for computing properties of the outcome functions without resorting to the tree and the tree measures. The same is true for the case of Markov chains. In particular, we shall now show how to obtain the vectors $W^{(n)}$ directly from the transition matrix. The key to our method is the following simple observation.

For a Markov chain process the second term in each product does not depend on n and is, in fact, p_{kj}. Therefore

$$\mathbf{w}^{(n+1)}(s_j) = \sum_k \mathbf{w}^{(n)}(s_k)p_{kj}.$$

In matrix language this is

$$W^{(n+1)} = W^{(n)} \cdot P.$$

Thus we see that the vector giving the probabilities for being in each of the states after $n + 1$ steps is obtained by multiplying the transition matrix on the left by the probability vector corresponding to n steps. Thus, if we start in s_i, $W^{(1)}$ is the ith row of P, $W^{(2)} = W^{(1)}P$, $W^{(3)} = W^{(2)}P$, etc.

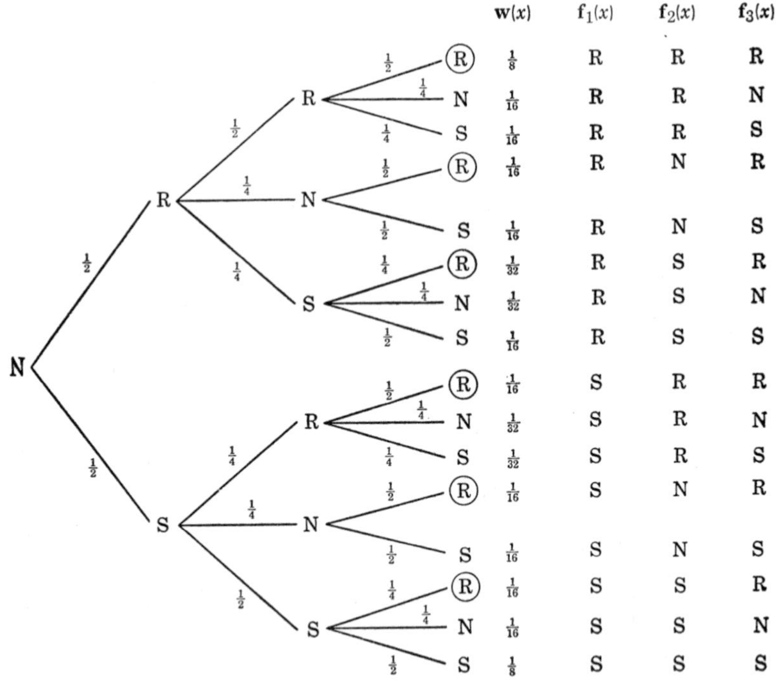

Figure 1

$$\mathbf{w}^{(n+1)}(s_j) = \mathbf{Pr}[\mathbf{f}_{n+1} = s_j] = \sum_k \mathbf{Pr}[\mathbf{f}_n = s_k \wedge \mathbf{f}_{n+1} = s_j]$$

$$= \sum_k \mathbf{Pr}[\mathbf{f}_n = s_k] \cdot \mathbf{Pr}[\mathbf{f}_{n+1} = s_j | \mathbf{f}_n = s_k]$$

Example (Continued). In the Land of Oz example, let us again start in state N. Then

$$W^{(1)} = (\tfrac{1}{2} \quad 0 \quad \tfrac{1}{2}).$$

$$W^{(2)} = (\tfrac{1}{2} \quad 0 \quad \tfrac{1}{2})\begin{pmatrix} \frac{1}{2} & \frac{1}{4} & \frac{1}{4} \\ \frac{1}{2} & 0 & \frac{1}{2} \\ \frac{1}{4} & \frac{1}{4} & \frac{1}{2} \end{pmatrix}$$

$$= (\tfrac{3}{8} \quad \tfrac{2}{8} \quad \tfrac{3}{8}).$$

$$W^{(3)} = (\tfrac{3}{8} \quad \tfrac{2}{8} \quad \tfrac{3}{8})\begin{pmatrix} \frac{1}{2} & \frac{1}{4} & \frac{1}{4} \\ \frac{1}{2} & 0 & \frac{1}{2} \\ \frac{1}{4} & \frac{1}{4} & \frac{1}{2} \end{pmatrix}$$

$$= (\tfrac{13}{32} \quad \tfrac{6}{32} \quad \tfrac{13}{32}).$$

Note that these vectors agree with those calculated earlier from the tree and its tree measure.

Observe that if we start in s_i, $W^{(1)}$ is the ith row of P, $W^{(2)} = W^{(1)}P$ is the ith row of P^2, etc. Hence $W^{(n)}$ is the ith row of P^n. Thus the various rows of P^n give us $W^{(n)}$ for various starting states.

Let $p_{ij}^{(n)}$ be the probability that the process will be in state s_j after n steps if it is started in state s_i. It is given by the ijth entry of the matrix P^n.

Example (Continued). In the Land of Oz example, we find P^3 to be

$$P^3 = \begin{array}{c} \\ \text{R} \\ \text{N} \\ \text{S} \end{array}\!\!\begin{array}{c} \begin{array}{ccc} \text{R} & \text{N} & \text{S} \end{array} \\ \begin{pmatrix} \frac{26}{64} & \frac{13}{64} & \frac{25}{64} \\ \frac{13}{32} & \frac{6}{32} & \frac{13}{32} \\ \frac{25}{64} & \frac{13}{64} & \frac{26}{64} \end{pmatrix} \end{array}.$$

Here we see that the probability for a nice day three days after rain is $p_{\text{R,N}}^{(3)} = \frac{13}{64}$. Note that the second row gives us the probabilities for each kind of weather three days after a nice day. These probabilities agree with those calculated earlier from the tree and tree measure.

The following examples of Markov chains will be used throughout the chapter for exercises. We shall refer to them simply by their number.

Example 1. The President of the United States tells person A his intention either to run or not to run in the next election. Then A relays the news to B, who in turn relays the message to C, etc., always to some new person. We assume that there is a probability a that a person will change the answer from "yes" to "no" when transmitting it to the next person and a probability b that he will change it from "no" to "yes." We choose as states the message, either "yes" or "no." The transition matrix is then

$$\begin{array}{c} \\ \text{yes} \\ \text{no} \end{array}\!\!\begin{array}{c} \begin{array}{cc} \text{yes} & \text{no} \end{array} \\ \begin{pmatrix} 1-a & a \\ b & 1-b \end{pmatrix} \end{array}.$$

The initial state represents the President's choice.

Example 2. Each time a certain horse runs a race he has probability $\frac{2}{5}$ of winning, $\frac{1}{5}$ of tying and $\frac{2}{5}$ of losing, independently of the outcome of any previous race. We have here an independent trials process but it may also be considered from the point of view of Markov chain theory. The transition matrix is

$$P = \begin{array}{c} \\ W \\ T \\ L \end{array} \begin{array}{c} \begin{array}{ccc} W & T & L \end{array} \\ \begin{pmatrix} \frac{2}{5} & \frac{1}{5} & \frac{2}{5} \\ \frac{2}{5} & \frac{1}{5} & \frac{2}{5} \\ \frac{2}{5} & \frac{1}{5} & \frac{2}{5} \end{pmatrix} \end{array}.$$

Example 3. Assume that of the sons of Harvard men 80 per cent go to Harvard and the rest to Yale, 40 per cent of the sons of Yale men go to Yale, and the remaining split evenly between Harvard and Dartmouth; and of the sons of Dartmouth men, 70 per cent go to Dartmouth, 20 per cent go to Harvard, and 10 per cent go to Yale. We form a Markov chain with transition matrix,

$$P = \begin{array}{c} \\ H \\ Y \\ D \end{array} \begin{array}{c} \begin{array}{ccc} H & Y & D \end{array} \\ \begin{pmatrix} .8 & .2 & 0 \\ .3 & .4 & .3 \\ .2 & .1 & .7 \end{pmatrix} \end{array}.$$

Example 4. Example 3 modified by assuming that the son of a Harvard man always goes to Harvard.

$$P = \begin{array}{c} \\ H \\ Y \\ D \end{array} \begin{array}{c} \begin{array}{ccc} H & Y & D \end{array} \\ \begin{pmatrix} 1 & 0 & 0 \\ .3 & .4 & .3 \\ .2 & .1 & .7 \end{pmatrix} \end{array}.$$

Example 5. The following is a special case of a model that has been used to explain diffusion of gases. The general model will be discussed in detail in Section 7. A box contains three balls. It has two compartments. Each second, one of the three balls is chosen at random and moved from the compartment it is in to the other. We choose as state the number of balls in the first compartment. The transition matrix is then

$$P = \begin{array}{c} \\ 0 \\ 1 \\ 2 \\ 3 \end{array} \begin{array}{c} \begin{array}{cccc} 0 & 1 & 2 & 3 \end{array} \\ \begin{pmatrix} 0 & 1 & 0 & 0 \\ \frac{1}{3} & 0 & \frac{2}{3} & 0 \\ 0 & \frac{2}{3} & 0 & \frac{1}{3} \\ 0 & 0 & 1 & 0 \end{pmatrix} \end{array}.$$

Example 6. The simplest type of inheritance of traits in animals occurs when a trait is governed by a pair of genes, each of which may be of two types, say G and g. An individual may have a GG combination or Gg (which is genetically the same as gG) or gg. Very often the GG and Gg types are indistinguishable in appearance, and then we say that the G gene *dominates* the g gene. An individual is called *dominant* if he has GG genes, *recessive* if he has gg, and *hybrid* with a Gg mixture.

In the mating of two animals, the offspring inherits one gene of the pair from each parent, and the basic assumption of genetics is that these genes are selected at random, independently of each other. This assumption determines the probability of occurrence of each type of offspring. Thus the offspring of two dominant parents must be dominant, of two recessive parents must be recessive, and of one dominant and one recessive parent must be hybrid. In the mating of a dominant and a hybrid animal, the offspring must get a G gene from the former and has probability $\frac{1}{2}$ for getting G or g from the latter, hence the probabilities are even for getting a dominant or a hybrid offspring. Again in the mating of a recessive and a hybrid, there is an even chance of getting either a recessive or a hybrid. In the mating of two hybrids, the offspring has probability $\frac{1}{2}$ of getting a G or a g from each parent. Hence the probabilities are $\frac{1}{4}$ for GG, $\frac{1}{2}$ for Gg, and $\frac{1}{4}$ for gg.

Let us consider a process of continued crossings. We start with an individual of unknown genetic character, and cross it with a hybrid. The offspring is again crossed with a hybrid, etc. The resulting process is a Markov chain. The states are dominant, hybrid, and recessive, and indicated by D, H, and R, respectively. The transition probabilities are

$$P = \begin{array}{c} \\ \text{D} \\ \text{H} \\ \text{R} \end{array} \begin{array}{c} \begin{array}{ccc} \text{D} & \text{H} & \text{R} \end{array} \\ \begin{pmatrix} \frac{1}{2} & \frac{1}{2} & 0 \\ \frac{1}{4} & \frac{1}{2} & \frac{1}{4} \\ 0 & \frac{1}{2} & \frac{1}{2} \end{pmatrix} \end{array} \tag{1}$$

as can be seen from the previous paragraph.

Example 7. The same as Example 6 except that we keep crossing the offspring with a dominant animal. The transition matrix is

$$P = \begin{array}{c} \\ \text{D} \\ \text{H} \\ \text{R} \end{array} \begin{array}{c} \begin{array}{ccc} \text{D} & \text{H} & \text{R} \end{array} \\ \begin{pmatrix} 1 & 0 & 0 \\ \frac{1}{2} & \frac{1}{2} & 0 \\ 0 & 1 & 0 \end{pmatrix} \end{array}.$$

Example 8. We start with two animals of opposite sex, cross them, select two of their offspring of opposite sex and cross those, etc. To simplify the example we will assume that the trait under consideration is independent of sex.

Here a state is determined by a pair of animals. Hence the states of our process will be: $s_1 =$ (D,D), $s_2 =$ (D,H), $s_3 =$ (D,R), $s_4 =$ (H,H), $s_5 =$ (H,R), and $s_6 =$ (R,R). Let us illustrate the calculation of transition probabilities in terms of s_2. When the process is in this state, one parent has GG genes, the other Gg. Hence the probability of a dominant offspring is $\frac{1}{2}$ for each. Then the probability of transition to s_1 (selection of two dominants) is $\frac{1}{4}$, transition to s_2 is $\frac{1}{2}$, and to s_4 is $\frac{1}{4}$. The transition matrix is

$$P = \begin{array}{c} \\ s_1 \\ s_2 \\ s_3 \\ s_4 \\ s_5 \\ s_6 \end{array} \begin{array}{c} \begin{array}{cccccc} s_1 & s_2 & s_3 & s_4 & s_5 & s_6 \end{array} \\ \begin{pmatrix} 1 & 0 & 0 & 0 & 0 & 0 \\ \frac{1}{4} & \frac{1}{2} & 0 & \frac{1}{4} & 0 & 0 \\ 0 & 0 & 0 & 1 & 0 & 0 \\ \frac{1}{16} & \frac{1}{4} & \frac{1}{8} & \frac{1}{4} & \frac{1}{4} & \frac{1}{16} \\ 0 & 0 & 0 & \frac{1}{4} & \frac{1}{2} & \frac{1}{4} \\ 0 & 0 & 0 & 0 & 0 & 1 \end{pmatrix} \end{array}.$$

EXERCISES

1. It is raining in the Land of Oz. Determine a tree and tree measure for the next three days' weather. Find $W^{(1)}$, $W^{(2)}$, and $W^{(3)}$ and compare with the results obtained from P, P^2, and P^3.

2. In Example 1, let $a = 0$ and $b = \frac{1}{2}$. Find P, P^2, and P^3. What would P^n be? What happens to P^n as n tends to infinity? Interpret this result. [*Ans.* After a long time the answer will be "yes."]

3. In Example 2, find P^2, and P^3. What is P^n? [*Ans.* $P^n = P$.]

4. For Example 3 find the probability that the grandson of a man from Harvard goes to Harvard.

5. In Example 4 find the probability that the grandson of a man from Harvard goes to Harvard. [*Ans.* The probability is 1.]

6. In Example 6, assume that we start with a hybrid. Find $W^{(1)}$, $W^{(2)}$ and $W^{(3)}$. What would $W^{(n)}$ be? [*Ans.* $W^{(n)} = W^{(1)}$.]

7. Find the matrices P^2, P^3, P^4, and P^n for the Markov chain determined by the transition matrix

$$P = \begin{pmatrix} 1 & 0 \\ 0 & 1 \end{pmatrix}.$$

Do the same for the Markov chain with transition matrix

$$P = \begin{pmatrix} 0 & 1 \\ 1 & 0 \end{pmatrix}.$$

Interpret what happens in each of these processes.

8. A certain calculating machine uses only the digits 0 and 1. It is supposed to transmit one of these digits through several stages. However, at every stage there is a probability p that the digit that enters this stage will be changed when it leaves and hence probability $q = 1 - p$ of being transmitted unchanged. We form a Markov chain to represent the process of transmission by taking as states the digits 0 and 1. What is the matrix of transition probabilities?

9. For the Markov chain in Exercise 8, draw a tree and assign a tree measure, assuming that the process begins in state 0 and moves through three stages of transmission. What is the probability that the machine after three stages produces the digit 0, i.e., the correct digit? What is the probability that the machine never changed the digit from 0? [*Ans.* $3p^2q + q^3$; q^3.]

10. Assume that a man's profession can be classified as professional, skilled laborer, or unskilled laborer. Assume that of the sons of professional men 80 per cent are professional, 10 per cent are skilled laborers, and 10 per cent are unskilled laborers. In the case of sons of skilled laborers, 60 per cent are skilled laborers, 20 per cent are professional, and 20 per cent are unskilled laborers. Finally, in the case of unskilled laborers, 50 per cent of the sons are unskilled laborers, and 25 per cent each are in the other two categories. Assume that every man has a son, and form a Markov chain by following a given family through several generations. Set up the matrix of transition probabilities. Find the probability that the grandson of an unskilled laborer is a professional man. [*Ans.* .375.]

11. In Exercise 10 we assumed that every man has a son. Assume instead that the probability a man has a son is .8. Form a Markov chain with four states. The first three states are as in Exercise 10, and the fourth state is such that the process enters it if a man has no son, and that the state cannot be left. This state represents families whose male line has died out. Find the matrix of transition probabilities and find the probability that an unskilled laborer has a grandson who is a professional man. [*Ans.* .24.]

12. Explain why the transition probabilities given in Example 5 are correct.

2. ERGODIC MARKOV CHAINS

The first important kind of Markov process that we shall study in detail is a regular Markov chain.

DEFINITION. A Markov chain is called a *regular chain* if some power of the transition matrix has only positive elements.

Of course, any transition matrix that has no zeros determines a regular Markov chain. The transition matrix for the Land of Oz example had $p_{NN} = 0$ but the second power P^2 has no zeros, so this too is a regular Markov chain. An example of a nonregular Markov chain is the chain with transition matrix

$$P = \begin{pmatrix} 1 & 0 \\ \frac{1}{2} & \frac{1}{2} \end{pmatrix}$$

Every power of this matrix will have a 0 in the upper right-hand corner. The probabilistic interpretation of regularity is the following: A Markov chain is regular if there is some time at which it is possible to be in any of the states regardless of the starting state. The easiest way to check regularity is to keep track of whether or not entries in the powers are positive. It is not necessary to compute the actual values of these entries. We do this by putting an x in the entry if it is positive and a 0 otherwise.

Let P be the transition matrix

$$P = \begin{pmatrix} 0 & 1 & 0 \\ 0 & 0 & 1 \\ \frac{1}{2} & \frac{1}{2} & 0 \end{pmatrix}.$$

We check regularity as follows:

$$P = \begin{pmatrix} 0 & x & 0 \\ 0 & 0 & x \\ x & x & 0 \end{pmatrix},$$

$$P^2 = \begin{pmatrix} 0 & 0 & x \\ x & x & 0 \\ 0 & x & x \end{pmatrix},$$

$$P^4 = \begin{pmatrix} 0 & x & x \\ x & x & x \\ x & x & x \end{pmatrix},$$

$$P^8 = \begin{pmatrix} x & x & x \\ x & x & x \\ x & x & x \end{pmatrix}.$$

It pays to try as high powers as possible when testing regularity. Hence we square the result each time.

We shall now discuss two important theorems relating to regular chains. The proofs will be given in the following section.

Theorem 1. If P is a transition matrix for a regular chain, then:

(1) The powers P^n approach a matrix T (that is, each entry of P^n approaches the corresponding entry of T).

(2) Each row of T is the same probability vector W.

(3) The components of W are all positive.

Recall that the i,jth entry of P^n, $p_{ij}^{(n)}$, is the probability that the process will be in state s_j after n steps if it starts in state s_i. Thus (1) states that long-range predictions (i.e., large n), are approximately the same for all n. That is, $p_{ij}^{(n)}$ is approximately t_{ij} for all large n. Result (2) states that these long-range predictions do not depend upon the starting state. That is, $t_{ij} = w_j$ depends only on the state s_j being considered and not on the starting state s_i. Thus the probability of being in s_j in the long run is approximately w_j, independently of the starting state.

Example 1. Let us consider several powers of the transition matrix for the Land of Oz example. These are, to three decimal places,

$$P = \begin{array}{c} \\ R \\ N \\ S \end{array} \begin{array}{c} \begin{array}{ccc} R & N & S \end{array} \\ \begin{pmatrix} .5 & .25 & .25 \\ .5 & 0 & .5 \\ .25 & .25 & .5 \end{pmatrix} \end{array},$$

$$P^2 = \begin{array}{c} \\ R \\ N \\ S \end{array} \begin{array}{c} \begin{array}{ccc} R & N & S \end{array} \\ \begin{pmatrix} .437 & .187 & .375 \\ .375 & .250 & .375 \\ .375 & .187 & .437 \end{pmatrix} \end{array},$$

$$P^4 = \begin{array}{c} \\ R \\ N \\ S \end{array} \begin{array}{c} \begin{array}{ccc} R & N & S \end{array} \\ \begin{pmatrix} .402 & .199 & .398 \\ .398 & .203 & .398 \\ .398 & .199 & .402 \end{pmatrix} \end{array},$$

$$P^8 = \begin{array}{c} \\ R \\ N \\ S \end{array} \begin{array}{c} \begin{array}{ccc} R & N & S \end{array} \\ \begin{pmatrix} .400 & .200 & .400 \\ .400 & .200 & .400 \\ .400 & .200 & .400 \end{pmatrix} \end{array}.$$

Thus we see that already by the eighth power the entries of P^n have rows the same to three decimal places. Thus the probability of rain eight days after a rainy day is very nearly the same as the probability of rain eight days after a nice day, or eight days after a snowy day. The next theorem gives a method for determining the matrix T.

Theorem 2. If P is a transition matrix for a regular chain, and T and W are as in Theorem 1, then the vector W is the unique probability vector such that $WP = W$.

A vector X with the property $XP = X$ will be called a *fixed vector* for P. Thus the common row of T is the unique vector W which is both a fixed vector for P and a probability vector.

Many interesting results concerning regular Markov chains depend only on the fact that the chain has a unique fixed probability vector that is positive. This property holds for a wider class of Markov chains.

DEFINITION. A Markov chain is called an *ergodic chain* if it is possible to go from every state to every other state.

Obviously a regular chain is ergodic, because if the nth power of the transition matrix is positive, then it is possible to go from every state to every other state in n steps. On the other hand, an ergodic chain may not be regular. For instance, if from a given state we can go to certain states only in an even number of steps and to others only in an odd number of steps, then all powers of the transition matrix will have 0's. This will be illustrated in Example 3 below. The following theorem is stated without proof.

Theorem 3. If P is a transition matrix for an ergodic chain, then:

(1) There is a unique probability vector W such that $WP = W$.

(2) All components of W are positive.

(3) If $h_j^{(n)}$ is the average number of times the process is in state s_j in the first n steps, then for any $\epsilon > 0$, $\mathbf{Pr}[|h_j^{(n)} - w_j| > \epsilon] \to 0$ no matter what the starting state is.

The interpretation given for W after Theorem 2 holds only for the special case of regular chains. Indeed, on any one step the probability of being in a given state may be 0 in an ergodic chain, no matter how large n is. But Theorem 3 provides a "law of large numbers" (see Chapter 3 Section 11) for all ergodic chains (including regular chains).

Example 1 (Continued). Returning again to the Land of Oz example, let us use Theorem 2 to find the limiting matrix T. We know that the common row W of T must be a probability vector, i.e., if $W = (w_1 \quad w_2 \quad w_3)$ then

$$w_1 + w_2 + w_3 = 1$$

and it must be a fixed vector, i.e.,

$$(w_1 \quad w_2 \quad w_3)\begin{pmatrix} \frac{1}{2} & \frac{1}{4} & \frac{1}{4} \\ \frac{1}{2} & 0 & \frac{1}{2} \\ \frac{1}{4} & \frac{1}{4} & \frac{1}{2} \end{pmatrix} = (w_1 \quad w_2 \quad w_3).$$

These two facts give us the following four equations which the components of W must satisfy.

$$\begin{aligned} w_1 + w_2 + w_3 &= 1, \\ \tfrac{1}{2}w_1 + \tfrac{1}{2}w_2 + \tfrac{1}{4}w_3 &= w_1, \\ \tfrac{1}{4}w_1 + \phantom{\tfrac{1}{2}w_2} + \tfrac{1}{4}w_3 &= w_2, \\ \tfrac{1}{4}w_1 + \tfrac{1}{2}w_2 + \tfrac{1}{2}w_3 &= w_3. \end{aligned}$$

The unique solution to these four equations is

$$W = (.4 \quad .2 \quad .4).$$

Thus P^n tends to the matrix

$$T = \begin{pmatrix} .4 & .2 & .4 \\ .4 & .2 & .4 \\ .4 & .2 & .4 \end{pmatrix},$$

and for any starting state, $W^{(n)}$ approaches $(.4 \quad .2 \quad .4)$ as n tends to infinity. We may interpret this by saying that in the long run it will rain 40 per cent of the time, be nice 20 per cent of the time, and snow 40 per cent of the time.

Example 2. The weather in the Land of Oz for the last 365 days was reported as follows:

SSRSSSSNRRRSNRRRRRRSNSSNRRSSNSSSNRNSNSSNSSSSRRNS
NRNRRRRNRRNSRRNSNRRSNSSSSRNRSRNSSSSNRRRNSSNSNS
RRSRRNRRRRRRSSSSSRRRNRRSSSSSSRNRSSNRRRRSRNSSSNS
RRSRSSRRRNSRNSSRRRRRRRRSNRSNRRNSNRRRRRRRRRRSS
RNSNSSNSSSRNRRNSRRRNRRSSNSNSSSRNRNRNRSSNSSSSRRR
RNSSRRNRSSRSSSRRRRRSSRRNRNRRRNSNSNSSRSSSNRSSSNR
RNRRNSRRSSSNSNRSSNSSNSRRNRRNRSNRSRRNSRRRSNSSSSS
SRRRRNSSRRNRNRSRNSNSSRNRNSSNSSSRNRRNSSS

There were 140 days of snow, 77 nice days, and 148 days of rain. The fraction of days of each kind of weather is given by the vector

$$\begin{array}{cccc} & R & N & S \\ W = & (.41 & .21 & .38). \end{array}$$

This vector agrees quite well with the theoretical vector

$$\begin{array}{cccc} & R & N & S \\ W' = & (.4 & .2 & .4). \end{array}$$

Finding the fixed vector for a regular Markov chain can be very difficult if the transition matrix is very large. It is often possible to guess the fixed vector on purely intuitive grounds. We shall see examples of this in Section 6 when we consider examples from physics. We give here a more simple example to illustrate this kind of situation.

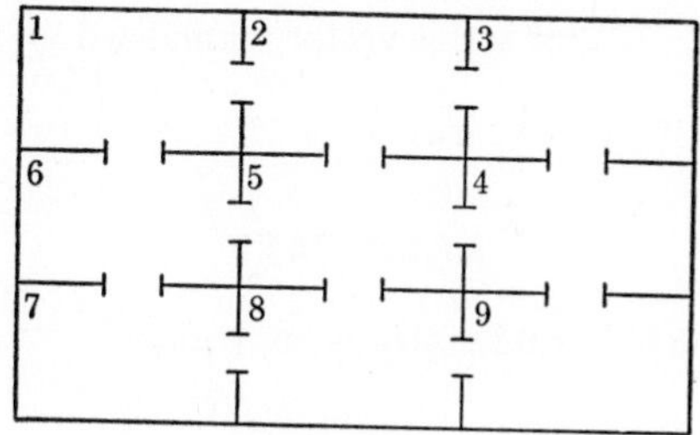

Figure 2

Example 3. A white rat is put into the maze of Figure 2. There are nine compartments with connections between the compartments as indicated. The rat moves through the compartments at random. That is, if there are k ways to leave a compartment, it chooses each of these with equal probability. We can represent the travels of the rat by a Markov chain process with transition matrix given by:

$$P = \begin{array}{c} \\ 1 \\ 2 \\ 3 \\ 4 \\ 5 \\ 6 \\ 7 \\ 8 \\ 9 \end{array}\begin{array}{c} \begin{array}{ccccccccc} 1 & 2 & 3 & 4 & 5 & 6 & 7 & 8 & 9 \end{array} \\ \begin{bmatrix} 0 & \frac{1}{2} & 0 & 0 & 0 & \frac{1}{2} & 0 & 0 & 0 \\ \frac{1}{3} & 0 & \frac{1}{3} & 0 & \frac{1}{3} & 0 & 0 & 0 & 0 \\ 0 & \frac{1}{2} & 0 & \frac{1}{2} & 0 & 0 & 0 & 0 & 0 \\ 0 & 0 & \frac{1}{3} & 0 & \frac{1}{3} & 0 & 0 & 0 & \frac{1}{3} \\ 0 & \frac{1}{4} & 0 & \frac{1}{4} & 0 & \frac{1}{4} & 0 & \frac{1}{4} & 0 \\ \frac{1}{3} & 0 & 0 & 0 & \frac{1}{3} & 0 & \frac{1}{3} & 0 & 0 \\ 0 & 0 & 0 & 0 & 0 & \frac{1}{2} & 0 & \frac{1}{2} & 0 \\ 0 & 0 & 0 & 0 & \frac{1}{3} & 0 & \frac{1}{3} & 0 & \frac{1}{3} \\ 0 & 0 & 0 & \frac{1}{2} & 0 & 0 & 0 & \frac{1}{2} & 0 \end{bmatrix} \end{array}.$$

That this chain is not regular can be seen as follows: from an odd numbered state the process can go only to an even numbered state, and from an even numbered state it can go only to an odd numbered one. Hence, starting in s_1 the process will be alternately in even and odd numbered states. Therefore each power of P will have 0's for the odd numbered entries or for the even numbered entries in row 1. On the other hand a glance at the maze shows that it is possible to go from every state to every other state, so that the chain is ergodic.

To find the fixed probability vector for this matrix we would have to solve ten equations in nine unknowns. However, we know that the components of the fixed vector will be proportional to the fraction of time the rat will spend in each of the compartments. It seems reasonable to think that this should be proportional to the number of entries to the compartments. Thus we try the vector with jth component the number of entries to the jth compartment. This is

$$X = (2 \quad 3 \quad 2 \quad 3 \quad 4 \quad 3 \quad 2 \quad 3 \quad 2).$$

It is easy to check that this vector is indeed a fixed vector so that the unique probability vector is this vector normalized to have sum 1. This is,

$$W = (\tfrac{1}{12} \quad \tfrac{1}{8} \quad \tfrac{1}{12} \quad \tfrac{1}{8} \quad \tfrac{1}{6} \quad \tfrac{1}{8} \quad \tfrac{1}{12} \quad \tfrac{1}{8} \quad \tfrac{1}{12}).$$

EXERCISES

1. Which of the following matrices are regular?

(a) $\begin{pmatrix} \frac{1}{2} & \frac{1}{2} \\ \frac{1}{2} & \frac{1}{2} \end{pmatrix}$. (b) $\begin{pmatrix} 0 & 1 \\ \frac{1}{4} & \frac{3}{4} \end{pmatrix}$. [Regular]

(c) $\begin{pmatrix} 1 & 0 \\ \frac{1}{3} & \frac{2}{3} \end{pmatrix}$. (d) $\begin{pmatrix} \frac{1}{5} & \frac{4}{5} \\ 1 & 0 \end{pmatrix}$. [Regular]

(e) $\begin{pmatrix} \frac{1}{2} & \frac{1}{2} \\ 0 & 1 \end{pmatrix}$. (f) $\begin{pmatrix} 0 & 1 \\ 1 & 0 \end{pmatrix}$. [Not regular]

(g) $\begin{pmatrix} \frac{1}{2} & \frac{1}{2} & 0 \\ 0 & \frac{1}{2} & \frac{1}{2} \\ \frac{1}{3} & \frac{1}{3} & \frac{1}{3} \end{pmatrix}$. (h) $\begin{pmatrix} \frac{1}{3} & 0 & \frac{2}{3} \\ 0 & 1 & 0 \\ 0 & \frac{1}{5} & \frac{4}{5} \end{pmatrix}$. [Not regular]

2. Show that the 2×2 matrix

$$S = \begin{pmatrix} 1-a & a \\ b & 1-b \end{pmatrix}$$

is a regular matrix if and only if neither a nor b is 0 and they are not both equal to 1.

3. Find the fixed point for the matrix in Exercise 2 for each of the cases listed there. [*Ans.* $\left(\frac{b}{a+b} \quad \frac{a}{a+b}\right)$.]

4. Find the fixed point probability vector W for each of the following regular matrices.

(a) $\begin{pmatrix} \frac{3}{4} & \frac{1}{4} \\ \frac{1}{2} & \frac{1}{2} \end{pmatrix}$. [*Ans.* $W = (\frac{2}{3} \quad \frac{1}{3})$.]

(b) $\begin{pmatrix} .9 & .1 \\ .1 & .9 \end{pmatrix}$.

(c) $\begin{pmatrix} \frac{3}{4} & \frac{1}{4} & 0 \\ 0 & \frac{2}{3} & \frac{1}{3} \\ \frac{1}{4} & \frac{1}{4} & \frac{1}{2} \end{pmatrix}$. [*Ans.* $W = (\frac{2}{7} \quad \frac{3}{7} \quad \frac{2}{7})$.]

5. Let the process start in s_1 and compute $W^{(1)}$, $W^{(2)}$, $W^{(3)}$ for each of the matrices in Exercises 4(a) and 4(b). Do they approach the fixed points of these matrices?

6. Consider the transition matrix in Exercise 2 with $a = b = 1$. Prove that this chain is ergodic but not regular. Find the fixed probability vector, and interpret it. Show that P^n does not tend to a limit.

7. Consider the transition matrix of Exercise 2 with $a = 0$ and $b = \frac{1}{2}$. Compute the unique fixed probability vector, and use your result to prove that the chain is not ergodic.

8. Show that the matrix

$$P = \begin{pmatrix} 1 & 0 & 0 \\ \frac{1}{4} & \frac{1}{2} & \frac{1}{4} \\ 0 & 0 & 1 \end{pmatrix}$$

has more than one fixed probability vector. Find the matrix that P^n

approaches, and verify that it is not a matrix all of whose rows are the same.

9. Prove that, if a 3-by-3 transition matrix has the property that its column sums are 1, then $(\frac{1}{3}\ \ \frac{1}{3}\ \ \frac{1}{3})$ is a fixed probability vector for it. State a similar result for n-by-n transition matrices. Interpret these results for ergodic chains.

Exercises 10–16 refer to the examples given in Section 1.

10. Show that Examples 4, 7, and 8 are not ergodic chains.

11. Show that, for reasonable assumptions concerning a and b, Example 1 is a regular chain. [*Hint.* Use the result of Exercise 2.]

12. Using the result of Exercise 3, give the approximate number of people who are told that the president will run. Interpret the fact that this proportion is independent of the starting state.

13. When an independent trials process is considered to be a Markov chain, what is its fixed probability vector? Is the chain always regular? Illustrate this for Example 2.

14. Show that Example 3 is regular, and find its fixed probability vector. Interpret the result.

15. Show that Example 5 is an ergodic chain, but not a regular chain. Find its fixed probability vector. Show that the same probabilities are obtained if the balls are put one at a time in the box, each one being put into the first compartment with probability $\frac{1}{2}$.

16. Show that Example 6 is regular. Use Exercise 6 of Section 1 to find the fixed probability vector.

17. A factory has two machines only one of which is used at any given time. A machine breaks down on any given day with probability p. There is a single repairman who takes two days to repair a machine and can work on only one machine at a time. We form a Markov chain by taking as states the pairs (x, y), where x is the number of machines in operating condition at the end of a day and y is 1 if a day's work has been put in on a machine not yet repaired and 0 otherwise. The transition matrix is

$$\begin{array}{c} \\ (2,0) \\ (1,0) \\ (1,1) \\ (0,1) \end{array} \begin{array}{c} \begin{array}{cccc} (2,0) & (1,0) & (1,1) & (0,1) \end{array} \\ \begin{pmatrix} q & p & 0 & 0 \\ 0 & 0 & q & p \\ q & p & 0 & 0 \\ 0 & 1 & 0 & 0 \end{pmatrix} \end{array},$$

where $p + q = 1$. Prove the chain regular and find the fixed vector.

[*Ans.* $\left(\dfrac{q^2}{p^2+1}\ \ \dfrac{p}{p^2+1}\ \ \dfrac{qp}{p^2+1}\ \ \dfrac{p^2}{p^2+1}\right)$.]

*3. PROOF OF THE BASIC THEOREMS FOR REGULAR CHAINS

We shall prove here the fundamental results concerning regular Markov chains stated in the previous section. We shall first show that there are several equivalent ways to state our basic result. We shall then prove one, and hence all, of these equivalent results.

Theorem 1. If P is any r-by-r transition matrix, the following statements are equivalent.

(a) $P^n \to T$ as n tends to infinity, where T is a matrix with each row the same vector W. The vector W is a probability vector.

(b) For any r component probability vector X,

$$XP^n \to W,$$

where W is a probability vector. The same vector W is obtained for all choices of X.

(c) For any r component column vector Y,

$$P^n Y \to C,$$

where C is a column vector with all components the same number c. The particular constant obtained depends upon the choice of Y.

Proof. We first prove that (a) and (b) are equivalent. We must show that (a) implies (b) and that (b) implies (a). Assume first that (a) is true. Let X be any r component probability vector. Since $P^n \to T$, we also have

$$XP^n \to XT.$$

By assumption T has all rows the same probability vector W. Hence

$$XT = W.$$

(See Exercise 12). Thus

$$XP^n \to XT = W.$$

Thus (a) implies (b).

Assume now that (b) is true. Let X_i be a row vector with 1 in the ith component and 0 in all other components. Then XP^n is the ith row of P^n. By (b) this approaches the same probability vector W for any choice of i. Hence all rows of P^n approach the same probability vector. This proves that (b) implies (a). We have thus shown that (a) and (b) are equivalent. A similar proof shows that (a) and (c) are equivalent. (See Exercise 8.)

The statement (c) has a simple interpretation as an averaging process. Let us consider the result of multiplying a column vector Y on the left by a probability matrix P. Since the row sums of P are one, each component of the vector PY is an average of the components of the vector Y. The components of P^2Y are an average of the components of the vector PY. In general the vector P^nY is the result of n such averaging operations. It seems reasonable that this averaging process should, for suitable P, smooth out the differences that may originally have existed in the components of the first vector. We shall first prove a theorem which shows that this "smoothing" does take place and then use this result to prove (c). Since (a), (b), and (c) are equivalent, we will have established the validity of all three of these statements for regular chains.

Theorem 2. Let P be an r-by-r transition matrix with no zero entries. Let d be the smallest entry of the matrix. Let Y be a column vector with r components, the largest of which is M_0 and the smallest m_0. Let M_1 and m_1 be the largest and smallest component, respectively, of the vector PY. Then

$$M_1 - m_1 \leq (1 - 2d)(M_0 - m_0).$$

Proof. The component m_1 of PY is an average of the components of Y. This average assigns weight at least d to the maximum component M_0 of Y. The result is surely greater than or equal to the average which would be obtained by assigning weight d to the component M_0 and all the rest of the weight to the minimum component m_0. That is,

$$m_1 \geq dM_0 + (1 - d)m_0. \tag{1}$$

The same argument shows that

$$M_1 \leq dm_0 + (1 - d)M_0. \tag{2}$$

Multiplying (1) by -1, we have

$$-m_1 \leq -dM_0 - (1 - d)m_0. \tag{3}$$

Adding (2) and (3), we have

$$\begin{aligned} M_1 - m_1 &\leq d(m_0 - M_0) + (1 - d)(M_0 - m_0) \\ &= (1 - 2d)(M_0 - m_0). \end{aligned}$$

This completes the proof.

Theorem 3. Each of the statements (a), (b), and (c) in Theorem 1 is true for a regular transition matrix.

Since we proved in Theorem 1 that the statements (a), (b), and (c) of Theorem 1 are equivalent, it is sufficient that we prove any one of them. We shall prove (c). We prove it only for the case that P has no zero elements, and the extension to the general case is indicated in Exercise 7.

Let Y be any r-component column vector. Let M_n and m_n be, respectively, the maximum and minimum components of the vector P^nY. The vector P^nY is obtained from the vector $P^{n-1}Y$ by multiplying on the left by the matrix P. Hence each component of P^nY is an average of the components of $P^{n-1}Y$. Thus

$$M_0 \geq M_1 \geq M_2 \geq \ldots$$

and

$$m_0 \leq m_1 \leq m_2 \leq \ldots.$$

Each sequence is monotone and bounded (since $m_0 \leq m_n \leq M_n \leq M_0$), hence each of these sequences will have a limit as n tends to infinity. Let M be the limit of M_n and let m be the limit of m_n. We shall prove that $M = m$. This will be the case if $M_n - m_n$ tends to 0. Let d be the smallest element of P. Then by Theorem 2,

$$M_n - m_n \leq (1 - 2d)(M_{n-1} - m_{n-1}).$$

From this we see that

$$M_n - m_n \leq (1 - 2d)^n(M_0 - m_0).$$

Since d can be at most $\frac{1}{2}$ (See Exercise 6), the difference $M_n - m_n$ tends to 0 as n tends to infinity. Every component of P^nY lies between m_n and M_n. Hence each component must approach the same number $c = M = m$. This proves statement (c) of Theorem 1 and hence also statements (a) and (b) of Theorem 1.

It is clear from the proof of Theorem 1 that the vector W which appears in (a) and (b) is in fact the same vector. The following theorem identifies this vector as the unique probability vector which is a fixed vector for P.

Theorem 4. Let P, T, and W be as in Theorem 1 part (a). Then W is the unique fixed point probability vector of P.

Proof. Since the powers of P approach T, $P^{n+1} = P^nP$ approaches T, but it also approaches TP; hence $TP = T$. Any one row of this matrix equation states that $WP = W$, hence W is a fixed point. We must still show that it is unique. Let Z be any probability vector which is a fixed point of P. By Theorem 1 part (b), we know that ZP^n approaches W. But since Z is a fixed point, $ZP^n = Z$. Hence Z remains fixed but "approaches" W. This is possible only if $Z = W$. Hence W is the only probability vector which is a fixed point of P.

We note that Theorem 1(b) is stronger than needed for a Markov chain process. For such a process we are interested only in the various rows of P^n, and hence we need only the special cases in which X has 1 as one component and 0 as its other components. But we can consider a more general kind of process. Suppose that we introduce a 0th experiment, in which we decide by a random (chance) device what the starting state should be. If X is any probability vector, we may think of its components as giving the probabilities of starting in various states. Then XP^n will give the probabilities of being in various states after n steps. The theorem establishes the fact that, even in this more general process, the probability of being in s_j approaches w_j, independently of the starting state.

We also obtain a new interpretation for W. Suppose that our random device picks state s_i as a starting state with probability w_i, for all i. Then the probability of being in the various states after n steps is given by $WP^n = W$, and is the same on all steps. Hence this method of starting provides us with a process that is stationary (or in "equilibrium"). The fact that W is the only probability vector for which $WP = P$ shows that we must have a random device of exactly the described kind to obtain a stationary process.

EXERCISES

1. Let $P = \begin{pmatrix} \frac{1}{2} & \frac{1}{2} \\ \frac{1}{4} & \frac{3}{4} \end{pmatrix}$. Let $Y = \begin{pmatrix} \frac{1}{2} \\ \frac{1}{2} \end{pmatrix}$. Compute PY, P^2Y, P^3Y, and P^4Y and show that the results approach a constant vector. What is this vector?

2. Let P be a regular r-by-r transition matrix and let Y be any r-component column vector. Show that the constant vector which P^nY approaches is TY, where T is the limiting matrix for P^n.

3. Let P be a regular matrix and assume Y is a vector such that $PY = Y$. Show then that $P^nY = Y$. Show that this means that Y must be a constant vector, that is, a vector each of whose components is the same number. Hence the only fixed column vectors for a regular transition matrix are constant vectors. Prove that if Y is any constant column vector, then $PY = Y$.

4. Show that if

$$P = \begin{pmatrix} 1 & 0 & 0 \\ \frac{1}{4} & 0 & \frac{3}{4} \\ 0 & 0 & 1 \end{pmatrix}, \quad Y = \begin{pmatrix} 1 \\ \frac{1}{4} \\ 0 \end{pmatrix}, \quad Z = \begin{pmatrix} 0 \\ \frac{3}{4} \\ 1 \end{pmatrix}$$

then $PY = Y$ and $PZ = Z$. Why does this show that the Markov chain with P as transition matrix is not regular? [*Hint:* Use the result of Exercise 3.]

5. Describe the set of all fixed column vectors for the chain given in Exercise 4.

6. Let P be the transition matrix with positive entries and let d be the minimum entry in the matrix. Show that d is at most $\frac{1}{2}$.

7. The theorem that $P^n \to T$ was proved only for the case that P has no zero entries. Fill in the details of the following extension to the case that P is regular. Because P is regular, for some N, P^N has no zeros. Thus the proof given shows that $M_{nN} - m_{nN}$ approaches 0 as n tends to infinity. However, the differences $M_n - m_n$ can never increase. Hence if we know that the differences obtained by looking at every Nth time tend to 0, then the entire sequence must also approach 0.

8. Prove that parts (a) and (c) in Theorem 1 are equivalent.

9. Let P be a regular transition matrix and let Y be a column vector which has a 1 in the jth component and 0 in all other components. Prove that C, the limit of P^nY, is the constant column vector with each component equal to w_j.

10. Let P, Y, and C be as in Exercise 9. Prove that the common component c of C is not zero. [*Hint:* Let N be such that P^N has no zeros. Let m_N be the minimum component of P^NY. Show that $0 < m_N \leq c$.]

11. Use the result of Exercises 9 and 10 to prove that for a regular chain the limiting vector W has all positive components.

12. Show that if T is the limiting matrix for a regular chain then $XT = W$ for any probability vector X.

13. Prove that in an r state ergodic chain it is possible to go from any state to any other state in at most $r - 1$ steps.

14. Let P be the transition matrix of an r state ergodic chain. Prove that if the diagonal entries p_{ii} are positive, then the chain is regular. [*Hint:* Show first that if the process can go from s_i to s_j in k steps, it can also go in any larger number of steps. Then use Exercise 13 to prove that P^{r-1} is positive.]

15. Prove that if P is the transition matrix of an ergodic chain, then $\frac{1}{2}(P + I)$ is the transition matrix of a regular chain. [*Hint:* Use Exercise 14.]

16. Prove that P and $\frac{1}{2}(P + I)$ have the same fixed vectors.

17. Prove, using Exercises 15 and 16, that an ergodic chain has a unique fixed probability vector, and that this vector is positive.

4. ABSORBING MARKOV CHAINS

In this section we shall consider a kind of Markov chain quite different from ergodic chains.

DEFINITION. A state in a Markov chain is an *absorbing state* if it is impossible to leave it. A Markov chain is *absorbing* if (1) it has at least one absorbing state, and (2) from every state it is possible to go to an absorbing state (not necessarily in one step).

Example. A particle moves on a line; each time it moves one unit to the right with probability $\frac{1}{2}$, or one unit to the left. We introduce barriers so that if it ever reaches one of these barriers it stays there, i.e., is absorbed. As a simple example, let the states be 0, 1, 2, 3, 4. States 0 and 4 are absorbing states. The transition matrix is then

$$\begin{array}{c} \\ 0 \\ 1 \\ 2 \\ 3 \\ 4 \end{array} \begin{array}{c} \begin{array}{ccccc} 0 & 1 & 2 & 3 & 4 \end{array} \\ \begin{pmatrix} 1 & 0 & 0 & 0 & 0 \\ \frac{1}{2} & 0 & \frac{1}{2} & 0 & 0 \\ 0 & \frac{1}{2} & 0 & \frac{1}{2} & 0 \\ 0 & 0 & \frac{1}{2} & 0 & \frac{1}{2} \\ 0 & 0 & 0 & 0 & 1 \end{pmatrix} \end{array}.$$

The states 1, 2, 3 are all nonabsorbing states, and from any of these it is possible to reach the absorbing states 0 and 4. Hence the chain is an absorbing chain. Such a process is usually called a *random walk.*

When a process reaches an absorbing state we shall say that it is absorbed.

Theorem. In an absorbing Markov chain the probability that the process will be absorbed is 1.

We shall indicate only the basic idea of the proof of the theorem. From each nonabsorbing state, s_j, it is possible to reach an absorbing state. Let n_j be the minimum number of steps required to reach an absorbing state, starting from state s_j. Let p_j be the probability that, starting from state s_j, the process will *not* reach an absorbing state in n_j steps. Then $p_j < 1$. Let n be the largest of the n_j and let p be the largest of the p_j. The probability of not being absorbed in n steps is less than p, in $2n$ steps is less than p^2, etc. Since $p < 1$, these probabilities tend to zero.

For an absorbing Markov chain we consider three interesting questions: (a) What is the probability that the process will end up in a given absorbing state? (b) On the average, how long will it take for the process to be absorbed? (c) On the average, how many times will the process be in each nonabsorbing state? The answer to all these questions depends, in general, on the state from which the process starts.

Consider then an arbitrary absorbing Markov chain. Let us renumber the states so that the absorbing states come first. If there are r absorbing states and s nonabsorbing states, the transition matrix will have the following *canonical* (or standard) *form.*

(1)
$$P = \begin{array}{c} \\ r \\ s \end{array}\begin{array}{c} \begin{array}{cc} r \text{ states} & s \text{ states} \end{array} \\ \left(\begin{array}{c|c} I & O \\ \hline R & Q \end{array}\right) \end{array}.$$

Here I is an r-by-r identity matrix, O is an r-by-s zero matrix, R is an s-by-r matrix, and Q is an s-by-s matrix. The first r states are absorbing and the last s states are nonabsorbing.

In Section 1 we saw that the entries of the matrix P^n gave the probabilities of being in the various states starting from the various states. It is easy to show that P^n is of the form

(2)
$$P^n = \begin{pmatrix} I & O \\ * & Q^n \end{pmatrix},$$

where the asterisk * stands for the s-by-r matrix in the lower left-hand corner of P^n, which we do not compute here. The form of P^n shows that the entries of Q^n give the probabilities for being in each of the nonabsorbing states after n steps for each possible nonabsorbing starting state. (After zero steps the process must be in the same nonabsorbing state in which it started. Hence $Q^0 = I$.) By our first theorem, the probability of being in the nonabsorbing states after n steps approaches zero. Thus every entry of Q^n must approach zero as n approaches infinity, i.e., $Q^n \to 0$.

Consider then the infinite series

$$I + Q + Q^2 + Q^3 + \ldots .$$

Suppose that Q were a nonnegative number x instead of a nonnegative matrix. To correspond to the fact that $Q^n \to O$ we take x to be less than 1. Then

$$1 + x + x^2 + \ldots = (1 - x)^{-1}.$$

It can be proved that the matrix series behaves in exactly the same way. That is,

$$I + Q + Q^2 + \ldots = (I - Q)^{-1}.$$

The matrix $N = (I - Q)^{-1}$ will be called the *fundamental matrix* for the given absorbing chain. It has the following important interpretation.

Consider the set of paths (see Chapter 3, Section 6) for the first n steps of an absorbing chain that starts at state s_i. Let $\mathbf{u}_{ij}^{(k)}$ be the characteristic function on this set of the statement "the kth outcome is s_j." Then

$$\mathbf{M}[\mathbf{u}_{ij}^{(k)}] = \mathbf{Pr}[\mathbf{u}_{ij}^{(k)} = 1] = q_{ij}^{(k)},$$

where $q_{ij}^{(k)}$ is the i,jth entry of Q^k. This equation holds even for $k = 0$ if we define $Q^0 = I$. Now let $t_{ij}^{(n)}$ be the function that gives the total number of times the chain is in state s_j. Then

$$\mathbf{t}_{ij}^{(n)} = \mathbf{u}_{ij}^{(0)} + \mathbf{u}_{ij}^{(1)} + \ldots + \mathbf{u}_{ij}^{(n)}$$

and

$$\mathbf{M}[\mathbf{t}_{ij}^{(n)}] = q_{ij}^{(0)} + q_{ij}^{(1)} + \ldots + q_{ij}^{(n)}.$$

This mean is the i,jth entry of the series $Q^0 + Q^1 + \ldots + Q^n$. Let us define n_{ij} as the limit of $\mathbf{M}[\mathbf{t}_{ij}^{(n)}]$ as n tends to infinity. The quantity n_{ij} may be interpreted as "the mean number of times the chain is in s_j if it starts in s_i and proceeds until it is absorbed." We see from above that n_{ij} is the i,jth entry of the matrix

$$N = I + Q + Q^2 + \ldots,$$

that is, of the fundamental matrix. Thus we have answered question (c) as follows.

Theorem. Let $N = (I - Q)^{-1}$ be the fundamental matrix for an absorbing chain. Then the entries of N give the mean number of times in each nonabsorbing state for each possible nonabsorbing starting state.

Example 1 (Continued). In Example 1 the transition matrix in canonical form is

$$\begin{array}{c} \\ 0 \\ 4 \\ \\ 1 \\ 2 \\ 3 \end{array}
\begin{array}{c} \begin{array}{ccccc} 0 & 4 & 1 & 2 & 3 \end{array} \\
\left(\begin{array}{cc|ccc} 1 & 0 & 0 & 0 & 0 \\ 0 & 1 & 0 & 0 & 0 \\ \hline \frac{1}{2} & 0 & 0 & \frac{1}{2} & 0 \\ 0 & 0 & \frac{1}{2} & 0 & \frac{1}{2} \\ 0 & \frac{1}{2} & 0 & \frac{1}{2} & 0 \end{array}\right) \end{array}.$$

From this we see that the matrix Q is

$$Q = \begin{pmatrix} 0 & \frac{1}{2} & 0 \\ \frac{1}{2} & 0 & \frac{1}{2} \\ 0 & \frac{1}{2} & 0 \end{pmatrix}$$

and
$$I - Q = \begin{pmatrix} 1 & -\frac{1}{2} & 0 \\ -\frac{1}{2} & 1 & -\frac{1}{2} \\ 0 & -\frac{1}{2} & 1 \end{pmatrix}.$$

Computing $(I - Q)^{-1}$, we find

$$N = (I - Q)^{-1} = \begin{matrix} \\ 1 \\ 2 \\ 3 \end{matrix} \begin{matrix} \begin{matrix} 1 & 2 & 3 \end{matrix} \\ \begin{pmatrix} \frac{3}{2} & 1 & \frac{1}{2} \\ 1 & 2 & 1 \\ \frac{1}{2} & 1 & \frac{3}{2} \end{pmatrix} \end{matrix}.$$

Thus, starting at state 2, the mean number of times in state 1 before absorption is 1, in state 2 it is 2, and in state 3 it is 1.

We next answer question (b). If we add all the entries in a row we will have the mean number of times in any of the nonabsorbing states for a given starting state, that is, the mean time required before being absorbed. This may be described as follows:

Theorem. Consider an absorbing Markov chain with s nonabsorbing states. Let C be an s-component column vector with all entries 1. Then the vector NC has as components the mean number of steps before being absorbed for each possible nonabsorbing starting state.

Example 1 (Continued). For Example 1 we have

$$NC = \begin{matrix} \\ 1 \\ 2 \\ 3 \end{matrix} \begin{matrix} \begin{matrix} 1 & 2 & 3 \end{matrix} \\ \begin{pmatrix} \frac{3}{2} & 1 & \frac{1}{2} \\ 1 & 2 & 1 \\ \frac{1}{2} & 1 & \frac{3}{2} \end{pmatrix} \end{matrix} \begin{pmatrix} 1 \\ 1 \\ 1 \end{pmatrix}$$
$$= \begin{matrix} 1 \\ 2 \\ 3 \end{matrix} \begin{pmatrix} 3 \\ 4 \\ 3 \end{pmatrix}.$$

Thus the mean number of steps to absorption starting at state 1 is 3, starting at state 2 it is 4, and starting at state 3 it is again 3. Since the process necessarily moves to 1 or 3 from 2 it is clear that it requires one more starting from 2 than from 1 or 3.

We now consider question (a). That is, what is the probability that an absorbing chain will end up in a particular absorbing state? It is clear that this probability will depend upon the starting state and be interesting only for the case of a nonabsorbing starting state. We write as usual our matrix in the canonical form

$$P = \left(\begin{array}{c|c} I & O \\ \hline R & Q \end{array}\right).$$

Theorem. Let b_{ij} be the probability that an absorbing chain will be absorbed in state s_j if it starts in the nonabsorbing state s_i. Let B be the matrix with entries b_{ij}. Then

$$B = NR,$$

where N is the fundamental matrix and R is as in the canonical form.

Proof. Let s_i be a nonabsorbing state and s_j be an absorbing state. If we compute b_{ij} in terms of the possibilities on the outcome of the first step we have the equation

$$b_{ij} = p_{ij} + \sum_k p_{ik} b_{kj},$$

where the summation is carried out over all nonabsorbing states k. Writing this in matrix form gives

$$B = R + QB$$

$$(I - Q)B = R,$$

and hence $$B = (I - Q)^{-1}R = NR.$$

Example 1 (Continued). In the random walk example we found that

$$N = \begin{pmatrix} \frac{3}{2} & 1 & \frac{1}{2} \\ 1 & 2 & 1 \\ \frac{1}{2} & 1 & \frac{3}{2} \end{pmatrix}.$$

From the canonical form we find that

$$R = \begin{pmatrix} \frac{1}{2} & 0 \\ 0 & 0 \\ 0 & \frac{1}{2} \end{pmatrix}.$$

Hence

$$B = NR = \begin{pmatrix} \frac{3}{2} & 1 & \frac{1}{2} \\ 1 & 2 & 1 \\ \frac{1}{2} & 1 & \frac{3}{2} \end{pmatrix} \begin{pmatrix} \frac{1}{2} & 0 \\ 0 & 0 \\ 0 & \frac{1}{2} \end{pmatrix}$$

$$= \begin{matrix} \\ 1 \\ 2 \\ 3 \end{matrix} \begin{matrix} \begin{matrix} 0 & \quad 4 \end{matrix} \\ \begin{pmatrix} \frac{3}{4} & \frac{1}{4} \\ \frac{1}{2} & \frac{1}{2} \\ \frac{1}{4} & \frac{3}{4} \end{pmatrix} \end{matrix}.$$

Thus, for instance, starting from s_1, there is probability $\frac{3}{4}$ of absorption in s_0 and $\frac{1}{4}$ for absorption in s_4.

Let us summarize our results. We have shown that the answers to questions (a), (b), and (c) can all be given in terms of the fundamental matrix $N = (I - Q)^{-1}$. The matrix N itself gives us the mean number of times in each state before absorption depending upon the starting state. The column vector NC gives us the mean number of steps before absorption, depending upon the starting state. The matrix NR gives us the probability of absorption for each of the absorbing states, depending upon the starting state.

EXERCISES

The examples referred to below are those in Section 1.

1. For what choices of a and b in Example 1 do we obtain an absorbing Markov chain? [*Ans.* $a = 0$ or $b = 0$.]

2. Show that Example 4 is an absorbing Markov chain.

3. Which of the genetics examples (Examples 6, 7, and 8) are absorbing chains? [*Ans.* Examples 7 and 8 are absorbing.]

4. Find the fundamental matrix N for Example 7.

5. Verify that for Example 8 the following matrix is the inverse of $I - Q$ and hence the fundamental matrix N:

$$N = \begin{pmatrix} \frac{8}{3} & \frac{1}{6} & \frac{4}{3} & \frac{2}{3} \\ \frac{4}{3} & \frac{4}{3} & \frac{8}{3} & \frac{4}{3} \\ \frac{4}{3} & \frac{1}{3} & \frac{8}{3} & \frac{4}{3} \\ \frac{2}{3} & \frac{1}{6} & \frac{4}{3} & \frac{8}{3} \end{pmatrix}.$$

Find NC and NR.

6. In the Land of Oz example let us change the transition matrix by making R an absorbing state. This gives

$$\begin{array}{c} \\ R \\ N \\ S \end{array} \begin{array}{c} \begin{array}{ccc} R & N & S \end{array} \\ \begin{pmatrix} 1 & 0 & 0 \\ \frac{1}{2} & 0 & \frac{1}{2} \\ \frac{1}{4} & \frac{1}{4} & \frac{1}{2} \end{pmatrix} \end{array}.$$

Find the fundamental matrix N, and also NC, and NR. What is the interpretation of these quantities?

7. In Example 5, make states 0 and 3 into absorbing states. Find the fundamental matrix N, and also NC, and NR for the resulting absorbing chain. Interpret the results.

[*Ans.* $N = \begin{pmatrix} \frac{9}{5} & \frac{6}{5} \\ \frac{6}{5} & \frac{9}{5} \end{pmatrix}$, $NR = \begin{pmatrix} \frac{3}{5} & \frac{2}{5} \\ \frac{2}{5} & \frac{3}{5} \end{pmatrix}$, $NC = \begin{pmatrix} 3 \\ 3 \end{pmatrix}$.]

8. In the random walk example of the present section, assume that the probability of a step to the right is $\frac{2}{3}$ and a step to the left is $\frac{1}{3}$. Find N, NC, and NR. Compare these with the results for probability $\frac{1}{2}$ for a step to the right and $\frac{1}{2}$ to the left.

9. A number is chosen at random from the integers 1, 2, 3, 4, 5. If x is chosen, then another number is chosen from the set of integers less than or equal to x. This process is continued until the number 1 is chosen. Form a Markov chain by taking as states the largest number that can be chosen. Show that

$$N = \begin{array}{c} \\ 2 \\ 3 \\ 4 \\ 5 \end{array} \begin{array}{c} \begin{array}{cccc} 2 & 3 & 4 & 5 \end{array} \\ \begin{pmatrix} 1 & 0 & 0 & 0 \\ 1 & \frac{1}{2} & 0 & 0 \\ 1 & \frac{1}{2} & \frac{1}{3} & 0 \\ 1 & \frac{1}{2} & \frac{1}{3} & \frac{1}{4} \end{pmatrix} \end{array} + I,$$

where I is the 4×4 identity matrix. What is the mean number of draws? [*Ans.* $\frac{25}{12}$.]

10. Using the result of Exercise 9, make a conjecture for the form of the fundamental matrix if we start with integers from 1 to n. What would the mean number of draws be if we started with numbers from 1 to 10?

11. Three tanks fight a three-way duel. Tank A has probability $\frac{1}{2}$ of destroying the tank it fires at. Tank B has probability $\frac{1}{3}$ of destroying, and Tank C has probability $\frac{1}{6}$ of destroying. The tanks fire together and each tank fires at the strongest opponent not yet destroyed. Form a Markov chain by taking as state the tanks which survive any one round. Find N, NC, NR, and interpret your results.

12. The following is an alternative method of finding the probability of absorption in a particular absorbing state, say s_j. Find the column vector d such that the jth component of d is 1, all other components corresponding to absorbing states are 0, and $Pd = d$. There is only one such vector. Component d_i is the probability of absorption in s_j if the process starts in s_i. Use this method to find the probability of absorption in state 1 in the random walk example given in this section.

13. Use the method of Exercise 12 to find in Example 8 of Section 1 the absorption probabilities for state s_1.

14. The following is an alternative method for finding the mean number of steps to absorption. Let t_i be the mean number of steps to absorption starting at state s_i. This must be the same as taking one more step and then adding $p_{ij}t_j$ for every nonabsorbing state s_j.

(a) Give reasons for the above claim that

$$t_i = 1 + \sum_j p_{ij}t_j,$$

where the summation is over the nonabsorbing states.

(b) Solve for t for the random walk example.

(c) Verify that the solution agrees with that found in the text.

The remaining problems concern the inheritance of color-blindness, which is a sex-linked characteristic. There is a pair of genes, g and G, of which the former tends to produce color-blindness, the latter normal vision. The G gene is dominant. But a man has only one gene, and if this is g, he is color-blind. A man inherits one of his mother's two genes, while a woman inherits one gene from each parent. Thus a man may be of type G or g, while a woman may be of type GG or Gg or gg. We will study a process of inbreeding similar to that of Example 8 of Section 1.

15. List the states of the chain. [*Hint:* There are six.] Compute the transition probabilities. Find the fundamental matrix N, and the vectors NC and NR.

16. Show that in both Example 8 of Section 1 and the example just given, the probability of absorption in a state having genes of a particular type is equal to the proportion of genes of that type in the starting state.

5. MEAN FIRST PASSAGE TIME FOR ERGODIC CHAINS

In this section we shall show how the theory developed for absorbing chains can be used to give information about ergodic chains.

Consider an ergodic chain with transition matrix P. Let us change this chain into a new Markov chain by making one state, say s_j, into an absorbing state. We do this by replacing the jth row of P by a row with a 1 in the jth component and 0 otherwise. If we start at any state other than s_j this new process will behave exactly like the old one up to the first time that state s_j is reached. Since the original chain was an ergodic chain, it was possible to reach s_j from any other state. Hence the new chain will be an absorbing chain with a single absorbing state s_j. We know that for an absorbing chain the process will eventually reach an absorbing state no matter where it is started. Hence we know that, in the original chain, state s_j is sure to be reached, no matter what the starting state is. (By this we mean, of course, that the probability of reaching s_j approaches 1.)

Let N be the fundamental matrix for the new chain. The entries of N give the mean number of times in each state before absorption. In terms of the original chain these quantities represent the mean number of times in each of the states before reaching state s_j for the first time. The ith component of the vector NC gives the mean number of steps before absorption in the new chain, starting in state s_i. In terms of the old chain this is the mean number of steps required to reach state s_j for the first time, starting at state s_i. This is called the *mean first passage time* from s_i to s_j.

Example 1. Let us return to Example 3 of Section 2. We shall make this ergodic chain into an absorbing chain by making state 5 an absorbing state. For example, we might assume that food is placed in the center of

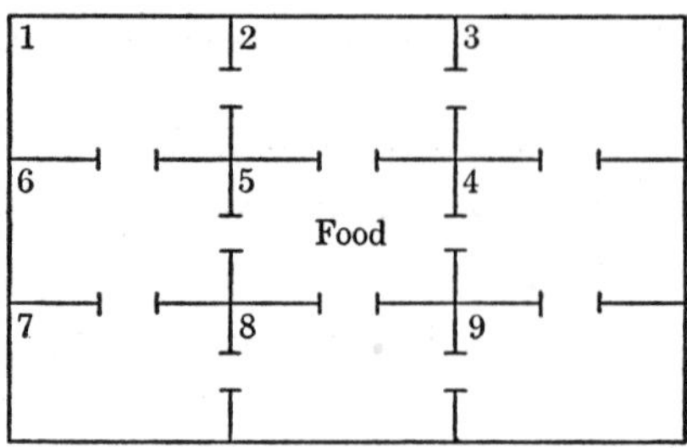

Figure 3

the maze and once the rat finds the food he stays to enjoy it. See Figure 3. The new transition matrix in canonical form is

$$P = \begin{array}{c} \\ 5 \\ 1 \\ 2 \\ 3 \\ 4 \\ 6 \\ 7 \\ 8 \\ 9 \end{array}\begin{array}{c} \begin{array}{c|cccccccc} 5 & 1 & 2 & 3 & 4 & 6 & 7 & 8 & 9 \end{array} \\ \left[\begin{array}{c|cccccccc} 1 & 0 & 0 & 0 & 0 & 0 & 0 & 0 & 0 \\ \hline 0 & 0 & \frac{1}{2} & 0 & 0 & \frac{1}{2} & 0 & 0 & 0 \\ \frac{1}{3} & \frac{1}{3} & 0 & \frac{1}{3} & 0 & 0 & 0 & 0 & 0 \\ 0 & 0 & \frac{1}{2} & 0 & \frac{1}{2} & 0 & 0 & 0 & 0 \\ \frac{1}{3} & 0 & 0 & \frac{1}{3} & 0 & 0 & 0 & 0 & \frac{1}{3} \\ \frac{1}{3} & \frac{1}{3} & 0 & 0 & 0 & 0 & \frac{1}{3} & 0 & 0 \\ 0 & 0 & 0 & 0 & 0 & \frac{1}{2} & 0 & \frac{1}{2} & 0 \\ \frac{1}{3} & 0 & 0 & 0 & 0 & 0 & \frac{1}{3} & 0 & \frac{1}{3} \\ 0 & 0 & 0 & 0 & \frac{1}{2} & 0 & 0 & \frac{1}{2} & 0 \end{array}\right] \end{array}.$$

If we compute the fundamental matrix N we obtain

$$N = \frac{1}{8}\begin{array}{c} \begin{array}{cccccccc} 1 & 2 & 3 & 4 & 6 & 7 & 8 & 9 \end{array} \\ \left[\begin{array}{cccccccc} 14 & 9 & 4 & 3 & 9 & 4 & 3 & 2 \\ 6 & 14 & 6 & 4 & 4 & 2 & 2 & 2 \\ 4 & 9 & 14 & 9 & 3 & 2 & 3 & 4 \\ 2 & 4 & 6 & 14 & 2 & 2 & 4 & 6 \\ 6 & 4 & 2 & 2 & 14 & 6 & 4 & 2 \\ 4 & 3 & 2 & 3 & 9 & 14 & 9 & 4 \\ 2 & 2 & 2 & 4 & 4 & 6 & 14 & 6 \\ 2 & 3 & 4 & 9 & 3 & 4 & 9 & 14 \end{array}\right] \end{array}\begin{array}{c} \\ 1 \\ 2 \\ 3 \\ 4 \\ 6 \\ 7 \\ 8 \\ 9 \end{array}.$$

The mean times to absorption are given by the vector NC, which is

$$NC = \begin{array}{c} 1 \\ 2 \\ 3 \\ 4 \\ 6 \\ 7 \\ 8 \\ 9 \end{array}\left[\begin{array}{c} 6 \\ 5 \\ 6 \\ 5 \\ 5 \\ 6 \\ 5 \\ 6 \end{array}\right].$$

We see that, starting from compartment 1, it will take on the average 6 steps to reach food. It is clear from symmetry that we should get the same answer for starting at state 3, 7, or 9. It is also clear that it should take one more step, starting at one of these states, than it would starting at 2, 4, 6, or 8. Some of the results obtained from N are not so obvious. For instance, we note that the mean number of times in the starting state is $\frac{14}{8}$ regardless of the state in which we start.

A quantity that is closely related to the mean first passage time is the mean recurrence time which is defined as follows. Assume that we start in state s_i. Consider the length of time before we return to s_i. It is clear that we must return, since we either return on the first step or go to some other state and from any other state we know that we will eventually reach s_i. The mean time required is called the *mean recurrence time.*

Theorem. For an ergodic Markov chain, the mean recurrence time for state s_i is $1/w_i$, where w_i is the ith component of the fixed probability vector for the transition matrix.

Proof. Consider the mean first passage time from s_i to the state s_j. This may be computed as follows: We consider the mean number of steps required, given the outcome of the first step, and multiply by the probability that this outcome occurs, and add. If the first step is to s_j the mean number of steps required is 1. If it is to some other state s_k the mean number of steps required is m_{kj} plus the one step already taken. Thus

$$m_{ij} = p_{ij} + \sum_{k \neq j} p_{ik}(m_{kj} + 1),$$

or since

$$\sum_k p_{ik} = 1,$$

$$m_{ij} = \sum_{k \neq j} p_{ik} m_{kj} + 1. \tag{1}$$

If we define m_{ii} to be the mean recurrence time for state s_i, then (1) holds for every choice of i and j. Let M be the matrix with entries m_{ij} and let M_{dg} be the matrix with diagonal entries the same as M but with all other entries 0. Let C be the r-by-r matrix with all entries 1. Then (1) may be written in matrix form as follows:

$$M = P(M - M_{dg}) + C. \tag{2}$$

Multiplying both sides of (2) by the fixed probability vector W gives

$$WM = WP(M - M_{dg}) + WC.$$

But since W is a fixed vector for P, then $WP = W$. Also since W is a probability vector, the sum of its components is 1. Hence

$WC = (1, 1, \ldots, 1)$. Thus we have

$$WM = W(M - M_{dg}) + (1 \quad 1 \quad \ldots \quad 1)$$

or

$$WM_{dg} = (1 \quad 1 \quad \ldots \quad 1).$$

But WM_{dg} is a row vector with ith component $w_i m_{ii}$. Hence $w_i m_{ii} = 1$ or

$$m_{ii} = 1/w_i$$

as was to be proved.

Example 1 (Continued). In Section 2 we found that the fixed probability vector for our example was

$$W = (\tfrac{1}{12} \quad \tfrac{1}{8} \quad \tfrac{1}{12} \quad \tfrac{1}{8} \quad \tfrac{1}{6} \quad \tfrac{1}{8} \quad \tfrac{1}{12} \quad \tfrac{1}{8} \quad \tfrac{1}{12}).$$

Hence the mean recurrences are given by the reciprocals of these probabilities. That is,

$$(12 \quad 8 \quad 12 \quad 8 \quad 6 \quad 8 \quad 12 \quad 8 \quad 12).$$

Example 2. In Section 7 of Chapter 3 we found that the weather in the Land of Oz could be represented by a Markov chain with states rain, nice, and snow. In Section 2 we found that the limiting vector was $W = (\tfrac{2}{5} \quad \tfrac{1}{5} \quad \tfrac{2}{5})$. From this we see that the mean number of days between rainy days is $\tfrac{5}{2}$, between nice days is 5, and between snowy days is $\tfrac{5}{2}$.

EXERCISES

1. In Example 3 of Section 1, make Dartmouth an absorbing state. Find the fundamental matrix and interpret your results in terms of the original chain. [*Ans.* $N = \begin{pmatrix} 10 & \frac{10}{3} \\ 5 & \frac{10}{3} \end{pmatrix}$.]

2. In Example 5 of Section 1 find for each state the mean first passage time to state 0. Do the same for state 2 and compare your results.

3. In Example 1 of Section 1 assume that the President says that he will run. Find the mean length of time before the first time the answer is passed on incorrectly.

4. Find the mean recurrence time for each state in Example 5 of Section 1. [*Ans.* $(8 \quad \tfrac{8}{3} \quad \tfrac{8}{3} \quad 8)$.]

5. Find the mean recurrence time for each state for Example 1 of Section 1.

6. A die is rolled repeatedly. Show by the results of this section that the mean time between occurrences of any given number is 6.

7. For the Land of Oz example, make rain into an absorbing state and find the fundamental matrix. Interpret the results obtained from this chain in terms of the original chain. [*Ans.* $\begin{pmatrix} \frac{4}{3} & \frac{4}{3} \\ \frac{2}{3} & \frac{8}{3} \end{pmatrix}$.]

8. For the Land of Oz example, write down the nine equations obtained by considering (1) for every i and j. Show then that the resulting equations have a unique solution.

9. Interpret the results of Exercise 7 of Section 4 in terms of the original process.

10. In Example 1 of this section assume that food is placed in compartment 5 and a trap is set in compartment 1. Form a Markov chain by making these states absorbing. Find the fundamental matrix N and the vectors NC and NR. Interpret your results in terms of the original chain.

11. In Exercise 17 of Section 2, find the mean number of days between days when no machine is working. If both machines are in working condition at the end of a particular day, what is the mean number of days before the first day that no machine is working?

[*Ans.* $(1 + p^2)/p^2$; $(1 + p)/p^2$.]

6. MARKOV CHAIN EXAMPLES FROM PHYSICS: ENTROPY

Many interesting examples of Markov chains have arisen in physics, particularly the study of gas mixtures. In the present section we shall discuss a simplified model of the molecular mixing of gases that was developed by two physicists named Ehrenfest. We also consider two simple diffusion models. Although the number of gas molecules considered here will be much smaller than can be physically observed, the kinds of result that we will obtain will help explain what is observed in experiments.

Example 1. In the first example, which is a model for the mixing of two gases, we consider a collection of $2n$ balls, of which n are white and n are black. They are placed in two urns in such a way that there are n balls in each urn. A single experiment consists in choosing a ball at random from each urn and placing the ball obtained from the first urn into the second urn, and the ball obtained from the second into the first urn. As a state for the process we take the number j of black balls in the first urn. Then there are $n - j$ white balls in the first urn, $n - j$ black balls and j white balls in the second urn. Suppose that we are at state j. Then, if the same color ball is chosen from each urn we remain at state j. If a black ball is chosen from urn 1 and a white ball from urn 2, we move to state $j - 1$. And if a white ball is chosen from urn 1 and a black ball from urn 2 we move to state $j + 1$. It is not possible to go from state j to any other state except these. The transition probabilities are given by (see Exercise 1):

$$p_{j,j-1} = \left(\frac{j}{n}\right)^2,$$

$$p_{j,j} = 2\frac{j(n-j)}{n^2},$$

$$p_{j,j+1} = \left(\frac{n-j}{n}\right)^2,$$

$$p_{jk} = 0, \quad \text{otherwise.}$$

It is easy to see that this Markov chain is ergodic. (In fact it is regular; see Exercise 2.) The physicist would be interested in the relative composition of the two urns after a large number of steps.

In order to answer the question it would be possible to solve for the fixed vector. But it is more instructive to try to guess the answer. It seems reasonable that after a large number of exchanges the balls should be quite mixed up and the probability that any particular n balls should be in urn 1 should be the same as if we simply took n balls at random from the $2n$ balls, and placed them in urn 1. If this were done, the probability that we would put j black balls in the urn is

$$(1) \qquad p_j = \frac{\binom{n}{j}\binom{n}{n-j}}{\binom{2n}{n}} = \frac{\binom{n}{j}^2}{\binom{2n}{n}}.$$

It can be checked that these probabilities do indeed satisfy the necessary equations for a fixed probability vector for the matrix. A special case of this problem is given in Exercise 3.

Example 2. Our second example is a model for the way in which the molecules of a gas would behave if put in a compartment in which there was a thin permeable membrane that divided the compartment into two cells. We again state the problem in terms of the probability urn model.

Imagine that we have two urns and $2n$ balls, this time of a single color. Every second one of the $2n$ balls is chosen at random and moved from the urn that it was in to the other urn. If there are j balls in the first urn then with probability $j/2n$ we take one of them out and put it in the second urn, and with probability $(2n - j)/2n$ we take a ball from the second urn and put it in the first urn. We let the number j of balls in the first urn be the state of the system. Then from state j we can pass only to state $j - 1$ and $j + 1$, and the transition probabilities are given by:

$$p_{j,j-1} = \frac{j}{2n},$$

$$p_{j,j+1} = \frac{2n-j}{2n},$$

$$p_{jk} = 0, \quad \text{otherwise.}$$

This defines the transition matrix of an ergodic but not regular Markov chain (see Exercise 4). Here, again, the physicist is interested in long-term predictions about the state occupied.

Again our intuition can be used to guess the answer. After many repetitions of the above mixing process we would expect, regardless of the initial distribution of balls, that the process should be equivalent to putting each ball in an urn chosen at random. This is an independent trials process. The probability that we would put j balls in the first urn is

$$p_j = \frac{\binom{2n}{j}}{2^{2n}}. \tag{2}$$

In Chapter 2, Section 9, we defined the entropy of a system of the type considered as $\log \binom{2n}{i}$ when the system is in state i. Note that the entropy differs from the logarithm of the ith component of the fixed probability vector only by a constant. We observed that the more even the division of molecules the larger the entropy.

The long-range prediction would thus say that the states of large entropy are more probable on the average than states of low entropy. In thermodynamics there is considerable interest in the question of the likelihood that a system will move from a state of high entropy to a state of low entropy. From the results of the previous section we know that from any one state we will reach any other state at some time. Hence we must expect transitions from high entropy states to low entropy states. However, the time required to go from high entropy to low entropy is very much greater than the time required to go from a low entropy state to a high entropy state.

Example 2 (Continued). Let us consider the special case of the situation described in Example 2 in which there are 4 balls. Then there are five states corresponding to there being 0, 1, 2, 3, or 4 balls in the first urn. The transition matrix is

$$P = \begin{array}{c} \\ 0 \\ 1 \\ 2 \\ 3 \\ 4 \end{array} \begin{array}{c} \begin{array}{ccccc} 0 & 1 & 2 & 3 & 4 \end{array} \\ \begin{pmatrix} 0 & 1 & 0 & 0 & 0 \\ \frac{1}{4} & 0 & \frac{3}{4} & 0 & 0 \\ 0 & \frac{1}{2} & 0 & \frac{1}{2} & 0 \\ 0 & 0 & \frac{3}{4} & 0 & \frac{1}{4} \\ 0 & 0 & 0 & 1 & 0 \end{pmatrix} \end{array}.$$

The fixed vector is

$$W = \left(\tfrac{1}{16} \quad \tfrac{4}{16} \quad \tfrac{6}{16} \quad \tfrac{4}{16} \quad \tfrac{1}{16}\right),$$

as can easily be checked. From the fixed vector we can immediately write down the mean recurrence time for each state. Thus if we start in state 0 it takes, on the average, 16 steps before we return to it. Similarly, starting at state 1 it takes an average of 4 steps, and starting at state 2 it takes an average of $2\frac{2}{3}$ steps before returning. The mean recurrence time for state 3 is the same as for state 1, and the mean recurrence time for state 4 is the same as for state 0.

The entropy of the system is $\log 1 = 0$ when it is in states 0 or 4, $\log 4$ when it is in states 1 or 3, and $\log 6$ when it is in state 2.

Let us consider now the mean first passage time to state 0, that is, to a low entropy state. To find these means we make state 0 into an absorbing state. Then the new transition matrix is

$$P' = \begin{array}{c} 0 \\ 1 \\ 2 \\ 3 \\ 4 \end{array} \left(\begin{array}{c|cccc} 1 & 0 & 0 & 0 & 0 \\ \hline \frac{1}{4} & 0 & \frac{3}{4} & 0 & 0 \\ 0 & \frac{1}{2} & 0 & \frac{1}{2} & 0 \\ 0 & 0 & \frac{3}{4} & 0 & \frac{1}{4} \\ 0 & 0 & 0 & 1 & 0 \end{array}\right).$$

The fundamental matrix N' is

$$N' = \begin{array}{c} \\ 1 \\ 2 \\ 3 \\ 4 \end{array} \begin{array}{c} \begin{array}{cccc} 1 & 2 & 3 & 4 \end{array} \\ \left(\begin{array}{cccc} 4 & 6 & 4 & 1 \\ 4 & 8 & \frac{16}{3} & \frac{4}{3} \\ 4 & 8 & \frac{20}{3} & \frac{5}{3} \\ 4 & 8 & \frac{20}{3} & \frac{8}{3} \end{array}\right) \end{array}.$$

By computing the product $N'C$, where C is a 4-component column vector all of whose entries are ones, we can obtain the mean number of steps before absorption depending on the starting state. This is

$$N'C = \begin{array}{c} 1 \\ 2 \\ 3 \\ 4 \end{array} \begin{pmatrix} 15 \\ 18\frac{2}{3} \\ 20\frac{1}{3} \\ 21\frac{1}{3} \end{pmatrix}.$$

Notice that all these times are very large, even the one from state 1. Thus we can expect the process to take a long time to reach a state of minimum entropy.

Let us now find the mean first passage time to the state of maximum entropy, i.e., state 2. For this we make state 2 absorbing. Our new transition matrix is then

$$P'' = \begin{array}{c} \\ 2 \\ 0 \\ 1 \\ 3 \\ 4 \end{array} \begin{array}{c} \begin{array}{c|cccc} 2 & 0 & 1 & 3 & 4 \end{array} \\ \left(\begin{array}{c|cccc} 1 & 0 & 0 & 0 & 0 \\ \hline 0 & 0 & 1 & 0 & 0 \\ \frac{3}{4} & \frac{1}{4} & 0 & 0 & 0 \\ \frac{3}{4} & 0 & 0 & 0 & \frac{1}{4} \\ 0 & 0 & 0 & 1 & 0 \end{array}\right) \end{array}.$$

The fundamental matrix is

$$N'' = \begin{array}{c} \\ 0 \\ 1 \\ 3 \\ 4 \end{array}\begin{array}{c} \begin{array}{cccc} 0 & 1 & 3 & 4 \end{array} \\ \begin{pmatrix} \frac{4}{3} & \frac{4}{3} & 0 & 0 \\ \frac{1}{3} & \frac{4}{3} & 0 & 0 \\ 0 & 0 & \frac{4}{3} & \frac{1}{3} \\ 0 & 0 & \frac{4}{3} & \frac{4}{3} \end{pmatrix} \end{array},$$

and

$$N''C = \begin{array}{c} 0 \\ 1 \\ 3 \\ 4 \end{array}\begin{pmatrix} 2\frac{2}{3} \\ 1\frac{2}{3} \\ 1\frac{2}{3} \\ 2\frac{2}{3} \end{pmatrix}.$$

Notice that these numbers are approximately a tenth as large as the components of $N'C$, indicating again that the process takes much less time to go to state 2 than to state 0 or state 4.

Example 3. As a final example, consider a region divided as in Figure 4. When a molecule leaves one region it is equally likely to go to each of the other two regions. The urn model for this is the following: We have $3n$ balls, all of the same color, distributed among three urns. Suppose there are i balls in the first urn, j in the second, and k in the third. Then with probability $i/3n$ we take a ball from the first urn and put it with equal probability in each of the other two urns. Similarly for the other urns. In order to describe this process we shall first perform a combining together or "lumping" of states in order to reduce the number of states and hence the size of the transition matrix. Lumping of states must be done with care (see Exercise 10).

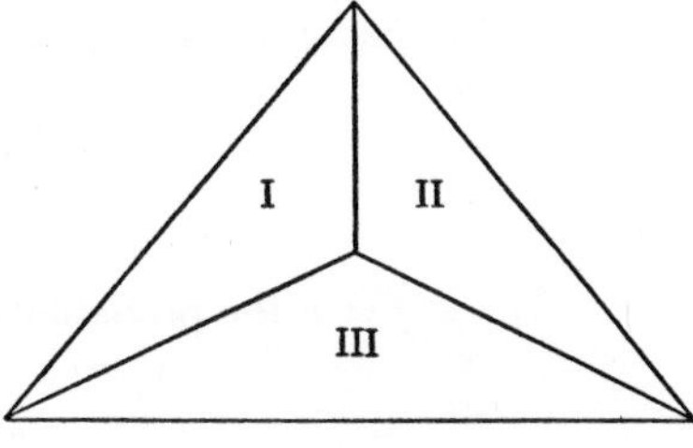

Figure 4

A state in the new process will be a triple of numbers (i, j, k), where $i \geq j \geq k$. This means that we have combined all the states that have the same three numbers regardless of which region contained the particular number in question. The transition probabilities may now be described:

The process goes from state (i, j, k) to states $(i - 1, j + 1, k)$ and $(i - 1, j, k + 1)$ each with probability $i/6n$.

The process goes from state (i, j, k) to states $(i + 1, j - 1, k)$ and $(i, j - 1, k + 1)$ each with probability $j/6n$.

The process goes from state (i, j, k) to states $(i + 1, j, k - 1)$ and $(i, j + 1, k - 1)$, each with probability $k/6n$.

In writing the states to which the process moves it is assumed that the numbers are rearranged, if necessary, in order of decreasing size.

If we wish to guess the limiting probabilities we can do so as before, but we must take into account the lumping of states that we have carried out. If there had been no lumping then we would expect that after a long period of time the probability of state (i, j, k) would be given by the expression

$$\frac{\binom{3n}{i, j, k}}{3^{3n}}.$$

However, when states are combined together their corresponding probabilities must be added. If $i = j = k = n$, then that state will not have been combined with any other; if $i = j \neq k$ or $i \neq j = k$, then there will have been exactly three such states combined together; and if $i \neq j \neq k$ then there will have been six states combined together. We thus have three kinds of limiting probability terms:

If $i = j = k = n$, then the probability of the state is

$$\frac{\binom{3n}{n, n, n}}{3^{3n}}.$$

If $i = j \neq k$ or $i \neq j = k$ the probability of the state is

$$\frac{\binom{3n}{i, j, k}}{3^{3n-1}}.$$

If $i \neq j \neq k$ the probability of the state is

$$\frac{2\binom{3n}{i, j, k}}{3^{3n-1}}.$$

In order to illustrate the problem we consider the case where $n = 2$, that is, where we have six balls to distribute among the three urns. Before combining states we have 28 states, and after combining we have seven (see Exercise 5). The transition matrix, after combining states, is

$$P = \begin{array}{c} \\ 6,0,0 \\ 5,1,0 \\ 4,2,0 \\ 4,1,1 \\ 3,3,0 \\ 3,2,1 \\ 2,2,2 \end{array} \begin{array}{c} \begin{array}{ccccccc} 6,0,0 & 5,1,0 & 4,2,0 & 4,1,1 & 3,3,0 & 3,2,1 & 2,2,2 \end{array} \\ \begin{bmatrix} 0 & 1 & 0 & 0 & 0 & 0 & 0 \\ \frac{1}{12} & \frac{1}{12} & \frac{5}{12} & \frac{5}{12} & 0 & 0 & 0 \\ 0 & \frac{1}{6} & 0 & \frac{1}{6} & \frac{1}{3} & \frac{1}{3} & 0 \\ 0 & \frac{1}{6} & \frac{1}{6} & 0 & 0 & \frac{2}{3} & 0 \\ 0 & 0 & \frac{1}{2} & 0 & 0 & \frac{1}{2} & 0 \\ 0 & 0 & \frac{1}{12} & \frac{1}{6} & \frac{1}{12} & \frac{5}{12} & \frac{1}{4} \\ 0 & 0 & 0 & 0 & 0 & 1 & 0 \end{bmatrix} \end{array}.$$

The limiting probability vector computed from the formulas given above is:

$$W = \left(\tfrac{1}{243} \quad \tfrac{4}{81} \quad \tfrac{10}{81} \quad \tfrac{10}{81} \quad \tfrac{20}{243} \quad \tfrac{40}{81} \quad \tfrac{10}{81}\right).$$

For a system considered in this example the entropy of a state is the logarithm of the number of distributions of the molecules that would yield the state under consideration. We consider the states before lumping. For a state with i balls in urn 1, j balls in urn 2, and k balls in urn 3, the entropy is

$$\log \binom{3n}{i, j, k}.$$

In the above example the types of states possible and their entropies are

Type of state	Entropy of state
6, 0, 0	$\log 1 = 0$
5, 1, 0	$\log 6$
4, 2, 0	$\log 15$
3, 3, 0	$\log 20$
4, 1, 1	$\log 30$
3, 2, 1	$\log 60$
2, 2, 2	$\log 90$

Observe that state 2, 2, 2 has the largest entropy. Other interesting facts can be observed, such as the fact that the entropy of state 3, 3, 0 is smaller than that of state 3, 2, 1, etc.

It can be shown that the mean time to go from any state to the lowest entropy state, 2, 2, 2, is no more than 12, while the mean number of steps needed to go from state 2, 2, 2, to state 6, 0, 0 is approximately 280.

As in the previous example the most uniform distribution has the largest entropy. The proof depends upon properties of the multinomial coefficients. We shall prove this fact for Example 3. The proof of the same fact for the other examples or for more complicated cases is exactly analogous.

Theorem. In Example 3 the entropy of the system when in state (n, n, n) is greater than when it is in any other state.

Proof. Consider some other state (i, j, k) where $i + j + k = 3n$. By renumbering the urns, if necessary, we can assume that $i \geq j \geq k$, and, of course, at least one of these inequalities is strict. We know that:

the entropy of the system when in state (n, n, n) is $\log \binom{3n}{n, n, n}$;

the entropy of the system when in state (i, j, k) is $\log \binom{3n}{i, j, k}$.

Now it is possible to go from state (n, n, n) to state (i, j, k) by a series of steps in which a 1 is taken from one of the entries of the triple and added to an entry to its left. Let us show that at each such step the entropy is decreased. Consider the step from state (r, s, t) to $(r+1, s, t-1)$, for example. The ratio of the corresponding multinomial coefficients is

$$\frac{\binom{3n}{r, s, t}}{\binom{3n}{r+1, s, t-1}} = \frac{(r+1)!s!(t-1)!}{r!s!t!} = \frac{(r+1)}{t} > 1,$$

where the last inequality comes from the fact that $r \geq t$. It is easy to show that all other such elementary steps also cause a decrease in entropy. And since it is possible to go from state (n, n, n) to state (i, j, k) by a sequence of such elementary steps, at each step decreasing the entropy, the entropy at (i, j, k) is less than the entropy at (n, n, n).

EXERCISES

1. Show that the transition probabilities and equation (1) are correct for Example 1.

2. In Example 1 show that $p_{jj} = 0$ only if $j = 0$ or n. Show that P^2 has all positive diagonal entries. Then use the results of Exercise 14 of Section 3 to show that the chain is regular.

3. Write the transition matrix for Example 1 in the case that $n = 3$. Show that the fixed probability vector is given by (1).

4. Write the transition matrix for Example 2 for the case that $n = 3$. Show that the chain is ergodic but not regular. Check to see that the limiting probability vector is given by (2).

5. In Example 3 use Exercise 11 of Chapter 2, Section 9 to show that the number of states, before combining, is

$$\binom{3n + r - 1}{3n}.$$

   Use this formula to show that there are 28 states for the case when $n = 2$ and $r = 3$. How many states would there be when $r = 3$ and $n = 3$? When $r = 3$ and $n = 4$?

6. In Example 3, find the mean recurrence times and show that these are generally (but not always) smaller for states of higher entropy.

7. Let $\mathbf{f}_m$ be the outcome function for the mth draw in Example 2. If m is large we may assume

$$\mathbf{Pr}[\mathbf{f}_m = j] = \binom{2n}{j} 2^{-2n}.$$

Find the mean and variance of $\mathbf{f}_m$. [*Hint:* Compare with the function giving the number of heads in $2m$ tosses of a coin.]

8. In Example 2 with $n = 2$, assume that the process is started in state 4. Let $\mathbf{f}_1$, $\mathbf{f}_2$, $\mathbf{f}_3$ be the first three outcome functions. Find the mean and variance for each function. Do the same assuming the process starts in state 2.

[*Partial Ans.* Starting in state 4 the means are $\mathbf{M}[\mathbf{f}_1] = 3$, $\mathbf{M}[\mathbf{f}_2] = 2\frac{1}{2}$, $\mathbf{M}[\mathbf{f}_3] = 2\frac{1}{4}$.]

9. Consider a regular Markov chain with transition matrix

$$P = \begin{matrix} & \begin{matrix} 1 & 2 & 3 \end{matrix} \\ \begin{matrix} 1 \\ 2 \\ 3 \end{matrix} & \begin{pmatrix} 0 & 0 & 1 \\ \frac{1}{3} & \frac{1}{3} & \frac{1}{3} \\ \frac{1}{2} & 0 & \frac{1}{2} \end{pmatrix} \end{matrix}.$$

Form a two-state process by considering the set (1, 2) to be one state and 3 the second state. Show that the knowledge that the system was in the set (1, 2) the last two times gives more information than the knowledge that the system was in the set (1, 2) last time. This means that the lumped process is not a Markov chain.

10. A sufficient condition that a Markov chain can be combined and still yield a Markov chain is as follows. Let $E_1, E_2, \ldots, E_r$ be the sets of states lumped together. The probability of moving from a state in E_i to the set E_j should be the same for any state in E_i. Verify that this condition is met in the lumping carried out in Example 3. Show that it is not the case in Exercise 9.

7. RANDOM WALKS

Let us consider a game played on a plane grid with an interior point selected as a starting point. A marker is placed at this point. This marker is moved to a neighboring point according to preassigned probabilities, and the game continues till one of the boundary points is reached. Each of the players of the game is assigned some of the boundary points and the winner is determined by noting which of the boundary points is reached.

In such a game there are two key questions we may want to ask: First of all we will want to know the probability of ending up at each of the boundary points. Secondly we may be interested in knowing the average length of such a game. Markov chain theory easily provides the answer to these questions, and even to such questions as to how many times we expect to pass through each point in a given game.

Example. In Figure 5 we find a grid with 7 interior and 10 boundary points. The interior points are numbered, and the boundary points are lettered. Any one of the interior points may be selected as a starting point, and we will be particularly interested in starting at the "center," i.e., at point 3. We will assume that the marker is moved with equal probability to each of the four neighboring points.

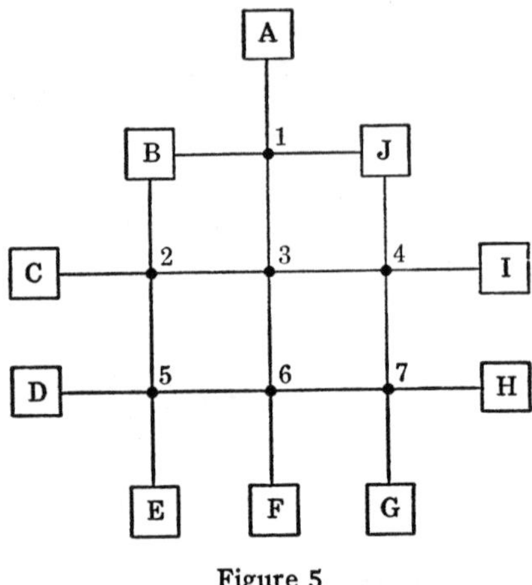

Figure 5

Since the boundary states are absorbing, this is an absorbing Markov chain. The lettered states are absorbing states, and the numbered states are transient states. The chain is determined by the two matrices (see Section 4).

$$Q = \begin{array}{c} \\ 1 \\ 2 \\ 3 \\ 4 \\ 5 \\ 6 \\ 7 \end{array} \begin{array}{c} \begin{array}{ccccccc} 1 & 2 & 3 & 4 & 5 & 6 & 7 \end{array} \\ \begin{bmatrix} 0 & 0 & \frac{1}{4} & 0 & 0 & 0 & 0 \\ 0 & 0 & \frac{1}{4} & 0 & \frac{1}{4} & 0 & 0 \\ \frac{1}{4} & \frac{1}{4} & 0 & \frac{1}{4} & 0 & \frac{1}{4} & 0 \\ 0 & 0 & \frac{1}{4} & 0 & 0 & 0 & \frac{1}{4} \\ 0 & \frac{1}{4} & 0 & 0 & 0 & \frac{1}{4} & 0 \\ 0 & 0 & \frac{1}{4} & 0 & \frac{1}{4} & 0 & \frac{1}{4} \\ 0 & 0 & 0 & \frac{1}{4} & 0 & \frac{1}{4} & 0 \end{bmatrix} \end{array},$$

$$R = \begin{array}{c} \\ 1 \\ 2 \\ 3 \\ 4 \\ 5 \\ 6 \\ 7 \end{array} \begin{array}{c} \begin{array}{cccccccccc} A & B & C & D & E & F & G & H & I & J \end{array} \\ \begin{bmatrix} \frac{1}{4} & \frac{1}{4} & 0 & 0 & 0 & 0 & 0 & 0 & 0 & \frac{1}{4} \\ 0 & \frac{1}{4} & \frac{1}{4} & 0 & 0 & 0 & 0 & 0 & 0 & 0 \\ 0 & 0 & 0 & 0 & 0 & 0 & 0 & 0 & 0 & 0 \\ 0 & 0 & 0 & 0 & 0 & 0 & 0 & 0 & \frac{1}{4} & \frac{1}{4} \\ 0 & 0 & 0 & \frac{1}{4} & \frac{1}{4} & 0 & 0 & 0 & 0 & 0 \\ 0 & 0 & 0 & 0 & 0 & \frac{1}{4} & 0 & 0 & 0 & 0 \\ 0 & 0 & 0 & 0 & 0 & 0 & \frac{1}{4} & \frac{1}{4} & 0 & 0 \end{bmatrix} \end{array}.$$

We know that all the quantities that interest us can be computed in terms of $(I - Q)^{-1}$, the fundamental matrix, denoted by N. The components of N give the mean number of times that we expect the marker to be in each transient state.

$$N = (I - Q)^{-1} = \begin{array}{c} \\ 1 \\ 2 \\ 3 \\ 4 \\ 5 \\ 6 \\ 7 \end{array} \begin{array}{c} \begin{array}{ccccccc} 1 & 2 & 3 & 4 & 5 & 6 & 7 \end{array} \\ \begin{bmatrix} 2415 & 225 & 780 & 225 & 120 & 255 & 120 \\ 225 & 2639 & 900 & 271 & 776 & 465 & 184 \\ 780 & 900 & 3120 & 900 & 480 & 1020 & 480 \\ 225 & 271 & 900 & 2639 & 184 & 465 & 776 \\ 120 & 776 & 480 & 184 & 2624 & 840 & 256 \\ 255 & 465 & 1020 & 465 & 840 & 2895 & 840 \\ 120 & 184 & 480 & 776 & 256 & 840 & 2624 \end{bmatrix} \end{array} \cdot \frac{1}{2220}.$$

Let us suppose that we start the random walk in the center state. Then the third row of N (denoted by N_3) gives us the mean number of times in each state. These entries can be simplified by dividing numerator and denominator by 60. This yields

$$N_3 = \tfrac{1}{37} \cdot (13 \;\; 15 \;\; 52 \;\; 15 \;\; 8 \;\; 17 \;\; 8).$$

The sum of these components, $\frac{128}{37}$, is the mean number of steps needed to reach the boundary. This is approximately 3.5. We see from Figure 5 that it must take at least 2 steps to reach the boundary, and we find that on the average it takes about $3\frac{1}{2}$. We know (see Section 4) that the probabilities of ending up at the various boundary points are given by the NR matrix. If we start in the center state, we need the third row of NR, which is N_3R.

$$B_3 = N_3R = \tfrac{1}{148} \cdot (13 \;\; 28 \;\; 15 \;\; 8 \;\; 8 \;\; 17 \;\; 8 \;\; 8 \;\; 15 \;\; 28).$$

This provides the answer for the case that we start in the center state. For any other starting state we proceed similarly.

The solution of the most general game played on a plane grid is exactly analogous. We number the interior points $1, 2, \ldots, s$ and the boundary points $1, 2, \ldots, r$. We then have an s-by-s matrix Q giving the probabilities of transition from a given interior point to another interior point. We also have the s-by-r matrix R giving the probabilities of stepping from a given interior point to a given boundary point. We know that the entries of the matrix $N = (I - Q)^{-1}$ tell us how many times we can expect to be in each interior state before hitting the boundary. If, for example, we want to start at interior point number 1, then the first row of N, call it N_1, will furnish this information. The mean number of steps needed to reach the boundary is the sum of the entries of this row. The probability of reaching a given boundary state is found in N_1R; that is, the jth component of N_1R gives us the probability of ending up at boundary point j if we start at interior point 1.

EXERCISES

Exercises 1–7 refer to the plane grid shown in Figure 6. A game is played on this grid by choosing a starting (interior) point, and moving with equal probability to one of the four neighboring points, till a boundary point is reached.

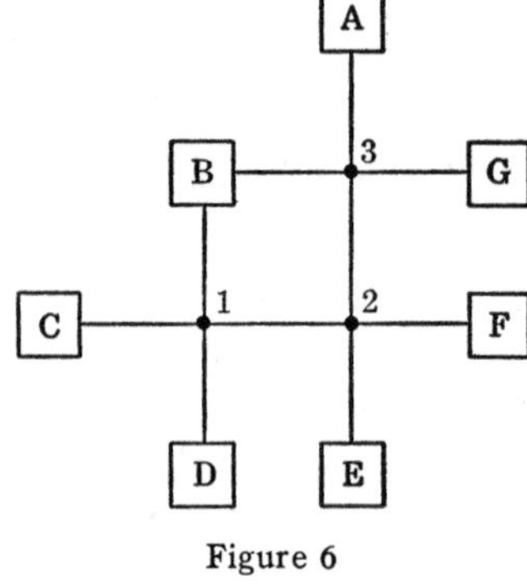

Figure 6

1. Set up the Q and R matrices. [*Hint:* Q is 3-by-3 and R is 3-by-7.]
2. Find the N matrix. If we start at point 1, how many times on the average can we expect to be in points 2 and 3? [*Ans.* $\frac{2}{7}$, $\frac{1}{14}$.]
3. For each possible starting position calculate the mean number of steps needed to reach the boundary. [*Ans.* $\frac{10}{7}$, $\frac{12}{7}$, $\frac{10}{7}$.]
4. For each possible starting point find the probability of ending up at the various boundary points.
5. We choose point 1 as the starting position. Player I wins if the marker ends up at points C or D, and player II wins otherwise. Show that the game is favorable to player I and find the odds in his favor. [*Ans.* 15 : 13.]
6. Suppose that the starting position is decided by tossing two coins. If we get two heads we start at point 1, if two tails at point 2, otherwise at point 3. What is the probability of ending up at B? [*Ans.* $\frac{1}{4}$.]
7. Check the answers obtained in Exercise 4 by the method of Section 4.
8. In the game in Figure 5 we start at the center and player I wins if and only if the marker ends up at B, C, E, G, or I. Show that the game is fair.
9. In the game in Figure 5 we start at the center and player I wins if and only if the marker ends up at B, F, or J. What are the odds against him? [*Ans.* 75 : 73.]

Exercises 10–15 refer to the plane grid shown in Figure 7. The rules of the game are as for Figure 6.

10. Set up the Q and R matrices.
11. Find the N matrix. If we start at the center, and we do *not* count the

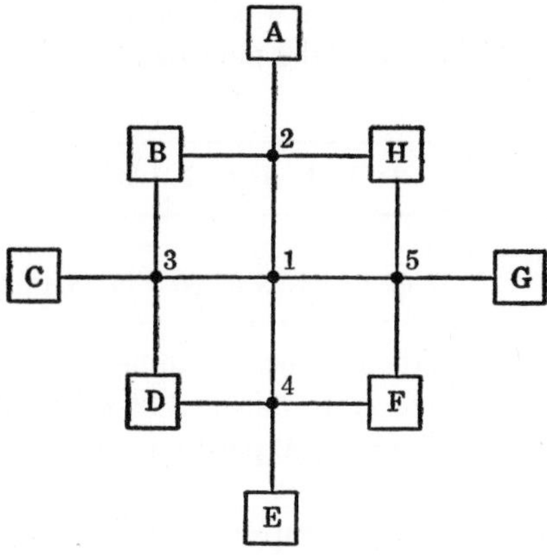

Figure 7

original position, show that we can expect to be the same number of times in each of the five interior positions.

12. Let us assume that from point 2 it takes an average of $\frac{5}{3}$ steps to reach the boundary. Use common sense arguments to find the mean number of steps needed from each of the other interior points. Use the N matrix to verify your answers.

13. Find the probabilities of ending up at each boundary point if we start at the center.

14. Find the probability of ending up at each boundary point if we start at point 2. [*Ans.* $\frac{13}{48}$ $\frac{7}{24}$ $\frac{1}{48}$ $\frac{1}{24}$ $\frac{1}{48}$ $\frac{1}{24}$ $\frac{1}{48}$ $\frac{7}{24}$.]

15. Using the grid in Figure 7 set up rules for three players so that they have equal chance of winning.

16. Suppose that we play the game described in the Example of the text, and that we receive prizes according to the following schedule: starting in state 3 we receive nothing if we land in states A, B, or C, \$1 in states D, E, F, and \$2 in the remaining states. Use B_3 calculated in the example to find the mean value of the prize we are to receive. [*Ans.* \$$\frac{151}{148}$.]

17. Generalize the result of Exercise 16 as follows: If there is a scale of payments at the boundary in a plane grid game, and if the payments are collected in a column vector V in the order in which boundary states are numbered, show that BV is the mean value of the payment.

18. Three sophomore research assistants at Dartmouth College carried out 148 random walks of the type discussed in the Example, always starting at point number 3. The following table shows the total number of times that the process was in each interior state (not counting the original position!) and the number of times that it ended at each boundary state.

State........	1	2	3	4	5	6	7	A	B	C	D	E	F	G	H	I	J
Number of times......	57	60	66	64	35	67	30	19	26	18	7	11	9	8	6	11	33

(a) From N_3 calculate the mean number of times that the process should be in each state during 148 random walks. (Remember that N_3 counts the original position, and then compare the results with the above table.)
(b) Carry out a similar comparison between the absorption probabilities given by B_3 and those estimated from the above table.
(c) How good is the estimate obtained from the 148 walks for the average number of steps needed to reach the boundary?
(d) Suppose that the game described in Exercise 8 were played with the results shown in the above table, what would the outcome be?

8. APPLICATION OF RANDOM WALKS TO ELECTRIC CIRCUITS

Let us suppose that in a complicated electric circuit the voltages at the boundary are fixed. We are then interested in finding the voltages at interior points. We will find that this type of problem is formally equivalent to a random walk problem.

Example 1. Let us suppose that we have the electric circuit of Figure 8. The voltages in the ten boundary positions are kept fixed at the indicated

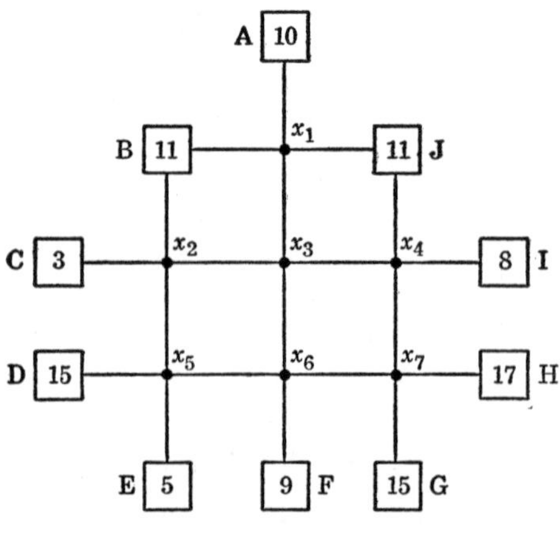

Figure 8

strengths. The various interior positions are connected to each other and to the boundary by equal resistances. The problem is to find the voltages at the interior positions.

It is an immediate consequence of Kirchhoff's laws that the voltage at an interior point must be the average of the four neighboring voltages. If we call the interior voltages $x_1, x_2, \ldots, x_7$ as in Figure 8, we arrive at the equations:

$$\begin{aligned}
x_1 &= \tfrac{1}{4}x_3 + \tfrac{1}{4} \cdot 10 + \tfrac{1}{4} \cdot 11 + \tfrac{1}{4} \cdot 11,\\
x_2 &= \tfrac{1}{4}x_3 + \tfrac{1}{4}x_5 + \tfrac{1}{4} \cdot 11 + \tfrac{1}{4} \cdot 3,\\
x_3 &= \tfrac{1}{4}x_1 + \tfrac{1}{4}x_2 + \tfrac{1}{4}x_4 + \tfrac{1}{4}x_6,\\
x_4 &= \tfrac{1}{4}x_3 + \tfrac{1}{4}x_7 + \tfrac{1}{4} \cdot 8 + \tfrac{1}{4} \cdot 11,\\
x_5 &= \tfrac{1}{4}x_2 + \tfrac{1}{4}x_6 + \tfrac{1}{4} \cdot 15 + \tfrac{1}{4} \cdot 5,\\
x_6 &= \tfrac{1}{4}x_3 + \tfrac{1}{4}x_5 + \tfrac{1}{4}x_7 + \tfrac{1}{4} \cdot 9,\\
x_7 &= \tfrac{1}{4}x_4 + \tfrac{1}{4}x_6 + \tfrac{1}{4} \cdot 15 + \tfrac{1}{4} \cdot 17.
\end{aligned}$$

To bring these equations into the usual form we would have to bring all the terms containing x_i's to the left side of the equation. Then we could solve the equations by our standard method. But it is worth comparing these equations with the matrices introduced in the Example in the last section. For this purpose we introduce two column vectors, one to represent the unknowns and one for the fixed voltages:

$$X = \begin{bmatrix} x_1 \\ x_2 \\ x_3 \\ x_4 \\ x_5 \\ x_6 \\ x_7 \end{bmatrix}, \qquad V = \begin{bmatrix} 10 \\ 11 \\ 3 \\ 15 \\ 5 \\ 9 \\ 15 \\ 17 \\ 8 \\ 11 \end{bmatrix}.$$

Then we note that our set of equations is of the form

$$X = QX + RV.$$

Hence

$$(I - Q)X = RV$$

$$X = (I - Q)^{-1}RV = NRV = BV.$$

Thus, for example, $x_3 = B_3V$. Using the B_3 vector computed in the last section we find that $x_3 = 10$.

In a similar problem involving a more complicated grid, we can also introduce the vectors X and V consisting of the variables and the fixed voltages, respectively. We know that voltage at any interior point is the average of the voltages at neighboring points. Thus we again find an equation of the form

(1) $$X = QX + RV,$$

where the first term is the contribution from neighboring interior states, and the second term from neighboring boundary states, if any. It is easily seen that if we set up the random walk on this grill with equal probabilities of transition to every neighboring state, then Q and R are the two transition matrices so denoted for Markov chains.

To bring our equations (1) into standard form we must collect the variables on the left side. This yields

(2) $$(I - Q)X = RV.$$

From physical considerations we believe that these equations have a solution no matter what V is. This would be assured if we knew that $I - Q$ has an inverse. If we tried to do this directly from the equations, it would involve a very lengthy computation. However, the existence of this inverse is assured from the Markov chain considerations. We know that the matrix has an inverse N which gives the mean number of times the process is in each interior state (see Section 4). Hence we can solve the equations (2) as in Example 1.

(3) $$X = NRV, \qquad X = BV.$$

This has a direct interpretation in terms of a game. Suppose that we play the game on the grid of the electric circuit, with equal probabilities of moving to neighboring points. Let us assume that we receive a payment at each boundary state, the amount of the payment given by the components of V. Then BV is the mean value of the payment we are to receive. (See Exercises 16 and 17 in the preceding section.)

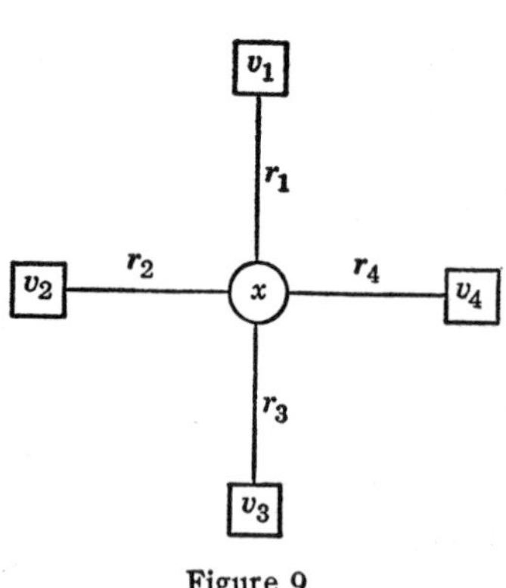

Figure 9

So far we have considered only a very specialized electrical problem. We have assumed that all the resistances connecting terminals were equal. Suppose now that we remove this restriction. Let us consider the simple network shown in Figure 9. The four voltages on the outside are known to be v_1, v_2, v_3, and v_4, while the resistances are r_1, r_2, r_3, and r_4. Let us call the unknown voltage at the center x. The total current flowing into the center from terminal j is $(v_j - x)/r_j$. By one of Kirchhoff's laws we know that the total current flowing into a terminal must be 0. Hence

$$(1/r_1)(v_1 - x) + (1/r_2)(v_2 - x) + (1/r_3)(v_3 - x) + (1/r_4)(v_4 - x) = 0.$$

Solving for x, we find that

$$x = \frac{(1/r_1)v_1 + (1/r_2)v_2 + (1/r_3)v_3 + (1/r_4)v_4}{(1/r_1) + (1/r_2) + (1/r_3) + (1/r_4)}.$$

This can be simplified by introducing the "normalized conductances." We define

$$p_j = \frac{1/r_j}{[(1/r_1) + (1/r_2) + (1/r_3) + (1/r_4)]} \tag{4}$$

and the solution can be written as

$$x = p_1v_1 + p_2v_2 + p_3v_3 + p_4v_4. \tag{5}$$

Since the sum of the p_j's is 1, this is again an average of the neighboring voltages, but the weights need no longer be equal. It is obvious, however, that such a circuit also has an analogous random walk, and that the treatment outlined above still holds, leading to the solution (3).

Example 2. Let us suppose that we have a network similar to that discussed in Exercises 1–7 of the last section, but with resistances as shown in Figure 10. The voltages are fixed on the boundaries as shown by the

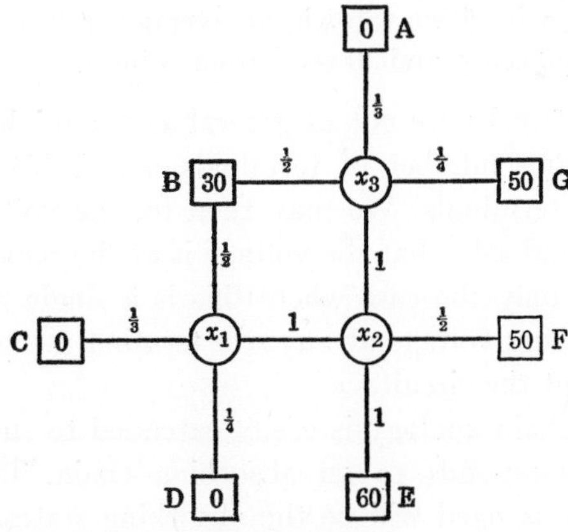

Figure 10

numbers in the boxes. We are to find the three interior voltages x_1, x_2, x_3. Two points are surrounded by resistances of 1, $\frac{1}{2}$, $\frac{1}{3}$, and $\frac{1}{4}$ units, hence the p_j's will be .1, .2, .3, and .4, respectively, according to formula (4). The remaining point is surrounded by 1, 1, 1, $\frac{1}{2}$, yielding p_j's of .2, .2, .2, .4. Thus we have the transition matrices

$$Q = \begin{pmatrix} 0 & .1 & 0 \\ .2 & 0 & .2 \\ 0 & .1 & 0 \end{pmatrix}, \qquad R = \begin{pmatrix} 0 & .2 & .3 & .4 & 0 & 0 & 0 \\ 0 & 0 & 0 & 0 & .2 & .4 & 0 \\ .3 & .2 & 0 & 0 & 0 & 0 & .4 \end{pmatrix}.$$

And the fixed voltage vector is

$$V = \begin{bmatrix} 0 \\ 30 \\ 0 \\ 0 \\ 60 \\ 50 \\ 50 \end{bmatrix}.$$

Hence $$N = (I - Q)^{-1} = \frac{1}{48}\begin{pmatrix} 49 & 5 & 1 \\ 10 & 50 & 10 \\ 1 & 5 & 49 \end{pmatrix}.$$

$$RV = \begin{pmatrix} 6 \\ 32 \\ 26 \end{pmatrix}, \qquad BV = N \cdot RV = \begin{pmatrix} 10 \\ 40 \\ 30 \end{pmatrix}.$$

Thus $x_1 = 10$, $x_2 = 40$, and $x_3 = 30$.

From our previous discussion we know that this result can also be interpreted in terms of a game. We play a game on the grid of Fig. 10. The transition probabilities are given by the normalized conductances (hence by the matrices Q and R shown above). A 30 cent prize is paid if we reach B, a 60 cent prize at E, and 50 cent prizes at F and G. Then by starting at point 1 we will win an average of 10 cents, from point 2 an average of 40 cents, and 30 cents from point 3.

Even these networks are not as general as one might want to solve. We could have any number of terminals, and arbitrary connections between pairs of terminals. We may then fix the voltage at a certain set of terminals, and ask what the voltage is at the remaining terminals. We will consider only the case where this is a single network, that is, where by introducing voltage at any one terminal we will get a flow of current throughout the circuit.

The Markov chain analogy is easily extended to such circuits. Any such network corresponds to an absorbing chain. The terminals at which the voltage is fixed will be the absorbing states. The remaining states will be transient. The transition probabilities from state i are found by considering all states to which it is connected in the circuit, and the probabilities are again proportional to the reciprocals of the resistances, hence they will again be normalized conductances. We can repeat the argument leading to equations (4) and (5), only now there need not be exactly four terms. There will be as many terms as there are "neighboring" states, that is, as many as the number of terminals to which terminal i is directly connected. The solution will again be given by equation (3). The voltages can still be interpreted as mean winnings if we carry out the absorbing Markov chain starting at a given state, and if we receive prizes equal to the fixed voltages.

Thus we see that any such circuit can be solved by solving the analogous absorbing Markov chain. But the procedure can also be reversed. If we have an absorbing Markov chain which has an electric network analog, then we can get valuable information about the chain by setting up the circuit and measuring "interior" voltages (see Exercises 7–8). It can be shown that this is a fairly large class of Markov chains, though there are many chains having no electric analog.

The two methods of solving a problem, by setting up an analogous problem in another field, serve to illustrate the difference between the two types of computing machines we have available, digital computers and analog computers.

If we have an electric network and wish to find interior voltages by means of the corresponding absorbing Markov chain, we are forced to invert the matrix $(I - Q)$, and to carry out matrix multiplications. These are numerical computations, and high-speed *digital* computers are ideally suited for the solution of the problem. On the other hand, if we wish to get information about a Markov chain, and we set up an analogous electric circuit, then this electric circuit plays the role of an *analog* computer. The digital computer carries out the mathematical operations necessary for a solution of the problem, while the analog computer furnishes us with a physical model in which some measurable quantity gives us the solution.

We can also see from this example what the relative advantages and disadvantages of the two types of computers are. At first glance the analog computer appears far superior. It furnishes us with an answer instantaneously, since the voltages at the interior states assume their values in negligible time. It is also a far cheaper and more easily available method. However, the method has severe limitations. The accuracy of the answer is no better than the accuracy of the parameters in the electric circuit, and we are quite unlikely to get three significant figures in our answer. We must also realize that each new Markov chain will require the rewiring of the circuit, and readjustment of the resistances. And finally, this method will be applicable only to absorbing Markov chains that happen to have a circuit analog.

The digital computer has no limit on the accuracy it can achieve, if we are willing to let it work on the problem for a sufficiently long time. And while each new type of problem will require a new set of instructions, a single set will work for all problems of the given type. And finally, the same digital computer can be used for millions of other types of problems. These advantages have so far outweighed those of the analog computer that digital computers will probably replace analog computers for most tasks.

EXERCISES

1. In the circuit of Figure 10 voltages are fixed as follows: $A = 10$, $B = 10$, $E = 20$, while the others are 0. Find the interior voltages. [*Ans.* $\frac{41}{16}$, $\frac{90}{16}$, $\frac{89}{16}$.]

2. Suppose that in Figure 8 the voltages are fixed as follows: $A = B = C = 5$, $D = E = 1$, the others are 0. Find the voltage at the center point.

Figure 11 shows a network. The numbers on the connections are resistances, while the numbers in the boxes are terminal voltages. Exercises 3–6 refer to this network.

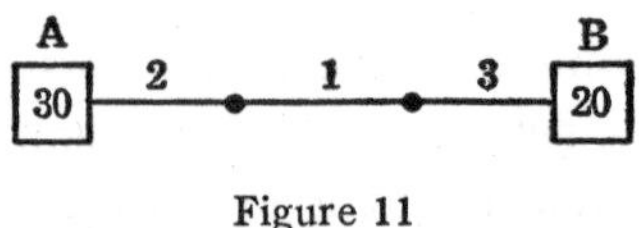

Figure 11

3. Set up the analogous Markov chain.

4. Find the N matrix.

5. For each interior point find the probability of reaching A.

6. Find the voltages at the interior points. [*Ans.* $26\frac{2}{3}$, 25.]

7. Suppose that in an electric network we put a unit voltage at one boundary point, and ground (0 voltage) the other boundary points. Prove that the voltage at each interior point is equal to the probability of ending up at the selected boundary point.

8. Use the result of Exercise 8 to obtain information about a Markov chain from an analogous electric circuit.

9. In Example 2, show that if the connection between x_2 and x_3 is broken, all interior voltages are decreased.

*9. AN APPLICATION OF LINEAR ALGEBRA

Let us apply some ideas from linear algebra to the related problems of random walk games and electric circuits. We have a network of arbitrary shape, with s interior points and r boundary points. The network must have the property that by introducing a voltage at any boundary point we can cause current to flow through the entire network.

This will also assure that the analogous Markov chain is absorbing.

We assign to each boundary point a number, positive, negative, or zero. In the circuit such a number will be the voltage at which the boundary point is kept. In the game the same number is the payment received (or made, if the number is negative) on reaching the boundary point. The connections between points have positive numbers assigned to them. For the game these are transition probabilities, while for the electric network resistances are given. These two sets of numbers are so related that the transition probabilities are proportional to the reciprocals of the resistances.

Let us represent the given boundary numbers (voltages or payments) as an r-dimensional column vector V. Since the components are arbitrary real numbers, V may be any element of $\mathfrak{X}_r$. Our problem is to find the resulting voltage at each interior point, or the mean payment received in a game starting at this point. We collect these numbers into an s-dimensional column vector X. This vector is an element of the vector space $\mathfrak{X}_s$. Thus we are interested in the transformation B that transforms the given boundary vector V into the interior vector X. From the previous section we know exactly how to find the matrix of this transformation, but let us see how much we can infer from linear algebra, without any computation.

Let us see what we can say about x_i, the ith component of X. It must be a function of the given boundary values, hence we may write $x_i = \mathbf{F}_i(V)$. We can easily see in either problem that $\mathbf{F}_i$ is a functional on $\mathfrak{X}_r$. First we must show that

$$\mathbf{F}_i(V + V') = \mathbf{F}_i(V) + \mathbf{F}_i(V').$$

In the electric circuit this is precisely what is known as the "superposition" theorem. In the game it states that if two sets of payments are to be made, the mean of the composite payment is the sum of the means of the individual payments, a fact easily deduced from the property of means. To show that $\mathbf{F}_i(kV) = k\mathbf{F}_i(V)$ is even simpler. We may think of multiplication by k as a change in the units used. This must certainly not change the answer, but rather change the units in which it is expressed. Hence if V becomes kV in the new units, then $\mathbf{F}_i(V)$ becomes $k\mathbf{F}_i(V)$ in the new units. Thus each $\mathbf{F}_i$ is a functional.

But we know that each functional on $\mathfrak{X}_r$ can be represented by an r-component row vector. We will also use $\mathbf{F}_i$ as the name of the row vector representing the functional $\mathbf{F}_i$. Then $x_i = \mathbf{F}_iV$. It is now clear that B is a linear transformation, and that its matrix has $\mathbf{F}_i$ as its ith row. (This $s \times r$ matrix is precisely the B matrix discussed in the last section.) Thus $X = BV$. While this result is already known to us, we were able to deduce the form of the answer here without resorting to complex calculations. We will even be able to prove an interesting theorem purely from abstract considerations.

Theorem. If there are more boundary points than interior points, then the boundary values can be chosen in infinitely many ways so that (1) the interior voltages are all 0, or (2) the game is fair no matter which interior state we start in.

Proof. Since B is a linear transformation from an r-dimensional space to an s-dimensional space, and since $r > s$, B cannot be one-one. Hence it has infinitely many vectors in its kernel. Choose any V in the kernel, and $BV = 0$, fulfilling condition (1) or (2).

The above representation of B resulted by choosing the natural basis on each vector space. It is worth discussing the natural basis on the boundary points in more detail. Let V_k be the kth element of this basis. Then V_k assigns value 1 to the kth boundary point, and 0's elsewhere. This may be interpreted as putting a unit voltage on this terminal, or as having a unit prize for reaching this boundary point. We know that the kth column of B is the vector BV_k, the result of transforming the basis vector V_k. This has as components the resulting interior voltages in the electric case, and hence the kth column of B shows the results of applying a unit voltage at terminal k. In the game the mean payment will simply be the probability of reaching this terminal, hence the kth column of B gives the probabilities of reaching terminal k from the various starting positions. This agrees with the results of the two previous sections.

These considerations are intended to illustrate that linear algebra enhances our understanding of a problem even when it does not furnish the solution.

EXERCISES

1. If $B = NR$, where $N = (I - Q)^{-1}$, show that B and R have the same kernel.

2. Let us define the *perimeter* to consist of those interior states that are directly connected with the boundary. Suppose there are p such states. Let R^* be the p-by-r matrix obtained from R by keeping only rows corresponding to perimeter states. What is the nature of the rows deleted? Prove that R and R^* have the same kernel.

3. Use the results of Exercises 1 and 2 to show that the range of B has dimension at most p.

4. Use the result of Exercise 3 to strengthen the theorem proved in this section.

5. Consider the network shown in Figure 12.

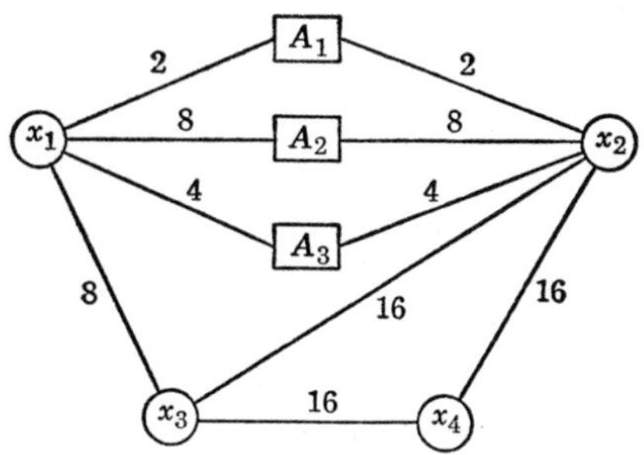

Figure 12

(a) Give three different ways of fixing voltages at A_1, A_2, and A_3 so that all the resulting "interior" voltages are 0.
(b) What is the dimensionality of the space of the possible interior voltages?
(c) Find the B matrix.
(d) Give a simpler meaning to the results of (b) and (c).

6. Use the result of Exercise 1 to prove the following theorem: A random walk game is fair if and only if the mean payment *on the next step* is 0 for every interior point.

7. Figure 13 illustrates a square network. In such a network we choose k^2 interior points arranged in a square, and we supply the minimum

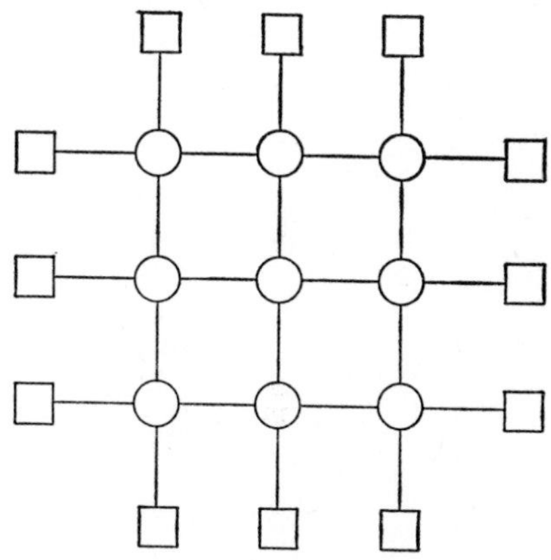

Figure 13

number of boundary points to isolate the interior from the outside. The figure illustrates $k = 3$. If k is any integer greater than 1, show that

(a) $p = 4(k - 1)$, $r = 4k$.

(b) The boundary values can always be chosen in infinitely many ways so that the game played on the square network is fair for every starting point.

8. Construct the square game with $k = 2$ and equal transition probabilities. Give three different ways of assigning boundary values so that the game is fair for all four starting positions.

SUGGESTED READING

Feller, W., *An Introduction to Probability Theory and Its Applications*, Wiley, New York, 2nd ed., 1957, Chapters XIV–XVI.

Kemeny, J. G., J. L. Snell, and G. L. Thompson, *Introduction to Finite Mathematics*, Prentice-Hall, Englewood Cliffs, N. J., 1957, Chapter VII.

Kemeny, J. G., and J. L. Snell, *Finite Markov Chains*, Van Nostrand, Princeton, N. J., 1959.

CHAPTER 7

Continuous Probability Theory

1. INTRODUCTION

As preparation for this chapter the reader should have covered the unstarred sections of Chapters 1, 2, 3, and he should understand thoroughly the content of a standard first-year calculus course.

In Chapter 3 we made an extensive study of the probabilities of statements relative to finite possibility spaces. But when we discussed the Poisson measure we found it convenient to look at the infinite set of all nonnegative integers as the possibility space. In the present chapter we shall consider even more general infinite possibility spaces—for instance, the set of all real numbers, or the set of all points in the plane. The techniques involved in assigning useful probability measures to such spaces will involve certain notions from elementary differential and integral calculus.

The Poisson measure provides an example of the most naive sort of infinite possibility space (sometimes called a "discrete" space), in which each point x_i is assigned a certain positive weight $\mathbf{w}(x_i)$ with

$$\sum_{i=1}^{\infty} \mathbf{w}(x_i) = 1.$$

Each subset is then assigned a measure equal to the sum of the weights of its points. There exist as many ways of setting up a discrete space as there exist positive infinite series of sum 1. Such an infinite probability space always satisfies the three axioms that we laid down for finite probability spaces.

1. $\mathbf{m}(X) = 0$ if and only if $X = \mathcal{E}$.
2. $0 \leq \mathbf{m}(X) \leq 1$.
3. $\mathbf{m}(X \cup Y) = \mathbf{m}(X) + \mathbf{m}(Y)$ if and only if $X \cap Y = \mathcal{E}$.

Suppose, however, that we want to consider as a possibility space $\mathcal{U}$ the interval of all real numbers between 0 and 1, an infinite set which we shall hereafter denote by $[0, 1]$. If our "experiment" consists in picking a point at random from $[0, 1]$, then the probability of picking a point in a given subset that happens to be itself an interval $[a, b]$ ought to equal the length $b - a$. Question: Is it possible to assign measures to all the subsets of $[0, 1]$ in such a way that all the subintervals are assigned their ordinary lengths as measures and in such a way that the axioms 1, 2, 3 still hold? Answer: No. We can satisfy only the weaker axioms obtained by deleting the "only if" parts of axioms 1 and 3. For it is clear that the measure of a unit set must be zero, since it must be smaller than the measure of any interval containing it. This makes it necessary that we delete the "only if" part of axiom 1. And as a consequence we must delete also the "only if" part of axiom 3. (See Exercise 8.) But if we are content to satisfy only these weakened axioms, then there does exist a measure of all the subsets of $[0, 1]$ satisfying them and assigning to every subinterval its ordinary length. The trouble now is that subsets other than intervals exist in bewildering abundance, and there is no way of determining what the measure should be on most of these, even when we specify the measures of all intervals. (We certainly cannot now define the measure of a subset to be the sum of the measures of its points!) There are, in fact, infinitely many solutions to the problem of assigning measures, no one more natural than any other. Hence we also abandon the attempt to assign measures to *all* subsets of $[0, 1]$ and instead agree to measure only *some* subsets, namely, finite unions of intervals, or subsets that are limits of these in a precise sense that we shall not need to spell out here. The class of subsets that we choose to measure is restricted enough so that their measures are completely determined once the measures of intervals are specified.

The above example leads us to write down the following requirements for a probability measure $\mathbf{m}$ defined on subsets of a general probability space $\mathcal{U}$.

1. $\mathbf{m}(\mathfrak{U}) = 1$.
2. $0 \leq \mathbf{m}(X) \leq 1$.
3. $\mathbf{m}(X \cup Y) = \mathbf{m}(X) + \mathbf{m}(Y)$ if $X \cap Y = \mathcal{E}$.

The measure **m** is defined only for certain subsets of $\mathfrak{U}$ (which are then called the "measurable" subsets). But we assume at least that unions, intersections, and complements of measurable subsets are again measurable subsets.

As special examples of general probability spaces we have so far all the finite spaces studied in Chapter 3, the Poisson space, and other discrete spaces, and (defined immediately above) the interval $[0, 1]$ with the "uniform" measure. This last example should be thought of as similar to the equiprobable measures (Chapter 3, Section 3) on finite sets. In Exercise 10 you are asked to prove that no reasonable analog of the equiprobable measure exists in the infinite discrete case.

On finite sets we did not restrict ourselves to the equiprobable case, and similarly on the interval $[0, 1]$ we do not restrict ourselves to the uniform case. But whatever the measure, we are still concerned primarily with finite unions of subintervals and with limits of these, so that we need never specify more than the measures of the subintervals themselves in order to determine (implicitly) the measures of all interesting subsets. Furthermore it is really enough to specify only the measures of those subintervals $[0, a]$ that have left-hand end point 0. For then the measure of an arbitrary subinterval $[a, b]$ can be found by subtracting $\mathbf{m}([0, a])$ from $\mathbf{m}([0, b])$. Hence it is very natural to associate with each probability measure **m** on the interval $\mathfrak{U} = [0, 1]$ a certain numerical function **G** (called a *distribution* function) with domain that same interval $\mathfrak{U}$ and assigning to each a in $\mathfrak{U}$ the value $\mathbf{G}(a) = \mathbf{m}([0, a])$. The function **G** is obviously positive and increasing. And if every unit set has measure zero, then **G** is continuous; the measure of a subinterval $[a, b]$ is $\mathbf{G}(b) - \mathbf{G}(a)$ whether or not the end points a and b are included.

Conversely it is possible to prove that every increasing continuous function **G** on the interval $[0, 1]$ with $\mathbf{G}(0) = 0$ and $\mathbf{G}(1) = 1$ defines a probability measure on $[0, 1]$. If we assume that **G** has a continuous derivative $\mathbf{G}'$ except possibly at 0 or 1 (and we always shall assume this), then by the fundamental theorem of the integral calculus

$$\mathbf{m}([a, b]) = \mathbf{G}(b) - \mathbf{G}(a) = \int_a^b \mathbf{G}'(x)\, dx.$$

The function $\mathbf{G}'$ is called the *density* function corresponding to the distribution function **G**.

For an arbitrary interval $[a, b]$ as possibility space we would require

$G(a) = 0$ and $G(b) = 1$. It will often be convenient to allow b to be $+\infty$ or a to be $-\infty$ or both. If $a = -\infty$, we replace the requirement $G(a) = 0$ by $\lim_{t\to-\infty} G(t) = 0$. If $b = +\infty$, we replace $G(b) = 1$ by $\lim_{t\to\infty} G(t) = 1$. Notice that the above integrals may be "improper."

Example 1. For the uniform measure on $[0, 1]$ the distribution function G has the formula $G(t) = t$. In Figure 1 is shown the uniform distribution

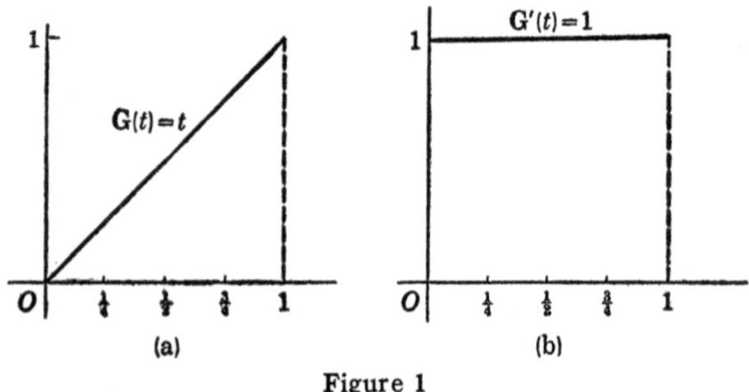

Figure 1

function $G(t) = t$, and its density $G'(t) = 1$. From Figure 1(a) it can be seen that there is probability of $\frac{1}{2}$ of choosing a number less than or equal to $\frac{1}{2}$, probability $\frac{3}{4}$ of choosing a number less than or equal to $\frac{3}{4}$, etc.

Example 2. In the study of radioactivity the *exponential distribution*

$$G(t) = 1 - e^{-t/a}$$

defined on the interval $[0, \infty]$ arises. Note that $G(0) = 0$ and $\lim_{t\to\infty} G(t) = 1$. Here $G(t)$ determines the probability that a particle will be emitted from a given radioactive substance before time t, and a is a positive constant depending on the nature of the substance. (The derivation of the distribution function and interpretation of a will be given in Section 2.) The density for $G(t)$ is

$$G'(t) = \frac{1}{a} e^{-t/a}.$$

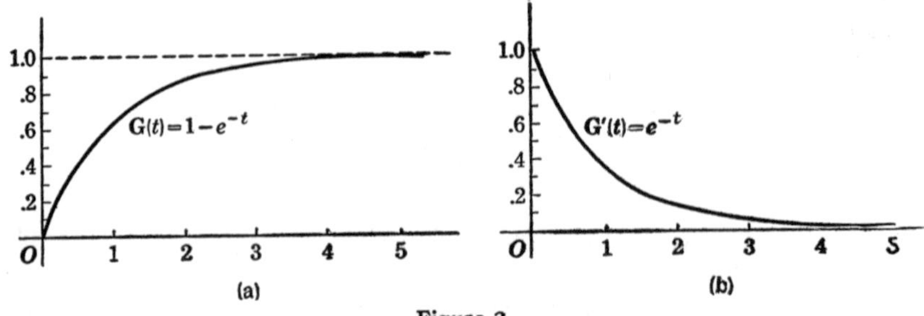

Figure 2

The graphs of $\mathbf{G}(t)$ and $\mathbf{G}'(t)$ for this example are shown in Figures 2(a) and 2(b). We have indicated the scale on each of these figures for later use in exercises.

From the expression for $\mathbf{G}(t)$ it is easy to find the probability that the particle is not emitted by time t. That is, if we let $\mathbf{x}$ be the identity function on $[0, \infty]$, then

$$\mathbf{Pr}[\mathbf{x} > t] = 1 - \mathbf{G}(t) = e^{-t/a}.$$

Further study of this example will be made in Section 2.

Example 3. Let us consider the outcome function $\mathbf{f}_n$ for an independent trials process (see Chapter 3). Let $\mathbf{f}_n^*$ be the standardized form of $\mathbf{f}_n$. Then by the central limit theorem (Chapter 3, Section 13),

$$\lim_{n\to\infty} \mathbf{Pr}[\mathbf{f}_n^* \le t] = \frac{1}{\sqrt{2\pi}} \int_{-\infty}^{t} e^{-x^2/2}\, dx$$

If we now regard the "limiting experiment" as one concerning continuous probability, we can set

$$\mathbf{G}(t) = \frac{1}{\sqrt{2\pi}} \int_{-\infty}^{t} e^{-x^2/2}\, dx$$

and it is clear that $\mathbf{G}(t)$ is an increasing function. It can be shown that $\lim_{t\to\infty} \mathbf{G}(t) = 1$ and $\lim_{t\to-\infty} \mathbf{G}(t) = 0$. Hence $\mathbf{G}(t)$ is a distribution function defined on $\mathcal{U} = [-\infty, \infty]$. The derivative of $\mathbf{G}$ is the function

$$\mathbf{G}'(t) = \frac{1}{\sqrt{2\pi}} e^{-t^2/2}.$$

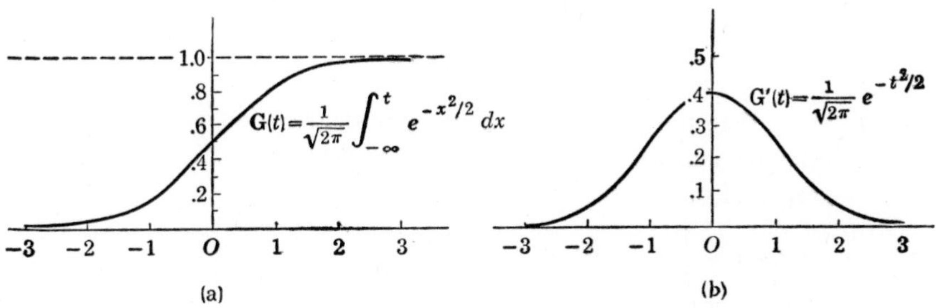

Figure 3

The graphs of $\mathbf{G}(t)$ and $\mathbf{G}'(t)$ are shown in Figures 3(a) and 3(b). The function $\mathbf{G}(t)$ is called the *normal distribution function* and $\mathbf{G}'(t)$ is called the *normal density function*. The scale is shown on these graphs for use in working problems.

If $\mathcal{U}$ is a finite possibility space, the weights assigned to points determine the measure of sets and could themselves be interpreted as probabilities. If $\mathcal{U}$ is an interval space and $\mathbf{G}(t)$ is a distribution function, then the value of $\mathbf{G}(t)$ represents a probability. However, the value of the density $\mathbf{G}'(t)$ does not represent a probability. We do have the following interpretation for the values $\mathbf{G}'(t)$. Let $[a, a + h]$ be an interval of $\mathcal{U}$ of length h. Then letting $\mathbf{x}$ stand for the identity function on $\mathcal{U}$,

$$Pr[a < \mathbf{x} < a + h] = \int_a^{a+h} \mathbf{G}'(t)\, dt.$$

By the mean value theorem of the integral calculus this gives us

$$Pr[a < \mathbf{x} < a + h] = \mathbf{G}'(t_0)h,$$

where t_0 is in the interval $[a, a + h]$. Hence it is more probable that the outcome will be in an interval of length h where $\mathbf{G}'(t)$ is large than where it is small. For example, in the case of the uniform measure, $\mathbf{G}'(t)$ is constant and all intervals of length h have the same measure. For the normal density a maximum for $\mathbf{G}'(t)$ occurs at 0 and intervals of length h near 0 have greater measure than intervals of the same length away from 0.

Specialists in probability theory often assign measures to possibility spaces that are much more outrageous than a mere interval of real numbers. In the present chapter, however, the most extreme case will be taken up in Section 4, where we will discuss a simple special method for assigning a probability measure on a 2-dimensional vector space, i.e., on the ordinary geometric plane. In this case we shall assign measures to rectangles and to sets obtained from these by our familiar set operations, and to limits of such sets.

EXERCISES

1. Show that the following functions are distribution functions on the intervals indicated. Find the associated density functions. Sketch the graphs of these functions.

(a) $\mathbf{G}(t) = \frac{1}{5}t$ on $[0, 5]$.

(b) $\mathbf{G}(t) = \frac{t^3}{2} + \frac{1}{2}$ on $[-1, 1]$.

(c) $\mathbf{G}(t) = \frac{2}{\pi}\arcsin\sqrt{t}$ on $[0, 1]$. [*Ans.* $\mathbf{G}'(t) = \frac{1}{\pi\sqrt{t(1-t)}}$.]

(d) $\mathbf{G}(t) = e^{3t}$ on $[-\infty, 0]$.

2. Show that the following functions are distribution functions on the intervals indicated. Find the associated density functions, and sketch the graphs in each case.

(a) $\mathbf{G}(t) = t(1 - \ln t)$ for t in $[0, 1]$.

(b) $\mathbf{G}(t) = \frac{1}{\pi} \arctan t + \frac{1}{2}$ for t in $(-\infty, \infty)$.

(c) $\mathbf{G}(t) = \frac{1}{2} e^t$ for $t < 0$

$= 1 - \frac{1}{2} e^{-t}$ for $t \geq 0$. [*Ans.* $\mathbf{G}'(t) = \frac{1}{2} e^{-|t|}$.]

(d) $\mathbf{G}(t) = \frac{1}{2} t^2$ for $0 \leq t \leq 1$

$= -\frac{1}{2} t^2 + 2t - 1$ for $1 < t \leq 2$.

3. Find the maximum, minimum, and inflection points of the normal density curve.

4. Determine values of a and b so that the function $\mathbf{G}'(x) = a/t$ is a density function on the interval $[1, b]$. [*Hint:* Find $\mathbf{G}(t)$ and test it.]

5. Determine numbers a, k, c, and d so that the function

$$\mathbf{G}'(t) = ke^{-(t-c)/d}$$

is a density function on the interval $[a, \infty]$. Find $\mathbf{G}(t)$.

6. A number x is chosen at random from the interval $[0, 5]$ with probabilities determined by the distribution function of Exercise 1(a). Consider the statements

p: $2 \leq \mathbf{x} \leq 4$.
q: $1 \leq \mathbf{x} \leq 2$.
r: $3 \leq \mathbf{x} \leq 4$.

Find the probabilities of the following statements:
(a) $\mathbf{Pr}[q \vee r]$.
(b) $\mathbf{Pr}[p \vee q]$.
(c) $\mathbf{Pr}[p \wedge (q \vee r)]$.

7. Assume that the distribution $\mathbf{G}(t) = (2/\pi) \arcsin \sqrt{t}$ has been assigned to the interval $[0, 1]$. Find the probability that the outcome lies in the interval $\frac{1}{4} \leq x \leq \frac{3}{4}$.

8. Show that if an infinite probability space contains nonempty subsets that have measure zero, then there must exist nondisjoint subsets A and B such that $\mathbf{m}(A \cup B) = \mathbf{m}(A) + \mathbf{m}(B)$.

9. Let $\mathcal{U}$ be the set of positive integers $\{1, 2, \ldots\}$ with the measure $\mathbf{m}$ defined by assigning the weight $1/2^i$ to the integer i. In the resulting infinite discrete probability space determine the measures of the following subsets.
(a) All even integers.

(b) All odd integers.
(c) All integers >5.
(d) All integers <5.
(e) All integers that are (exactly) divisible by 3.

10. Show that in an infinite discrete probability space, an "equiprobable" measure (analogous to the equiprobable measure on a finite set, studied in Section 3 of Chapter 3) is impossible.

11. Let $\mathcal{U}$ be the interval $[0, 1]$ with the uniform measure. Determine the measures of the following subsets:
(a) $A = [\frac{1}{5}, \frac{2}{5}] \cup [\frac{3}{5}, \frac{4}{5}]$.
(b) $B = [\frac{1}{5}, \frac{3}{5}] \cup [\frac{2}{5}, \frac{4}{5}]$.
(c) $C = [0, \frac{1}{2}] \cup [\frac{3}{4}, \frac{7}{8}] \cup [\frac{15}{16}, \frac{31}{32}] \cup \ldots$.
(d) $A \cap B$.
(e) $\tilde{C}$.

12. Show that a function $\mathbf{G}'$ is a density for a distribution $\mathbf{G}$ on the interval space $\mathcal{U} = [a, b]$ if and only if it has the following two properties.
(a) $\mathbf{G}'(x) \geq 0$ for all x in $\mathcal{U}$.
(b) $\int_a^b \mathbf{G}'(x)\, dx = 1$.

13. Show that the function $\mathbf{G}'(x) = \sin x$ on the interval $[0, \pi/2]$ satisfies the conditions given in Exercise 12 for a density function. Find the distribution function which has this density.

14. Assume that $\mathbf{G}_1'$ and $\mathbf{G}_2'$ are density functions defined on an interval space $\mathcal{U}$. Show that $\mathbf{G}_1' + \mathbf{G}_2'$ is not a density function. Show that $a\mathbf{G}_1' + (1 - a)\mathbf{G}_2'$ is a density function if a is a constant between 0 and 1.

2. THE DETERMINATION OF A DISTRIBUTION

We cannot actually perform an experiment with an infinite number of possible outcomes. Therefore it is not surprising that distribution functions are obtained from somewhat less direct considerations than are weight functions. In this section we shall discuss three different ways that distribution functions arise and give an example of each case.

The first method that we consider is the case that a distribution function is obtained as a limiting situation from a sequence of finite experiments. We have already seen one example of this, namely the normal distribution arising from the central limit theorem. We now give a second example that leads to quite a different kind of distribution function.

Example 1. Peter and Paul match pennies. They start with equal fortunes and we consider the number of times that Peter is ahead of Paul in the first n matches. (To avoid ties we make the convention that when they are equal the player that was ahead last time is considered still to be ahead.) In the case of 6 matches the outcome for Peter may be, for example $WLWLLW$. Then Peter's winnings are 1, 0, 1, 0, -1, 0, and by our convention he would be ahead on the first four matches and behind on the last two. Hence he would be ahead $\frac{2}{3}$ of the time. In an even number of matches it is possible to be ahead only an even number of times. If this problem is studied as a finite problem, the following elegant solution is obtained, which is here presented without proof.

Theorem 1. Let $\mathbf{g}_{2n}$ be the number of plays that Peter is in the lead in $2n$ matches. Then

$$\mathbf{Pr}[\mathbf{g}_{2n} = 2k] = \binom{2k}{k}\binom{2n-2k}{n-k}2^{-2n}.$$

It might be thought that the most probable number of times for Peter to lead is $n/2$ or one half of the time. But in fact this is the most unlikely number of times that he will lead. The most probable such number of times are never or always. The probabilities are given in Fig. 4 for the case of 12 matches. Note that it is more than twice as likely for Peter never to be in the lead than for him to be in the lead exactly 6 times.

$2k$	$\mathbf{Pr}[\mathbf{g}_{2n} = 2k]$
0	.226
2	.123
4	.103
6	.098
8	.103
10	.123
12	.226

Figure 4

Just as was true for the binomial measure, for large n these probabilities are difficult to compute. But for the binomial measure the central limit theorem gave an approximation for these probabilities for large n. And here also an approximating theorem has been proved.

Theorem 2. Let $\mathbf{g}_n$ be the number of times that Peter leads in n matches and let $\mathbf{h}_n = \mathbf{g}_n/n$ be the fraction of the times that he leads. Then for

$0 < a < 1$, as $n \to \infty$,

$$\mathbf{Pr}[\mathbf{h}_n < t] \to \frac{1}{\pi} \int_0^t \frac{dx}{\sqrt{x(1-x)}} = \frac{2}{\pi} \arcsin \sqrt{t}.$$

This theorem leads to a new distribution function

$$\mathbf{G}(t) = \frac{2}{\pi} \arcsin \sqrt{t}.$$

The domain of **G** is the interval $[0, 1]$. The corresponding density function is

$$\mathbf{G}'(t) = \frac{1}{\pi\sqrt{t(1-t)}}.$$

The graphs of these functions are shown in Figures 5(a) and 5(b).

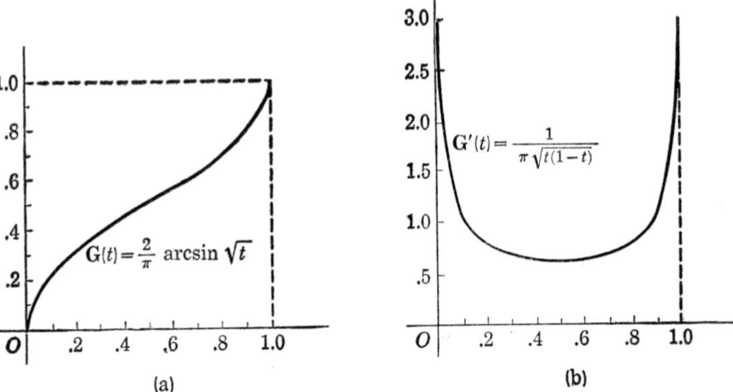

Figure 5

For details of the proofs of these theorems and an interesting discussion of their consequences, see Chapter 2 of the book by W. Feller, listed under suggested readings at the end of Chapter 3.

We now give a second method for obtaining new distribution functions. Let $\mathcal{U}$ be an interval and assume that a measure has been assigned to $\mathcal{U}$. Let **f** be a function with domain $\mathcal{U}$ and range an interval R. Assume that for every t in R the truth set of the statement $\mathbf{f}(x) < t$ is a measurable set. Then we consider the set R to be a new possibility space, with distribution $\mathbf{G}(t)$ defined by

$$\mathbf{G}(t) = \mathbf{Pr}[\mathbf{f} < t].$$

This distribution on R is called the *distribution for* **f**. And the derivative $\mathbf{G}'$, when it exists, is called the *density* for **f**. When **f** is a continuous function of its domain $\mathcal{U}$, then its range R is an interval $[a, b]$ and the distribution $\mathbf{G}$ defines a probability measure on $[a, b]$ satisfying the axioms 1, 2, 3 on page 441. Furthermore, all probability questions about the single function $\mathbf{f}$ defined on the possibility space $\mathcal{U}$ now can be reduced to equivalent questions about the identity function $\mathbf{y}$ on a certain interval possibility space. Specifically,

$$Pr[\mathbf{f} < t] = Pr[\mathbf{y} < t],$$

where the probability on the left-hand side is computed with respect to the measure on the original space, and the probability on the right-hand side is computed with respect to the measure defined by $\mathbf{G}$ on the interval $[a, b]$.

Example 2. Assume that the normal measure has been assigned to $\mathcal{U} = [-\infty, \infty]$. Let $\mathbf{f}$ be defined by $\mathbf{f}(x) = x^2$. Then the range of $\mathbf{f}$ is $R = [0, \infty]$. The truth set of the statement $\mathbf{f}(x) < t$ is the interval $[-\sqrt{t}, \sqrt{t}]$. By the symmetry of the normal curve

$$\mathbf{G}(t) = \mathbf{Pr}[\mathbf{f} < t] = \frac{2}{\sqrt{2\pi}} \int_0^{\sqrt{t}} e^{-x^2/2}\, dx.$$

Recall that if u is a function of t, then

$$\frac{d}{dt} \int_0^u \mathbf{w}(x)\, dx = \mathbf{w}(u) \frac{du}{dt}.$$

Thus the derivative of $\mathbf{G}$ is

$$\mathbf{G}'(t) = \frac{e^{-t/2}}{\sqrt{2\pi t}}.$$

An important special function is $\mathbf{f}(x) = cx + d$, $c > 0$. When we decide to change the scale in which the outcome is measured we are led to the consideration of such a function. The constant d corresponds to a change of the origin, and the constant c determines the change of unit. The density of $\mathbf{f}$ is then the appropriate density for the new possibility space. The next theorem gives the new density and distribution functions in terms of the old ones.

Theorem 3. Let $\mathcal{U}$ be an interval with end points a and b for which a measure has been defined by a distribution function $\mathbf{G}_0$. Let $\mathbf{f}(x) = cx + d$ be defined on $\mathcal{U}$, with $c > 0$; then the range R of $\mathbf{f}$ is the interval with end points $ca + d$ and $cb + d$. The distribution for $\mathbf{f}$ is given by

$$\mathbf{G}_1(t) = \mathbf{G}_0\left(\frac{t - d}{c}\right) \quad \text{for } t \text{ in } R.$$

If $\mathbf{G}_0$ has a density $\mathbf{G}_0'$, then $\mathbf{G}_1$ has a density

$$\mathbf{G}_1'(t) = \frac{1}{c}\,\mathbf{G}_0'\left(\frac{t-d}{c}\right) \quad \text{for } t \text{ in } R.$$

Proof. By a straightforward calculation we have

$$\begin{aligned}\mathbf{G}_1(t) &= \mathbf{Pr}[\mathbf{f} < t] = \mathbf{Pr}[c\mathbf{x} + d < t] \\ &= \mathbf{Pr}\left[\mathbf{x} < \frac{t-d}{c}\right] = \mathbf{G}_0\left(\frac{t-d}{c}\right).\end{aligned}$$

To obtain the density, $\mathbf{G}_1'(t)$, we use the chain-rule.

Example 3. Let $\mathbf{G}$ be the exponential distribution $1 - e^{-t}$ defined on $[0, \infty]$. Now let $\mathbf{f}(x) = 2x + 3$. The range of $\mathbf{f}$ is $[3, \infty]$. The distribution for $\mathbf{f}$ is

$$\mathbf{G}_1(t) = \mathbf{G}_0\left(\frac{t-3}{2}\right) = 1 - e^{-(t-3)/2} \quad \text{for } 3 \le t < \infty,$$

and the density for $\mathbf{f}$ is

$$\mathbf{G}_1'(t) = \frac{1}{2}e^{-(t-3)/2} \quad \text{for } 3 \le t < \infty.$$

Example 4. Let us assume that $\mathfrak{U} = [-\infty, \infty]$ and that the measure has been assigned by the normal distribution. Then

$$\mathbf{G}_0'(t) = \frac{1}{\sqrt{2\pi}}\,e^{-t^2/2}.$$

Let $\mathbf{f}(x) = cx + d$. Then the density for $\mathbf{f}$ is

$$\mathbf{G}_1'(t) = \frac{1}{\sqrt{2\pi c^2}}\,e^{-(t-d)^2/2c^2}.$$

A distribution with a density of this form is called a *normal distribution* with mean d and variance c^2. The reason for this notation will be explained in the next section.

As a final method for determining a distribution function we shall show that it is possible to determine uniquely a distribution function by requiring that the probabilities determined by it should satisfy some simple property suggested from physical considerations.

Example 5. Assume that a radioactive source is emitting alpha particles. We observe the source at a given time and measure the length of time before the first particle is emitted. The possibility space is then $[0, \infty]$. From physical considerations it is reasonable to assume that knowing that a particle was not emitted in the first s seconds should not affect the probability that it will not be emitted in the next t seconds. This condition may be stated as

$$\mathbf{Pr}[\mathbf{x} > s + t \mid \mathbf{x} > s] = \mathbf{Pr}[\mathbf{x} > t]$$

for all s. We shall prove that this condition determines the form of the distribution function.

We need the following result from calculus.

Theorem 4. Let $\mathbf{f}$ be a function with domain $[0, \infty]$, that has a derivative at each point, that is not the zero function, and that satisfies the condition

$$\mathbf{f}(s + t) = \mathbf{f}(s) \cdot \mathbf{f}(t) \tag{1}$$

for all s and t. Then

$$\mathbf{f}(s) = e^{ks},$$

where $k = \mathbf{f}'(0)$.

Proof. Since $\mathbf{f}$ is not the zero function, $\mathbf{f}(r) \neq 0$ for some r. From (1), $\mathbf{f}(r) = \mathbf{f}(r + 0) = \mathbf{f}(r) \cdot \mathbf{f}(0)$. Hence $\mathbf{f}(0) = 1$. Again from condition (1) we have

$$\frac{\mathbf{f}(s + h)}{h} = \frac{\mathbf{f}(s)\mathbf{f}(h)}{h}.$$

This implies

$$\frac{\mathbf{f}(s + h) - \mathbf{f}(s)\mathbf{f}(0)}{h} = \frac{\mathbf{f}(s)\mathbf{f}(h) - \mathbf{f}(s)\mathbf{f}(0)}{h},$$

or, since $\mathbf{f}(0) = 1$,

$$\frac{\mathbf{f}(s + h) - \mathbf{f}(s)}{h} = \mathbf{f}(s) \frac{\mathbf{f}(h) - \mathbf{f}(0)}{h}.$$

Letting h tend to 0 gives

$$\mathbf{f}'(s) = \mathbf{f}(s)\mathbf{f}'(0).$$

This differential equation has the general solution

$$\mathbf{f}(s) = ce^{\mathbf{f}'(0)s}$$

where c is an arbitrary constant. Since $\mathbf{f}(0) = 1$, then c must be 1, proving the theorem.

We now use Theorem 4 to prove the following theorem:

Theorem 5. Let $\mathfrak{U}$ be the possibility space $[0, \infty]$ and assume that a measure has been assigned by a distribution $\mathbf{G}$ with density $\mathbf{G}'$. Then the condition

$$\mathbf{Pr}[\mathbf{x} > s + t | \mathbf{x} > s] = \mathbf{Pr}[\mathbf{x} > t] \tag{2}$$

for all s and t is a necessary and sufficient condition for $\mathbf{G}$ to be the exponential distribution.

Proof. Assume first that $\mathbf{G}$ has been assigned and that (2) is satisfied. Let $\mathbf{H} = \mathbf{1} - \mathbf{G}$. That is $\mathbf{H}(t) = \mathbf{Pr}[\mathbf{x} > t]$. By analogy with the finite case we may write the conditional probability in (2) in the form

$$\mathbf{Pr}[\mathbf{x} > s + t | \mathbf{x} > s] = \frac{\mathbf{Pr}[(\mathbf{x} > s + t) \wedge (\mathbf{x} > s)]}{\mathbf{Pr}[\mathbf{x} > s]}$$

$$= \frac{\mathbf{Pr}[\mathbf{x} > s + t]}{\mathbf{Pr}[\mathbf{x} > s]}.$$

Thus from (2) we have that

$$\mathbf{Pr}[\mathbf{x} > s + t] = \mathbf{Pr}[\mathbf{x} > s] \cdot \mathbf{Pr}[\mathbf{x} > t].$$

That is, that $\mathbf{H}(s + t) = \mathbf{H}(s)\mathbf{H}(t)$ for all s and t. We know that **H** has a derivative since **G** has a derivative. Hence the conditions for the previous theorem are satisfied. Therefore $\mathbf{H} = e^{kt}$. Since $\mathbf{G}(t) = 1 - \mathbf{H}(t)$ we have $\mathbf{G}(t) = 1 - e^{kt}$. Since **G** is nondecreasing, k is negative. Finally, letting $a = -1/k$ we have the exponential distribution

$$\mathbf{G}(t) = 1 - e^{-t/a}.$$

The proof that the exponential measure does have property (2) is left as an exercise (see Exercise 4).

To summarize, we have given three different methods which lead to the assignment of measures to intervals: first as a limiting situation from finite experiments; second, as a measure on the range of a function determined from a measure given on the domain; third, by imposing conditions, suggested by physical considerations, that the measure must fulfill.

EXERCISES

1. In Example 1, find the exact probability that Peter leads $2k$ times in 20 matches for $k = 0, 1, \ldots, 10$.

2. Using the arcsine distribution estimate the probability that Peter leads more than 9000 times in 10,000 matches. On the other hand, using the central limit theorem estimate the probability that his final fortune is greater than \$3. [*Ans.* .20; .001.]

3. In Example 1 construct a tree and tree measure for four matches. Compute the probability that Peter leads 0, 2, 4 times from the tree measure and verify that the result is as given in Theorem 1.

4. If the exponential distribution is assigned to the interval $[0, \infty]$, prove that

$$\mathbf{Pr}[\mathbf{x} > s + t \mid \mathbf{x} > s] = \mathbf{Pr}[\mathbf{x} > s].$$

5. If the distribution $\mathbf{G}(t) = 1 - e^{-t}$ has been assigned to the space $\mathcal{U} = [0, \infty]$, use the result of Theorem 3 to find the distribution for the function $\mathbf{f}$ defined by $\mathbf{f}(x) = ax + b$.

6. Assume that the normal distribution with density

$$\mathbf{G}'(t) = \frac{1}{\sqrt{2\pi}} e^{-t^2/2}$$

has been assigned on $\mathcal{U} = [-\infty, \infty]$ and let $\mathbf{f}$ be the function defined by $\mathbf{f}(x) = |x|$. Find the distribution function $\mathbf{G}_0(t)$ and the density $\mathbf{G}_0'(t)$ for $\mathbf{f}$. [*Ans.* $\mathbf{G}_0'(t) = \frac{\sqrt{2}}{\sqrt{\pi}} e^{-t^2/2}$ on $[0, \infty]$.]

7. Assume that a distribution function $\mathbf{G}_0$ has been assigned to the interval $[0, \infty]$. Let $\mathbf{f}$ be the function defined by $\mathbf{f}(x) = x^2$. Show that the distribution for $\mathbf{f}$ is $\mathbf{G}_1(t) = \mathbf{G}_0(\sqrt{t})$ and the density $\mathbf{G}_1'$ is given by $\mathbf{G}_1'(t) = \mathbf{G}_0'(\sqrt{t})/2\sqrt{t}$.

8. If the exponential measure has been assigned to the interval $[0, \infty]$, use the result of Exercise 7 to find the density for the function $\mathbf{f}$ defined by $\mathbf{f}(x) = x^2$.

9. An angle θ is chosen at random between $-\pi/2$ and $\pi/2$. A line is drawn from $\begin{pmatrix} 0 \\ 1 \end{pmatrix}$ making an angle θ with the y-axis. Show that the distribution function for the point x at which the line crosses the x-axis is

$$\mathbf{G}(t) = \frac{1}{2} + \frac{1}{\pi} \arctan t$$

for $\mathcal{U} = [-\infty, \infty]$. Find the density $\mathbf{G}'(t)$.

10. Assume that the uniform measure is assigned to the interval $[-1, 1]$. Find the distribution for $\mathbf{f}(x) = x^2$.

11. Assign the exponential distribution $1 - e^{-t}$ to the interval $[0, \infty]$. Find the distribution function for $\mathbf{f}(x) = 1 - e^{-x}$.

[*Ans.* $\mathbf{G}(t) = t$ on $[0, 1]$.]

12. Let $\mathcal{U}$ be an interval for which a measure determined by the distribution function $\mathbf{G}$ has been assigned. Now consider $\mathbf{G}$ as a function on $\mathcal{U}$. Prove that the distribution for $\mathbf{G}$ is the uniform distribution on the interval $[0, 1]$.

13. Assume that a measure has been assigned to $[-\infty, \infty]$ by the normal distribution with mean c and variance d^2. Let $\mathbf{f}(x) = rx + s$. Show that the distribution for $\mathbf{f}$ is the normal measure with mean $s + rc$ and variance $(rd)^2$.

3. THE MEAN AND VARIANCE OF FUNCTIONS

The concepts of the mean and variance of functions defined over finite possibility spaces were discussed in Chapter 3. The concepts generalize readily to the case of infinite possibility spaces, and we shall discuss them here. We shall assume throughout this section that all functions considered on an interval possibility space are continuous functions.

DEFINITION. Let $\mathcal{U} = [a, b]$ be an interval space for which a measure has been determined by a distribution function $\mathbf{G}$ having a density $\mathbf{G}'$. Then if $\mathbf{f}$ is a real valued function with domain $\mathcal{U}$, the mean of $\mathbf{f}$, denoted by $\mathbf{M}[\mathbf{f}]$ is given by

$$\mathbf{M}[\mathbf{f}] = \int_a^b \mathbf{f}(x)\mathbf{G}'(x)\,dx.$$

The basic properties of means developed for finite possibility spaces remain valid for the mean defined as an integral. Specifically we have the following theorem.

Theorem 1. Let $\mathcal{U} = [a, b]$ be an interval possibility space for which a measure has been assigned. Then

(a) For any two function $\mathbf{f}$ and $\mathbf{g}$,

$$\mathbf{M}[\mathbf{f} + \mathbf{g}] = \mathbf{M}[\mathbf{f}] + \mathbf{M}[\mathbf{g}].$$

(b) For any constant $\mathbf{c}$,

$$\mathbf{M}[c\mathbf{f}] = c\mathbf{M}[\mathbf{f}].$$

(c) For any constant function $\mathbf{c}$,

$$\mathbf{M}[\mathbf{c}] = c.$$

Parts (a) and (b) of this theorem are standard theorems from the calculus. To prove (c) we note that

$$\mathbf{M}[\mathbf{c}] = \int_a^b c\mathbf{G}'(x)\,dx = c\int_a^b \mathbf{G}'(x)\,dx = c.$$

Example 1. Let $\mathcal{U}$ be the unit interval and assume that the uniform distribution has been assigned. Then $\mathbf{G}'(x) = 1$. Let $\mathbf{x}$ be the identity function on $\mathcal{U}$.

$$\mathbf{M}[\mathbf{x}] = \int_0^1 x\,dx = \frac{1}{2}.$$

$$\mathbf{M}[\mathbf{x}^2] = \int_0^1 x^2\,dx = \frac{1}{3}.$$

Example 2. Let $\mathcal{U}$ be the interval $[0, \infty]$ and assume that the exponential distribution $\mathbf{G}(x) = 1 - e^{-x/a}$ has been assigned. Then $\mathbf{G}'(x) = (1/a)e^{-x/a}$. Hence

$$\mathbf{M}[\mathbf{x}] = \frac{1}{a}\int_0^\infty xe^{-x/a}\,dx$$

$$= -e^{-x/a}(x + a)\Big]_0^\infty = a.$$

We thus see that the constant a which determines the distribution is the mean of the identity function. For this reason we refer to this distribution as the exponential distribution with mean a.

In general when we refer to the *mean of a distribution* we shall understand this to be the mean of the identity function with respect to this distribution.

In the finite case every function had a mean value. When our possibility space is an infinite interval the function may not have a finite mean because it becomes too large. For instance, let $\mathcal{U} = [0, \infty]$ and assume that the exponential distribution with mean 1 has been assigned. Let $\mathbf{f}(x) = e^x$. Then the mean would be

$$\mathbf{M}[\mathbf{f}] = \int_0^\infty e^x \cdot e^{-x}\, dx = \int_0^\infty dx,$$

which is infinite. We shall speak of the mean of a function only when the defining integral is finite.

The variance of a function is defined as in the finite case by

$$\mathbf{V}[\mathbf{f}] = \mathbf{M}[(\mathbf{f} - \mathbf{a})^2],$$

where a is the mean of $\mathbf{f}$. Similarly the standard deviation is defined as $\mathbf{D}[\mathbf{f}] = \sqrt{\mathbf{V}[\mathbf{f}]}$. Thus if $\mathbf{f}$ is defined on $\mathcal{U} = [c, d]$ and a measure has been assigned by the distribution $\mathbf{G}$, we have

$$\mathbf{V}[\mathbf{f}] = \int_c^d [\mathbf{f}(x) - a]^2 \mathbf{G}'(x)\, dx.$$

We define the *variance of a distribution* to be the variance of the identity function with respect to this distribution.

Again the properties of variance proved for the finite case remain valid.

Theorem 2. Let $\mathcal{U}$ be an interval space for which a measure has been assigned. Let $\mathbf{f}$ be any function on $\mathcal{U}$ and c be any constant. Then

(a) $\mathbf{V}[\mathbf{f}] = \mathbf{M}[\mathbf{f}^2] - \mathbf{M}[\mathbf{f}]^2$.
(b) $\mathbf{V}[\mathbf{f} + \mathbf{c}] = \mathbf{V}[\mathbf{f}]$.
(c) $\mathbf{V}[c\mathbf{f}] = c^2\mathbf{V}[\mathbf{f}]$.
(d) $\mathbf{V}[\mathbf{c}] = 0$.

The proofs of these facts are left as exercises (see Exercise 3).

Example 1 (Continued). Let us find the variance of the identity function. That is,

$$\mathbf{V}[\mathbf{x}] = \int_0^1 (x - \tfrac{1}{2})^2\, dx = \frac{1}{3}\left(x - \frac{1}{2}\right)^3\Bigg]_0^1 = \tfrac{1}{24} + \tfrac{1}{24} = \tfrac{1}{12}.$$

Example 2 (Continued). For the exponential distribution we have for the identity function $\mathbf{x}$

$$\mathbf{M}[\mathbf{x}^2] = \frac{1}{a}\int_0^\infty x^2 e^{-x/a}\,dx = 2a^2.$$

By Theorem 2(a),

$$\mathbf{V}[\mathbf{x}] = \mathbf{M}[\mathbf{x}^2] - (\mathbf{M}[\mathbf{x}])^2 = 2a^2 - a^2 = a^2.$$

Thus the standard deviation $\mathbf{D}[\mathbf{x}] = a$. Hence for the exponential measure the mean and standard deviation are the same. Recall that for the Poisson measure the mean and variance were the same.

Example 3. Let $\mathcal{U} = [-\infty, \infty]$ and assume that a measure has been assigned by the normal distribution function with density

$$\mathbf{G}'(t) = \frac{1}{\sqrt{2\pi}}\,e^{-t^2/2}.$$

Consider the identity function on $\mathcal{U}$. It can be shown that the mean value is finite and it is clear from symmetry that it must be 0. Thus $\mathbf{V}[\mathbf{x}] = \mathbf{M}[\mathbf{x}^2]$. Integrating by parts we obtain

$$\begin{aligned}\mathbf{M}[\mathbf{x}^2] &= \frac{1}{\sqrt{2\pi}}\int_{-\infty}^{\infty} x^2 e^{-x^2/2}\,dx \\ &= -\frac{1}{\sqrt{2\pi}}\,xe^{-x^2/2}\Big]_{-\infty}^{\infty} + \frac{1}{\sqrt{2\pi}}\int_{-\infty}^{\infty} e^{-x^2/2}\,dx = 1.\end{aligned}$$

Then $$\mathbf{V}[\mathbf{x}] = 1.$$

Example 4. Let $\mathcal{U} = [-\infty, \infty]$ and assume that a measure has been assigned by a normal distribution function having the density

$$\mathbf{G}'(t) = \frac{1}{\sqrt{2\pi b^2}}\,e^{-(t-a)^2/2b^2}.$$

Then by integration it is possible to verify that $\mathbf{M}[\mathbf{x}] = a$ and $\mathbf{V}[\mathbf{x}] = b^2$. This explains the terminology "normal distribution with mean a and variance b^2." We could also find the mean and variance of $\mathbf{x}$ from the previous example. To do this let $\mathbf{h} = (\mathbf{x} - \mathbf{a})/b$. Then by Theorem 3 of the previous section the distribution for $\mathbf{h}$ has density

$$\mathbf{G}_0'(t) = \frac{1}{\sqrt{2\pi}}\,e^{-t^2/2}.$$

Hence, from Example 4 of Section 2, we have

$$\mathbf{M}[\mathbf{h}] = 0 \quad \text{and} \quad \mathbf{V}[\mathbf{h}] = 1.$$

Since $\mathbf{x} = b\mathbf{h} + \mathbf{a}$, $\mathbf{M}[\mathbf{x}] = a$, and $\mathbf{V}[\mathbf{x}] = b^2$.

We conclude this section with some remarks to tie up the mean value theorem of the integral calculus with the mean of a function.

The extended mean value theorem of the integral calculus (see, for example, Courant, *Differential and Integral Calculus*, p. 127) may be stated as follows:

Theorem. If $\mathbf{f}(x)$ is continuous on the finite interval $[a, b]$ and $\mathbf{p}(x)$ is continuous and nonnegative, then

$$\int_a^b \mathbf{f}(x)\mathbf{p}(x)\,dx = \mathbf{f}(x_0) \int_a^b \mathbf{p}(x)\,dx,$$

where x_0 is a number between a and b.

Let us assume that we have an interval space $\mathfrak{U}$ for which a measure has been assigned by a distribution function $\mathbf{G}(t)$ with density $\mathbf{G}'(t)$. Let $I_0 = [a, b]$ be any subinterval of $\mathfrak{U}$. We apply the mean value theorem to

$$\int_a^b \mathbf{f}(x)\mathbf{G}'(x)\,dx$$

and obtain

$$\int_a^b \mathbf{f}(x)\mathbf{G}'(x)\,dx = \mathbf{f}(x_0) \int_a^b \mathbf{G}'(x)\,dx = \mathbf{f}(x_0)\mathbf{m}(I_0),$$

where x_0 is in I_0.

In this case

$$\mathbf{f}(x_0) = \frac{\int_a^b \mathbf{f}(x)\mathbf{G}'(x)\,dx}{\mathbf{m}(I_0)}.$$

But $\mathbf{G}'(x)/\mathbf{m}(I_0)$ may be considered the density function of a measure defined on I_0. It clearly should be interpreted as the conditional measure given that the outcome lies in I_0. Then $\mathbf{f}(x_0)$ gives the mean of $\mathbf{f}$ given that the outcome lies in I_0. If I_0 is $\mathfrak{U}$ then we obtain

$$\mathbf{M}[\mathbf{f}] = \mathbf{f}(x_0)$$

for some point x_0 in $\mathfrak{U}$. Thus when dealing with measures assigned by a distribution function which has a continuous density we can always be sure that there is a possibility for which the function value is the same as the mean value of the function. This was of course not the case when we dealt with finite possibility spaces. For example the mean number of heads in three tosses of a coin is $\frac{3}{2}$. There is no possibility which results in $\frac{3}{2}$ heads. Note that when $\mathbf{f}$ is the identity function then x_0 is the mean value of $\mathbf{f}$. In Example 1, $\mathbf{M}[\mathbf{x}] = \frac{1}{2}$ and $x_0 = \frac{1}{2}$.

It is also interesting to observe that probability considerations make the mean value theorem intuitively clear. The conditional mean of $\mathbf{f}$, given that the outcome lies in I_0, must be between the maximum and minimum value of $\mathbf{f}$ in I_0. Since a continuous function takes on all values between its maximum and minimum, there must be some point x_0 in I_0 which gives the exact value of the conditional mean.

Using the above results we can show that an experiment on an interval space can be approximated by an experiment with a finite number of possibilities. To do this divide $\mathcal{U} = [a, b]$ nonoverlapping intervals $I_0, I_1, \ldots, I_n$. On each interval $I_j = [a_j, b_j]$ we can find an x_j such that

$$x_j = \frac{\int_{a_j}^{b_j} x\mathbf{G}'(x)\,dx}{\mathbf{m}(I_j)}.$$

We consider then a finite possibility space $\hat{\mathcal{U}} = \{x_0, x_1, \ldots, x_n\}$ and assign weights $\mathbf{w}(x_j) = \mathbf{m}(I_j)$. Then the mean of the outcome function for this finite experiment is

$$\Sigma\, x_j\mathbf{m}(I_j),$$

which is clearly equal to

$$\sum_j \int_{a_j}^{b_j} x\mathbf{G}'(x)\,dx = \int_a^b x\mathbf{G}'(x)\,dx.$$

Hence the mean of the outcome function for the finite experiment and the infinite experiment are the same.

Furthermore, the probability of any statement relative to $\mathcal{U}$ whose truth set is a finite union of intervals I_j will have the same probability computed as a statement relative to $\hat{\mathcal{U}}$ by means of the weight function $\mathbf{w}$. The larger the number of intervals we take, the larger the class of statements we can consider as statements relative to a finite possibility space.

Example 5. Assume that $\mathcal{U} = [0, 1]$ and that the uniform measure is assigned. We choose n intervals defined by $I_j = \left[\frac{j}{n}, \frac{j+1}{n}\right]$, for $j = 0, 1, \ldots, n - 1$. Then $\mathbf{m}(I_j) = 1/n$. Clearly the mean value of the outcome function given that it lies in I_j is the mid-point of I_j. Hence the space for our finite experiment would have n points, namely, the mid-points of the intervals and the measure would be the equiprobable measure.

The above procedure can be carried out when $\mathcal{U}$ is an infinite interval. In this case if we take a sequence of intervals $I_0, I_1, \ldots$ we will be led to a measure defined on a sequence of points $x_0, x_1, \ldots$ (see Exercise 8).

In the finite case we observed that the mean of a function could be computed by two different methods: first from the definition

$$\mathbf{M}[\mathbf{f}] = \Sigma\, \mathbf{f}(x_j)\mathbf{w}(x_j),$$

and second from the range values by

$$\mathbf{M}[\mathbf{f}] = \sum_j y_j\mathbf{Pr}[\mathbf{f} = y_j].$$

The corresponding fact for continuous probabilities is the following: Let **f** be a function defined on an interval space $\mathcal{U} = [a, b]$ with range $R = [c, d]$. Assume that a measure has been assigned to $\mathcal{U}$ by a distribution function $\mathbf{G}(t)$. Let $\mathbf{H}(t)$ be the distribution function for **f**. Then from the definition of the mean

$$\mathbf{M}[\mathbf{f}] = \int_a^b \mathbf{f}(x)\mathbf{G}'(x)\, dx.$$

However it can also be proved that

$$\mathbf{M}[\mathbf{f}] = \int_c^d y\mathbf{H}'(y)\, dy.$$

That is, the mean of **f** is the mean of its distribution function computed on R.

Example 6. Let $\mathcal{U} = [0, 1]$ and assume that the uniform measure has been assigned. Let $\mathbf{f}(x) = x^2$. Then **f** has the distribution function $\mathbf{H}(t) = \sqrt{t}$ defined again on the interval $[0, 1]$. The mean of this distribution function is

$$\int_0^1 y\mathbf{H}'(y)\, dy = \int_0^1 \frac{\sqrt{y}}{2}\, dy = \frac{1}{3}.$$

This agrees with the value for $\mathbf{M}[\mathbf{f}^2]$ obtained directly from the definition in Example 1.

All of the discussion above was related to interval spaces. As indicated in the first section it is often necessary to consider more general spaces. In all these cases it is possible to define integration in such a way that the mean of a function is an integral of the function over the entire space. For example, if $\mathcal{U}$ is the plane this is the familiar double integration. For all cases it turns out that the mean and variance may be computed either directly or from the distribution of the function. Since the distribution of the function is a measure on the range it is possible to reduce the calculations to integrals on the line.

EXERCISES

1. Assume that the uniform measure has been assigned to $\mathcal{U} = [0, 1]$. Let $\mathbf{f}(x) = x^3$. Find the mean and variance of **f**.

2. The exponential distribution with mean a is assigned to the interval $[0, \infty]$. Let $\mathbf{f}(x) = x + 2$. Find the mean and variance of **f**.

3. Prove each of the assertions in Theorem 2.

4. Let $\mathcal{U} = [0, \pi/2]$ and let the distribution $\mathbf{G}(t)$ be defined by $\mathbf{G}(t) = 1 - \cos t$. Find the mean and variance for the identity function.
[*Ans.* $\mathbf{M}[\mathbf{x}] = 1$; $\mathbf{V}[\mathbf{x}] = \pi - 3$.]

5. Assume that the exponential measure with mean a has been assigned to represent the time required for a radioactive particle to be emitted. The half life of the particle is the time t_0 such that the probability is $\frac{1}{2}$ that the particle will be emitted before time t. Show that $t_0 = a \ln 2$.

6. A distribution function with density $\mathbf{G}'(x) = \frac{1}{\sqrt{2\pi x}} e^{-(x/2)}$ has been assigned to $\mathfrak{U} = [0, \infty]$. Find the mean and variance for this distribution.

7. In Example 5 assume that $n = 10$. Find the mean and variance for the identity function of the finite experiment discussed in this example. Compare your result with the mean and variance for the identity function for the continuous experiment.

[*Ans.* Mean is $\frac{1}{2}$ in each case. Variance is .0833 in continuous case, .0825 in the finite case.]

8. The exponential distribution with mean a is assigned to $\mathfrak{U} = [0, \infty]$. Let I_j be the interval $[j, j + 1]$. Show that the measure of I_j is of the form $(1 - \lambda)\lambda^j$ for some constant λ. Show that the conditional mean for the outcome given that it is in I_j is of the form $x_j = j + c$, where c is a constant between 0 and 1. Show that when a is very large, this constant is near $\frac{1}{2}$, and when a is very small it is near 0.

9. Consider an experiment with possible outcomes 0, 1, 2, . . . and assume that the weight function $\mathbf{w}(j) = (1 - \lambda)\lambda^j$ has been assigned. Show that

$$\mathbf{Pr}[\mathbf{x} > s + t \mid \mathbf{x} > s] = \mathbf{Pr}[\mathbf{x} > t]$$

for any positive numbers s and t.

10. Prove that for any function $\mathbf{f}$ on an interval space $\mathfrak{U}$, $\mathbf{M}[\mathbf{f}^2] \geq (\mathbf{M}[\mathbf{f}])^2$.

11. Assign the uniform measure to the interval $[0, 1]$. Let $\mathbf{f}(x) = x^2$. Find the mean of $\mathbf{f}$. Find the distribution of $\mathbf{f}$. Compute the mean of this distribution and show that it is the same as the mean of $\mathbf{f}$.

12. Let $\mathfrak{U} = [0, \infty]$ and assume that the exponential distribution with mean a has been assigned. Let $\mathbf{f}(x) = x^2$. Find the distribution of $\mathbf{f}$ and compute the mean of this distribution. Show that the result agrees with the mean of $\mathbf{f}$ as computed directly.

4. INDEPENDENT FUNCTIONS

Consider two experiments carried out independently. Let $\mathfrak{U}_1$ be the possibility space of the first, and $\mathfrak{U}_2$ of the second, and let $\mathbf{m}_1$ and $\mathbf{m}_2$ be the measures determined by the experiments, respectively. Let $\mathbf{f}_1$ be a numerical function on $\mathfrak{U}_1$ and $\mathbf{f}_2$ on $\mathfrak{U}_2$. If we wish to compute probabilities of statements involving the individual functions, such as

$\mathbf{f}_1 < 5$ or $\mathbf{f}_2 > 2$, we can carry out the computation in one of the original spaces. But often we wish to assign a probability to a statement involving both functions, such as $\mathbf{f}_1 + \mathbf{f}_2 < 5$. For this purpose we need to construct a combined space $\mathcal{U}$ and a measure $\mathbf{m}$ on $\mathcal{U}$.

Let us suppose that $\mathbf{f}_1$ has as range $[a_1, b_1]$, and $\mathbf{f}_2$ has range $[a_2, b_2]$. Then as the points of $\mathcal{U}$ we will take all possible pairs of values, that is, all $\begin{pmatrix} x \\ y \end{pmatrix}$ such that $a_1 \leq x \leq b_1$ and $a_2 \leq y \leq b_2$. We may conveniently picture $\mathcal{U}$ as a rectangle in the plane, as shown in Figure 6.

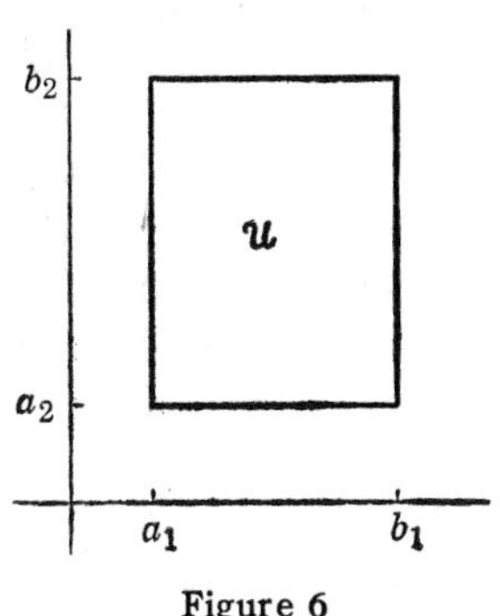

Figure 6

We wish to construct a measure $\mathbf{m}$ on $\mathcal{U}$ that has two properties. First of all, probability statements involving only one function should yield the same value as on the original space. Second, we want the functions to turn out to be independent according to the new measure. More specifically, we must require that

(1) $$\mathbf{Pr_m}[c_1 < \mathbf{f}_1 < d_1] = \mathbf{Pr_{m_1}}[c_1 < \mathbf{f}_1 < d_1]$$

and $$\mathbf{Pr_m}[c_2 < \mathbf{f}_2 < d_2] = \mathbf{Pr_{m_2}}[c_2 < \mathbf{f}_2 < d_2].$$

(2) $$\mathbf{Pr_m}[(c_1 < \mathbf{f}_1 < d_1) \wedge (c_2 < \mathbf{f}_2 < d_2)]$$
$$= \mathbf{Pr_m}[c_1 < \mathbf{f}_1 < d_1] \cdot \mathbf{Pr_m}[c_2 < \mathbf{f}_2 < d_2].$$

We know that instead of considering the functions $\mathbf{f}_1$, $\mathbf{f}_2$ on their domains we may consider the identity functions on their range. In the combined space $\mathcal{U}$ it is convenient to introduce "coordinate functions" $\mathbf{x}$ and $\mathbf{y}$ such that $\mathbf{x}\left[\begin{pmatrix} x \\ y \end{pmatrix}\right] = x$ and $\mathbf{y}\left[\begin{pmatrix} x \\ y \end{pmatrix}\right] = y$. Then in (1) and (2) the function $\mathbf{x}$ will replace $\mathbf{f}_1$, and $\mathbf{y}$ will replace $\mathbf{f}_2$. Then the left side of (2) is the measure of a rectangle A, as shown in Figure 7, according to the new measure. From (2) and (1) we know that this measure is

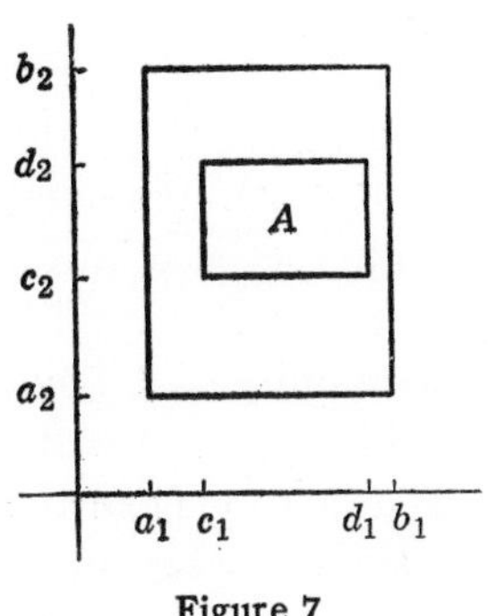

Figure 7

$$\mathbf{Pr_{m_1}}[c_1 < \mathbf{x} < d_1] \cdot \mathbf{Pr_{m_2}}[c_2 < \mathbf{y} < d_2].$$

Thus, if $\mathbf{G}_1$ and $\mathbf{G}_2$ are the distribution functions of the two functions, then

$$\mathbf{m}(A) = [\mathbf{G}_1(d_1) - \mathbf{G}_1(c_1)]\cdot[\mathbf{G}_2(d_2) - \mathbf{G}_2(c_2)]. \tag{3}$$

Thus we see that the measure of each rectangle is uniquely determined by our two requirements. But since, as we asserted in Section 1, the entire measure in the case of a plane region is determined by the measures of rectangles, we have a uniquely determined $\mathbf{m}$. The regions in $\mathcal{U}$ to which we assign measure are limits of unions of rectangles, hence the measures will in general be limits of sums of terms like (3).

Whenever we discuss two independent functions jointly, we will tacitly assume that the combined space $\mathcal{U}$ has been constructed, and all probability statements will be relative to the measure just constructed, the so-called *product measure.*

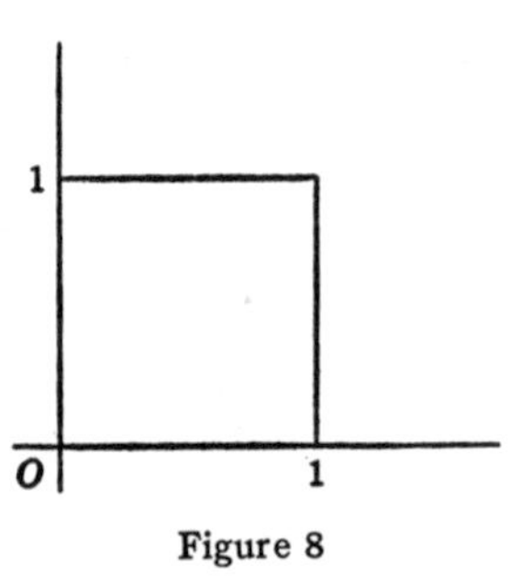

Figure 8

Example 1. Let us suppose that two points are picked at random from the unit interval. Then $0 \leq x \leq 1$, $0 \leq y \leq 1$, and $\mathcal{U}$ is a unit square (see Figure 8). From Section 1 we know that $\mathbf{G}_1(t) = \mathbf{G}_2(t) = t$, and hence (3) yields that $\mathbf{m}(A) = (d_1 - c_1)(d_2 - c_2)$. Thus the measure of the rectangle A is simply its area, and hence the measure of every region (to which we assign a measure) in $\mathcal{U}$ will be its area.

Theorem. Let $\mathbf{g}$ be a function such that $\mathbf{g}$ is continuous and $a_2 \leq \mathbf{g}(x) \leq b_2$ for all x in $[a_1, b_1]$, with the possible exceptions of $x = a_1$ and $x = b_1$. Then for independent coordinate functions $\mathbf{x}$, $\mathbf{y}$ on the combined space $\mathcal{U}$,

$$\mathbf{Pr}[\mathbf{y} < \mathbf{g}(\mathbf{x})] = \int_{a_1}^{b_1} \mathbf{G}_1'(x)\mathbf{G}_2[\mathbf{g}(x)]\,dx. \tag{4}$$

Proof: The desired probability, $\mathbf{Pr}[\mathbf{y} < \mathbf{g}(\mathbf{x})]$ is the measure of the shaded area in Figure 9 (which is the truth set of $\mathbf{y} < \mathbf{g}(\mathbf{x})$). We must approximate this region by rectangles. First we divide the base into n equal parts, each of length $h = (b_1 - a_1)/n$. We know that for the ith such interval we can select a point x_i so that the probability of $\mathbf{x}_1$ lying in this interval is $\mathbf{G}_1'(x_i)\cdot h$. We choose the ith rectangle to have the ith interval as base, and to have altitude $\mathbf{g}(x_i)$. (See Figure 10.) Then the probability of $\mathbf{y}$ lying in the vertical interval is

$$\mathbf{Pr}[\mathbf{y} < \mathbf{g}(x_i)] = \mathbf{G}_2[\mathbf{g}(x_i)].$$

Hence the measure of the ith rectangle is

$$\mathbf{G}_1'(x_i)\mathbf{G}_2[\mathbf{g}(x_i)]\cdot h. \tag{5}$$

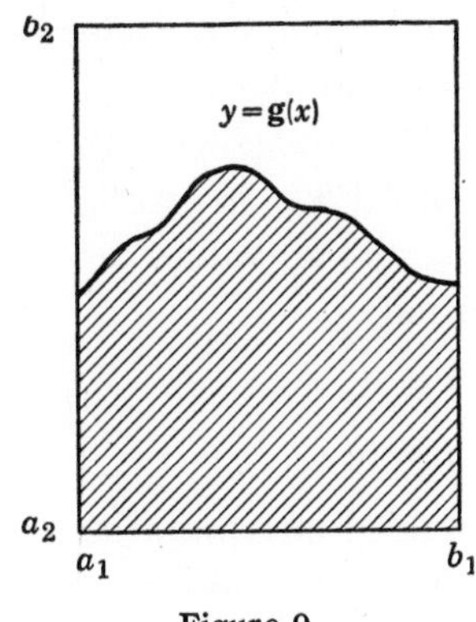

Figure 9

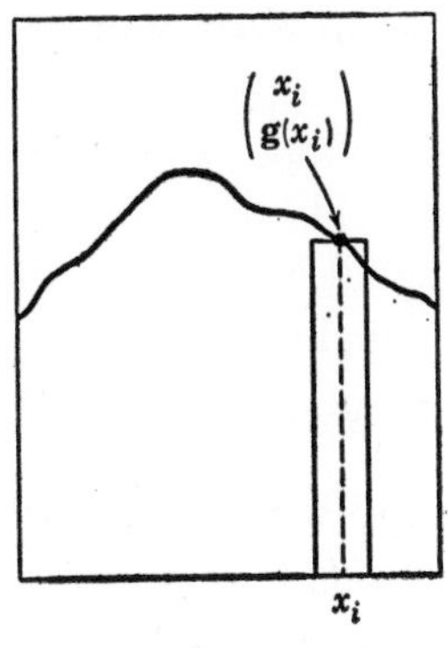

Figure 10

The measure of the entire region will be the limit as n goes to infinity of the sum of the terms (5). It is convenient to introduce the abbreviation $\mathbf{F}(x) = \mathbf{G}_1'(x)\mathbf{G}_2[\mathbf{g}(x)]$. Then the total measure is

$$\operatorname*{Lim}_{n\to\infty} \sum_{i=1}^{n} \mathbf{F}(x_i)\cdot h = \int_{a_1}^{b_1} \mathbf{F}(x)\, dx.$$

The equality follows from the definition of the definite integral. If we replace $\mathbf{F}$ by what it stands for, we obtain our theorem.

This theorem is of great importance. Its one shortcoming is that $\mathbf{g}$ is restricted to have values within $[a_2, b_2]$. But it is easy to see how this restriction can be removed. Suppose that we wish to find $\mathbf{Pr}[\mathbf{y} < \mathbf{g}(\mathbf{x})]$,

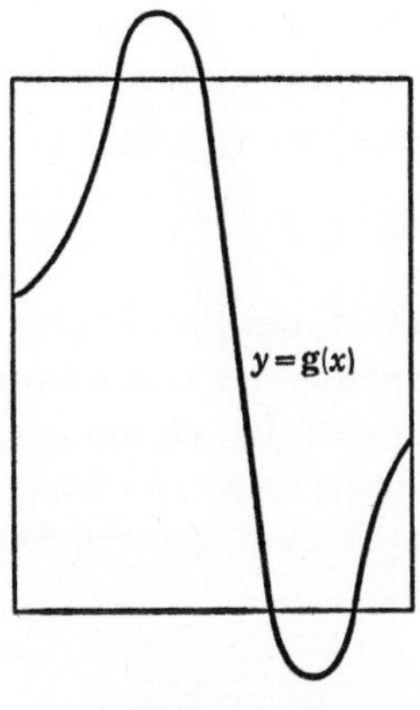

Figure 11

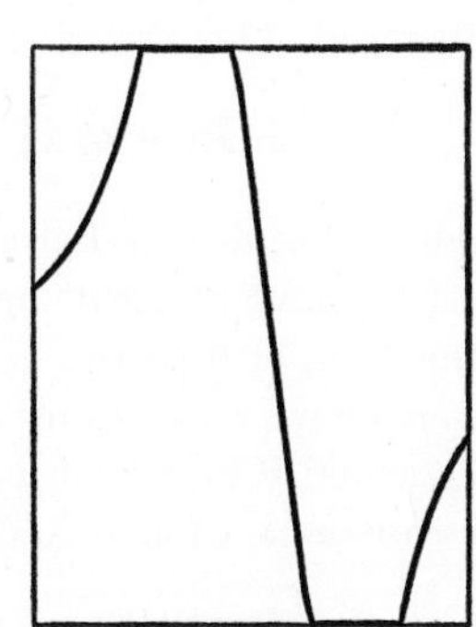

Figure 12

where $\mathbf{g}$ is as in Figure 11. Then we see that we may replace $\mathbf{g}$ by the function $\mathbf{g}_1$ shown in Figure 12, which will not change the probability. The latter function satisfies the condition of the theorem.

There is an even simpler trick for extending the usefulness of the theorem. Why can $\mathbf{g}$ not be used directly, in the case of Figure 10? Because $\mathbf{g}$ will be sometimes below a_2 and sometimes above b_2, and hence $\mathbf{G}_2[\mathbf{g}(x)]$ is not defined. The trick of using $\mathbf{g}_1$ in place of $\mathbf{g}$ amounts to replacing all values of $\mathbf{g}$ above b_2 by b_2, and all values below a_2 by a_2. We could equally well adopt the convention:

If $t > b_2$, then $\quad \mathbf{G}_2(t) = \mathbf{G}_2(b_2) = 1.$

If $t < a_2$, then $\quad \mathbf{G}_2(t) = \mathbf{G}_2(a_2) = 0.$

This convention agrees well with the intended interpretation of $\mathbf{G}_2$, and it is in common use. Once we adopt the convention, we may in our theorem use any continuous function $\mathbf{g}$.

Example 2. Let us ask in Example 1 what the probability is that the product of the two numbers selected is less than $\frac{1}{2}$. That is, we are trying to find $\mathbf{Pr}[x \cdot y < \frac{1}{2}] = \mathbf{Pr}[y < 1/2x]$. Our theorem is applicable with $\mathbf{g}(x) = 1/2x$. Hence the answer is

$$\int_0^1 \mathbf{G}_1'(x)\mathbf{G}_2(1/2x)\,dx = \int_0^1 1 \cdot \mathbf{G}_2(1/2x)\,dx.$$

In evaluating this integral we must be careful of values of x for which $1/2x > 1$, that is, for $x < \frac{1}{2}$. Here $\mathbf{G}_2$ is equal to 1, by our convention. Hence we have

$$\int_0^{1/2} 1\,dx + \int_{1/2}^1 1/2x\,dx = \tfrac{1}{2}(1 + \ln 2) = .847.$$

As a special case of our theorem let us consider two independent functions, both of which have range $[0, b]$. Then $\mathcal{U}$ is a square of side b at the origin. Let us choose $\mathbf{g}(x) = x$, so that the bounding curve is the upward slanting diagonal. Our theorem is applicable in this case, and we find that

$$\mathbf{Pr}[\mathbf{y} < \mathbf{x}] = \int_0^b \mathbf{G}_1'(x)\mathbf{G}_2(x)\,dx. \tag{6}$$

Example 3. Let us consider a mixture of two types of radioactive atoms, in which we have "tagged" an atom of each kind. What is the probability that the atom of type two will be emitted first? Let us suppose that the two atoms have mean times of a_1 and a_2, respectively, for being emitted. Letting $\mathbf{x}$ and $\mathbf{y}$ be the outcome functions (that is, the respective times before emission), we may apply (6) to yield

$$\int_0^\infty \frac{1}{a_1} e^{-x/a_1}(1 - e^{-x/a_2})\,dx = \frac{a_1}{a_1 + a_2}.$$

Similarly, the probability that the first type of atom is emitted first is $a_2/(a_1 + a_2)$. The fact that the sum of these two probabilities is 1 shows that the probability of being emitted at exactly the same time is 0. It should also be noted that if the atoms are alike, that is $a_1 = a_2$, then the probability that a particular one is emitted first is $\frac{1}{2}$.

Example 4. A floor is made of planks of uniform width. We take a match whose length equals the width of one plank, and toss it up in the air. What is the probability that the match will fall on a crack between planks? Let us take the width of a plank (and hence the length of our match) to be two units. The position of the fallen match is determined by two numbers: the angle it makes with a fixed line, and the position of its center. Actually, it suffices to take the distance of the center from the nearest crack, and it is convenient to measure the angle relative to a line perpendicular to the crack. Let **x** be the angle, and **y** be the distance. (See Figure 13.)

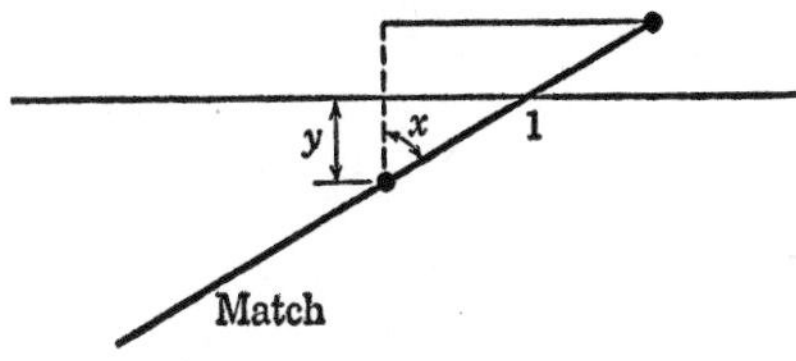

Figure 13

Then $\mathfrak{U}_1 = [-\pi/2, \pi/2]$ and $\mathfrak{U}_2 = [0, 1]$. If the match is tossed in the air without regard to the position of the planks, we may assume that **x** and **y** have the uniform distribution and that they are independent. Hence $\mathbf{G}_1(t) = (t + \pi/2)/\pi$, and $\mathbf{G}_2(t) = t$.

For the match to cross a crack we must have $\mathbf{y} < \cos(\mathbf{x})$, as can be seen from Figure 13. Hence our theorem is applicable with $\mathbf{g}(x) = \cos x$. Thus the desired probability is

$$\int_{-\pi/2}^{\pi/2} \mathbf{G}_1'(x)\mathbf{G}_2(\cos x)\, dx = \int_{-\pi/2}^{\pi/2} \frac{1}{\pi} \cos x\, dx = \frac{2}{\pi}.$$

It is very interesting to note that this problem, whose formulation has nothing to do with circles requires π for its solution. It also furnishes us with a simple "experimental" method of finding an approximate value of π.

Example 5. Let us generalize Example 4 to the case where the length of the match is k times the width of a plank. Then our inequality becomes $\mathbf{y} < k \cos(\mathbf{x})$, and hence we obtain

$$\int_{-\pi/2}^{\pi/2} \mathbf{G}_1'(x)\mathbf{G}_2(k \cos x)\, dx = \int_{-\pi/2}^{\pi/2} \frac{1}{\pi} k \cos x\, dx = \frac{2k}{\pi}.$$

This states that the probability of crossing a crack is proportional to the length of the match. But this is, in general, absurd. For example, if the match is π times the width of the plank, then we obtain a probability of 2.

This is a case where we did not pay sufficient attention to our convention. If $k > 1$, then $k \cos x$ will take on values greater than 1, and hence will lie outside the range of $\mathbf{y}$. For such values we must replace $\mathbf{G}_2(k \cos x)$ by 1. Hence we note that the answer just obtained is correct for $k \leq 1$, but for $k > 1$ we must proceed as follows:

$$\begin{aligned}\int_{-\pi/2}^{\pi/2} \mathbf{G}_1'(x)\mathbf{G}_2(k \cos x)\,dx &= \frac{1}{\pi}\int_{-\pi/2}^{\pi/2} \mathbf{G}_2(k \cos x)\,dx \\ &= \frac{2}{\pi}\int_0^{\pi/2} \mathbf{G}_2(k \cos x)\,dx \\ &= \frac{2}{\pi}\left[\int_0^{\arccos(1/k)} 1\,dx + \int_{\arccos(1/k)}^{\pi/2} k \cos x\,dx\right] \\ &= \frac{2}{\pi}\left[\arccos\frac{1}{k} + k - \sqrt{k^2 - 1}\right].\end{aligned}$$

EXERCISES

1. In Example 3 find $\mathbf{Pr}[\mathbf{y} < \mathbf{x} + 1]$, that is, the probability that the second atom decays at most 1 second after the first one.

2. In Example 3 find $\mathbf{Pr}[\mathbf{y} \leq \mathbf{x} - 1]$, that is, the probability that the second atom decays at least 1 second before the first. (*Hint:* The lower limit of the integral in this case is not 0.)

3. Using the results of Exercises 1 and 2 find $\mathbf{Pr}[|\mathbf{x} - \mathbf{y}| < 1]$, that is, the probability that the two atoms decay within 1 second of each other. [*Ans.* $1 - a_1/(a_1 + a_2)e^{-1/a_1} - a_2/(a_1 + a_2)e^{-1/a_2}$.]

4. Obtain the answer of Exercise 3 by the following alternative argument: The desired probability may be obtained by adding the probability that atom 1 decays first and atom 2 decays within a second afterwards to the probability that atom 2 decays first and atom 1 decays within a second afterwards. (*Hint:* Use the result of Example 3, and recall that the probability of decay within any one-second interval is always the same for a given atom.)

5. Pick two numbers from 0 to 1 at random. What is the probability that their sum is less than 1.2? [*Ans.* .68.]

6. In Example 2 draw the truth set of $\mathbf{xy} < 1/2$, and verify that the answer obtained is the area of the truth set.

7. From (6) prove that $\mathbf{Pr}[(\mathbf{y} < \mathbf{x}) \vee (\mathbf{x} < \mathbf{y})] = 1$, in all cases where (6) is applicable. What is $\mathbf{Pr}[\mathbf{x} = \mathbf{y}]$?

8. In Example 5 verify that both formulas give the correct answer if $k = 1$.

9. In Example 5 prove that the probability tends to 1 as the length of the match is increased indefinitely.

10. In Example 5 find the probability that a match twice the width of a plank crosses a crack. [*Ans.* .837.]

11. What is the probability that two numbers picked at random from 0 to 1 will differ by less than $\frac{1}{2}$?

12. Prove that if two points are picked at random from 0 to 1 the probability that they differ by less than k (where $0 \le k \le 1$) is $2k - k^2$.

13. If $\mathbf{x}$ and $\mathbf{y}$ both have range $[0, b]$ and have distribution functions $\mathbf{G}_1$ and $\mathbf{G}_2$, prove that the function $\mathbf{f} = \mathbf{y}/\mathbf{x}$ has distribution

$$\mathbf{G}(t) = \int_0^b \mathbf{G}_1'(x)\mathbf{G}_2(tx)\,dx.$$

14. In Exercise 13 find the distribution of $\mathbf{f} = \mathbf{xy}$.

15. In Example 2 find the distribution of $\mathbf{y}/\mathbf{x}$. [*Hint:* Use the result of Exercise 13, and observe the convention on $\mathbf{G}_2$. The range of the quotient will be $[0, +\infty]$.]

16. In Example 2 find the distribution of $\mathbf{x} \cdot \mathbf{y}$ and verify that it yields the correct value for $t = \frac{1}{2}$. [*Ans.* $\mathbf{G}(t) = t(1 - \ln t)$.]

17. It can be shown that for any pair of independent functions $\mathbf{M}[\mathbf{f}_1\mathbf{f}_2] = \mathbf{M}[\mathbf{f}_1] \cdot \mathbf{M}[\mathbf{f}_2]$. Using the result of Exercise 16, verify this for the case of Example 2.

18. Let $\mathfrak{U}$ be the interval $[-\pi, \pi]$ and assume that the uniform measure has been assigned. Let $\mathbf{f}_n(x) = \sin nx$. Prove that $\mathbf{M}[\mathbf{f}_n] = 0$ and $\mathbf{V}[\mathbf{f}_n] = \frac{1}{2}$. Prove that $\mathbf{M}[\mathbf{f}_n \cdot \mathbf{f}_m] = \mathbf{M}[\mathbf{f}_n] \cdot \mathbf{M}[\mathbf{f}_m]$ for $n \neq m$. Are $\mathbf{f}_n$ and $\mathbf{f}_m$ independent?

19. From the interval $[0, \pi/2]$ we pick two points: the first is picked at random, the second with a method leading to the distribution $1 - \cos t$. What is the probability that the first is smaller than the second? Give an intuitive reason why the answer must be greater than $\frac{1}{2}$. [*Ans.* $2/\pi$.]

5. SUMS OF INDEPENDENT FUNCTIONS

If $\mathbf{f}_1$ and $\mathbf{f}_2$ are independent functions, a particularly important new function to consider is $\mathbf{f} = \mathbf{f}_1 + \mathbf{f}_2$. If we know the distribution functions $\mathbf{G}_1$ and $\mathbf{G}_2$ of the original functions, we may use the results of the previous section to obtain the distribution function $\mathbf{G}$ of $\mathbf{f}$.

Let the range of $\mathbf{f}_1$ be $[a_1, b_1]$ and of $\mathbf{f}_2$ be $[a_2, b_2]$. As usual we construct the combined space $\mathfrak{U}$ on which $\mathbf{f} = \mathbf{x} + \mathbf{y}$. The range of $\mathbf{f}$ is the interval $[a_1 + a_2, b_1 + b_2]$. For any t in this interval, by definition

$$\mathbf{G}(t) = \mathbf{Pr}[\mathbf{f} < t] = \mathbf{Pr}[\mathbf{x} + \mathbf{y} < t] = \mathbf{Pr}[\mathbf{y} < t - \mathbf{x}].$$

This may be obtained by the method of the general theorem if we choose

$\mathbf{g}(x) = t - x$, where t is taken as a fixed number. The boundary curve $y = t - x$ is a straight line, which in a typical position appears as in Figure 14. From our theorem we obtain

$$\mathbf{G}(t) = \int_{a_1}^{b_1} \mathbf{G}_1'(x)\mathbf{G}_2(t - x)\, dx \tag{1}$$

where $\mathbf{G}_2(t - x)$ has to be interpreted according to the convention we adopted for values of x to the left of c and to the right of d. This $\mathbf{G}(t)$

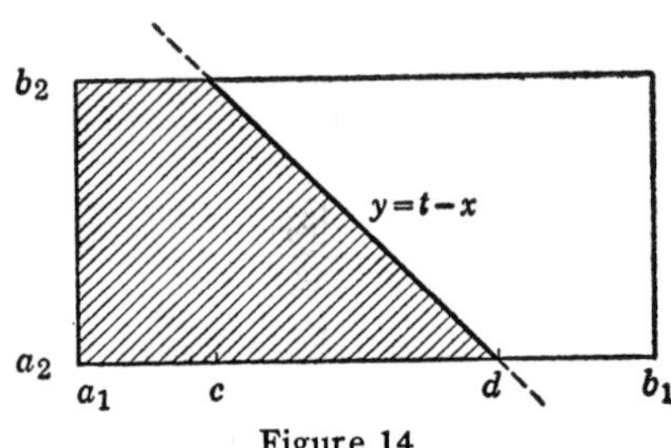

Figure 14

need not have a continuous density function. But if it has a continuous density $\mathbf{G}'(t)$, then we may obtain a formula for the new density function by differentiating with respect to t. (This can be justified, even though the derivative of $\mathbf{G}_2$ does not exist at c and d.)

$$\mathbf{G}'(t) = \int_{a_1}^{b_1} \mathbf{G}_1'(x)\mathbf{G}_2'(t - x)\, dx. \tag{2}$$

Actually we need to carry out the integral only over a smaller interval in most cases. Since by our convention $\mathbf{G}_2$ is a constant (0 or 1) outside of $[a_2, b_2]$, its derivative is 0 here. Hence we need only integrate over those values of x for which $t - x$ lies within $[a_2, b_2]$. In Figure 14 this would mean integrating from c to d.

Example 1. Assume that in two independent experiments the outcome functions $\mathbf{x}$ and $\mathbf{y}$ have normal distribution, with mean 0 and variance 1. Let us find the density for $\mathbf{x} + \mathbf{y}$. Since the ranges are $[-\infty, +\infty]$, then $t - x$ will always lie in the range of $\mathbf{y}$.

$$\begin{aligned}
\mathbf{G}(t) &= \int_{-\infty}^{\infty} \mathbf{G}_1'(x)\mathbf{G}_2'(t - x)\, dx \\
&= \frac{1}{2\pi} \int_{-\infty}^{\infty} e^{-x^2/2} e^{-(t-x)^2/2}\, dx \\
&= \frac{1}{2\pi} \int_{-\infty}^{\infty} e^{-x^2 - t^2/2 + tx}\, dx \\
&= \frac{1}{2\pi} \int_{-\infty}^{\infty} e^{-(x-t/2)^2 - t^2/4}\, dx \\
&= \frac{1}{2\sqrt{\pi}} e^{-t^2/4} \int_{-\infty}^{\infty} \frac{1}{\sqrt{\pi}} e^{-(x-t/2)^2}\, dx.
\end{aligned}$$

The integrand for the last integral is the normal density with mean $t/2$ and variance $\frac{1}{2}$. Hence the value of this integral is 1. Thus

$$\mathbf{G}'(t) = \frac{1}{2\sqrt{\pi}} e^{-t^2/4}.$$

But this is the density of the normal distribution with mean 0 and variance 2. Thus we see that the sum of two functions with normal distribution having mean 0 and standard deviation 1 is a function with normal distribution having mean 0 and standard deviation 2. This is a special case of the following more general result which may be proved by a computation similar to that given above.

Theorem. Let $\mathbf{f}_1$ and $\mathbf{f}_2$ be two independent functions such that $\mathbf{f}_1$ has normal distribution with mean a_1 and variance b_1^2, and $\mathbf{f}_2$ has normal distribution with mean a_2 and variance b_2^2. Then $\mathbf{f}_1 + \mathbf{f}_2$ has normal distribution with mean $a_1 + a_2$ and variance $b_1^2 + b_2^2$.

Both the law of large numbers and the central limit theorem stated for finite experiments hold also under very general conditions for experiments with interval possibility spaces. In particular, consider an experiment with interval possibility space $\mathcal{U}$ and outcome function $\mathbf{f}$. If this experiment is repeated n times independently, we obtain n outcome functions $\mathbf{f}_1, \mathbf{f}_2, \ldots, \mathbf{f}_n$. Let $\mathbf{s}_n = \mathbf{f}_1 + \mathbf{f}_2 + \ldots + \mathbf{f}_n$. Assume that both the mean and variance of $\mathbf{f}_1$ are finite. Let $\mathbf{M}[\mathbf{f}_1] = a$ and $\mathbf{V}[\mathbf{f}_1] = b^2$. Then $\mathbf{M}[\mathbf{s}_n/n] = a$ and $\mathbf{V}[\mathbf{s}_n/n] = b^2/n$.

Law of large numbers. For any $\epsilon > 0$,

$$\mathbf{Pr}\left[\left|\frac{\mathbf{s}_n}{n} - a\right| > \epsilon\right] \to 0$$

as n tends to infinity.

The proof of this theorem follows exactly the proof in the finite case using Chebychev's inequality.

As in the finite case the fact that the variance of the average of independent outcomes approaches 0 suggests that the average of the outcomes will be with high probability near the mean. It is important to realize that this need not be the case without some restriction on the distribution of $\mathbf{f}_1$. We have here assumed that the mean and variance are finite. To see that some restriction is necessary consider the case where the distribution of $\mathbf{f}_1$ is the Cauchy distribution

$$\mathbf{G}(t) = \frac{1}{2} + \frac{1}{\pi} \arctan t$$

on $[-\infty, \infty]$. Then the average of two such functions $(\mathbf{f}_1 + \mathbf{f}_2)/2$ will have a distribution given by

$$\mathbf{Pr}\left[\frac{\mathbf{f}_1 + \mathbf{f}_2}{2} < t\right] = \mathbf{Pr}[\mathbf{f}_1 + \mathbf{f}_2 < 2t]$$
$$= \int_{-\infty}^{\infty} \mathbf{G}'(x)\mathbf{G}(2t - x)\, dx$$
$$= \frac{1}{\pi}\int_{-\infty}^{\infty} \frac{1}{1 + x^2}\left[\frac{1}{2} + \frac{1}{\pi}\arctan(2t - x)\right] dx.$$

If this integration is carried out we obtain

$$\mathbf{Pr}\left[\frac{\mathbf{f}_1 + \mathbf{f}_2}{2} < t\right] = \frac{1}{2} + \frac{1}{\pi}\arctan t.$$

But this states that the average of the two outcomes has exactly the same distribution as each individual outcome. Hence the average of any number of outcomes is no more likely to be near 0, for example, than is a single outcome. For the distribution we have considered the mean is defined only in a certain restricted sense and the variance is in any case infinite.

As in the finite case, it is possible to prove that under suitable conditions the average of a large number of independent outcomes will have a distribution which is approximately normal.

Central Limit Theorem. Let $\mathbf{s}_n$ be the sum of n independent functions $\mathbf{f}_1, \mathbf{f}_2, \ldots, \mathbf{f}_n$, each having the same distribution, having a finite variance not 0. Let $\mathbf{s}_n^*$ be $\mathbf{s}_n$ normalized to have mean 0 and standard deviation 1. Then for any choice of c and d,

$$\mathbf{Pr}[c < \mathbf{s}_n^* < d] \to \frac{1}{\sqrt{2\pi}} \int_c^d e^{-x^2/2}\, dx$$

as $n \to \infty$.

It is interesting to consider the central limit theorem for the special case where the outcome functions themselves have a normal distribution. In this case we know that the sum $\mathbf{s}_n = \mathbf{f}_1 + \ldots + \mathbf{f}_n$ will also have a normal distribution. Hence $\mathbf{s}_n^*$ will have a normal distribution with mean 0 and standard deviation 1. For this case the central limit theorem is trivially true, the limiting situation being exact for every n. We consider now an example where the common distribution is not normal.

Example 2. Consider the experiment of choosing a point at random on the unit interval. We perform this experiment twice. Let $\mathbf{f}_1$ and $\mathbf{f}_2$ be the outcome functions and let $\mathbf{f} = \mathbf{f}_1 + \mathbf{f}_2$. Then $\mathbf{G}_1(t) = \mathbf{G}_2(t) = t$, and

$$\mathbf{G}(t) = \int_0^1 \mathbf{G}_1'(x)\mathbf{G}_2(t - x)\, dx = \int_0^1 \mathbf{G}_2(t - x)\, dx.$$

If $t \leq 1$, $\mathbf{G}_2(t-x) = 0$ for $x > t$. Hence

$$\mathbf{G}(t) = \int_0^t (t-x)\,dx = \tfrac{1}{2}t^2.$$

If $t > 1$, $\mathbf{G}_2(t-x) = 1$ for $x < t-1$. Hence

$$\mathbf{G}(t) = \int_0^{t-1} 1\,dx + \int_{t-1}^{1} (t-x)\,dx = -\tfrac{1}{2}t^2 + 2t - 1.$$

The density is

$$\mathbf{G}'(t) = \begin{cases} t & 0 \leq t \leq 1 \\ 2-t & 1 \leq t \leq 2. \end{cases}$$

The graph of $\mathbf{G}'(t)$ is shown in Figure 15.

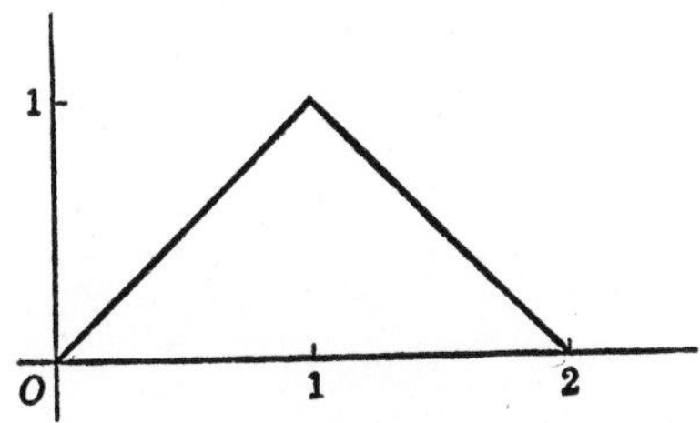

Figure 15

Similarly we can find the density for the sum of four such functions. If the computation is carried out the result is

$$\mathbf{G}'(t) = \begin{cases} \tfrac{1}{6}t^3, & 0 \leq t \leq 1 \\ -\tfrac{1}{2}t^3 + 2t^2 - 2t + \tfrac{2}{3}, & 1 \leq t \leq 2 \\ \mathbf{G}'(4-t) & 2 \leq t \leq 4 \end{cases}$$

We have seen that $\mathbf{M}[\mathbf{f}_1] = \frac{1}{2}$ and $\mathbf{V}[\mathbf{f}_1] = \frac{1}{12}$. Hence the mean and variance for the sum of four experiments would be 2 and $\frac{4}{12} = \frac{1}{3}$, respectively. The central limit theorem suggests comparing this with a normal density with mean 2 and variance $\frac{1}{3}$. We have shown in Figure 16, p. 472, the two density functions, and it will be seen that they are indeed quite similar.

We shall now give two other applications of sums of independent functions.

Example 3. Assume that a gun is to be fired at a target. We determine a coordinate system on the target putting the origin at the bull's-eye. Let $\mathbf{x}$ be the x coordinate of the shot and $\mathbf{y}$ the y coordinate. Assume that $\mathbf{x}$ and $\mathbf{y}$ are independent functions having normal distribution with mean 0. By a suitable choice of units we can make them have standard deviation 1. (The assumption of normality is often justified on the grounds of the central limit theorem. The values of $\mathbf{x}$ and $\mathbf{y}$ are thought of as the sum of a large number of small chance effects.) We shall now find the distribu-

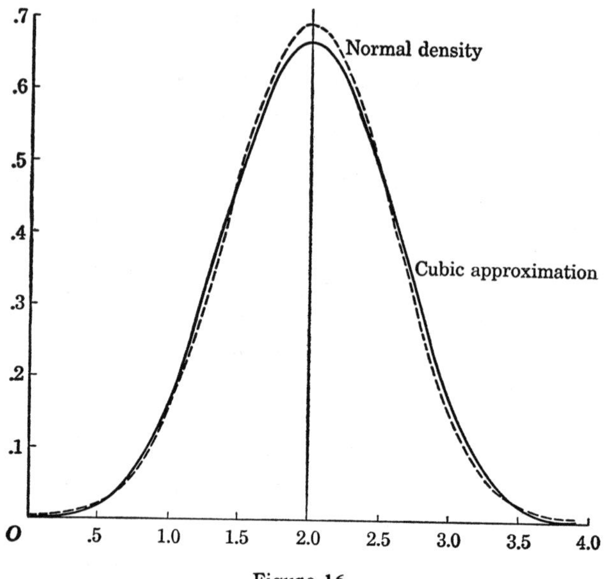

Figure 16

tion function for the square of the distance $\mathbf{r}$ from the origin, that is for $\mathbf{r}^2 = \mathbf{x}^2 + \mathbf{y}^2$. The function $\mathbf{r}^2$ has range $[0, +\infty]$.

The functions $\mathbf{x}^2$ and $\mathbf{y}^2$, being squares of functions with normal distribution with mean 0 and variance 1, have density

$$\mathbf{G}_1'(t) = \mathbf{G}_2'(t) = \frac{1}{\sqrt{2\pi t}} e^{-t/2}.$$

Hence if $\mathbf{G}(t)$ is the distribution of $\mathbf{r}^2$,

$$\begin{aligned} \mathbf{G}(t) &= \int_0^t \mathbf{G}_1'(x)\mathbf{G}_2'(t-x)\,dx \\ &= \int_0^t \frac{1}{\sqrt{2\pi x}} e^{-x/2} \frac{1}{\sqrt{2\pi(t-x)}} e^{-(t-x)/2}\,dx \\ &= \frac{1}{2\pi} e^{-t/2} \int_0^t \frac{dx}{\sqrt{x(t-x)}}. \end{aligned}$$

But
$$\int_0^t \frac{dx}{\sqrt{x(t-x)}} = \arcsin \frac{2x-t}{t}\Big]_0^t = \pi.$$

Therefore
$$\mathbf{G}'(t) = \frac{1}{2} e^{-t/2}$$

and
$$\mathbf{G}(t) = 1 - e^{-t/2}.$$

Thus the square of the distance from the center has an exponential distribution with mean 2 and standard deviation 2.

Example 4. As an extension of the previous example we consider an example from physics. Consider a large number of gas molecules in a container. Let the vector velocity of a molecule be represented by $\mathbf{V}$ and its cartesian components by $\mathbf{v}_1$, $\mathbf{v}_2$, and $\mathbf{v}_3$. Then the speed of a molecule $\mathbf{s}$ is determined by

$$\mathbf{s}^2 = \mathbf{v}_1^2 + \mathbf{v}_2^2 + \mathbf{v}_3^2.$$

It is usually assumed that if a molecule is chosen at random its velocity components may be assumed to have normal distributions with mean 0. By a proper choice of units we may assure that the variance is 1. Let us then find the distribution for $\mathbf{s}^2$. Let $\mathbf{G}_1$ be the distribution for $\mathbf{v}_1^2$ and $\mathbf{G}_2$ for $\mathbf{v}_2^2 + \mathbf{v}_3^2$. From our previous results we know that

$$\mathbf{G}_1'(t) = \frac{1}{\sqrt{2\pi t}}\, e^{-t/2} \quad \text{and} \quad \mathbf{G}_2'(t) = \frac{1}{2}\, e^{-t/2}.$$

Then the density function $\mathbf{G}'$ for $\mathbf{s}^2$ is given by

$$\mathbf{G}'(t) = \int_0^t \frac{1}{\sqrt{2\pi x}}\, e^{-x/2} \cdot \frac{1}{2}\, e^{-(t-x)/2}\, dx$$

$$= \frac{1}{2\sqrt{2\pi}}\, e^{-t/2} \int_0^t \frac{dx}{\sqrt{x}} = \frac{\sqrt{t}}{\sqrt{2\pi}}\, e^{-t/2}.$$

Therefore $$\mathbf{G}(t) = \frac{1}{\sqrt{2\pi}} \int_0^t \sqrt{x}e^{-x/2}\, dx.$$

We have found the distribution for the square of the speed. To find the distribution $\mathbf{G}_0$ for the speed itself we proceed as follows.

$$\mathbf{G}_0(t) = \mathbf{Pr}[\mathbf{s} < t] = \mathbf{Pr}[\mathbf{s}^2 < t^2] = \frac{1}{\sqrt{2\pi}} \int_0^{t^2} \sqrt{x}\, e^{-x/2}\, dx.$$

The density is given by differentiation,

$$\mathbf{G}_0'(t) = \frac{\sqrt{2}}{\sqrt{\pi}}\, t^2 e^{-t^2/2}.$$

EXERCISES

1. An experiment has possibility space $[0, \infty]$ and outcome function with density e^{-t}. Assume that the experiment is performed twice. Find the density function for the sum of the two outcomes. Do the same for the case of four experiments. [*Ans.* xe^{-x}, $\frac{1}{6}x^3e^{-x}$.]

2. In Exercise 1, let $\mathbf{g}$ be the sum of the four experiments. Then $\mathbf{M}[\mathbf{g}] = 4$ and $\mathbf{V}[\mathbf{g}] = 4$. Using the result of Exercise 1, find the density for $\mathbf{g}^* = (\mathbf{g} - 4)/2$ and compare this with a normal density with mean 0 and variance 1.

3. In Example 2 find the probability of a deviation of more than one standard deviation from the mean in the sum of four experiments. Do the same for two and three standard deviations. Compare the results with those obtained from a normal density.

4. In Example 2 find the point of inflection for the cubic density function on Figure 16 and compare with the point of inflection for the normal density function.

5. Let **f** be a function with range $[0, \infty]$ and density $\mathbf{G}'$. Show that the density function for $\sqrt{\mathbf{f}}$ is $\mathbf{G}_0'$ given by $\mathbf{G}_0'(t) = 2\mathbf{G}'(t^2)$ for $t > 0$.

6. Use the result of Exercise 5 to find the density for the distance from the origin in Example 3. Find the mean of the distance.

[*Ans.* $te^{-t^2/2}, \dfrac{1}{2\sqrt{2\pi}}$.]

7. Use the result of Exercise 5 to find the density for the speed of a molecule (see Example 4). Find the mean of the speed.

8. In Example 3 of Section 4, assume that a molecule is tagged and observed until the first time it collides with another molecule. Let **f** be the time required. Assume that

$$\mathbf{Pr}[\mathbf{f} \geq t + s \mid \mathbf{f} \geq t] = \mathbf{Pr}[\mathbf{f} \geq s].$$

What would the density for **f** be? Compare this assumption in the case (a) the velocity of the particle is known and (b) the velocity is unknown.

9. Assume that $\mathbf{f}_1, \mathbf{f}_2, \ldots, \mathbf{f}_n$ are independent functions, each with uniform distribution on the interval $[a, b]$. Find the mean and variance of the sum.

10. Assume that 10 people are waiting in a line for service. Assume further that the probability that a single person is served during the first t seconds after he becomes first in the line is $1 - e^{-t}$. What is the mean and variance for the total time it takes to get served? Use the central limit theorem to estimate the probability that the total time is greater than half an hour.

11. The energy associated with a particle with speed s is $w = \frac{1}{2}ms^2$, where m is the mass of the particle. Using the result of Example 4 find the mean value of the energy. [*Ans.* $\frac{3}{2}m$.]

6. ERRORS IN MEASUREMENT AND COMPUTATION

In this section we shall show that the theory of probability can give insight into the accuracy of results obtained by measurements and computations.

We begin with a simple example from machine computations. Let us suppose that the machine carries out N multiplications in a given problem. If the machine carries its answers to k decimal places, it will have to round off each product in the kth place. This introduces an error between $-5\cdot 10^{-(k+1)}$ and $5\cdot 10^{-(k+1)}$. It is convenient in the machine to carry all numbers as proper fractions, and in this case errors are roughly added. If we want to be absolutely safe, we must allow for a cumulative rounding error of $5N\cdot 10^{-(k+1)}$. If $N = 10^6$, and $k = 10$, then this will be $5\cdot 10^{-5}$, which may introduce an error of 1 in the fourth decimal place.

However, it is unrealistic to assume that there will be no cancellation among the errors, and that each error will be of maximum size. Instead, it is often reasonable to assume that a rounding error of $\mathbf{f}_j$ occurs on the jth multiplication, and that its distribution is uniform on $[-5\cdot 10^{-(k+1)}, 5\cdot 10^{-(k+1)}]$. If we take the total error $\mathbf{s}_N$ to be the sum of these errors, and assume that the errors are independent, then the central limit theorem states that $\mathbf{s}_N^*$ will have a distribution that is very nearly normal with mean 0 and variance 1. For each j, $\mathbf{M}[\mathbf{f}_j] = 0$ and $\mathbf{V}[\mathbf{f}_j] = \frac{1}{12}\cdot 10^{-2k}$. Hence $\mathbf{M}[\mathbf{s}_N] = 0$ and $\mathbf{V}[\mathbf{s}_N] = (N/12)\cdot 10^{-2k}$. Hence $\mathbf{s}_N^* = \mathbf{s}_N\cdot(\sqrt{12}\,10^k/\sqrt{N})$. Thus, for example,

$$\mathbf{Pr}\left[-3 < \frac{\sqrt{12}\,10^k}{\sqrt{N}}\mathbf{s}_N < +3\right] = \mathbf{Pr}\left[-\frac{3\sqrt{N}}{\sqrt{12}\,10^k} < \mathbf{s}_N < +\frac{3\sqrt{N}}{\sqrt{12}\,10^k}\right]$$
$$\approx .997.$$

If we again take $N = 10^6$ and $k = 10$, we find that a cumulative rounding error of $3\sqrt{10^6}/\sqrt{12}\,10^{10}$, which is less than 10^{-7}, is quite unlikely. Hence we are safe in trusting six decimal places in the answer. We also see that $10^{-k}\sqrt{N}$ is a fairly safe estimate of the cumulative rounding error in all such cases.

In the above example our error was the sum of functions such that for each function we knew the mean and variance. We now consider a case where this is not true. Assume that we are trying to measure some physical object, say the length of a rod. Let us hypothesize that our rod has a "true length" a, but that our measuring devices are subject to error. Let $\mathbf{f}$ be the value we get on measuring the rod. It is customary to assume that $\mathbf{f}$ is a function with normal distribution with mean a and variance b^2. This is suggested by the central limit theorem, it being assumed that the actual error in measurement is the sum of a large number of small chance effects. We do not know a or b^2. The variance b^2 will, of course, depend upon the measuring device used. A large variance would correspond to a crude instrument and a small variance to a precise instrument. We would like to estimate a. We might also be interested in estimating b^2, which is a descriptive quantity associated with the measuring technique.

We take a series of N measurements. Let $\mathbf{f}_1, \mathbf{f}_2, \ldots, \mathbf{f}_N$ be the outcomes for these measurements. We begin by estimating a. This is done by means of the function

$$\mathbf{h}_N = \frac{\mathbf{f}_1 + \mathbf{f}_2 + \ldots + \mathbf{f}_N}{N}.$$

The function $\mathbf{h}_N$ is called the *sample mean*. If we assume that the measurements are independent and each with the same distribution, then the law of large numbers states that for any $\epsilon > 0$

$$\mathbf{Pr}[|\mathbf{h}_N - a| > \epsilon] \to 0$$

as N tends to infinity. Hence we know that by taking sufficiently many experiments we can obtain a to any desired accuracy. We now see what accuracy we can assure for a given number of experiments.

Each $\mathbf{f}_j$ is assumed to have normal distribution with mean a and variance b^2. Hence $\mathbf{h}_N$ will have normal distribution with mean a and variance b^2/N. Therefore

$$\mathbf{h}_N^* = \frac{\mathbf{h}_N - \mathbf{a}}{(b/\sqrt{N})}$$

will have a normal distribution with mean 0 and variance 1. Hence from tables of the normal distribution we can find for any k

$$\mathbf{Pr}\left[-k < \frac{\mathbf{h}_N - \mathbf{a}}{(b/\sqrt{N})} < k\right]$$

or equivalently

$$\mathbf{Pr}\left[\mathbf{h}_N - \frac{kb}{\sqrt{N}} < a < \mathbf{h}_N + \frac{kb}{\sqrt{N}}\right].$$

Assume now that the variance b^2 is known. For example, assume that $b = .4$ and $N = 10^4$. Then if we take $k = 2$ we have

$$\mathbf{Pr}[\mathbf{h}_N - .008 < a < \mathbf{h}_N + .008] = .95.$$

We then perform the experiments, find the value of $\mathbf{h}_N$ and assert that a lies in the interval $\mathbf{h}_N \pm .008$. We have asserted a statement to be true, when in fact we are only willing to assign probability .95 for its being true. For this reason the interval obtained is called the 95 per cent *confidence interval*. Had we chosen $k = 3$ we would have obtained a larger interval but we would have a higher confidence (.997) in our assertion.

The above procedure depended on our knowing b. In general this may not be known. There are two procedures which are used. The first is to estimate b^2 from the experiments performed and use this estimate in carrying out the above procedure. We estimate b^2 by use of the function

$$\mathbf{s}^2 = \sum_{j=1}^{N} \frac{(\mathbf{f}_j - \mathbf{h}_N)^2}{N-1}.$$

The function $\mathbf{s}^2$ is called the *sample variance.* It can be shown that $\mathbf{M}[\mathbf{s}^2] = b^2$ and $\mathbf{V}[\mathbf{s}^2] \to 0$ as N tends to infinity. Hence for large N we know that this will be a good estimate. For small N this procedure cannot be justified. In this case a more advanced technique, beyond the scope of this book, is used.

One must be quite careful, however, in the indiscriminate assumption that measurements of the same quantity are normally distributed. For example, if we assume that two quantities $\mathbf{f}_1$ and $\mathbf{f}_2$ are both normally distributed, it is not true that their quotient is normally distributed.

Example. Suppose that $\mathbf{x}$ and $\mathbf{y}$ both have normal distributions with mean 0 and variance 1. Let us find the distribution of their quotient. We wish to compute the probability $\mathbf{Pr}[(\mathbf{y}/\mathbf{x}) < t]$. This may be written as

$$\mathbf{G}(t) = \mathbf{Pr}[\mathbf{x} > 0] \cdot \mathbf{Pr}_+[\mathbf{y} < t\mathbf{x}] + \mathbf{Pr}[\mathbf{x} < 0] \cdot \mathbf{Pr}_-[\mathbf{y} > t\mathbf{x}],$$

where $\mathbf{Pr}_+$ is a conditional probability given that $\mathbf{x} > 0$, and $\mathbf{Pr}_-$ is given that $\mathbf{x} < 0$. Hence

$$\mathbf{G}(t) = \tfrac{1}{2}\mathbf{Pr}_+[\mathbf{y} < t\mathbf{x}] + \tfrac{1}{2}(1 - \mathbf{Pr}_-[\mathbf{y} < t\mathbf{x}]).$$

Restricting $\mathbf{x}$ to be positive gives it a new range $[0, \infty]$, and renormalizes its density function by a factor of 2. $\mathbf{Pr}_-$ is similarly obtained. Then from our general theorem we obtain

$$\mathbf{G}(t) = \frac{1}{2}\int_0^\infty 2\mathbf{G}_1'(x)\mathbf{G}_2(tx)\,dx + \frac{1}{2}\left[1 - \int_{-\infty}^0 2\mathbf{G}_1'(x)\mathbf{G}_2(tx)\,dx\right]$$

$$\mathbf{G}'(t) = \frac{1}{2}\int_0^\infty 2x\mathbf{G}_1'(x)\mathbf{G}_2'(tx)\,dx - \frac{1}{2}\int_{-\infty}^0 2x\mathbf{G}_1'(x)\mathbf{G}_2'(tx)\,dx$$

$$= \int_0^\infty 2x\mathbf{G}_1'(x)\mathbf{G}_2'(tx)\,dx$$

$$= \frac{1}{\pi}\int_0^\infty xe^{-x^2/2}e^{-(tx)^2/2}\,dx$$

$$= \frac{1}{\pi}\int_0^\infty xe^{-(1+t^2)x^2/2}\,dx$$

$$= \frac{1}{\pi(1+t^2)}$$

$$\mathbf{G}(t) = \int_{-\infty}^{t} \frac{1}{\pi(1 + x^2)}\, dx = \frac{1}{\pi} \arctan t + \frac{1}{2}.$$

Hence the ratio of two independent functions with mean 0 and variance 1 is a Cauchy distribution. We have seen that the average of functions with a Cauchy distribution behaves quite differently than the average of functions with a normal distribution.

In particular, if a series of measurements are known to have a normal distribution with mean 0 it can be expected that in a large number of measurements it is very likely that the average of the measurements will be near to 0. Assume now that the measurements each have a Cauchy distribution. Then this has a perfectly symmetric density function and we would expect that the average of our measurements should be near 0. However, we observed in Section 5 that the average of any number of such measurements would have the same distribution. Thus it is no more likely that the average of a million such measurements will be near to 0 than it is that a single measurement will be near to 0.

EXERCISES

1. Assume that for a certain calculation the roundoff errors are uniformly distributed on the interval $(-5 \cdot 10^{-8}, 5 \cdot 10^{-8})$. What is the maximum error that can occur in 10^6 multiplications? Estimate a reasonable accuracy to place on the answer assuming that the errors are independent. [*Ans.* .05, 10^{-4}.]

2. A certain measuring device gives measurements with an error which is normal with mean 0 and variance 2. A series of 10 measurements is made and an average of 25 is obtained for the measurements. Give 95 per cent confidence limits for the true value of the quantity being measured.

3. Assume that when one buys a 10 per cent resistor claimed to be a k-ohm resistor the outcome may be assumed to be uniformly distributed on the interval $k \pm .10k$. A man needs to have a 20-ohm resistance. He considers (a) buying one 20-ohm resistor or (b) buying two 10-ohm resistors, putting the two in series to obtain an expected sum of 20 ohms. Find the mean and variance for the resistance which he would obtain by each of the two procedures. Which seems to be the better procedure? [*Ans.* (a) 20, $\frac{4}{3}$ (b) 20, $\frac{2}{3}$.]

4. Assume that a machine does not round off but simply drops the digits after k decimal places. Assuming that the multiplications are equally likely to be by a positive or by a negative number, this may be considered a process which results in an error uniformly distributed on

the interval -10^{-k} and 10^{-k}. If $k = 10$ and $N = 10^6$ what is a reasonable accuracy to place on the answer? Compare this with the error caused by rounding off.

5. The following ten measurements were obtained for the length of a certain rod: 2.13, 2.34, 2.16, 2.17, 2.18, 2.19, 2.21, 2.13, 2.17, 2.50. Assume that the measurements are normal with mean the true length of the rod. Estimate the variance from the measurements and find 95 per cent confidence limits for the true mean.

6. Assume that whenever measurements from a certain instrument are made it is observed that the sample mean is always very near the square root of the sample variance. What might be assumed about the distribution of the measurements?

7. Assume that the number of particles emitted from a radioactive source in a unit time interval has a Poisson distribution. For a large number of measurements how should the sample mean compare with the sample variance?

8. Assume that two independent measurements are made of the time before a particle is emitted from a radioactive source. Assume that each time may be considered to have an exponential measure with the same mean a. Show that the distribution of the ratio of the two times is

$$\mathbf{G}(t) = \frac{t}{1+t} \qquad \text{on } [0, \infty].$$

Show that this distribution does not have a finite mean or variance.

SUGGESTED READING

Cramer, Harold, *The Elements of Probability Theory*, Wiley, New York, 1955.

Fry, T. C., *Probability and its Engineering Uses*, Van Nostrand, Princeton, 1928.

Bizley, M. T. L., *Probability, An Intermediate Textbook*, Cambridge University Press, Cambridge, 1957.

Munroe, M. E., *Theory of Probability*, McGraw-Hill, New York, 1951.

Arley, N. and K. Rander Buch, *Introduction to the Theory of Probability and Statistics*, Wiley, New York, 1950.

Index

Absorbing Markov chain, 404
  absorbing state of, 404
  cannonical form of matrix of, 405
Abstract euclidean vector spaces, 330
  orthonormal basis for, 334
Abstract vector spaces, 250
  subspace of, 260
Alias transformation, 286
Alibi transformation, 286
Alternatives, complete set of, 30
Analysis of logical possibilities, 20
Arguments, valid, 32
Aristotle, 2
Assignment of branch weights, 138

Barycentric coordinates of a vector, 352
Base of a number system, 100
Bases:
  dual natural, 293
  for polyhedral convex sets, 350
Basic conjunction, 42
Basic series circuit, 47
Basis:
  cannonical, of a convex set, 354
  dual of a functional, 291
  dual of a natural, 292
  functional, 290
  natural, 269
  of a possibility space, 80, 82
  of a vector space, 269
  orthonormal basis for abstract vector space, 334
  trivial, 83
Beer and ale experiment, 197
Beginner variable, 228
Biconditional, 10
Binary number system, 99
Binomial coefficients, 90
Binomial measures, 180
  Poisson approximation of, 110
Birthday problem, 125
Boole, George, 2
Bounded convex set, 346
Bounding hyperplanes, 344
Branch of a tree, 21
Branch point, star of, 146
Branch weights, assignment of, 138
Bridge:
  number of deals, 88
  number of hands, 92

Cannonical basis of a convex set, 354
Cannonical form of transition matrix, 405
Cantor, George, 103
Cardinal numbers, 102, 104
  hierarchy of, 107
Cartesian coordinate system, 208, 321
Cauchy distribution, 469
Cauchy-Schwarz inequality, 322
Central limit theorem, 187, 189, 470
Chain:
  absorbing, 404
  ergodic, 391, 394
  Markov, 148, 384
  regular, 391
Characteristic equation of a linear differential equation, 294
Characteristic function:
  of a statement, 73
  of a subset, 72
Chebyshev's inequality, 173
Circuit:
  basic series, 47
  electric, 428
  switching, 45
Closed half plane, 339
Closed half space, 339
Coefficients:
  binomial, 90
  multinomial, 87
Column vector, 205
Complete permutation, 125
Complete set of alternatives, 30
Component:
  of a matrix, 206
  of a vector with respect to a basis, 269

Compound statement, 1
relation to a subset, 60
Conclusion, 32
Conditional, 9
contrapositive of, 37
converse of, 36
variants of, 36
Conditional probability, 129
Conductance, 431
Confidence interval, 476
Conjunction, 4
basic, 42
Connectives, 4
Constant function, 71
Continuum hypothesis, 109
generalized, 111
Contradictories, 29
Contrapositive, 37
Converse, 36
Convex combination of vectors, 346
Convex sets, 337
bases for, 350
bounded, 346
cannonical basis for, 354
extreme edge of, 352
extreme point of, 345
extreme value of a functional on, 355
polyhedral, 341
unbounded, 346
Coordinate system;
cartesian, 208
oblique, 209
Coordinates:
barycentric, 352
of a vector with respect of a basis, 269
Coplanar lines, 304
Counting problems, 85
Courant, Richard, 457

Density function, 441, 448
exponential, 442
for the arc sine distribution, 448
normal, 443, 450
uniform, 442
Denumerable infinity, 106
Denumerably infinite set, 106
Dependent statements, 28
Describe (a possibility space), 81
Difference (of sets), 57
Differential equations:
characteristic equation of, 294
initial conditions for, 294
linear, 294
non-homogeneous, 299
Diffusion of gases, 388, 415
Dimension of a vector space, 272
uniqueness of, 274
Discrete possibility space, 439
Disjoint (sets), 57
Disjunction, 4
exclusive, 5
inclusive, 5
Distribution function, 441, 446, 448
arc sine, 448
Cauchy, 469
exponential, 442
normal, 443, 450
uniform, 442
Domain of a function, 70
Dual functional basis, 291
of the natural basis, 292
Dual (linear programming) problem, 363
Duality theorem, 366

Ehrenfest, 94, 415
Electric circuits and linear algebra, 434
Electric circuits and random walks, 428
Empty set, 52
Entropy, 94, 415, 420
Equations:
linear, 223
linear differential, 294
locus of, 337
Equiprobable measure, 120
Equivalence of statements, 11, 26
Ergodic Markov chain, 391, 394
law of large numbers for, 394
mean first passage time, 411
mean recurrence time, 413
Errors, measurement of, 474
Euclidean geometry, 248, 320
Euclidean vector spaces, 330
orthonormal basis for, 334
Exclusive disjunction, 5
Existential statement, 96
Exponential distribution, 442
Extraneous roots, 68
Extreme edge of a convex set, 352
Extreme points of polyhedral convex sets, 344, 345
Extreme values of functionals on convex sets, 355

Factorial, 86
Fallacy, 34
Feasible vectors, 366, 373
Finite dimensional vector space, 272
Fixed point of a permutation, 125
Fixed vector of a Markov chain, 393
Flat, 311
Function:
arc sine, 448
characteristic, 72, 73
constant, 71
definition of, 70
density, 441

distribution, 441, 446, 448
domain of, 70
exponential density, 442
exponential distribution, 442
graph of, 325
identity, 71
mean of, 159, 453, 455
normal density, 443
normal distribution, 443
numerical, 74
numerical linear (functional), 255, 288
of two real variables, 325
path weight, 138
range of, 70
standard deviation of, 169
standardized, 169
value of, 70
uniform density, 442
uniform distribution, 442
variance of, 165, 453, 455
weight, 113
Functional, 255, 288
basis, 290
dual basis, 291
extreme values of, 355
level planes of, 302
Functions:
basis of a possibility space, 80, 82
equality of, 72
independent, 132, 460
logically independent, 82
negative of, 75
numerical, 74
one-one, 84
outcome, 81
product of, 75
quotient of, 75
sum of, 75
Fundamental matrix of an absorbing chain, 405
Fundamental row operations, 234

Gases, diffusion of, 388, 415
Generalized continuum hypothesis, 111
Genetics, 388
Geometric vectors, 245, 246
Geometry:
euclidean, 248, 320
vector, 299, 306
Goldbach conjecture, 97
Graph of a function, 325

Half plane:
closed, 339
open, 339
Half space:
open, 339
closed, 339

Hat-check problem, 126, 164
Hilbert, David, 104
Homogeneous linear equations, 229
Hyperplane, 224, 311
bounding, 344

Identity function, 71
Identity matrix, 216
if statement, 9
if and only if statement, 10, 37
Implication, 24
Implicit representation of a line, 308
Implicit representation of a plane, 302
Inclusive disjunction, 5
Inconsistent statements, 26, 28
Independent functions, 132, 460
Independent process, 146
Independent statements, 17, 28, 131
Independent trials process, 147, 152
Indicators, 374
Indirect method of proof, 38
Inequality:
Cauchy-Schwarz, 322
Chebyshev's, 173
statement, 338
superfluous, 338
Infinite possibility space, 439
Infinity:
denumerable, 106
non-denumerable, 108
Initial conditions for linear differential equations, 294
Inner product of vectors, 214, 320
Intersection (of sets), 56
Interval, 440
measure of, 440
Inverse of a square matrix, 240
Inverse transformations, 259
Invertible:
matrix, 241
transformation, 259, 283

Kernel, of a transformation, 257

Labeling, 86
Land of Oz, 149, 385
Law of large numbers, 172, 174, 394, 469
Length of a vector, 321
Level planes of a functional, 302
Line, 224
implicit representation, 308
parametric representation, 300
translate of, 300
Linear combination of vectors, 265
Linear equations:
differential, 294
homogeneous, 229
reduced set of, 228, 231
simultaneous, 223

Linear independence of vectors, 266, 267
Linear numerical function (functional), 255, 288
Linear programming:
  constraints, equality form, 373
  duality theorem of, 366
  feasible vectors for, 366, 373
  maximum problem of, 364, 366, 372
  minimum problem of, 360, 366, 372
  problems, 359
  simplex method for, 372, 376
Linear transformations, 255
  alias and alibi, 286
  composite, 283
  examples of, 255, 260
  inverse, 259
  invertible, 259, 283
  kernel of, 257
  matrix of, 278
  projection, 262, 282
  shear, 263, 282
Lines, coplanar, 304
Locus:
  of a linear equation, 224, 337
  of a linear inequality, 338
Logical possibilities, 2, 13
  analysis of, 20
  main requirement of, 14
Logical relations, 24
  systematic analysis of, 28
Logically false statement, 16
Logically independent functions, 82
Logically true statement, 11, 15

Markov chains:
  absorbing, 404
  absorbing state of, 404
  ergodic, 391, 394
  finite, 148, 384
  mean first passage time, 411
  mean recurrence time, 413
  regular, 391
  starting state of, 148
  states of, 184, 384
  transition matrix of, 150, 384
  transition probability, 148
Matrix:
  columns of, 205
  component of, 206
  fundamental, of an absorbing chain, 405
  identity, 216
  inverse of a square, 240
  invertible, 241
  multiple of, 206
  multiplication, 214
  of a transformation, 278
  orthogonal, 335
  product (of two), 214
  rows of, 205
  square, 205
  square, inverse of, 240
  sum of two, 206
  transition, 150
  transition, cannonical form of, 405
  zero, 207
Maximum problem, 364, 366, 372
Maze, rat, 396, 412
Mean first passage time, 411
Mean of a distribution, 455
Mean of a function, 159, 453
Mean recurrence time, 413
Measure:
  binomial, 180
  equiprobable, 120
  for infinite possibility spaces, 440
  of a set, 113
  of an interval, 440
  Poisson, 180
  probability, 116, 441
  product, 462
  properties of, 116, 440, 441
  uniform, 442
Measurable subsets, 441
Measurement of errors, 474
Median, 164
Minimum problem, 360, 366, 372
Multinomial coefficients, 87

Natural basis, 269
  dual of, 292, 293
Necessary condition, 37
  and sufficient condition, 38
Negation, 5
  of an existential statement, 96
  of a universal statement, 96
Network:
  electric, 428
  switching, 45
Non-denumerably infinite set, 108
Non-homogeneous differential equations, 299
Normal:
  curve, 189
  distribution function, 443
  with given mean and variance, 450
Normal to a plane, 324
Normalized equation of a plane, 324
n-simplex, 350
Number of elements in a set, 76
Number system, base of, 100
Numbers:
  binary, 99
  cardinal, 102, 104
  octal, 102
  transfinite, 107
Numerical function, 74

Oblique coordinate system, 209
Odds, 118
One-one function, 84
only if statement, 37
Open half plane, 339
Open half space, 339
Open statement, 65
Orthogonal matrix, 335
Orthonormal basis, 323
  for an abstract vector space, 334
Outcome functions, 81
Oz, Land of, 149, 385

Parametric representation:
  of a flat, 311
  of a line, 300
Pascal triangle, 92
Path of a tree, 21, 137
Path weight function, 138
Permutation, 87
  complete, 125
  fixed point of, 125
Plane:
  explicit equation for, 326
  implicit representation of, 302
  level, of a functional, 302
  normal to, 324
  normalized equation of, 324
Polyhedral convex set, 341
  bases for, 350
  extreme edge of, 352
  extreme points of, 344, 345
Possibilities, logical, 2, 13
  main requirement of, 14
Possibility space:
  basis of, 80, 82
  discrete, 439
  infinite, 439
Premise, 32
Prices, shadow, 364
Prime number, 97
Probability:
  conditional, 129
  fundamental assumption of, 112
  vector, 385
Probability measure, properties of, 116, 441
Process:
  independent, 146
  independent trials, 147, 152
  Markov chain, 148, 384
  random walk, 193, 404, 423
  stochastic, 146
Product, inner or scalar, 320
Product measure, 462
Projection of a vector on a plane, 325
Proof, indirect method of, 38

Quantifiers:
  existential, 96
  universal, 96
Quotient of two numerical functions, 75

Random walk, 193, 404, 423
  application to electric circuits, 428
Range, of a function, 70
Reduced set (of rows), 228
reductio ad absurdum, 39
Regular Markov chain, 391
  law of large numbers for, 394
Relations:
  logical, 25
  one-fold, 28
  two-fold, 28
Roots, extraneous, 68
Row operations, 234
Row vector, 205

Sample:
  mean, 476
  variance, 477
Scalar product, 320
Self-contradiction, 16
Set:
  bounded, 346
  convex, 337, 340
  characteristic function of, 72
  definition of, 51
  description of, 51
  empty, 52
  listing of, 51
  measure of, 113
  polyhedral convex, 341
  subset of, 52
  translate of, 300
  unbounded, 346
  unit, 52
  universal, 52
Shadow prices, 364
Simplex, 350
Simplex method, 372, 376
  indicators, 374
Simultaneous linear equations, 223
Space, vector, 250
  basis of, 269
  examples of, 260
  spanned by vectors, 266
  subspace of, 260
Square matrix, inverse of, 240
Standard deviation of a function, 169
Standardized function, 169
Star of a branch point, 146
Stars, equal, 147

State, of a Markov chain, 148, 348
  starting, 148
  absorbing, 404
Statement:
  characteristic function of, 73
  complete set of alternatives for, 30
  compound, 1
  conclusion of, 32
  existential, 96
  fallacy, 34
  logically false, 16
  independent, 28, 131
  open, 65
  premise of, 32
  probability of, 113
  self-contradiction, 16
  simple parts of, 1
  tautology, 15
  truth set of, 61
  universal, 96
Statements:
  contradictories, 29
  dependent, 28
  equivalent, 11
  having given truth tables, 41
  inconsistent, 26
  independent, 17, 28
  independent relative to a measure, 131
  subcontraries, 28
Stochastic process, 146
Subcontraries, 28, 29
Subset:
  complement of, 56
  empty, 52
  measurable, 441
  proper, 52
  unit, 52
  universal, 52
Subsets:
  difference of two, 57
  disjoint, 57
  intersection of two, 56
  relation to compound statements, 61
  truth sets, 61
  union of two, 56
Subspace of a vector space, 260
Subspace spanned by vectors, 266
Sufficient condition, 38
Superfluous inequality, 344
Switching circuits, 45

Transformations, linear:
  alias and alibi, 286
  composite, 283
  definition, 255
  examples of, 255, 260
  inverse of, 259
  invertible, 259, 283
  kernel of, 257
  matrix of, 278
  projection, 262, 282
  shear, 263, 282
Transition matrix, 384
  cannonical form of, 405
Transition probability, 148
Translate:
  of a line, 300
  of a set, 300
Tree:
  description of, 20, 21
  branches of, 21, 137
  path of, 21, 137
Trivial basis, 83
Truth set (of a statement), 61
Truth tables, 4

Uniform distribution, 442
Uniform measure, 442
Union of sets, 56
Unit set, 52
Universal set, 52
Universal statement, 96

Valid arguments, 32
Value of a function, 70
Variable, beginner, 228
Variance:
  of a distribution, 455
  of a function, 165, 453
Vector geometry, 299, 306
Vector space:
  abstract euclidean, 330
  basis of, 269
  dimension of, 272
  examples of, 251, 260
  finite dimensional, 272
  orthonormal basis for, 334
  spanned by vectors, 266
  subspace of, 260
  uniqueness of dimension of, 274
Vectors:
  barycentric coordinates of, 352
  column, 205
  components (coordinates) of, with respect to a basis, 269
  convex combination of, 346
  feasible, 366, 373
  fixed, of a Markov chain, 393
  geometric, 245, 246
  inner product of, 214, 320
  length of, 321

linear combination of, 265
linearly independent, 266, 267
probability, 385
row, 205
spanning a subspace, 266
Venn diagrams, 56

Weight function, 113
Weights, assignment of branch, 138
World's Series, 22, 83, 144

Zero matrices, 207